C A R S

OF THE LATE 60'S

BRITISH AND IMPORTED MODELS 1965-1969

If you want a car that's more spacious, powerful, handsome and luxurious, this one has it all.

NEW CRESTA. BY VAUXHALL

Vauxhall's new Cresta is a big, impressive 6-seater, beautifully proportioned and five inches longer than the previous model. The new curved design gives four inches extra shoulder room without increasing overall width—plus a boot with room for 30 cu. ft. of luggage.

Acceleration is sensational! From the traffic lights the new Cresta will out-accelerate practically every other saloon car on the road. Its great 3.3 litre 6-cylinder engine now develops 140 brake horse power! This masterful performance is blended with docility and quietness; the Cresta is a true 'top gear car' as it glides smoothly and silently through traffic.

You choose the gearbox that suits you best!

4-speed all synchromesh with floor-mounted lever. Regular 3-speed (column-mounted) lever (with or without overdrive) or, if you'd rather let the car do all the work, Powerglide—the smoothest automatic transmission in the world!

And power brakes, of course—with discs at front and self-adjusting drum brakes at rear.

There are two versions: the Cresta, with two headlamps, and the Cresta de Luxe with four headlamps (illustrated). Both are elegantly appointed cars with lavish soundproofing and superbly comfortable seats. In addition, the de Luxe model offers you individual front seats, with the option of Ambla or leather upholstery.

If you want a car that is more spacious, powerful, handsome and luxurious, Vauxhall's new Cresta has it all. See it at the Motor Show now, and at your Vauxhall dealer's soon.

Cresta £956.2.11.
Cresta de Luxe *(shown here)* **£1058.17.1.**
Prices include P.T. and are ex-works.

VAUXHALL. BRED FOR SUCCESS. — BETTER THAN EVER FOR '66.
See the new Vauxhalls at the Motor Show. NEW Viva 90. NEW Viva SL. NEW Cresta & Cresta de Luxe. Plus the famous Viva, Victor 101 & VX 4/90.

EXPRESS NEWSPAPERS PLC

C A R S

OF THE LATE 60'S

BRITISH AND IMPORTED MODELS 1965-1969

This edition published 1995 by
The Promotional Reprint Company Limited,
Deacn House, 65 Old Church Street,
London SW3 5BS

Exclusively in the UK for
Bookmart Limited,
Desford Road, Enderby,
Leicester LE9 5AD

ISBN 1 85648 223 5

Printed and bound in Hong Kong

CONTENTS

INTRODUCTION

Cars of the late 60's is a comprehensive guide to all new models exhibited at the annual motor shows in England between 1965 - 1969. The book is a compilation of the Daily Express publication "Review of World Cars" and provides detailed information on all vehicles displayed at the shows, as well as car prices and an illustrated overview of the state of the world car market as it was in the late 60's.

The 1965 motor show was the 50th international exhibition to be held, with over 68 manufacturers from 12 countries taking part, and for the first time there will be manufacturers from Japan exhibiting. The shows main theme was on vehicle safety, with over 12 million vehicles on the road.

1966 was again emphasising the commitment by manufacturers to create more safety features into all of its models. More cars are now being fitted with seat belts as standard equipment. Barbara Castle the Transport Minister says "that they will be compulsory in Britain next year". 1966 also saw the introduction of the 70 mile per hour speed limit. This measure was brought in after Ministerial panic over a series of multiple crashes on motorways mainly in fog.

The 1967 show saw the Government relax it's restrictions by reducing the hire purchase down payment to 25% with three years to pay. This was a much need boost to an industry that for the past year had cut back production. The trend of all manufacturers is to combine comfort with safety and efficiency on a scale never before attempted.

The 1968 show opened on a note of higher optimism among British car manufacturers. Optimism because of the effects of devaluation which, by slashing prices in foreign markets, has given new life to sales of British cars abroad. There are now over 14 million cars on the road. Britain's roads are now the most congested in the world. Last year road users paid £1.2 billion in tax, including £820 million in fuel tax, with very little of it returned in the form of road building.

1969 saw exports reach an all time record of £890 million an increase on the previous year of over £150 million. Optimism in the motor industry stems from many new and vital changes in her factories in the past 12 months which have led to economies in production, streamlining effort, smoother organisation and cheaper products. Much of the success of British cars comes from the fact that only four big car empires remain in Britain, British Leyland, Ford, Rootes and Vauxhall. Together with the smaller established manufacturers such as Rolls Royce, Aston Martin and Jensen.

More than a vast shop-window – it's part of our life

A MESSAGE FROM SIR PATRICK HENNESSY

SIR PATRICK HENNESSY
President of the Society of
Motor Manufacturers and
Traders, & Chairman of the
Ford Motor Company

BRITISH motorists, who buy more than a million new cars every year, have come to regard the Motor Show, I suspect, as the industry's annual shop window—the biggest car showroom in the country.

But it is a lot more than that.

It represents the accumulated hard work, energy and inspiration of more than 500,000 people who have helped to make the motor industry the most vital cornerstone of our export economy.

These half a million people—a hundredth part of our nation—account for as much as 18 per cent of the nation's visible exports. They sell more abroad than any other industry in the country and we particularly welcome the many overseas visitors who will visit us again this year to see what we have to offer.

They are backed by up-to-date plants and equipment—some in advance of anything the rest of the world can show. Investment by motor vehicle manufacturers alone in the last ten years has exceeded £650 million.

This is the vast complex which produces a staggering range of products demonstrating world technical leadership in innovation,

feature and manufacturing methods.

Quality and value for money coupled with continuous improvement, development and refinement are the themes of the 1965 Motor Show. The British car still costs in basic price little more than it did ten years ago—and we have come a long way since then.

Several new and improved British models are making their first appearance at Earls Court this year and there are challenging models from many overseas manufacturers.

Along the gallery are many new accessories and components and the sporting enthusiast will be able to examine cars which have won fame for Britain on tracks and courses all over the world.

This invaluable Review will help visitors to the exhibition to make the most of their time. There is so much to see that it is equally valuable to the annual visitors to Earls Court as well as the newcomer.

---

50 up – and stronger than ever

WHY is it that the Society of Motor Manufacturers and Traders are expecting the unprecedented total of more than 500,000 visitors to this year's Show?

It is not simply that the 50th exhibition should be marked by specially spectacular display.

The fact is that motor manufacturers the world over now can realise the dream of producing cars for all kinds of conditions which combine the most advanced techniques and inventions.

Put briefly, class distinction in cars is now being broken down. Technologically, the man who is going to buy an £800 car is almost on a par with the man who is able to afford a much more expensive model.

No longer is there one level for the rich and another for the not-so-rich. Now most can buy the most advanced models.

This significant stride forward does not mean, of course, the complete standardisation of all

motor cars but more excitingly it heralds an entirely new development so that all motorists are competing on a much more equal footing. This is what makes the Motor Show of 1965 a momentous event for every motorist.

What, in effect does this new era, now on exhibition, add up to? Most important of all, compact engines so that more cars can take up less room.

These engines, as a result of skill and research, are more efficient and cheaper to run. Along with this is the functional bonus of more room inside the cars without their bodies being enlarged. This amounts to an all-round saving.

And—reassuring note—extra special attention has been given to the safety factor, now more vital than ever on account of the huge numbers who use our roads.

For speed-with-safety is the keynote of this Exhibition. It is not only an ideal but a necessity recognised by all to-day. So you will see, for instance, more padded interiors, easier-to-handle gearboxes with synchromesh on all four forward gears, higher braking standards and two-position anti-dazzle mirrors to mention just a few additions.

Leading manufacturers from 12 nations are exhibiting; and, for the first time, Japanese firms who constitute a formidable challenge will be showing. In the past most car companies have tended to unveil their new models as and when these were ready. But now the bulk of motor car makers have withheld their new models until autumn showtime.

In the world to-day the sales honeymoon is over. Certainly, in the last six months we, in these islands and indeed other nations as well, have felt the shrinking in the sales demand. This has sharpened the ingenuity and inventive-

ness of car makers and so has provided a fresh stimulus.

Earls Court can truly be termed the spearhead of our export drive because British cars are the biggest foreign currency earners of all. In this sense, the Exhibition is the greatest showpiece of British engineering and expertise which is held anywhere.

I believe that this superb assembly, which glitters and glows under a myriad arclights, forms a splendid springboard to project the products of 68 of the world's greatest motor car producers.

The Daily Express Motor Show Review is above all designed as a guide to the drivers and owners of 12 million vehicles (contributing £1,000 million a year in tax) who will enjoy the colour and excitement of this supreme event of the motoring year.

For the many who are not able to share the adventure and experience of visiting Earls Court, my aim has been to compile a review that will communicate to them the atmosphere and diversity of the 500 car and accessory stands in Hall and Balcony.

BASIL CARDEW
Daily Express
Motoring Reporter
& Editor of the
Daily Express
Motor Show Review

CARS
OF THE LATE 60'S
BRITISH AND IMPORTED MODELS 1965-1969

MOTOR SHOW REVIEW GUIDE
1965

A - Z
SECTION

And very nice too—but now let's talk of ENGINES

says GORDON WILKINS

"HOW big is the engine? What is the motorway cruising speed? And what is the fuel consumption?"

These, a German motor salesman told me, are the first things a Continental buyer asks about a new car. Mr. Fraser's obsession with speed limits and the cuts in our already inadequate road programme will keep Britain limping along behind Europe for a long time yet, but the lesson is clear. In Europe, the fastest-growing export market, swift transcontinental travel on modern motorways is creating a demand for more powerful cars with a fast top-gear pick-up, a high cruising speed and a moderate fuel consumption. Already some of our popular models are beginning to look underpowered by Continental standards, but manufacturers are getting the message. So in spite of interesting ideas like self-levelling suspensions, new automatic transmissions, the switch to negative-earth electrical systems and the trend towards alternators instead of dynamos, the big interest this year is in the engines. Big, smooth, multi-bearing engines with the hefty torque that means real top-gear punch; engines with ingenious carburation

The AUDI engine, designed by Mercedes-Benz, has pistons with combustion chambers in the top.

systems, high compression ratios, and free-flow manifolds to deliver power with economy; low-priced engines with overhead camshafts for higher revs; canted engines; Vee engines; engines with flat heads and bowl-in-piston combustion chambers and more Wankel engines.

Rootes got into line by increasing engine sizes from 1,592 c.c. to 1,725 c.c. right through the range; Hillman, Singer, Sunbeam and Humber. The new engines have five main bearings instead of three and come in two versions; cast-iron head, 8.4 to 1 compression, 65 h.p., or aluminium head, 9.2 to 1 compression and 85 h.p. The more powerful version has the modern feature of a twin-choke compound carburetter, using only one choke for economy at low speeds, two for maximum power.

In France, Citroen follow the same recipe. Bigger bores, shorter stroke and new valve gear enable their big four to gain an extra 1,000 revs a minute and five bearings keep it smooth. When it was introduced ten years ago the DS 19, with 1,911 c.c. had 75 h.p. The new DS 21 with 2,175 c.c. has 100 h.p.

In Germany, Volkswagen have given the "beetle" its second major increase in engine size (now 1,285 c.c. and 40 h.p. against 1,192 c.c. and 34 h.p.) and there's a new engine of 1,584 c.c. with 54 h.p. for the larger cars.

General Motors' German factory, Opel, are fighting back by pushing the engine of their Kadett from 993 to 1,078 c.c. which gives it 55 h.p. in its hottest version. (They are not at the Show because they don't compete with General Motors Vauxhall on their home ground.)

The search for lightness and compactness is producing new types of engine. Ford of Dagenham give the Corsair a new V-four in two sizes: 1.7-litre developing 76½ h.p. or 2-litre producing 88 h.p. Compared with the 1½-litre Corsair GT engine, capacity has gone up by 33 per cent but engine length is reduced by 11 per cent.

In the search for high efficiency and low weight, designers of touring car engines are adopting overhead camshafts, once the prerogative of sports and racing cars. Opel have switched to o.h.c. for their medium and large cars: a four-cylinder in three versions, 1.5, 1.7 and 1.9 litres giving up to 90 h.p. and a six of 2,784 c.c. producing 125 h.p. This is a direct challenge to Mercedes who always use o.h.c., but have now given their four-cylinder engine five bearings and 1,988 c.c. (95 h.p.) and produced a splendid new seven-bearing six of 2,496 c.c. which achieves 150 h.p. when equipped with fuel injection.

Just what o.h.c. can mean in weight saving is illustrated by the Opel 1½-litre engine, which has five bearings instead of the previous three, and delivers more power but weighs 35 lb. less. But still greater savings are achieved by using light alloys. There are few engines in production more advanced than the excellent Coventry-Climax-designed light alloy o.h.c. unit in the Hillman Imp and as another example, take a look at the Peugeot 204. At first glance the arrangement is basically BMC; crosswise engine and front-wheel drive; but the engine is an up-to-the-minute little unit in light alloy, with wet cylinder liners and a chain-driven overhead camshaft, producing 53 h.p. from 1,130 c.c.

As you can see on the Peugeot, an overhead camshaft makes it easy to use hemispherical combustion chambers, with the gas flowing in from the carburetter on one side of the block and out into the exhaust on the other side. NSU do it on their unusual air-cooled o.h.c. four, which is mounted across the back of their saloon models, and in line with the modern trend, they have increased the size from 996 to 1,085 c.c. for the fast 1000 TT. coupe and the new 110 long wheelbase saloon.

In the middle range, BMW have developed a fine new 2-litre o.h.c. engine from their 1800 for their graceful 2000 CS coupe.

Certainly the boldest design is that of Glas, the enterprising German manufacturer who

The Glas V8 engine, above, has an overhead camshaft driven by a cogged belt instead of a chain. The NSU twin-rotor Wankel unit (right) develops up to 120 h.p.

has been driving his overhead camshaft by a cogged belt instead of a chain. It's quieter and cheaper. After successful experience on four-cylinder engines, he is using the same method on a new V8 of 2,576 c.c. which provides 140 h.p. for his elegant new four-seater GT coupe styled by Frua.

And now the overhead camshaft is even invading the United States, with the announcement of an entirely new o.h.c. six by Pontiac, for not even the Americans with their big, extravagantly powered engines can ignore the attractions of high efficiency and low weight.

Rover started something when they adopted a flat head with a combustion chamber formed by a bowl in the piston on their 2000 engine. It was an idea originated by S. D. Heron, a British born engineer, in the U.S.A. Now the same principle is used on Ford's V4 and it is employed with a new twist on the Audi engine designed by Mercedes-Benz engineers for Auto Union. Here a corkscrew inlet passage imparts a high-speed swirl to the mixture as it enters the cylinder. This makes it possible to use a compression ratio of 11.2 to 1, the highest in the world for touring cars at the moment, yet ordinary premium fuel can be used. As a result, Audi claim exceptional economy for a 1.7-litre unit (30 m.p.g. at a cruising speed of 70 m.p.h.) and the engine has such a hefty low-speed punch that it will pull away from a tick-over in top gear.

Another idea that's catching on is the valve rocker pivoted on a ball joint instead of a rocker shaft. The Audi has them; so does the Ford V4.

With our cold, wet English summers, we don't have much trouble through fuel vaporising in the pipelines from the heat of the sun, but in export markets it can be a serious problem. On the new Mercedes range and the Ford Corsair fuel now circulates from tank to carburetter and back again to keep it cool. And as a measure to speed up running in and reduce cylinder wear after cold starts, several makers are now using piston rings with slippery molybdenum inserts.

With all this intensive development, the old piston engine has obviously got plenty of life in it yet, but the opposition is slowly taking shape. Quite a few of the little NSU Prinz convertibles with Wankel engines are now running about and NSU have just revealed a

twin-rotor Wankel unit developing up to 120 h.p. which will go into a new sports car due next year. They are also working with Citroen on a Wankel unit for a new Citroen model due in 1977. The Japanese too are pouring money into development of compact Wankel engines with three-lobed rotors instead of pistons. They have twin-rotor units already and are developing engines with four rotors.

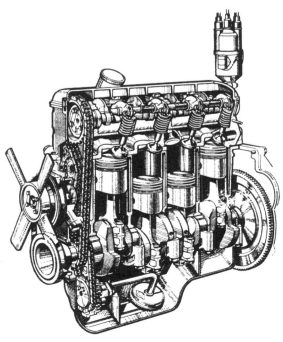

Cut-away section of the BMW development.

In all this talk of increased power, there's one very confusing element. How do you measure your horsepower? The publicity-conscious Americans quote the highest power that can be squeezed out of the engine on the test bed. This is the SAE power, but it bears little relation to what is available to drive the car after the engine has expended some of its power driving fan, water pump, ignition distributor and fuel pump and has been deprived of some of its power by the car's silencing system. For this reason Continental manufacturers have been in the habit of quoting nett power as installed in the car. The difference can be considerable. For example, the 1,725 c.c. Rootes engine that powers the Sunbeam Rapier, Singer Vogue and Humber Sceptre, produces 91 horsepower according to American SAE standards, but when it is installed in the car there is only 85 h.p. left to drive you along the road. The new 2,496 c.c. Mercedes-Benz 250 SE engine delivers 170 h.p. SAE on the test bed, but the amount available to drive the car according to German DIN standards is 150 h.p. Similar differences exist in the torque figures. Unfortunately, some Continental manufacturers, not wishing to let their engines appear inefficient in comparison with American engines, have taken to quoting SAE figures. And the British quote gross horsepower, nett horsepower or something in between indiscriminately, so that it becomes extremely difficult to compare one car with another. As far as possible, the figures quoted in this year's Motor Show Review show the nett power available to drive the car. Where these could not be obtained, the gross test-bed power is given, with the word "gross" after it.

Yesterday, today – and tomorrow Alvis stands out from the crowd

It was exciting enough to own an Alvis in 1920. Today it is even more exciting. Five speed syncro-mesh gear box, 130 B.H.P. engine, immaculate gleaming coach work . . . the Alvis Series III is one of the few really distinctive cars on the road.

SALOON £2,998. 4. 7d.*
COUPE £3,239. 17. 11d.*
Power assisted steering and automatic transmission are available as extras.
* Recommended prices ex-works including tax.

See today's Alvis on stand no. 144 Earls Court

ALVIS OF COVENTRY

LONDON SHOWROOMS: DEVONSHIRE HOUSE · PICCADILLY
LONDON W.1 · TELEPHONE HYDE PARK 9151

12

ŠKODA 1000 MB

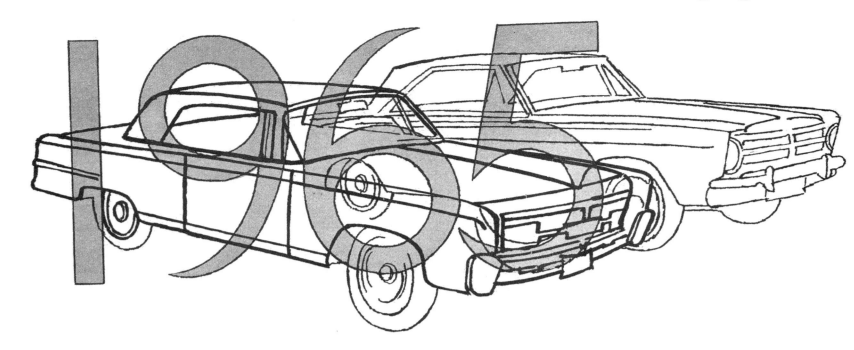

INTRODUCING . . . *The Show's handiest companion*

ALL THE CARS IN A-TO-Z ORDER

ABARTH SIMCA 2000

MORE Abarth than Simca, this racing coupe has won many successes in sprints and hill climbs. No car for the commuter, but a rewarding if temperamental steed for the sportsman. Underframe and some suspension parts are from Simca 1000. Twin-cam engine is by Abarth with two twin-choke Webers and two plugs per cylinder. Choice of four or six-speed gearbox. 1600 c.c. engine also available.

CLOSE-UP

Four-cyl.; o.h.c.; 88 × 80 mm.; 1,948 c.c.; 195 b.h.p.; 9.8 to 1 comp.; coil ign.; 2 Weber twin-choke carbs.; 4-speed, 13.82, 8.25, 5.75, 4.71 to 1; cen. lvr.; susp., f. ind. transv. leaf, r. ind. coil; 2-door; 2-seat; disc brks.; max. 155 m.p.h.; cruise 130; m.p.g. 19-21; whl. base 6ft. 10¼in.; track f. and r. 4ft. 2in.; lgth. 11ft. 10½in.; width 4ft. 10½in.; ht. 3ft. 11⅛in.; g.c. 5in.; turng. cir. 29ft. 6in.; kerb wt. 13½ cwt.; tank 12 gals.; 12-volt.

ABARTH FIAT OT 1600

HAVING successfully installed his light alloy double-overhead camshaft engine with two twin-choke Webers in the back of a Fiat 850 saloon, the irrepressible Abarth goes all the way with this racing spider using Fiat underbody but with Girling discs on double circuits. One of more than 20 models engineered with jewel-like precision (and cost) at a model factory at Turin.

CLOSE-UP

Four-cyl.; o.h.c.; 86 × 68.5 mm.; 1,592 c.c.; 170 b.h.p.; 9.5 to 1 comp.; coil ign.; 2 Weber twin-choke carbs.; 6-speed; cen. lvr.; susp., f. ind. transv. leaf, r. ind. coil; 2-door; 2-seat; disc servo brks.; max. 145 m.p.h.; cruise 120; m.p.g. 22-25; whl. base 6ft. 7⅜in.; track, f. 3ft. 11½in., r. 4ft. 3¼in.; lgth. 12ft. 2in.; width 4ft. 11¾in.; ht. 2ft. 8in.; g.c. 4in.; turng. cir. 30ft.; kerb wt. 12¼ cwt.; tank 6½ gals.; 12-volt.

A.C. COBRA

THIS Cobra won't be charmed by music; it simply wouldn't be heard when the Ford V8 7-litre engine gets going. The sports racing Cobra II strikes out to win under the banner of American racing driver Carroll Shelby and collected this year's GT Championship. If a 7-litre engine is too big Cobra I with 4.7-litre engine has a top speed around 150 m.p.h. Built at Thames Ditton and mostly exported.

CLOSE-UP

Eight-cyl.; o.h.v.; 101.6×72.9 mm.; 4,727 c.c.; 280 b.h.p.; 11 to 1 comp.; coil ign.; Holley carb.; 4-speed, 8.36, 6.30, 4.99, 3.54 to 1; cen. lvr.; susp. f. and r. ind. coil; 2-door; 2-seat; disc brks.; max. 150 m.p.h.; cruise 130; m.p.g. 20; whl. base 7ft. 6in.; track, f. 4ft. 3½in., r. 4ft. 4½in.; lgth. 12ft. 7in.; width 5ft. 1in.; ht. 4ft. 1in.; g.c. 7in.; turng. cir. 34ft.; kerb wt. 18 cwt.; tank 15 gals.; 12-volt.

£2,030+£425 p.t. = £2,455

ALFA ROMEO GIULIA SPIDER

SHORTER in the wheelbase but faster off the mark than the saloon models, Alfa Romeo's Giulia Spider has quality coachwork from the production line in Pininfarina's well-equipped factory outside Turin. All the thrill of open air motoring in fine weather, plus the comfort of snug convertible bodywork with glass windows and an efficient heater for the winter. Fine road holding, steering accurate to a hair and a five-speed gearbox add to driving pleasure.

CLOSE-UP

Four-cyl.; o.h.c; 78×82 mm.; 1,570 c.c.; 92 b.h.p.; 9 to 1 comp.; coil ign.; Solex carb.; 5-speed, 16.93, 10.19, 6.94, 5.12, 4.05 to 1; cen. lvr.; susp., f. ind. coil, r. coil; 2-door; 2-seat; hyd. brks., disc front; max. 108 m.p.h.; cruise 90; m.p.g. 27-29; whl. base 7ft. 5in.; track f. 4ft. 3in., r. 4ft. 2in.; lgth. 13ft.; width 5ft. 1in.; ht. 4ft. 3in.; g.c. 5½in.; turng. cir. 34ft. 6in.; kerb wt. 18½ cwt.; tank, 11¾ gals.; 12-volt.

£1,155+£242 p.t. = £1,397

ALFA ROMEO GIULIA SPRINT G.T.

ROMEO, Romeo, Wherefore art thou Juliet? The name may be a little confusing, but a spell behind the wheel proves there's no confusion in the minds of the engineers who designed this fast, roadworthy eye-catching coupe with the fine road holding, responsive controls and silken-smooth five-speed gearbox. Bertone did the body styling. There are saloons too and a Spider by Pininfarina.

CLOSE-UP

Four-cyl.; o.h.c.; 78×82 mm.; 1,570 c.c.; 105 b.h.p.; 9.1 to 1 comp.; coil ign.; 2 Weber twin-choke carbs.; 5-speed, 15.05, 9.06, 6.17, 4.55, 3.6 to 1; cen. lvr.; susp., f. ind. coil, r. coil; 2-door; 2/4-seat; disc servo brks.; max. 109 m.p.h.; cruise 95; m.p.g. 22-26; whl. base 7ft. 9in.; track, f. 4ft. 3½in., r. 4ft. 2in.; lgth. 13ft. 5in.; width 5ft. 2in.; ht. 4ft. 4in.; g.c. 5½in.; turng. cir. 35ft.; kerb wt. 19¾ cwt.; tank 10½ gals.; 12-volt.

£1,529+£320 p.t. = £1,849

ALFA ROMEO SPRINT 2600

BERTONE does the coupe, Touring the Spider, on Alfa Romeo's quick-off-the-mark six-cylinder chassis. Twin overhead camshafts, three twin-choke carburetters and a fine five-speed gearbox endear it to real enthusiasts. With competitions in mind, Zagato builds a lean, sleek light alloy coupe that has disc brakes all round, not just in front and maximum speed is said to be 120 m.p.h.

CLOSE-UP

Six-cyl.; o.h.c.; 83×79.6 mm.; 2,584 c.c.; 145 b.h.p.; 8.5 to 1 comp.; coil ign.; 3 Solex twin-choke carbs.; 5-speed, 15.79, 9.50, 6.47, 4.77, 3.77 to 1; cen. lvr.; susp., f. ind. coil, r. coil; 4-door; 4-seat; hyd. servo brks., disc front; max. 120 m.p.h.; cruise 110; m.p.g. 18-20; whl. base 8ft. 5in.; track, f. 4ft. 7in., r. 4ft. 6in.; lgth. 14ft. 4in.; width 5ft. 7in.; ht. 4ft. 4in.; g.c. 4¾in.; turng. cir. 32ft.; kerb wt. 25¼ cwt.; tank 13¼ gals.; 12-volt.

£2,440+£510 p.t. = £2,950

Abbreviations—g.c.—ground clearance; susp.—suspension; f.—front; r.—rear; comp.—compression; s.v.—side-valves; o.h.v.—overhead valves; o.h.c.—overhead camshaft; hyd.—hydraulic.

15

ALVIS 3-LITRE

FUSION of Alvis and Rover brings together two old-established companies with interests in fine cars, cross-country vehicles and aviation, but Alvis continues a separate car policy with this long established six-cylinder model. It is available in England with two-door saloon built by Park Ward bodies or on the Continent with light coupe and convertible bodies by the Swiss coachbuilder Graber.

CLOSE-UP

Six-cyl.; o.h.v.; 84×90 mm.; 2,993 c.c.; 130 b.h.p.; 8.5 to 1 comp.; coil ign.; 2 S.U. carbs.; 5-speed, 11.38, 6.97, 4.86, 3.77, 3.07 to 1; cen. lvr.; BW auto opt.; susp., f. ind. coil, r. half-elliptic; 2-door; 4-seat; disc servo brks.; max. 112 m.p.h.; cruise 90; m.p.g. 18-22; whl. base 9ft. 3½in.; track f. 4ft. 7¾in., r. 4ft. 6 3/16 in.; lgth. 15ft. 8½in.; width 5ft. 6in.; ht. 5ft.; g.c. 7in.; turng. cir. 39ft. 6in.; kerb wt. 30½ cwt.; tank 14¼ gals.; 12-volt.

£2,480 + £518 p.t. = £2,998

AMPHICAR

FERRIES? Tunnels? Who wants them? Drive across rivers, harbours, and lakes in your own time on this sturdy German-built amphibian. It looks just like a normal car that other people may call out the lifeboat when you take the plunge. Its British Triumph Herald engine propels it at about 6 m.p.h. in the water through two nylon propellers, or 68 on land.

CLOSE-UP

Four-cyl.; o.h.v.; 69.3×76 mm.; 1,147 c.c.; 38 b.h.p.; 8 to 1 comp.; coil ign.; Solex carb.; 4-speed, 21.22, 13.73, 8.26, 4.91 to 1; cen. lvr.; susp. f. and r. ind. coil; 2-door; 4-seat; hyd. brks.; max. 68 m.p.h.; cruise 55; m.p.g. 28; whl. base 7ft.; track, f. 4ft., r. 4ft. 2in.; lgth. 14ft. 3in.; width 5ft. 2in.; ht. 5ft.; g.c. 10in.; turng. cir. 37ft.; kerb wt. 20¾ cwt.; tank 10½ gals.; 12-volt.

£886 + £187 p.t. = £1,073

ASTON MARTIN DB6 CONVERTIBLE

THIS exciting new model has more rear-seat, head, body and leg room than any Aston Martin previously built. It is also the first model from this company with full four-seater capacity. The new body design incorporates an aerodynamic spoiler on the familiar fast-back styling which gives greater road holding and safety at speed. Coming from a long line of thoroughbreds, this car more than upholds tradition.

CLOSE-UP

Six-cyl.; o.h.c.; 96×92 mm.; 3,995 c.c.; 282 b.h.p.; 8.75 to 1 comp.; coil ign.; 3 S.U. carbs.; 5-speed, 10.18, 6.64, 4.64, 3.77, 3.14 to 1; cen. lvr., auto opt.; susp., f. ind. coil, r. coil; 2-door; 4-seat; disc servo brks.; max. 148 m.p.h.; cruise 120; m.p.g. 15-18; whl. base 8ft. 2in.; track f. 4ft. 6in., r. 4ft. 5½in.; lgth 15ft.; width 5ft. 6in.; ht. 4ft. 5in.; g.c. 4in.; turng. cir. 34ft.; kerb wt. 29½ cwt.; tank 16 gals.; 12-volt.

£3,775 + £788 p.t. = £4,563

ASTON MARTIN DB6

EXTENDING the appeal of a famous high performance car comes a new, longer model with four full-sized seats. Not just James Bond with a blonde this time, but the whole family or four business associates can now enjoy the comfort and superb performance of one of the world's great quality cars. David Brown engineering and design know-how reinforced by racing experience have done it again.

CLOSE-UP

Six-cyl.; o.h.c.; 96×92 mm.; 3,995 c.c.; 282 b.h.p.; 8.75 to 1 comp.; coil ign.; 3 S.U. carbs.; 5-speed, 10.29, 6.64, 4.64, 3.77, 3.14 to 1; cen. lvr., auto opt.; susp. f. ind. coil, r. coil; 2-door; 4-seat; disc servo brks.; max. 150 m.p.h.; cruise 125; m.p.g. 15-18; whl. base 8ft. 2in.; track f. 4ft. 6in., r. 4ft. 5½in.; lgth. 15ft.; width 5ft. 6in.; ht. 4ft. 4in.; g.c. 4in.; turng. cir. 34ft.; kerb wt. 29 cwt.; tank 22 gals.; 12-volt.

£3,515 + £734 p.t. = £4,249

AUSTIN MINI COOPER S

MONTE Carlo Rally twice in a row and countless other successes in rallies and racing have proved the mettle of this David among the Goliaths. Here is the Mini formula pushed to its peak of perfection, with competition twin-carburetter high compression engine, close gear ratios, more powerful brakes, special broad-rim wheels and braced-tread tyres. Instrument panel and interior trim are adapted to its active role.

CLOSE-UP
Four-cyl.; o.h.v.; 70.64 81.33 mm.; 1,275 c.c.; 75 b.h.p.; 9.75 to 1 comp.; coil ign.; 2 S.U. carbs.; 4-speed, 11.02, 6.6, 4.67, 3.44 to 1; cen. lvr.; susp. f. and r. ind. rubber-hydraulic; 2-door; 4-seat; hyd. servo brks., disc front; max. 95 m.p.h.; cruise 85; m.p.g. 28-32; whl. base 6ft. 8in.; track, f. 4ft. 0⅜in.; r. 3ft. 10⅞in.; lgth. 10ft. 0¼in.; width 4ft. 7½in.; ht. 4ft. 5in.; g.c. 6in.; turng. cir. 32ft. 10in.; kerb wt. 13 cwt.; tank 5½ gals.; 12-volt.

£642+£136 p.t. = £778

AUSTIN A40

FIRST of the British Motor Corporation cars to be body-designed by Italian Pininfarina this car is still very much in demand. It has smooth, straight lines and lots of space for passengers and baggage or goods. It has a robust performance with light running costs and is a particular favourite with Mums who take their children to school. The Italians turn out their own versions of the saloon model.

CLOSE-UP
Four-cyl.; o.h.v.; 64.6×83.7 mm.; 1,098 c.c.; 48 b.h.p. gross; 8.5 to 1 comp.; coil ign.; S.U. carb.; 4-speed, 16.52, 10.82, 6.43, 4.56 to 1; cen. lvr.,; susp., f. ind. coil, r. half-elliptic; 2-door; 4-seat; hyd. brks.; max. 83 m.p.h.; cruise 70; m.p.g. 31-33; whl. base 7ft. 3in.; track f. and r. 3ft. 11in.; lgth. 12ft. 0¼in.; width 4ft. 11⅜in.; ht. 4ft. 8½in.; g.c. 7½in.; turng. cir. 36ft.; kerb wt. 15⅝ cwt.; tank 7 gals.; 12-volt.

£460+£97 p.t. = £557

AUSTIN 1800

MINI major, a brilliant formula adapted to the medium range. More interior space and a bigger luggage boot than you'd think possible within its compact, easily parkable overall dimensions. Crosswise engine, front-wheel drive and Hydrolastic suspension, all proclaim its descent from the Mini and the 1100. Front brakes are discs. Like other members of the BMC front-drive family this is a bold design with lots of development potential.

CLOSE-UP
Four-cyl.; o.h.v.; 80.26×88.9 mm.; 1,798 c.c.; 80 b.h.p.; 8.2 to 1 comp.; coil ign.; S.U. carb.; 4-speed, 13.78, 9.28, 5.79, 4.19 to 1; cen. lvr.; susp., f. and r. ind. rubber hydraulic; 4-door; 5-seat; hyd. servo brks., disc front; max. 90 m.p.h.; cruise 80; m.p.g. 28-30; whl. base 8ft. 10in.; track f. 4ft. 8½in., r. 4ft. 7½in.; lgth. 13ft. 8½in.; width 5ft. 7in.; ht. 4ft. 7½in.; g.c. 6½in.; turng. cir. 35ft. 6in.; kerb wt. 22¼ cwt.; tank 10¾ gals.; 12-volt.

£721+£152 p.t. = £873

AUSTIN A/110 WESTMINSTER

THIS is a first-class car for the motorist who wants a good-looking car that will do its job without fuss, smoothly and silently. Among the favourites of the British Motor Corporation's wide range, it appeals both to the family man and the man of commerce. Changes made in suspension, braking and silencers have paid off well.

CLOSE-UP
Six-cyl.; o.h.v.; 83×89 mm.; 2,912 c.c.; 120 b.h.p.; 8.3 to 1 comp.; coil ign.; 2 S.U. carbs.; 4-speed, 10.31, 8.1, 5.11, 3.91 to 1; cen. lvr. BW overdrive or auto. opt.; susp., f. ind. coil, r. half-elliptic; 4-door; 5/6-seat; servo brks., disc front; max. 102 m.p.h.; cruise 80; m.p.g. 18-23; whl. base 9ft. 2in.; track f. 4ft. 6in., r. 4ft. 5¼in.; lgth. 15ft. 7½in.; width 5ft. 8½in.; ht. 5ft. 0½in.; g.c. 6½in.; turng. cir. 41ft.; kerb wt. 28½ cwt.; tank 16 gals.; 12-volt.

£825+£173 p.t. = £998

Abbreviations—g.c.—ground clearance; susp.—suspension; f.—front; r.—rear; comp.—compression; s.v.—side-valves; o.h.v.—overhead valves; o.h.c.—overhead camshaft; hyd.—hydraulic.

AUSTIN HEALEY 3000 MARK III

STANDBY of BMC rally teams, driven with particular brilliance by the Morleys, this veteran work-horse provides an extraordinary amount of performance for the money and is still scoring international successes against much later designs. A tough six-cylinder engine, solid structure and suspension refined in the hard school of rally motoring keep it going when many more exotic machines have stopped.

CLOSE-UP
Six-cyl.; o.h.v.; 88.4×83.9 mm.; 2,912 c.c.; 148 b.h.p.; 9 to 1 comp.; coil ign.; 2 S.U. carbs.; 4-speed, 10.209, 7.302, 4.743, 3.545 to 1; cen. lvr., de Normanville overdrive opt.; susp., f. ind. coil, r. half-elliptic; 2-door; 2/3 seat; hyd. servo brks., disc front; max. 120 m.p.h.; cruise 100; m.p.g. 20-23; whl. base 7ft. 7¾in.; track f. 4ft. 0¾in., r. 4ft. 2in.; lgth. 13ft. 1½in.; width 5ft.; ht. 4ft. 1in.; g.c. 4½in.; turng. cir. 35ft.; kerb wt. 23 cwt.; tank 12 gals.; 12-volt.

£915+£192 p.t.=£1,107

AUDI

REVIVING a famous pre-war name, Auto Union present a front-wheel drive car with a unique engine. World's highest compression ratio and high-swirl bowl-in-piston combustion chamber give it enviable economy and astonishing flexibility. They claim 33 m.p.g. at 70 m.p.h.—with 1.7 litres. Other talking points; rustproof stainless steel bumpers, disc front brakes mounted inboard, glass fibre and nylon fan, five-position adjustable backrest.

CLOSE-UP
Four-cyl.; o.h.v.; 80×84.4 mm.; 1,695 c.c.; 72 b.h.p.; 11.2 to 1 comp.; coil ign.; Solex carb.; 4-speed, 13.22, 7.56, 5.13, 3.76 to 1; col. lvr.; susp. f. ind. torsion bar, r. torsion bar; 2/4-door; 4/5-seat; hyd. brks., disc front; max. 92 m.p.h.; cruise 85; m.p.g. 32-38; whl. base 8ft. 2in.; track, f. 4ft. 4⅞in., r. 4ft. 4½in.; lgth. 14ft. 0½in.; width 5ft. 4in.; ht. 4ft. 8in.; g.c. 6¼in.; turng. cir. 34ft. 9in.; kerb wt. 19¾ cwt.; tank 11⅝ gals.; 12-volt.

AUTO UNION DKW F.102

LATEST and most sophisticated of a two-stroke front wheel drive line that began with little economy cars long ago. Three cylinders in line, with pump lubrication, drive the front wheels through an all-synchro gearbox. Sealed cooling system, no chassis greasing and 6,000-mile service intervals fit it for hard work. Front brakes are discs. Wings are detachable for repair.

CLOSE-UP
Three-cyl.; two-stroke; 81×76 mm.; 1,175 c.c.; 60 b.h.p.; 7.5 to 1 comp.; coil ign.; Solex carb.; 4-speed, 14.91, 7.78, 4.79, 3.63 to 1; col. lvr.; susp., f. ind. torsion bar, r. torsion bar; 2/4-door; 5-seat; hyd. brks.; max. 81 m.p.h.; cruise 75; m.p.g. 28-33; whl. base 8ft. 1⅛in.; track f. and r. 4ft. 4⅜in.; lgth. 14ft. 0½in.; width 5ft. 3⅞in.; ht. 4ft. 9⅛in.; g.c. 6¼in.; turng. cir. 36ft.; kerb wt. 18½ cwt.; tank 9⅞ gals.; 6-volt.

£806+£170 p.t.=£976

BENTLEY T-TYPE

SHARING all features of the fabulous new Rolls-Royce except the radiator grille, this Bentley satisfies top people's yearnings for a car that is roomier, easier to park and still faster. Besides the unit-structure, all-independent self-levelling suspension, and disc brakes with hydraulic servos, note details like electrically operated seats that rise and tilt, warning lamps with test button.

CLOSE-UP
Eight-cyl.; o.h.v.; 104.1×91.4 mm.; 6,230 c.c.; b.h.p. not revealed; 9 to 1 comp.; coil ign.; 2 S.U. carbs.; 4-speed auto., 11.75, 8.1, 4.46, 3.08 to 1; col. lvr.; susp. f. and r. ind. coil, hyd. levelling; 4-door; 5-seat; disc, hyd. servo brks.; max. 120 m.p.h.; cruise 100; m.p.g. 13-16; whl. base 9ft. 11½in.; track f. and r. 4ft. 9½in.; lgth. 16ft. 11½in.; width 5ft. 11in.; ht. 4ft. 11¾in.; g.c. 6½in.; turng. cir. 38ft.; kerb wt. 41½ cwt.; tank 24 gals.; 12-volt.

Abbreviations—g.c.—ground clearance; susp.—suspension; f.—front; r.—rear; comp.—compression; s.v.—side-valves; o.h.v.—overhead valves; o.h.c.—overhead camshaft; hyd.—hydraulic.

BENTLEY S.3 CONTINENTAL

IF you believe that the introduction of a new model enhances the value of an existing classic, why not invest in a Continental Bentley? Separate chassis, drum brakes, mechanical brake servo, half-elliptic rear springs and rigid axle are retained for this great car, as for all special coachwork Rolls-Royce and Bentley models. The price is high but 20 years from now there will still be buyers.

CLOSE-UP

Eight-cyl.; o.h.v.; 104.14×91.44 mm.; 6,230 c.c.; b.h.p. not revealed; 9 to 1 comp.; coil ign.; 2 SU. carbs.; 4-speed auto., 11.75, 8.10, 4.46, 3.08 to 1; col. lvr.; susp., f. ind. coil, r. half-elliptic, 2/4-door; 4-seat; hyd. servo brks.; max. 120 m.p.h.; cruise 90-100; m.p.g. 14-16; whl. base 10ft. 3in.; track, f. 4ft. 10½in., r. 5ft.; lgth. 17ft. 8in.; width 6ft. 0¾in.; ht. 5ft. 4in.; g.c. 7in.; turng. cir. 41ft. 9in.; kerb wt. 39¼ cwt.; tank 18 gals.; 12-volt.

£6,640 + £1,385 p.t. = £8,025

B.M.W. 1800 TI

FROM a 1500 c.c. family saloon BMW have developed a range of high performance models including this fast rally and racing car which has a formidable record of success. High power from its overhead camshaft engine is matched by fine road holding from its all-independent suspension and fade-free stopping with servo-assisted brakes (discs in front). Maximum performance comes from TI.SA., with 130 h.p., Weber carburetters, five-speeds.

CLOSE-UP

Four-cyl.; o.h.c.; 84×80 mm.; 1,773 c.c.; 110 b.h.p.; 9.5 to 1 comp.; coil ign.; 2 Solex carbs.; 4-speed, 15.69, 8.50, 5.46, 4.11 to 1; cen. lvr.; susp., f. and r. ind. coil; 4-door; 4-seat; hyd. servo brks., disc front; max. 109 m.p.h.; cruise 90; m.p.g. 20; whl. base 8ft. 4½in.; track f. 4ft. 4in., r. 4ft. 6in.; lgth. 14ft. 9in.; width 5ft. 7½in.; ht. 4ft. 9in.; g.c. 6in.; turng. cir. 31ft. 6in.; kerb wt. 21¼ cwt.; tank 12 gals.; 12-volt.

£1,446 + £302 p.t. = £1,748

BMW 2000 CS

CHOICE of two engines and transmissions gives BMW's attractive new 2-litre coupe a wide appeal. Two twin-choke carburetters and 120 h.p. with four speeds, all synchromesh, or one carburetter and 100 h.p. with the new ZF automatic transmission. Two oval and two circular headlamps make an easily-identified combination. Engine design is derived from the 1800 but with bigger bores, new crankshaft, bigger valves, modified cylinder head.

CLOSE-UP

Four-cyl.; o.h.c.; 89×80 mm.; 1,990 c.c.; 120 b.h.p.; 9.3 to 1 comp.; coil ign.; 2 Solex twin-choke carbs.; 4-speed, 00.0, 0.00, 0.00, 3.89 to 1; cen. lvr.; susp. f. and r. ind. coil; 2-door; 4-seat; hyd. brks., disc front; max. 115 m.p.h.; cruise 100; m.p.g. 23-26; whl. base 8ft. 4½in.; track, f. 4ft. 4in., r. 4ft. 6in.; lgth. 14ft. 8½in.; width 5ft. 6in.; ht. 4ft. 2¼in.; g.c. 5½in.; turng. cir. 30ft.; kerb wt. 20½ cwt.; tank 12 gals.; 12-volt.

BOND EQUIPE G.T. 4S

REPLACING the original two-seater Equipe, the GT 4S offers reasonable space for two rear passengers and the luggage trunk now has an external lid. Triumph Herald chassis, Spitfire Mk 2 engine, and a glass fibre body built round the Herald scuttle, screen frame, doors and instrument panel, make a distinctive car at a practical price. And it can be serviced by Triumph agents.

CLOSE-UP

Four-cyl.; o.h.v.; 69.3×76 mm.; 1,147 c.c.; 67 b.h.p.; 9 to 1 comp.; coil ign.; 2 S.U. carbs.; 4-speed; 15.7, 11.3, 7.3, 4.2 to 1; cen. lvr.; susp., f. ind. coil, r. ind. trans. leaf; 2-door; 2/4-seat; hyd. brks., disc front; max. 85 m.p.h.; cruise 75; m.p.g. 30-35; whl. base 7ft. 7½in.; track, f. 4ft. 1in.; r. 4ft. 0½in.; lgth. 13ft. 2⅜in.; width 5ft. 0½in.; ht. 4ft. 4½in.; g.c. 6in.; turng. cir. 25ft.; kerb wt. 16 cwt.; tank 10 gals.; 12-volt.

£685 + £144 p.t. = £829

Abbreviations—g.c.—ground clearance; susp.—suspension; f.—front; r.—rear; comp.—compression; s.v.—side-valves; o.h.v.—overhead valves; o.h.c.—overhead camshaft; hyd.—hydraulic.

BRISTOL 408

LATEST version of this clean-lined beauty has redesigned brakes, softer front suspension, better steering by redistributing the weight and more engine-urge which gives the car a higher top speed. Radiator air intake shape has been altered to improve air flow over a lighter and more efficient radiator, incorporating a sealed cooling system. This is the model for the car connoisseur.

CLOSE-UP
Eight-cyl.; o.h.v.; 98.55 · 84.07 mm.; 5,130 c.c.; 250 b.h.p. gross; 9 to 1 comp.; coil ign.; Carter carb.; 3-speed auto, 8.10, 4.80, 3.31 to 1; push button control; susp., f. ind. coil, r. torsion bar; 2-door; 4-seat; disc servo brks.; max. 125 m.p.h.; cruise 100; m.p.g. 18-20; whl. base 9ft. 6in.; track f. 4ft. 5in., r. 4ft. 6½in.; lgth. 16ft. 1½in.; width 5ft. 8in.; ht. 5ft.; g.c. 6½in.; turng. cir. 39ft. 6in.; kerb wt. 32 cwt.; tank 18 gals.; 12-volt.

£4,012 + £837 p.t. = £4,849

BUICK RIVIERA

REVISED body design plus a host of luxury features give extra interest to this fine high performance model. Power operated windows, power adjusted seats, automatic boot lid release, head rests, cornering lights, rear window demister, remote control outside mirror, twin-operated radio and wood-rimmed steering wheel are features which will appeal to those who love comfort, while the body lines will attract attention in any company.

CLOSE-UP
Eight-cyl.; o.h.v.; 109.5 \ 92.5 mm.; 6,965 c.c.; 340 b.h.p. gross; 10.25 to 1 comp.; coil ign.; four-choke carb.; 3-speed auto., 8.01, 4.78, 3.23 to 1; cen. lvr.; susp., f. ind. coil, r. coil; 2-door; 5-seat; hyd. servo brks.; max. 120 m.p.h.; cruise 100; m.p.g. 13-17; whl. base 9ft. 11in.; track, f. 5ft. 3½in., r. 5ft. 3in.; lgth. 17ft. 7¼in.; width 6ft. 6¾in.; ht. 4ft. 5⅜in.; g.c. 6in.; turng. cir. 44ft.; kerb wt. 38½ cwt.; tank 18¼ gals.; 12-volt.

BUICK SKYLARK

SPORTING lines of the two-door hard-top saloon are backed by an engine that produces 325 h.p. on the test bed. Transmission is two-speed automatic and there are many special items of equipment: 7-position tilting steering wheel, power adjusted seat, power-operated windows, reclining passenger seat and headrests for both front seats. The gear selector is on the centre console and the steering is power assisted.

CLOSE-UP
Eight-cyl.; o.h.v.; 106.3 × 92.5 mm.; 6,572 c.c.; 325 b.h.p. gross; 10.25 to 1 comp.; coil ign.; four-choke carb.; 2-speed, 5.43, 3.08 to 1; cen. lvr.; susp., f. ind. coil, r. coil; 2-door; 5-seat; hyd. servo brks.; max. 110 m.p.h.; cruise 90; m.p.g. 13-17; whl. base 9ft. 7in.; track, f. 4ft. 10in., r. 4ft. 11in.; lgth. 17ft.; width 6ft. 3in.; ht. 4ft. 6in.; turng. cir. 40ft. 8in.; kerb wt. 29 cwt.; tank 16½ gals.; 12-volt.

CADILLAC FLEETWOOD

GONE are the sharp sky-tilted fins that identified Cadillacs for so long. The Fleetwood Brougham has a long, low line and vinyl-padded roof in a choice of five colours. Inside, wooden trim, carpeted foot-rests, swivelling reading lamps and fold-down picnic tables provide the luxury touches that thousands of Cadillac owners throughout the world expect. Power operation for seats, steering, windows and brakes and of course automatic transmission.

CLOSE-UP
Eight-cyl.; o.h.v.; 104.9 · 101.6 mm.; 7,025 c.c.; 340 b.h.p. gross; 10.5 to 1 comp.; coil ign.; Carter carb.; 3-speed auto., 7.49, 4.55, 2.94 to 1; col. lvr.; susp., f. ind. coil, r. coil; 4-door; 6-seat; hyd. servo brks.; max. 120 m.p.h.; cruise 100; m.p.g. 12-15; whl. base 11ft. 1in.; track f. and r. 5ft. 2½in.; lgth. 18ft. 11½in.; width 6ft. 7⅞in.; ht. 4ft. 7¼in.; g.c. 5¾in.; turng. cir. 45ft. 9in.; kerb wt. 43¼ cwt.; tank 21 gals.; 12-volt.

Abbreviations—g.c.—ground clearance; susp.—suspension; f.—front; r.—rear; comp.—compression; s.v.—side-valves; o.h.v.—overhead valves; o.h.c.—overhead camshaft; hyd.—hydraulic

CHEVROLET IMPALA CONVERTIBLE

STYLING and mechanical changes appear on the 1966 models of the world's top selling car range. Heavier perimeter-type chassis frame, stronger dampers are new points. Also on the stand is the Corvette Mako Shark II, an experimental fast-back two seater coupe with 7-litre engine, concealed headlamps and transmission selector controls on the steering wheel. It has all-independent suspension and electrically operated stabilising flaps.

CLOSE-UP

Eight-cyl.; o.h.v.; 98.4 × 76.2 mm.; 4,638 c.c.; 198 b.h.p gross; 9.25 to 1 comp.; coil ign.; Rochester carb. 3-speed, 8.66, 4.97, 3.36 to 1; col. lvr.; 4-speed, overdrive or auto. opt.; susp., f. ind. coil, r. coil; 2-door; 5/6-seat; hyd. brks., servo opt.; max. 105 m.p.h.; cruise 90; m.p.g. 15-18; whl. base 9ft. 10⅞in.; track, f. 5ft. 1⅞in., r. 5ft. 3¼in.; lgth. 17ft. 9in.; width 6ft. 7½in.; ht. 4ft. 7⅛in.; g.c. 7½in.; turng. cir. 39ft. 6in.; kerb wt. 33½ cwt.; tank 19½ gals.; 12-volt.

CHEVROLET IMPALA

IMPALA, Chevelle, Chevy II, Caprice, Corvair and Corvette; the Chevrolet range covers a vast variety of sizes and body styles, with front or rear engines. Fourteen of the 50 models are station wagons. Among the options are tilt-telescope steering wheel, F.M. stereo radio with four speakers. Padded instrument panel and visors, dual speed wipers with non-glare arms and blades, and reversing lamps are standard equipment.

CLOSE-UP

Eight-cyl.; o.h.v.; 98.4 × 76.2 mm.; 4,638 c.c.; 198 b.h.p. gross; 9.25 to 1 comp.; coil ign.; Rochester carb.; 2-speed auto., 6.11, 3.36 to 1; col. lvr.; susp., f. ind. coil, r. coil; 2 or 4-door; 6-seat; hyd. brks., servo opt.; max. 108 m.p.h.; cruise 90; m.p.g. 15-18; whl. base 9ft. 10⅞in.; track, f. 5ft. 1⅞in., r. 5ft. 3¼in.; lgth. 17ft. 9in.; width 6ft. 7½in.; ht. 4ft. 8½in.; g.c. 7½in.; turng. cir. 39ft. 6in.; kerb wt. 33 cwt.; tank 16¾ gals.; 12-volt.

CHRYSLER NEWPORT

HERE'S Chrysler prestige in an economy model which is available as saloon, coupe or hardtop with two or four doors. Transmission is manual three-speed, with option of automatic. Chrysler becomes one of the first American manufacturers to offer disc brakes with their appearance as an optional extra on front wheels of the high performance 300 model. In all there are 13 models in the Chrysler 1966 range.

CLOSE-UP

Eight-cyl.; o.h.v.; 108 × 85.8 mm.; 6,276 c.c.; 270 b.h.p. gross; 9.2 to 1 comp.; coil ign.; twin-choke carb.; 3-speed; col. lvr., auto. opt.; susp., f. ind. torsion bar, r. half-elliptic; 4-door; 6-seat; hyd. brks.; max. 100 m.p.h.; cruise 90; m.p.g. 15-19; whl. base 10ft. 4in.; track, f. 5ft. 2in., r. 5ft. 0¾in.; lgth. 18ft. 3in.; width 6ft. 7½in.; ht. 4ft. 7½in.; g.c. 6in.; turng. cir. 44ft.; kerb wt. 37¾ cwt.; tank 20 gals.; 12-volt.

CHRYSLER NEW YORKER

BIGGER engine and higher performance, plus a long line of optional equipment will hold the interest of buyers in 1966. Six-way seat adjusters, better dampers, thicker brake linings are included. Body styles include 2-door and 4-door hardtops, 4-door saloon and station wagons with a variety of seating layouts. Styling is planned to give stronger separate identity to New York, Newport and the sporting 300 series.

CLOSE-UP

Eight-cyl.; o.h.v.; 109.7 × 95 mm.; 7,210 c.c.; 365 b.h.p. gross; 10 to 1 comp.; coil ign.; four-choke carb.; 3-speed; col. lvr., auto. opt.; susp., f. ind. torsion bar, r. half-elliptic; 4-door; 6-seat; hyd. brks.; max. 120 m.p.h.; cruise 95; m.p.g. 12; whl. base 10ft. 4in.; track, f. 5ft. 2in., r. 5ft. 0¾in.; lgth. 18ft. 3in.; width 6ft. 7½in.; ht. 4ft. 7¾in.; g.c. 6in.; turng. cir. 44ft.; kerb wt. 38½ cwt.; tank 20 gals.; 12-volt.

Abbreviations—g.c.—ground clearance; susp.—suspension; f.—front; r.—rear; comp.—compression; s.v.—side-valves; o.h.v.—overhead valves; o.h.c.—overhead camshaft; hyd.—hydraulic.

CITREON DS 21 PALLAS

BIGGER bore, shorter stroke, bigger valves and five-bearing crankshaft form the recipe for an extra 1000 r.p.m. and an increase to 100 h.p. which raises maximum speed to 109 m.p.h. Other advances over the DS 19; quartz iodine lamps, synchromesh first gear on the hydraulic-shift model, constant velocity drive shaft joints throughout for smoother steering, improved disc brakes with a warning light to show when pads need renewing.

CLOSE-UP

Four-cyl.; o.h.v.; 90 × 85.5 mm.; 2,175 c.c.; 100 b.h.p.; 8.75 to 1 comp.; coil ign.; Weber twin-choke carb.; 4-speed, 14.22, 8.49, 5.56, 3.72 to 1; dash lvr.; susp. f. and r. ind. hyd.-pneu.; 4-door; 5/6-seat; hyd. servo brks., disc front; max. 109 m.p.h.; cruise 95; m.p.g. 25-30; whl. base 10ft. 3in.; track, f. 4ft. 11in., r. 4ft. 3½in.; lgth. 15ft. 10in.; width 5ft. 10½in.; ht. 4ft. 11in.; g.c. 6½in.; turng. cir. 36ft.; kerb wt. 25 cwt.; tank 14 gals.; 12-volt.

£1635+£342 p.t. = £1977

CITREON DS 21 CABRIOLET

TEN years have not dated the body style or Citroen's unique chassis design with self-levelling hydraulic-pneumatic suspension. It has influenced many later designs. More power, stronger dampers, revised gear ratios enhance performance for 1966 and stopping distances from various speeds are shown on the speedometer. Citroen's unique single-bolt wheel fixing is abandoned in favour of the usual five studs.

CLOSE-UP

Four-cyl.; o.h.v.; 90 ∕ 85.5 mm.; 2,175 c.c.; 100 b.h.p.; 8.75 to 1 comp.; coil ign.; Weber twin-choke carb.; 4-speed, 14.22, 8.49, 5.56, 3.72 to 1; dash lvr.; susp. f. and r. ind. hyd.-pneu.; 2-door; 5-seat; hyd. servo brks., disc front; max. 106 m.p.h.; cruise 90; m.p.g. 25-30; whl. base 10ft. 3in.; track, f. 4ft. 11in.; r. 4ft. 3½in.; lgth. 15ft. 10in.; width 5ft. 10½in.; ht. 4ft. 11in.; g.c. 6½in.; turng. cir. 36ft.; kerb wt. 26 cwt.; tank 14 gals.; 12-volt.

£2,560+£535 p.t. = £3,095

DAF DAFFODIL

DETAIL improvements to body style go along with better lubrication for the automatic transmission and improved road holding on Holland's unique economy car. Its belt-drive automatic transmission, long thought suitable only for small light cars, now drives an experimental transporter for the American army and emerged triumphantly from its first try-out in a racing car at Monte Carlo. Standard body style is the two-door saloon.

CLOSE-UP

Two-cyl.; o.h.v. air cooled; 85.5 ∕ 65 mm.; 746 c.c.; 26 b.h.p.; 7.5 to 1 comp.; coil ign. BCI carb.; auto. belt drive 16.4 to 3.9 to 1; cen. lvr.; susp., f. ind. trans. leaf, r. ind. coil; 2-door; 4-seat; hyd. brks.; max. 65 m.p.h.; cruise 65; m.p.g. 38-48; whl. base 6ft. 9in.; track f. and r. 3ft. 10½in.; lgth. 11ft. 10½in.; width 4ft. 9in.; ht. 4ft. 6½in.; g.c. 6¾in.; turng. cir. 31ft.; kerb wt. 13¼ cwt.; tank, 7 galls.; 6-volt.

£490+£104 p.t. = £594

DAIHATSU 800

MADE in Osaka for the developing Japanese assault on world car markets, the little Daihatsu has a 797 c.c. engine with pushrod-operated valves in a light alloy head. Hydraulically operated clutch, four-speed all-synchromesh gearbox and hypoid final drive are modern features. Drum brakes are used all round and suspension is conventional: There is also a more powerful model with 1000 c.c. engine.

CLOSE-UP

Four-cyl.; o.h.v.; 62 × 66 mm.; 797 c.c.; 41 b.h.p.; 9 to 1 comp.; coil ign.; Solex carb.; 4-speed, 22.35, 11.94, 7.58, 5.125 to 1; col. lvr.; susp., f. ind. torsion bar, r. half-elliptic; 2-door; 4-seat; hyd. brks.; max. 69 m.p.h.; cruise 62; m.p.g. 33-36; whl. base 7ft. 4in.; track, f. 3ft. 10½in., r. 3ft. 10in.; lgth 12ft. 5½in.; width 4ft. 9in.; ht. 4ft. 7½in.; g.c. 6in.; turng. cir. 29ft. 3in.; kerb wt. 14½ cwt.; tank 5½ gals.; 12-volt.

£658+£141 p.t. = £799

Abbreviations—g.c.—ground clearance; susp.—suspension; f.—front; r.—rear; comp.—compression; s.v.—side-valves; o.h.v.—overhead valves; o.h.c.—overhead camshaft; hyd.—hydraulic.

DAIMLER MAJESTIC

ALTHOUGH produced only in small numbers, this big, powerful saloon from one of Britain's oldest-established manufacturers sets a high standard of performance with its powerful V8 engine and automatic transmission. Disc brakes on all wheels, with servo assistance, enable its performance to be used safely and the luxurious interior finish stamps it as a car suitable for private or official occasions.

CLOSE-UP

Eight-cyl.; o.h.v.; 95.25 × 89 mm.; 4,560 c.c.; 220 b.h.p. gross; 8 to 1 comp.; coil ign.; 2 S.U. carbs.; 3-speed auto., 8.7, 5.41, 3.77 to 1; col. lvr.; susp., f. ind. coil, r. half-elliptic; 4-door; 5/6-seat; disc servo brks.; max. 110 m.p.h.; cruise 90; m.p.g. 13-18; whl. base 9ft. 6in.; track f. and r. 4ft. 9in.; lgth. 16ft. 10in.; width 6ft. 1¾in.; ht. 5ft. 2⅜in.; g.c. 7in.; turng. cir. 42ft.; kerb wt. 37 cwt.; tank 21½ gals.; 12-volt.

£2,235 + £468 p.t. = £2,703

DAIMLER 2½-LITRE V8

NATURALLY bears a strong resemblance to its bed-mate the Jaguar. It stems from a combination of two outstandingly successful projects—the Daimler 2½-litre V8 engine and the Jaguar Mark 2 body shell. Result: a car combining the grace and beauty of Jag styling with the smoothness and high-performance of the Daimler power plant. Standard equipment includes disc brakes all round, comprehensive heater and demister, and Borg Warner automatic transmission.

CLOSE-UP

Eight-cyl.; o.h.v.; 76.2 × 69.85 mm.; 2,548 c.c.; 140 b.h.p. gross; 8.2 to 1 comp.; coil ign.; 2 S.U. carbs.; 3-speed, BW auto., 10.02, 6.19, 4.27 to 1; col. lvr.; susp., f. ind. coil, r. cantilever leaf; 4-door; 5-seat; disc servo brks.; max. 110 m.p.h.; cruise 80-90; m.pg. 20-22; whl. base 8ft. 11⅜in.; track f. 4ft. 7in., r. 4ft. 5⅜in.; lgth. 15ft. 0¾in.; width 5ft. 6¾in.; ht. 4ft. 9½in.; g.c. 7in.; turng. cir. 37ft. 6in.; kerb wt. 30 cwt.; tank 12 gals.; 12-volt.

£1,362 + £285 p.t. = £1,647

DAIMLER LIMOUSINE

ECONOMICALLY a difficult exercise, the production of limousines caters for a small market where buyers expect top quality. The Jaguar group holds its place in the market with this comfortable, quiet and very fast car, while producing Jaguar Cars, Coventry Climax engines, Guy trucks, Daimler buses, Cummins diesel engines and who knows what else besides. Also available with the same fine 4½-litre V8 engine is the Daimler Majestic saloon.

CLOSE-UP

Eight-cyl.; o.h.v.; 95.25 × 80.01 mm.; 4,561 c.c.; 220 b.h.p. gross; 8 to 1 comp.; coil ign.; 2 S.U. carbs.; 3-speed, auto. 8.7, 5.4, 3.77 to 1; col. lvr.; susp., f. ind. coil, r. half-elliptic; 4-door; 8-seat; disc servo brks.; max. 110 m.p.h.; cruise 90; m.p.g. 17-20; whl. base 11ft. 6in.; track f. and r. 4ft. 9in.; lgth. 18ft. 10in.; width 6ft. 1¼in.; ht. 5ft. 5½in.; g.c. 7in.; turng. cir. 44ft.; kerb wt. 40 cwt.; tank 16 gals.; 12-volt.

£2,893 + £604 p.t. = £3,497

DODGE DART

CANTED-OVER six, or straight-mounted V8, the Dodge power units cover a vast range from 145 to 425 test-bed horsepower and there is all the usual wide selection of body styles, including this sleek Polara V8 Convertible. The Dart has a lot in common mechanically with Chrysler's Valiant and among the optional equipment are disc brakes for the front wheels.

CLOSE-UP

Six-cyl.; o.h.v.; 86.3 × 104.8 mm.; 3,690 c.c.; 145 b.h.p. gross; 8.4 to 1 comp.; coil ign.; Holley carb.; 3-speed, 9.59, 6.05, 3.31 to 1; col. lvr., auto. opt.; susp. f. ind. torsion bar, r. half-elliptic; 2 or 4-door; 5/6-seat; hyd. servo brks.; max. 90 m.p.h.; cruise 80; m.p.g. 16-20; whl. base 9ft. 11in.; track, f. 4ft. 11½in., r. 4ft. 11½in.; lgth. 16ft. 8⅝in.; width 6ft. 3in.; ht. 4ft. 7in.; g.c. 5½in.; turng. cir. 45ft. 6in.; kerb wt. 23 cwt.; tank 15 gals.; 12-volt.

Abbreviations—g.c.—ground clearance; susp.—suspension; f.—front; r.—rear; comp.—compression; s.v.—side-valves; o.h.v.—overhead valves; o.h.c.—overhead camshaft; hyd.—hydraulic.

23

ELVA COURIER

THIS model stems from a successful sports racing car and has proved to be smart, quick and lion-hearted. Its body is glass fibre reinforced with steel and has disc brakes at the front, winding windows and independent rear suspension. It is a model that appeals to the sporting type who wants a reasonably priced car with moderate running costs. The inside matches the splendid finish of the exterior.

CLOSE-UP
Four-cyl.; o.h.v.; 80.3×89 mm.; 1,798 c.c.; 95 b.h.p. gross; 8.9 to 1 comp.; coil ign.; 2 S.U. carbs.; 4-speed, 14.2, 8.66, 5.37, 3.91 to 1; cen. lvr.; susp. f. and r. ind. coil; 2-door; 2-seat; hyd. brks., disc front; max. 110 m.p.h.; cruise 95; m.p.g. 28; whl. base 7ft. 6in.; track, f. 4ft. 1½in., r. 4ft. 1in.; lgth. 12ft. 5½in.; width 5ft.; ht. 3ft. 9½in.; g.c. 6in.; turng. cir. 35ft.; kerb wt. 12¾ cwt.; tank 9 gals.; 12-volt.

£823+£173 p.t. = £996

FAIRTHORPE EM-3

ODD-LOOKING but fast, the Fairthorpes have been built with a variety of engines, many from Ford and Standard Triumph. Their bodies are in glass fibre and many cars have been supplied in kit form for assembly by enthusiastic amateurs in their own garages at home. Regular appearances by works cars in rallies have helped to develop the chassis design.

CLOSE-UP
Four-cyl.; o.h.v.; 69.3×76 mm.; 1,147 c.c.; 67 b.h.p.; 9 to 1 comp.; coil ign.; 2 S.U. carbs.; 4-speed, 15.41, 8.88, 5.75, 4.11 to 1; cen. lvr.; susp. f. and r. ind. coil; 2-door; 2-seat; hyd. brks., disc front; max. 95 m.p.h.; cruise 80; m.p.g. 36-42; whl. base 6ft. 11⅞in.; track f. and r. 4ft.; lgth. 11ft. 10in.; width 4ft. 9¾in.; ht. 3ft. 5⅜in.; g.c. 6ins.; turng. cir. 24ft.; kerb wt. 9¾ cwt.; tank 9¾ gals.; 12-volt.

£625+£132 p.t. = £757

FERRARI 275 GTB

GONE is the rear axle with half elliptics and radius arms; Ferrari takes the all-independent line in this spell-binding successor to the 250GT. Magnesium alloy wheels complement the lean lines of the coupe body built to Pininfarina designs by Scaglietti. After quarrels over homologation, 275 GTB is ready to add to Ferrari's fabulous racing record or bring jet-age thrills to ordinary road driving.

CLOSE-UP
Twelve-cyl.; o.h.c.; 77×58.8 mm.; 3,286 c.c.; 275 b.h.p.; 9.2 to 1 comp.; coil ign.; 3 Weber twin-choke carbs.; 5-speed, 10.15, 6.99, 5.18, 4.12, 3.43 to 1; cen. lvr.; susp. f. and r. ind. coil; 2-door; 2-seat; disc servo brks.; max. 160 m.p.h.; cruise 130; m.p.g. 15-20; whl. base 7ft. 10½in.; track, f. 4ft. 6⅜in., r. 4ft. 6¾in.; lgth. 14ft. 3⅜in.; width 5ft. 6¾in.; ht. 4ft. 5⅛in.; g.c. 4⅜in.; turng. cir. 46ft.; kerb wt. 25 cwt.; tank 18¾ gals.; 12-volt.

£4,900+£1,074 p.t. = £5,974

FERRARI 330 GT

EVEN at prices over £6,500 discriminating buyers to whom money is no problem are ordering this great car which unites Ferrari's long racing experience and Pininfarina's flair for the production of fine coachwork in a car of breath-taking performance and luxurious comfort. V-12 4-litre engine with an overhead camshaft to each bank and three twin-choke Weber carburetters. Transmission via four-speed gearbox with de Normanville overdrive.

CLOSE-UP
Twelve-cyl.; o.h.c.; 77×71 mm.; 3,967 c.c.; 300 b.h.p.; 8.8 to 1 comp.; coil ign.; 3 Weber carbs.; 4-speed with overdrive, 10.78, 7.22, 5.34, 4.25, 3.31 to 1; cen. lvr.; susp., f. ind. coil, r. half-elliptic; 2-door; 2-seat; disc servo brks.; max. 152 m.p.h.; cruise 130; m.p.g. 12-16; whl. base 8ft. 8⅜in.; track f. 4ft. 7⅛in.; r. 4ft. 6⅞in.; lgth. 15ft. 10½in.; width 5ft. 7⅛in.; ht. 4ft. 5⅜in.; g.c. 4⅜in.; turng. cir. 50ft.; kerb wt. 27 cwt.; tank 19¾ gals.; 12-volt.

£5,350+£1,172 p.t. = £6,522

FIAT 500D

FIAT'S baby has passed the 1½ million sales mark in world markets. Two-cylinder air-cooled engine at the rear, for stamina and economy with no freezing troubles; all-independent suspension for a good ride over rough roads. The folding top is an unusual feature and doors on current models are hinged at front instead of rear. There's a station wagon, too, with a longer wheelbase.

CLOSE-UP

Two-cyl.; o.h.v.; air cooled; 67.4×70 mm.; 499 c.c.; 21.5 b.h.p. gross; 7.1 to 1 comp.; coil ign.; Weber carb.; 4-speed, 18.96, 10.59, 6.66, 4.48 to 1; cen. lvr.; susp., f. ind. transv. leaf, r. ind. coil; 2-door; 2/4-seat; hyd. brks.; max. 60 m.p.h.; cruise 55; m.p.g. 55; whl. base 6ft. 0½in.; track f. 3ft. 8½in., r. 3ft. 8½in.; lgth. 9ft. 9in.; width 4ft. 4in.; ht. 4ft. 4½in.; g.c. 5in.; turng. cir. 28ft. 6in.; kerb wt. 10¼ cwt.; tank 4½ gals.; 12-volt.

£338 + £72 p.t. = £410

FIAT 850

FIAT'S most grown-up small car, the 850 has now been in production for some 18 months and continues to gather popularity. It is a sturdy little car with immaculate manners, especially in traffic. A two-door four-seater, it is compact enough to be parked almost on the space of a postage stamp. Engine is rear-mounted, the gearbox is all-synchromesh and the drum brakes are more than adequate.

CLOSE-UP

Four-cyl.; o.h.v.; 65×63.5 mm.; 843 c.c.; 37 b.h.p.; 8.8 to 1 comp.; coil ign.; Weber carb.; 4-speed, 16.82, 9.27, 6.51, 4.16 to 1; cen. lvr.; susp., f. ind. transv. leaf, r. ind. coil; 2-door; 4-seat; hyd. brks.; max. 76 m.p.h.; cruise 65; m.p.g. 40; whl. base 6ft. 7¾in.; track f. 3ft. 9½in., r. 3ft. 11⅝in.; lgth. 11ft. 8¾in.; width 4ft. 8½in.; ht. 4ft. 6½in.; g.c. 6¼in.; turng. cir. 31ft. 6in.; kerb wt. 13½ cwt.; tank 6½ gals.; 12-volt.

£475 + £101 p.t. = £576

FIAT 1500

FAVOURITE Italian family car brought up-to-date with longer wheelbase, more rear-seat room, new grille and tail lamp clusters, servo brakes, improved equipment. Thermostatic fan clutch helps quick warming up, cuts noise while cruising. Included in the price are reversing lamps, map light, rubber-faced bumper overriders, lockable fuel filler, anti-theft steering lock, pedal-operated windscreen washers.

CLOSE-UP

Four-cyl.; o.h.v.; 77×79 mm.; 1,481 c.c.; 75 b.h.p.; 8.8 to 1 comp.; coil ign.; Weber carb.; 4-speed, 15.37, 9.43, 6.1, 4.1 to 1; col. lvr.; susp., f. ind. coil, r. half-elliptic; 4-door; 5-seat; hyd. servo brks, disc front; max. 93 m.p.h.; cruise 82; m.p.g. 27-30; whl. base 7ft. 11½in.; track, f. 4ft. 3in., r. 4ft. 2in.; lgth. 13ft. 4½in.; width 5ft. 0¾in.; ht. 4ft. 8½in.; g.c.; 5in.; turng. cir. 39ft.; kerb wt. 19¼ cwt.; tank 10 gals.; 12-volt.

£772 + £162 p.t. = £934

FIAT 2300

SALOON, station wagon, or four-seater sports coupe; Fiat's six-cylinder range caters for a wide variety of motoring needs. On the family models automatic transmission is an optional extra and the engine has a twin-choke carburetter. The sports coupe comes in two versions, 2300 with single carburetter; 2300 S with twin-carburetter engine modified by Abarth. In its faster form speeds up to 120 m.p.h. are achieved.

CLOSE-UP

Six-cyl.; o.h.v.; 78×79.5 mm.; 2,279 c.c.; 105 b.h.p.; 8.8 to 1 comp; coil ign.; twin choke Weber carb.; 4-speed, 13.82, 8.15, 6.03, 4.30 to 1; de Normanville overdrive opt.; col. lvr.; susp., f. ind. torsion bar, r. half-elliptic; 4-door; 5-seat; disc servo brks.; max. 100 m.p.h.; cruise 90; m.p.g. 22; whl. base 8ft. 8½in.; track, f. 4ft. 5in., r. 4ft. 3½in.; lgth. 14ft. 8½in.; width 5ft. 3½in.; ht. 4ft. 10in.; g.c. 5¾in.; turng. cir. 37ft. 9in.; kerb wt. 25 cwt.; tank 13¼ gals.; 12-volt.

£1,100 + £231 p.t. = £1,331

Abbreviations—g.c.—ground clearance; susp.—suspension; f.—front; r.—rear; comp.—compression; s.v.—side-valves; o.h.v.—overhead valves; o.h.c.—overhead camshaft; hyd.—hydraulic.

FORD ANGLIA

CHOICE of engines, either 997 c.c. or 1,198 c.c. gives Ford's veteran family car a range of performance, with accent on economy or on speed and acceleration to suit a variety of needs. Besides the saloon, there is a very practical, good looking station wagon. Despite rumours of replacement, Ford seem determined to keep this highly successful model running.

CLOSE-UP

Four-cyl.; o.h.v.; 80.96 × 48.41 mm.; 997 c.c.; 39 b.h.p.; 8.9 to 1 comp.; Super: 80.96 × 58.17 mm.; 1,198 c.c.; 48.5 b.h.p.; 8.7 to 1 comp.; coil ign.; Solex carb.; 4-speed, 16.99, 9.88, 5.83, 4.125 to 1; Super: 14.61, 9.88, 5.83, 4.125 to 1; cen. lvr.; susp., f. ind. coil, r. half-elliptic; 2-door; 4-seat; hyd. brks.; max. 75 m.p.h.; cruise 65; Super: 80 and 70; m.p.g. 35-40; whl. base 7ft. 6½in.; track, f. 3ft. 10in., r. 3ft. 9¾in.; lgth. 12ft. 10in.; width 4ft. 9½in.; ht. 4ft. 9½in.; g.c. 6½in.; turng. cir. 32ft.; kerb wt. 15 cwt.; tank 7 gals.; 12-volt.

Anglia: £395 + £84 p.t. = £479
Super: £485 + £103 p.t. = £588

FORD CORSAIR

TRANSFORMED by the new British Ford V4 engine, the Corsair reaches a high level of flexibility and performance. The engine has a counter-rotating balance shaft to ensure smooth running. There are two versions 1.7-litre and 2-litre. The latter gets the GT label but both have single carburetters. Flat cylinder heads and bowl-in-piston combustion chambers.

CLOSE-UP

Four-cyl.; o.h.v.; 93.7 × 60.3 mm.; 1,663 c.c.; 76.5 b.h.p.; 9.1 to 1 comp. or 93.7 × 72.4 mm.; 1,996 c.c.; 88 b.h.p.; 8.9 to 1 comp.; coil ign.; carb.; 4-speed, 13.38, 9.05, 5.33, 3.78 to 1; cen. or col. lvr.; susp., f. ind. coil, r. half-elliptic; 4-door; 5-seat; hyd. brks., disc front; max. 85-95 m.p.h.; cruise 75-85; m.p.g. 26-30; whl. base 8ft. 5in.; track, f. 4ft. 2½in., r. 4ft. 1½in.; lgth. 14ft. 8⅝in.; width 5ft. 3⅜in.; ht. 4ft. 9in.; g.c. 6½in.; turng. cir. 36ft. 6in.; kerb wt. 19½ cwt.; tank 8 gals.; 12-volt.

De Luxe: £650 + £135 p.t. = £785
G.T.: £752 + £157 p.t. = £909

FORD CORTINA

STANDARD and GT models with saloon or station wagon bodywork give the Cortina a broad coverage in the important 1½-litre market and it is one of the best-selling British-built cars. Positive ventilation system, air extractors on rear quarter panels keep interior air fresh and speeds demisting. Two sizes, 1200 or 1500 c.c.; Borg Warner automatic transmission if desired.

CLOSE-UP

Four-cyl.; o.h.v.; 80.96 × 58.17 mm.; 1,198 c.c.; 48.5 b.h.p.; 8.7 to 1 comp.; or 80.96 × 72.82 mm.; 1,499 c.c.; 59.5 b.h.p.; coil ign.; Solex or Weber carb.; 4-speed, 14.61, 9.88, 5.83, 4.125 to 1; or 13.8, 9.34, 5.51, 3.9; cen. lvr., col. opt.; susp., f. ind. coil, r. half-elliptic; 2 or 4-door; 4/5-seat; hyd. brks, disc front; max. 78-85 m.p.h.; cruise 65-75; m.p.g. 32-40; whl. base 8ft. track f. and r. 4ft. 1½in.; lgth. 14ft. 0½in.; width 5ft. 2½in.; ht. 4ft. 8½in.; g.c. 6½in.; turng. cir. 34ft. 8in.; kerb wt. 16½-16¾ cwt.; tank 8 gals.; 12-volt.

1200: £480 + £102 p.t. = £582
1500: £570 + £120 p.t. = £690

FORD ZEPHYR FOUR

THIS is the car for the motorist who wants a lot of motor car with a four-cylinder engine and modest running costs. One of the steady sellers in the wide Ford of Dagenham range, it is as well-suited for the family man as the businessman. It is a car which thrives on hard work and its performance matches its splendid economy.

CLOSE-UP

Four-cyl.; o.h.v.; 82.55 × 79.50 mm.; 1,703 c.c.; 68 b.h.p.; 8.3 to 1 comp.; coil ign.; Zenith carb.; 4-speed, 17.21, 9.17, 5.87, 3.9 to 1; col. lvr., BW overdrive or auto. opt.; susp., f. ind. coil, r. half-elliptic; 4-door; 5/6-seat; hyd. brks., disc front; max. 76 m.p.h.; cruise 70; m.p.g. 23-27; whl. base 8ft. 11in.; track f. 4ft. 5in., r. 4ft. 5½in.; lgth. 15ft. 0½in.; width 5ft. 9in.; ht. 4ft. 9½in.; g.c. 6½in.; turng. cir. 36ft. 6in.; kerb wt. 23 cwt.; tank 12½ gals.; 12-volt.

£675 + £142 p.t. = £817

Abbreviations—g.c.—ground clearance; susp.—suspension; f.—front; r.—rear; comp.—compression; s.v.—side-valves; o.h.v.—overhead valves; o.h.c.—overhead camshaft; hyd.—hydraulic.

FORD ZEPHYR SIX & ZODIAC

THIS is among the most luxurious and powerful of the Ford of Dagenham models and continues to scoop up orders both here and in foreign parts. Certainly it is one of the lowest priced cars for its size, appointments and performance anywhere in the world. No important changes are made on this superfunctional car as it does its job so well.

CLOSE-UP

Six-cyl.; o.h.v.; 82.55 × 79.50 mm.; 2,553 c.c.; 98 b.h.p., Zod. 109 b.h.p.; 8.3 to 1 comp.; coil ign.; Zenith carb.; 4-speed, 11.21, 7.85, 5.00, 3.54 to 1; col. lvr., BW overdrive or auto. opt.; susp., f. ind. coil, r. half-elliptic; 4-door; 5/6 seat; hyd. servo brks., disc front; max. 96-100 m.p.h.; cruise 85; m.p.g. 19-24; whl. base 8ft. 11in.; track, f. 4ft. 5in., r. 4ft. 5½in.; lgth 15ft. 2¾in.; width 5ft. 9in.; ht. 4ft. 9½in.; g.c. 6¾in.; turng. cir. 36ft. 6in.; kerb wt. 24½ cwt., Zod. 25½ cwt.; tank 12½ gals.; 12-volt.

Zephyr: £735 + £155 p.t. = £890
Zodiac: £850 + £179 p.t. = £1,029

FORD TAUNUS 20M

V6 ENGINE and clear cut styling give this German Ford from Cologne its individual character. The gearbox has synchromesh on all four speeds, and automatic transmission is optional. Heater, cigarette lighter, two-speed wipers, reversing lamp are standard and a sliding roof is available; one you push or one worked by an electric motor. There's also a 100 m.p.h. TS model with 90 h.p. high compression engine.

CLOSE-UP

Six-cyl.; o.h.v.; 84 × 60 mm.; 1,998 c.c.; 85 b.h.p.; 8 to 1 comp.; coil ign.; Twin-choke Solex carb.; 4-speed, 12.7, 7.29, 5.07, 3.7 to 1; col. lvr., auto. opt.; susp., f. ind. coil, r. half-elliptic; 2/4-door; 4/5-seat; hyd. brks., disc front, servo opt.; max. 95 m.p.h.; cruise 87; m.p.g. 20-23; whl. base 7ft. 10½in.; track, f. 4ft. 8½in., r. 4ft. 7½in.; lgth 15ft. 2½in.; width 5ft. 7½in.; ht. 4ft. 10½in.; g.c. 7in.; turng. cir. 34ft. 4in.; kerb wt. 20½ cwt.; tank 9¾ gals.; 6-volt.

£975 + £205 p.t. = £1,180

FORD MUSTANG

DETROIT'S dark horse that proved a winner. Sporty appearance with roomy interior and good luggage space made a hit with America's young generation and soon half a million were sold. Lots of options in six-in-line or V8 engines, cover the power spectrum from 100 to 250 horsepower. 3- or 4-speed gearbox, automatic transmission, power steering, disc front brakes are among the options.

CLOSE-UP

Six-cyl.; o.h.v.; 93.5 × 79.5 mm.; 3,273 c.c.; 120 b.h.p. gross; 9.2 to 1 comp.; coil ign.; Ford carb.; 3-speed, 8.83, 5.41, 3.2 to 1; cen. lvr., four-speed or auto. opt.; susp., f. ind. coil, r. half-elliptic; 2-door; 4-seat; hyd. brks., servo and disc opt.; max.   m.p.h.; cruise   ; m.p.g. 14-17; whl. base 9ft.; track f. and r. 4ft. 8in.; lgth. 15ft. 1½in.; width 5ft. 8½in.; ht. 4ft. 3in.; g.c. 6in.; turng. cir. 40ft.; kerb wt. 24¾ cwt.; tank 16 gals.; 12-volt.

£1,519 + £318 p.t. = £1,837

FORD G.T.

NOW in production, after development in racing, the sleek Slough-built projectile will soon be homologated for participation in production car events. Already successful on American tracks, it has shown terrific speed at Le Mans. Its V8 engine behind the two seats is coupled to a five-speed ZF gearbox. The centre section is monocoque in steel sheet; other panels are in glass fibre.

CLOSE-UP

Eight-cyl.; o.h.v.; 101.6 × 72.9 mm.; 4,736 c.c.; 380 b.h.p. gross; 10 to 1 comp.; coil ign.; 2 Weber carbs.; 5-speed, 10.21, 6.20, 4.60, 4.05, 3.59 to 1; susp. f. and r. ind. coil; 2-door; 2-seat; disc brks.; max. 185 m.p.h.; cruise 150; m.p.g. 11-13; whl. base 7ft. 11in.; track f. and r. 4ft. 7in.; lgth. 13ft. 4in.; width 5ft. 10in.; ht. 3ft. 4½in.; g.c. 4in.; kerb wt. 17⅞ cwt.; tank 30½ gals.; 12-volt.

Abbreviations g.c.—ground clearance; susp.—suspension; f.—front; r.—rear; comp.—compression; s.v.—side-valves; o.h.v.—overhead valves; o.h.c.—overhead camshaft; hyd.—hydraulic.

27

FORD GALAXIE

BIG bold, but cheap to buy and run in its native United States, the model on show is only one from a bewildering range of body styles and engine options. An electric wiper and screen washer are still new enough to be mentioned, on American cars. Three-speed or four-speed manual gearboxes are supplied, engines can be sixes or V8s, servo brakes and servo steering are optional.

CLOSE-UP

Eight-cyl.; o.h.v.; 102.9 × 96 mm.; 6,392 c.c.; 280 b.h.p. gross; 9.3 to 1 comp.; coil ign.; Ford 4-choke carb.; 3-speed auto., 7.2, 4.41, 3.0 to 1; col. lvr.; susp., f. ind. coil, r. half-elliptic; 4-door; 6-seat; hyd. servo brks.; max. 120 m.p.h.; cruise 100; m.p.g. 15-18; whl. base 9ft. 11in.; track f. and r. 5ft. 2in.; lgth. 17ft. 6in.; width 6ft. 5½in.; ht. 4ft. 5⅞in.; g.c. 7in.; turng. cir. 41ft.; kerb wt. 34⅜ cwt.; tank 16½ gals.; 12-volt.

GILBERN

ALREADY familiar to visitors to the Racing Car Show, the Gilbern now comes to Earls Court. Built in South Wales, it uses an MGB engine in a tubular chassis with coil spring front suspension and a rigid rear axle on radius arms and Panhard rod with coil springs. The trim glass fibre coupe body is well finished. Cars are also sold in kit form for home assembly.

CLOSE-UP

Four-cyl.; o.h.v.; 80.26 × 88.9 mm.; 1,798 c.c.; 95 b.h.p.; 8.9 to 1 comp.; coil ign.; 2 S.U. carbs.; 4-speed, 14.21, 8.66, 5.37, 3.91 to 1; cen. lvr. de Normanville overdrive opt.; susp., f. ind. coil, r. coil; 2-door; 2/4-seat; hyd. brks.; disc front; max. 104 m.p.h.; cruise 90; m.p.g. 24-30; whl. base 7ft. 8in.; track f. and r. 4ft. 1½in.; lgth. 12ft. 10½in.; width 5ft. 0½in.; ht. 4ft. 5¼in.; g.c. 6in.; turng. cir. 30ft. 6in.; kerb wt. 17⅛ cwt.; tank 9¼ gals.; 12-volt.

£1,100 + £230 p.t. = £1,330

HILLMAN SUPER MINX

NOW gets far more power with an entirely new 1,725 c.c. engine which replaces the well-tested 1,592 c.c. power plant in the previous model. Also extra reliability from a 5-bearing crankshaft which takes less stress out of the engine and allows a smoother performance. Also big improvements to the super-detailed comfort in the interior of this Rootes car. Top speed now raised to more than 80 m.p.h. and overall thirst lowered to 30 m.p.g.

CLOSE-UP

Four-cyl.; o.h.v.; 81.5 × 82.55 mm.; 1,725 c.c.; 69.5 b.h.p. gross; 8.4 to 1 comp.; coil ign.; Solex carb.; 4-speed, 13.04, 8.32, 5.41, 3.89 to 1; cen. lvr.; BW auto. or de Normanville overdrive opt.; susp., f. ind. coil, r. half-elliptic; 4-door; 4/5-seat; hyd. brks., disc front; max. 85 m.p.h.; cruise 75; m.p.g. 28-30; whl. base 8ft. 5in.; track, f. 4ft. 3¾in., r. 4ft. 0½in.; lgth. 13ft. 10½in.; width 5ft. 3¾in.; ht. 4ft. 10in.; g.c. 5¼in.; turng. cir. 36ft.; kerb wt. 21 cwt.; tank 11 gals.; 12-volt.

£665 + £140 p.t. = £805

HILLMAN IMP DE LUXE

BIGGER valves boost the output of the Imp's willing little overhead camshaft light alloy engine to 42 h.p. Better seats, more powerful heater, more sound insulation also distinguish the Series II. The rear window lifts up and rear backrest folds flat for extra luggage capacity. New for 1966 is the Super Imp with two-tone horns, door-operated courtesy lights, wheel embellishers, more luxurious interior.

CLOSE-UP

Four-cyl.; o.h.c.; 68 × 60.4 mm.; 875 c.c.; 39 b.h.p.; 10 to 1 comp.; coil ign.; Solex carb.; 4-speed, 16.59, 8.91, 5.70, 4.14 to 1; cen. lvr.; susp. f. and r. ind. coil; 2-door; 4-seat; hyd. brks.; max. 80 m.p.h.; cruise 75; m.p.g. 40; whl. base 6ft. 10in.; track, f. 4ft. 1½in., r. 4ft. 0½in.; lgth. 11ft. 9in.; width 5ft. 0½in.; ht. 4ft. 6½in.; g.c. 6½in.; turng. cir. 30ft.; kerb wt. 14¼ cwt.; tank 6 gals.; 12-volt.

£445 + £94 p.t. = £539

Abbreviations—g.c.—ground clearance; susp.—suspension; f.—front; r.—rear; comp.—compression; s.v.—side-valves; o.h.v.—overhead valves; o.h.c.—overhead camshaft; hyd.—hydraulic.

HINO CONTESSA 1300

HAVING started by making rear-engined Renaults under licence, Hino continued the rear-engined theme with their own new model and got Michelotti to do the styling. Result, a lively, well-endowed beauty with international appeal. Four-door saloon with single carburetter engine giving 55 h.p. is said to do 80 m.p.h.; two-door coupe with twin-carburetter 65 h.p. engine is credited with 90.

CLOSE-UP
Four-cyl.; o.h.v.; 71×79 mm.; 1,251 c.c.; 55 b.h.p.; 8.5 to 1 comp.; coil ign.; Hitachi twin-choke carb.; 3-speed, 14.17, 7.68, 4.11 to 1; cen. lvr., 4-speed opt.; susp., f. ind. torsion bar, r. ind. coil; 4-door; 4-seat; hyd. brks.; max. 80 m.p.h.; cruise 65; m.p.g. 33; whl. base 7ft. 5⅝in.; track, f. 4ft. 0⅞in., r. 4ft.; lgth. 13ft. 7¾in.; width 5ft. 0¼in.; ht. 4ft. 6⅞in.; g.c. 6⅜in.; turng. cir. 30ft. 2in.; kerb wt. 18¼ cwt.; tank 7 gals.; 12-volt.

HUMBER SUPER SNIPE

HIGH-GRADE finish and a lot of space at a strictly moderate price keeps customers coming back for the Rootes Group's big six-cylinder model. Further detail improvements enhance its appeal for 1966. Laycock de Normanville overdrive is available to the man whose business involves fast cruising on motorways. Borg Warner automatic transmission is the alternative for the chaffeur-driven town car.

CLOSE-UP
Six-cyl.; o.h.v.; 87.3 × 82.55 mm.; 2,965 c.c.; 128 b.h.p.; 8 to 1 comp.; coil ign.; 2 Stromberg carbs.; 3-speed, 11.84, 6.13, 4.22 to 1; col. lvr.; de Normanville overdrive or BW auto. opt.; susp., f. ind. coil, r. half-elliptic; 4-door; 6-seat; servo brks., disc front; max. 105 m.p.h.; cruise 90; m.p.g. 20-25; whl. base 9ft. 2in.; track, f. 4ft. 9in., r. 4ft. 7½in.; lgth. 15ft. 8in.; width 5ft. 9½in.; ht. 5ft. 1in.; g.c. 7in.; turng. cir. 38ft.; kerb wt. 32 cwt.; tank 16 gals.; 12-volt.
£1,250+£262 p.t.=£1,512

HUMBER SCEPTRE

RE-STYLED front-end with quadruple headlamps moved from wings to grille, hides the new 1.7-litre five-bearing engine in potent alloy-head form with twin-choke carburetter. An alternator gives full battery charge at city speeds; press button ventilating panes, lockable fuel filler and lockable illuminated glove box give extra security. Front disc brakes, rear drums, are all self adjusting.

CLOSE-UP
Four-cyl.; o.h.v.; 81.5 × 82.55 mm.; 1,725 c.c.; 91 b.h.p. gross; 9 to 1 comp.; coil ign.; 2 Zenith carbs.; 4-speed, 14.6, 9.04, 5.88, 4.22 to 1, de Normanville overdrive; cen. lvr.; susp., f. ind. coil, r. half-elliptic; 4-door; 4/5-seat; hyd. servo brks., disc front; max. 90 m.p.h.; cruise 80; m.p.g. 25; whl. base 8ft. 5in.; track, f. 4ft. 3¾in., r. 4ft. 0½in.; lgth. 13ft. 9in.; width 5ft. 3½in.; ht. 4ft. 9in.; g.c. 5½in.; turng. cir. 36ft.; kerb wt. 21½ cwt.; tank 10½ gals.; 12-volt.
£850+£179 p.t. = £1,029

HUMBER HAWK

THIS is the car for the family man in the upper income brackets. It is good looking, thoroughly reliable, roomy and quiet running. Saloon and station wagon models are equally functional with moderate operating costs. The interior of these cars has the legendary plush comforts expected from Rootes. Latest versions have automatic transmission as an optional extra. A robust car that remains a big favourite.

CLOSE-UP
Four-cyl.; o.h.v.; 81 / 110 mm.; 2,267 c.c.; 73 b.h.p.; 7.5 to 1 comp.; coil ign.; Zenith carb.; 4-speed, 14.13, 9.04, 5.88, 4.22 to 1; de Normanville overdrive opt.; col. lvr.; susp., f. ind. coil, r. half-elliptic; 4-door; 6-seat; servo brks., disc front; max. 85 m.p.h.; cruise 70-75; m.p.g. 20-25; whl. base 9ft. 2in.; track, f. 4ft. 9in., r. 4ft. 7½in.; lgth. 15ft. 4½in.; width 5ft. 9½in.; ht. 4ft. 11½in.; g.c. 7in.; turng. cir. 38ft.; kerb wt. 28¾ cwt.; tank 16 gals.; 12-volt.
£905+£190 p.t. = £1,095

Abbreviations—g.c.—ground clearance; susp.—suspension; f.—front; r.—rear; comp.—compression; s.v.—side-valves; o.h.v.—overhead valves; o.h.c.—overhead camshaft; hyd.—hydraulic.

HUMBER IMPERIAL

ALL the luxury of a top-class town carriage for under £2,000. West of England cloth interior by Thrupp and Maberly, with occasional tables, cigar lighters in armrests, adjustable backrests, reading lamps and radio with speakers at front and rear. For driving pleasure there are power-assisted steering, power-assisted brakes (discs in front), Selectaride adjustable rear dampers and now the latest BW automatic transmission.

CLOSE-UP

Six-cyl.; o.h.v.; 87.3 × 82.6 mm.; 2,965 c.c.; 128 b.h.p.; 8 to 1 comp.; coil ign.; 2 Zenith carbs.; 3-speed auto., 9.75, 6.04, 4.22 to 1; col. lvr.; susp., f. ind. coil, r. half-elliptic; 4-door; 5/6-seat; hyd. servo brks., disc front; max. 100 m.p.h.; cruise 90; m.p.g. 16-20; whl. base 9ft. 2in.; track f. 4ft. 8½in., r. 4ft. 7½in.; lgth. 15ft. 7½in.; width 5ft. 10¼in.; ht. 5ft.; g.c. 7in.; turng. cir. 39ft.; kerb wt. 32¾ cwt.; tank 16 gals.; 12-volt.

£1,485+£311 p.t. = £1,796

ISO-RIVOLTA

BODY by Bertone; V8 Corvette engine by Chevrolet; a formula for performance with elegance from a new Italian manufacturer. Steel body panels on a reinforced underframe make it virtually a unit structure. The rear axle is de Dion with radius arms and Watt linkage. The disc servo brakes have twin fluid circuits. Transmission is four-speed all-synchromesh or automatic with torque converter and two speeds.

CLOSE-UP

Eight-cyl.; o.h.v.; 101.6 × 82.55 mm.; 5,354 c.c.; 300 b.h.p. gross; 10.5 to 1 comp.; coil ign.; Carter carb.; 4-speed, 7.3, 5.5, 4.34, 2.88 to 1; cen. lvr.; susp., f. ind. coil, r. de Dion coil; 2-door; 4-seat; disc servo brks.; max. 135 m.p.h.; cruise 120; m.p.g. 14-18; whl. base 8ft. 10¾in.; track f. and r. 4ft. 7½in.; lgth. 15ft. 8¾in.; width 5ft. 9in.; ht. 4ft. 4¾in.; g.c. 4¾in.; turng. cir. 44ft.; kerb wt. 30½ cwt.; tank 21 gals.; 12-volt.

£3,840+£801 p.t. = £4,641

JAGUAR E-TYPE

4.2-LITRE engine, a fine new all-synchromesh gearbox and improved seats with adjustable backrests have helped to make the latest version of this sleek speedster one of the best buys among the world's fast cars. Top gear flexibility is now terrific, the brake servo is more responsive and the alternator keeps the battery fully charged even in town driving. All-independent suspension gives fabulous road holding.

CLOSE-UP

Six-cyl.; o.h.c.; 92 × 106 mm.; 4,235 c.c.; 265 b.h.p. gross; 9 to 1 comp.; coil ign.; 3 S.U. carbs.; 4-speed, 11.18, 6.16, 4.25, 3.31 to 1; cen. lvr.; susp., f. ind. torsion bar, r. ind. coil; 2-door; 2-seat; servo disc brks.; max. 150 m.p.h.; cruise 130; m.p.g. 18-22; whl. base 8ft.; track f. and r. 4ft. 2in.; lgth. 14ft. 7¾in.; width 5ft. 5¼in.; ht. 4ft. 0½in.; g.c. 5½in.; turng. cir. 40ft. 6in.; kerb wt. 25¾ cwt.; tank 14 gals.; 12-volt.

Coupe: £1,681+£352 p.t. = £2,033

JAGUAR 2.4 LITRE MARK 2

IN this car's price bracket you see more of these models on the road than any other. It continues to be one of the best sellers in the magnificent Jaguar range. It appeals because it gives fast motoring at a very reasonable price. Add comfort and good fittings and you know the reason for the car's tremendous popularity. The engine, which stems from the 3.4 litre Jaguar, seems just right for the job.

CLOSE-UP

Six-cyl.; o.h.c.; 83 × 76.5 mm.; 2,483 c.c.; 120 b.h.p. gross; 8 to 1 comp.; coil ign.; 2 Solex carbs.; 4-speed, 14.42, 7.94, 5.48, 4.27 to 1; cen. lvr.; susp., f. ind. coil, r. cantilever leaf; 4-door; 5-seat; servo disc brks.; max. 105 m.p.h.; cruise 75-80; m.p.g. 23; whl. base 8ft. 11¾in.; track, f. 4ft. 7in., r. 4ft. 5¾in.; lgth 15ft. 0¾in.; width 5ft. 6¾in.; ht. 4ft. 9½in.; g.c. 7in.; turng. cir. 33ft. 6in. kerb wt. 28¼ cwt.; tank 12 gals.; 12-volt.

£1,148+£241 p.t. = £1,389

Abbreviations—g.c.—ground clearance; susp.—suspension; f.—front; r.—rear; comp.—compression; s.v.—side-valves; o.h.v.—overhead valves; o.h.c.—overhead camshaft; hyd.—hydraulic.

JAGUAR S-TYPE

RACE-BRED road holding, with all-independent suspension, precise steering and disc servo brakes added to Jaguar's luxuriously planned interior and a really big luggage boot makes the S-type an obvious choice for the business man who has to travel fast and far during the week and find space for the family at week-ends. Choice of 3.4 or 3.8-litre engines, the latter with limited-slip differential.

CLOSE-UP

Six-cyl.; o.h.c.; 83 × 106 mm.; 3,442 c.c.; 210 b.h.p. gross; 8 to 1 comp.; or 87 × 106 mm.; 3,781 c.c.; 220 b.h.p. gross; coil ign.; 2 S.U. carbs.; 4-speed, 11.95, 6.58, 4.54, 3.54 to 1; cen. lvr., de Normanville overdrive or BW auto. opt.; susp. f. and r. ind. coil; 4-door; 4-seat; disc servo brks.; max. 118 m.p.h. (3.4), 123 m.p.h. (3.8); cruise 90-100; m.p.g. 16-23; whl. base 8ft. 11⅜in.; track f. 4ft. 7½in., r. 4ft. 6½in.; lgth. 15ft. 7⅞in.; width 5ft. 6½in.; ht. 4ft. 6½in.; g.c. 7in.; turng. cir. 33ft. 6in.; kerb wt. 31¼ cwt.; tank 14 gals.; 12-volt.

3.4: £1,422 + £298 p.t. = £1,720
3.8: £1,499 + £314 p.t. = £1,813

JAGUAR MARK X

AN elegant and spacious car that continues to be among the best sellers in the brilliant Jaguar range. Extra power from the 4.2 litre engine is particularly appreciated by its many overseas buyers. Its low, long look has set new standards for this class of beauty and is much copied. Lion-hearted at speed, it is a docile lamb in traffic—and moderate in price and running costs.

CLOSE-UP

Six-cyl.; o.h.c.; 92 × 106 mm.; 4,235 c.c.; 265 b.h.p. gross; 8 to 1 comp.; coil ign.; 3S. U. carbs.; 4-speed 10.76, 6.98, 4.70, 3.54 to 1; cen. lvr.; overdrive or BW auto. opt.; susp. f. and r. ind. coil; 4-door; 5-seat; disc servo brks.; max. 120 m.p.h.; cruise 100; m.p.g. 15-20; whl. base 10ft.; track f. and r. 4ft. 10in.; lgth. 16ft. 10in.; width 6ft. 4½in.; ht. 4ft. 6½in.; g.c. 5½in.; turng. cir. 38 ft. 8in.; kerb wt. 37½ cwt.; tank 20 gals.; 12-volt.

£1,819 + £381 p.t. = £2,200

JENSEN C-V8 MK. III

HAPPY dove-tailing of British and American interests results in this powerful and graceful saloon that would adorn any motorist's garage. All-British chassis and body and a Chrysler engine. Improvements to the latest model include a dual braking system, re-designed wood-veneer dashboard, improved heating and demisting system and electrically-heated rear window. Probably the most successful hybrid car anywhere in the world.

CLOSE-UP

Eight-cyl.; o.h.v.; 108 × 86 mm.; 6,276 c.c.; 335 b.h.p. gross; 10 to 1 comp.; coil ign.; Carter carb.; 3-speed auto., 7.52, 4.45, 3.07 to 1; col. lvr., manual opt.; susp., f. ind. coil, r. half-elliptic; 2-door; 4-seat; disc servo brks.; max. 138 m.p.h.; cruise 115; m.p.g. 16-18; whl. base 8ft. 9in.; track, f. 4ft. 7⅞in., r. 4ft. 8½in.; lgth. 15ft. 3½in.; width 5ft. 7½in.; ht. 4ft. 7in.; g.c. 6in.; turng. cir. 38ft.; kerb wt. 30 cwt.; tank 16 gals; 12-volt.

£3,043 + £636 p.t. = £3,679

JENSEN F.F.

FERGUSON Formula four-wheel drive, with master differential to conquer wheelspin is the basis of this new model which could make history in fast-car design. Besides super-safe cornering on slippery surfaces it offers skid-free braking through Dunlop's Maxaret, already used on aircraft; now making its debut on a production car. Chrysler engine, transmission, glass fibre bodywork, similar to Jensen's C-V8.

CLOSE-UP

Eight-cyl.; o.h.v.; 108 × 86 mm.; 6,276 c.c.; 335 b.h.p. gross; 10 to 1 comp. coil ign.; Carter carb.; 3-speed auto., 7.52, 4.45, 3.07 to 1; col. lvr.; susp., f. ind. coil, r. half-elliptic; 2-door; 4-seat; disc servo brks. with Maxaret; max. 130 m.p.h.; cruise 110; m.p.g. 15-17; whl. base 8ft. 9in.; track f. 4ft. 4⅞in., r. 4ft. 8½in.; lgth. 15ft. 3½in.; width 5ft. 7½in.; ht. 4ft. 7in.; g.c. 6in.; turng. cir. 38ft.; kerb wt. 31 cwt.; tank 16 gals.; 12-volt.

LANCIA FLAMINIA COUPE

ADVANCED engineering made the name of Lancia right from the start and after years in production the Flaminia is still ahead. Compact V6 engine in front, clutch, gearbox and differential at the rear, plus De Dion rear axle give it a strong individual character. The range comprises saloon and coupe bodies styled by Pininfarina. GT coupe and convertible by Touring and an exotic lightweight coupe by Zagato.

CLOSE-UP
Six-cyl.; o.h.v.; 84×81.5 mm.; 2,775 c.c.; 139 b.h.p.; 9 to 1 comp.; coil ign.; 2 Solex carbs.; 4-speed, 11.64, 7.76, 5.38, 5.77 to 1; col. lvr.; susp., f. ind. coil, r. de Dion half-elliptic; 4-door; 6-seat; disc servo brks.; max. 112 m.p.h.; cruise 90; m.p.g. 24-28; whl. base 9ft.; track f. and r. 4ft. 6in.; lgth. 15ft. 4in.; width 5ft. 8in.; ht. 4ft. 7in.; g.c. 5in.; turng. cir. 40ft.; kerb wt. 30 cwt.; tank 12¾ gals.; 12-volt.
£2,803+£703 p.t. = £3,508

LANCIA FLAVIA

RARE, but rewarding to those who can afford it, the Flavia is one of the most exclusive models in the 1.8-litre class. Its flat four light alloy engine drives the front wheels and is available in various stages of tune in saloon, Pininfarina coupe, Vignale convertible and Zagato sports coupe. Maximum speeds range up to about 112 m.p.h. and disc brakes on all wheels ensure safe stopping.

CLOSE-UP
Four-cyl.; o.h.v.; 88×74 mm.; 1,800 c.c.; 92 b.h.p.; 9 to 1 comp.; coil ign.; Solex carb.; 4-speed, 13.65, 8.08, 5.70, 4.1 to 1; col. lvr.; susp., f. ind. trans. leaf, r. half-elliptic; 4-door; 5-seat; disc servo brks.; max. 100 m.p.h.; cruise 85; m.p.g. 26-32; whl. base 8ft. 8¼in.; track, f. 4ft. 3½in., r. 4ft. 2⅜in.; lgth. 15ft. 0½in.; width 5ft. 3½in.; ht. 4ft. 11in.; g.c. 5in.; turng. cir. 34ft.; kerb wt. 24 cwt.; tank 10½ gals.; 12-volt.
£1,562+£327 p.t. = £1,889

LANCIA FULVIA

EXOTIC and individual, the sports coupe, latest addition to the Fulvia range, is a typical Lancia and it has a close family resemblance to the saloon. Both have light narrow V4 engines canted over, driving the front wheels and disc brakes with twin fluid circuits. But whereas the saloon has a 1,091 c.c. engine developing 58 h.p., the coupe has 1,216 c.c. and 80 h.p.

CLOSE-UP
Four-cyl.; o.h.c.; 72×67 mm.; 1,091 c.c.; 58 b.h.p.; 7.8 to 1 comp.; coil ign.; Solex carb.; 4-speed, 21.18, 12.16, 7.36, 4.78 to 1; cen. lvr.; susp., f. ind. trans. leaf, r. half-elliptic; 4-door; 4-seat; disc brks.; max. 85 m.p.h.; cruise 75; m.p.g. 28-34; whl. base 8ft. 1⅛in.; track, f. 4ft. 3½in., r. 4ft. 2½in.; lgth. 13ft. 7in.; width 5ft. 1⅛in.; ht. 4ft. 7in.; g.c. 5in.; turng. cir. 37ft.; kerb wt. 19½ cwt.; tank 8½ gals.; 12-volt.
£1,140+£239 p.t. = £1,379

LOTUS CORTINA

EUROPEAN Touring Car Champion in the hands of Sir John Whitmore, this wolf in sheeps clothing is hard to catch on road or track. Under the Cortina shell is very special suspension and steering by Lotus and a high-powered competition engine with twin overhead camshafts and two twin-choke Weber carburetters. Racing seats, wood-rimmed wheel, special instrumentation and servo-assisted disc brakes fit it for the job.

CLOSE-UP
Four-cyl.; o.h.c.; 82.5×72.7 mm.; 1,558 c.c.; 105 b.h.p.; 9.5 to 1 comp.; coil ign.; 2 Weber carbs.; 4-speed, 9.75, 6.39, 4.79, 3.9 to 1; cen. lvr.; susp., f. ind. coil, r. coil; 2-door; 4/5-seat; hyd. servo brks., disc front; max. 115 m.p.h.; cruise 100; m.p.g. 20-25; whl. base 8ft. 2½in.; track, f. 4ft. 3½in., r. 4ft. 2½in.; lgth. 14ft. 0½in.; width 5ft. 2½in.; ht. 4ft. 5½in.; g.c. 5⅝in.; turng. cir. 37ft.; kerb wt. 17½ cwt.; tank 8 gals.; 12-volt.
£820+£172 p.t. = £992

LOTUS ELAN S2

AFTER selling over 2000 of the convertible Elan models, Colin Chapman introduces a neat coupe with electrically operated windows. There are interior lights in each quarter panel and a map reading light on the dash. No major change in the backbone chassis with all-independent suspension, which brings road holding of near-G.P. standards into the sports car market, but gear ratios are revised for the coupe.

CLOSE-UP
Four-cyl.; o.h.c.; 82.6×72.75 mm.; 1,558 c.c.; 105 b.h.p.; 9.5 to 1 comp.; coil ign.; 2 twin choke Weber carbs.; 4-speed 9.76, 6.4, 4.8, 3.9 to 1; cen. lvr.; susp. f. and r. ind. coil; 2-door; 2/3-seat; disc brks.; max. 125 m.p.h.; cruise 100; m.p.g. 30; whl. base 7ft.; track f. and r. 3ft. 11in.; lgth. 12ft. 1½in.; width 4ft. 8in.; ht. 3ft. 5in.; g.c. 6in.; turng. cir. 31ft.; wt. kerb 13¼ cwt.; tank 10 gals.; 12-volt.
£1,187+£249 p.t. = £1,436

MARCOS 1800

PLYWOOD chassis and glass fibre body are the unique Marcos formula for high performance and good lines at a moderate price. Choice of two rear suspensions for 1966; full independent by cross-braced leading links and coil springs, or rigid axle on radius arms, torque link and Panhard rod, with coil springs. Engine is by Volvo. Car kits are available for tax-free home assembly.

CLOSE-UP
Four-cyl.; o.h.v,; 84×80 mm.; 1,780 c.c.; 114 b.h.p. gross; 10 to 1 comp.; coil ign.; 2 Stromberg carbs.; 4-speed; 12.24, 7.78, 5.32, 3.91 to 1; cen. lvr., de Normanville overdrive opt.; susp., f. ind. coil, r. de Dion coil; 2-door; 2-seat; hyd. brks., disc front; max. 115 m.p.h.; cruise 95; m.p.g. 22-30; whl. base 7ft. 5½in.; track, f. 4ft. 0¾in., r. 4ft. 3in.; lgth. 13ft. 4½in.; width 5ft. 2½in.; ht. 3ft. 6½in.; g.c. 4½in.; turng. cir. 29ft. 6in.; kerb wt. 18⅞ cwt.; tank 12 gals.; 12-volt.
£1,650+£285 p.t. = £1,935

MASERATI MISTRALE

MISTRALE: the sub-tropical wind you'll be gone with when the throttle opens on this superb six-cylinder sports coupe from one of Italy's most famous fast-car factories. Frua evolved the exotic lines for the coupe and the long, lean convertible. Lucas provides the fuel injection; Girling the disc brakes with double fluid circuits and vacuum servo, Burman the recirculating ball steering.

CLOSE-UP
Six-cyl.; o.h.c.; 86 × 106 mm.; 3,692 c.c.; 245 b.h.p.; 8.8 to 1 comp.; coil ign.; Lucas injection; 5-speed, 11.38, 6.97, 4.86, 3.77, 3.2 to 1; cen. lvr.; susp., f. ind. coil, r. half-elliptic; 2-door; 2-seat; disc servo brks.; max. 155 m.p.h.; cruise 135; m.p.g. 17-20; whl. base 7ft. 10½in.; track, f. 4ft. 6¾in., r. 4ft. 5⅜in.; lgth. 14ft. 7in.; width 5ft. 6in.; ht. 4ft. 2in.; g.c. 5½in.; turng. cir. 35ft.; kerb wt. 25 cwt.; tank 16 gals.; 12-volt.
£4,705+£981 p.t. = £5,686

MASERATI V8

BREATH-TAKING performance and eye-catching lines are combined in this unusual four-speed saloon by a world-famous sports car manufacturer. A 4.1-litre V8 engine with four overhead camshafts provides the power. Frua did the body styling. Transmission is ZF five-speed all-synchromesh, or Borg Warner 3-speed automatic. The De Dion rear axle is located on radius arms and a transverse Watt linkage.

CLOSE-UP
Eight-cyl.; o.h.c.; 88×85 mm.; 4,136 c.c.; 260 b.h.p.; 8.5 to 1 comp.; coil ign.; 4 Weber carbs.; 5-speed, 9.66, 6.22, 4.35, 3.54, 3.0 to 1; cen. lvr.; BW auto. opt.; susp., f. ind. coil, r. de Dion coil; 4-door; 5-seat; disc servo brks.; max. 143 m.p.h.; cruise 110; m.p.g. 17-18; whl. base 8ft. 10½in.; track, f. 4ft. 6¾in., r. 4ft. 7 1/16in.; lgth. 16ft. 5in.; width 5ft. 6½in.; ht. 4ft. 5½in.; g.c. 7in.; turng. cir. 42ft. 9in.; kerb wt. 33 cwt.; tank 20 gals.; 12-volt.
£4,953+£1,033 p.t. = £5,986

Abbreviations—g.c.—ground clearance; susp.—suspension; f.—front; r.—rear; comp.—compression; s.v.—side-valves; o.h.v.—overhead valves; o.h.c.—overhead camshaft; hyd.—hydraulic.

33

MERCEDES-BENZ 200

ENLARGED engine with five bearings and twin carburetters, revised gear ratios, twin-circuit servo brakes, bring new performance, higher safety margins to the lowest-priced Mercedes. Rear legroom is increased, seats are improved, an alternator provides the electricity. Indicators, fog and parking lamps are grouped under the headlamps. Self-levelling rear suspension compensator is an optional extra. There's 200D with diesel engine for ultimate economy.

CLOSE-UP
Four-cyl.; o.h.c.; 87 × 83.6 mm.; 1,988 c.c.; 95 b.h.p.; 9 to 1 comp.; coil ign.; 2 Solex carbs.; 4-speed, 12.52, 9.3, 5.79, 4.08 to 1; cen. or col. lvr., auto. opt.; susp. f. and r. ind. coil; 4-door; 5-seat; servo brks., disc front; 100 m.p.h.; cruise 90; m.p.g. 22-28; whl. base 8ft. 10½in.; track, f. 4ft. 10½in., r. 4ft. 10½in.; lgth. 15ft. 6½in.; width 5ft. 10⅜in.; ht. 4ft. 10¾in.; g.c. 7½in.; turng. cir. 36ft.; kerb wt. 25 cwt.; tank 14¼ gals.; 12-volt.

MERCEDES 230 SL

MOST popular sports car ever built by Mercedes, the 230 SL comes in two versions: coupe and convertible. "Pagoda" roof gives maximum all-across headroom and door height. Coil spring all-independent suspension and broad-based tyres give it uncanny road grip; the smooth six-cylinder injection engine and four-speed all-synchromesh gearbox make driving a joy. Automatic transmission and power steering are optional.

CLOSE-UP
Six-cyl.; o.h.c.; 82×72 mm.; 2,306 c.c.; 150 b.h.p.; 9.3 to 1 comp.; coil ign.; Bosch injection; 4-speed, 16.57, 8.55, 5.32, 3.75 to 1; cen. lvr., auto. opt.; susp. f. and r. ind. coil; 2-door; 2-seat; hyd. servo brks., disc front; max. 125 m.p.h.; cruise 110; m.p.g. 20-24; whl. base 7ft. 10½in.; track f. and r. 4ft. 10½in.; lgth. 14ft. 1½in.; width 5ft. 9¼in.; ht. 4ft. 3½in.; g.c. 5in.; turng. cir. 33ft. 4in.; kerb wt. 25½ cwt.; tank 14¼ gals.; 12-volt.

£2,800 + £682 p.t. = £3,482

MERCEDES-BENZ 250 SE

ONE of the world's most advanced cars, crammed with ideas for pleasanter motoring. Choice of three engines; 130 h.p. twin-carburetter 250S, 150 h.p. injection 250SE, 170 h.p. injection 300SE. Manual or automatic transmission, self-levelling suspension, twin-circuit disc servo brakes. Reclining seats slide, tilt, rise and fall. Rubber strip protects side panels, alternator boosts electrical output, fluid fan coupling cuts noise when cruising fast.

CLOSE-UP
Six-cyl.; o.h.c.; 82×78.8 mm.; 2,496 c.c.; 150 b.h.p.; 9.3 to 1 comp.; coil ign.; Bosch injection; 4-speed, 15.88, 8.94, 5.57, 3.92 to 1; cen. or col. lvr., auto opt.; susp. f. and r. ind. coil; hyd-pneu. levelling; 4-door; 5-seat; disc servo brks.; max. 118 m.p.h.; cruise 100; m.p.g. 18-28; whl. base 9ft. 0½in.; track, f. 4ft. 10½in., r. 4ft. 10⅜in.; lgth. 16ft. 1in.; width 5ft. 11½in.; ht. 4ft. 8¾in.; g.c. 6in.; turng. cir. 37ft.; kerb wt. 29¼ cwt.; tank 18 gals.; 12-volt.

MERCEDES-BENZ 600 PULLMAN

MAJESTIC mammoth Pullman with eight seats or mighty big saloon with six seats; in either form the 600 is a powerhouse full of way-ahead features. Hydraulically operated windows, rising-sliding-tilting seats, press-button sliding roof, self-levelling pneumatic suspension, disc brakes operated by compressed air. Power steering and automatic transmission are fitted naturally, and a light alloy fuel-injection V8 engine.

CLOSE-UP
Eight-cyl.; o.h.c.; 103.1×95 mm.; 6,329 c.c.; 300 b.h.p. gross; 9.0 to 1 comp.; coil ign.; Bosch injection; 4-speed auto., 12.85, 8.14, 5.10, 3.23 to 1; col. lvr.; susp., f. and r. ind. pneu.; 4-door; 7/8-seat; disc compressed air brks.; max. 125 m.p.h.; cruise 100; m.p.g. 18; whl. base 12ft. 9½in.; track f. 5ft. 2½in., r. 5ft. 2in.; lgth. 20ft. 6in.; width 6ft. 6¾in.; ht. 4ft. 11½in.; g.c. 8in.; turng. cir. 47ft. 9in.; kerb wt. 51¾ cwt.; tank 24½ gals.; 12-volt.

£8,270 + £1,724 p.t. = £9,994

MERCURY COMET

REAPPEARANCE at Earls Court of a medium-price compact car from the Ford group. Available with six-cylinder or V8 engines, it offers the buyer a wide range of choice in saloon, station wagon, hardtop and convertible bodies, with three-speed manual, four-speed manual, or 3-speed automatic transmissions. There is also the option of servo-assisted steering and vacuum servo brakes.

CLOSE-UP

Eight-cyl.; o.h.v.; 101.6 × mm.; 4,727 c.c.; 200 b.h.p. gross; 9.3 to 1 comp.; coil ign.; Ford twin-choke carb.; 3-speed, 7.81, 4.76, 2.80 to 1; col. lvr.; susp., f. ind. coil, r. half-elliptic; 2- or 4-door; 6-seat; hyd. brks., servo opt.; max. 100 m.p.h.; cruise 85; m.p.g. 15-18; whl. base 9ft. 8in.; track, f. 4ft. 8in., r. 4ft. 7in.; lgth. 16ft. 11in.; width 6ft. 1¾in.; ht. 4ft. 7in.; g.c. 6in.; turng. cir. 43ft. 4in.; kerb wt. 25¼ cwt.; tank 16¾ gals.; 12-volt.

M.G. MIDGET

"SAFETY FAST" is not just a catch-phrase for this sports car which is one of the safest in the world. It is the type of car that young men like to motor along with a girl-friend. It has snazzy looks, the punch of a sports car much about its business, and is extremely economical in operating costs. Few rallies or speed tests fail to have this hot favourite listed in their programmes.

CLOSE-UP

Four-cyl.; o.h.v.; 64.6 / 83.7 mm.; 1,098 c.c.; 59 b.h.p.; 8.9 to 1 comp.; coil ign.; 2 S.U. carbs.; 4-speed, 13.5, 8.09, 5.73, 4.22 to 1; cen. lvr.; susp., f. ind. coil, r. half-elliptic; 2-door; 2-seat; hyd. brks., disc front; max. 90 m.p.h.; cruise 75; m.p.g. 29-32; whl. base 6ft. 8in.; track, f. 3ft. 9¾in., r. 3ft. 8¾in.; lgth. 11ft. 5¼in.; width 4ft. 5in.; ht. 4ft. 1¾in.; g.c. 5in.; turng. cir 32ft.; kerb wt. 14¼ cwt.; tank 6 gals.; 12-volt.
£515+£109 p.t. = £624

M.G. MGB

APPEAL of this popular British sports car now broadened by a graceful new GT coupe body, with comfortable seats and really useful luggage space. In the latest version the engine has five main bearings and a Laycock de Normanville overdrive supplements the four-speed gearbox. Unit body-chassis, rack and pinion steering, coil spring front suspension, semi-elliptic rear, and disc front brakes are salient points.

CLOSE-UP

Four-cyl.; o.h.v.; 80.26 / 89 mm.; 1,798 c.c.; 95 b.h.p.; 8.9 to 1 comp.; coil ign.; 2 S.U. carbs.; 4-speed, 14.21, 8.66, 5.37, 3.91 to 1; cen. lvr., de Normanville overdrive opt.; susp., f. ind. coil, r. half-elliptic; 2-door; 2/3 seat; hyd. brks., disc front; max. 108 m.p.h.; cruise 85; m.p.g. 26-28; whl. base 7ft. 7in.; track, f. 4ft. 1in., r. 4ft. 1¼in.; lgth. 12ft. 9¼in.; width 4ft. 11⅞in.; ht. 4ft. 1¾in.; g.c. 5in.; turng. cir. 32ft. 10in.; kerb wt. 18 cwt.; tank 10 gals.; 12-volt.
£707+£148 p.t. = £855

MORGAN PLUS 4

THIS zestful sports car from a small Malvern firm continues to have a special following of enthusiasts. Small improvements are made each year so that the models are always well abreast of the times. The new competition car has a lower bonnet and bodyline along with 72-spoke wire wheels and wide-base tyres. Tested in 1,000 rallies, these cars are robust and reliable.

CLOSE-UP

Four-cyl.; o.h.v.; 86 × 92 mm.; 2,138 c.c.; 100 b.h.p.; 9 to 1 comp.; coil ign.; 2 Stromberg carbs.; 4-speed, 11.08, 6.5, 4.49, 3.73 to 1; cen. lvr.; susp., f. ind. coil, r. half-elliptic; 2-door; 2-seat; hyd. brks., disc front; max. 110 m.p.h.; cruise 95; m.p.g. 25-28; whl. base 8ft.; track f. and r. 3ft. 11in.; lgth. 12ft.; width 4ft. 8in.; ht. 4ft. 4in.; g.c. 6½in.; turng. cir. 33ft. 9in.; kerb wt. 13½ cwt.; tank 8½ gals.; 12-volt.
£675+£142 p.t. = £817

Abbreviations—g.c.—ground clearance; susp.—suspension; f.—front; r.—rear; comp.—compression; s.v.—side-valves; o.h.v.—overhead valves; o.h.c.—overhead camshaft; hyd.—hydraulic.

35

MORRIS MINI MINOR

MINI surprises are becoming an annual event, last time, Hydrolastic suspension, this time automatic transmission as an optional extra. Fluid torque converter and an ingenious four-speed gear system bring clutchless automatic driving to Britain's versatile baby. Effortless town driving, holiday trips, production car racing, international rallies, local deliveries or farm transport; there's a Mini for every kind of motoring.

CLOSE-UP

Four-cyl.; o.h.v.; 63×68.3 mm.; 848 c.c.; 34 b.h.p.; 8.3 to 1 comp.; coil ign.; S.U. carb.; 4-speed, 13.66, 8.18, 5.32, 3.76 to 1; cen. lvr., auto opt.; susp. f. and r. ind. rubber-hydraulic; 2-door; 4-seat; hyd. brks.; max. 73 m.p.h.; cruise 60; m.p.g. 45; whl. base 6ft. 8in.; track, f. 3ft. $11\frac{3}{8}$in., r. 3ft. $9\frac{7}{8}$in.; lgth. 10ft.; width 4ft. $7\frac{1}{2}$in.; ht. 4ft. 5in.; g.c. $6\frac{1}{8}$in.; turng. cir. 31ft. 7in.; kerb wt. $11\frac{3}{4}$ cwt.; tank $5\frac{1}{2}$ gals.; 12-volt.

£387+£83 p.t.=£470

MORRIS MINOR 1000

THIS extremely successful car seems to go on forever. And it well deserves its brilliant reputation. One of the first British Motor Corporation models designed by that genius Alec Issigonis. It has the magnificent virtue of being viceless on the road while providing heaps of room for the driver and passengers. It has been a No. 1 favourite with the public for more than 14 years. What more can you ask?

CLOSE-UP

Four-cyl.; o.h.v.; 64.6×83.7 mm.; 1.098 c.c.; 48 b.h.p.; 8.5 to 1 comp.; coil ign.; S.U. carb.; 4-speed, 15.27, 9.16, 5.96, 4.22 to 1; cen. lvr.; susp., f. ind. torsion bar, r. half-elliptic; 2- or 4-door; 4-seat; hyd. brks.; max. 75 m.p.h.; cruise 55; m.p.g. 36-48; whl. base 7ft. 2in.; track f. 4ft. $2\frac{3}{8}$in., r. 4ft. $2\frac{1}{4}$in.; lgth. 12ft. 4in.; width 5ft.; ht. 5ft.; g.c. $6\frac{3}{4}$in.; turng. cir. 33ft.; kerb wt. $15\frac{1}{4}$ cwt.; tank $6\frac{1}{2}$ gals.; 12-volt.

£426+£90 p.t.=£516

MORRIS 1100

FIRST of the many front-drive 1100 models from the BMC, this popular saloon with the steady-riding Hydrolastic rubber-and-water suspension is now available with automatic transmission. The ingenious new system by Automotive Products uses a fluid torque converter and gives a choice of four speeds with remarkably few gears. A new hit for the versatile crosswise engine-cum-transmission unit.

CLOSE-UP

Four-cyl.; o.h.v.; 64.58×83.72 mm.; 1,098 c.c.; 48 b.h.p.; 8.5 to 1 comp.; coil ign.; S.U. carb.; 4-speed, 14.99, 8.98, 5.83, 4.13 to 1; cen. lvr.; susp. f. and r. ind. rubber-hyd.; 2- or 4-door; 4-seat; hyd. brks., disc front; max. 76 m.p.h.; cruise 60; m.p.g. 34-38; whl. base 7ft. $9\frac{1}{2}$in.; track f. 4ft. $3\frac{1}{2}$in., r. 4ft. $2\frac{7}{8}$in.; lgth. 12ft. $2\frac{3}{4}$in.; width 5ft. $0\frac{3}{8}$in.; ht. 4ft. 5in.; g.c. $5\frac{1}{4}$in.; turng. cir. 34ft.; kerb wt. $16\frac{1}{2}$ cwt.; tank $8\frac{1}{2}$ gals.; 12-volt.

£507+£107 p.t.=£614

MOSKVITCH

FOUR headlamps are a capitalist excess the Russians have not been able to resist, but despite up-to-date styling, rugged construction and a full toolkit remain their protection against their bad roads and lack of service stations. Besides the 4-door saloon there is a good-looking station wagon. Some Moskvitch cars are now assembled in Belgium with Perkins diesel engines.

CLOSE-UP

Four-cyl.; o.h.v.; 76×75 mm.; 1,357 c.c.; 60 b.h.p. gross; 7 to 1 comp.; coil ign.; K-59 carb.; 4-speed, 17.34, 10.19, 6.60, 4.55 to 1; col. lvr.; susp., f. ind. coil, r. half-elliptic; 4-door; 4-seat; hyd. brks.; max. 72 m.p.h.; cruise 60; m.p.g. 35; whl. base 7ft. 9in.; track f. and r. 4ft.; lgth. 13ft. 4in.; width 5ft. 1in.; ht. 5ft. $1\frac{1}{4}$in.; g.c. $7\frac{1}{2}$in.; turng. cir. $39\frac{3}{4}$ft.; kerb wt. 18 cwt.; tank $7\frac{3}{4}$ gals.; 12-volt.

Abbreviations—g.c.—ground clearance; susp.—suspension; f.—front; r.—rear; comp.—compression; s.v.—side-valves; o.h.v.—overhead valves; o.h.c.—overhead camshaft; hyd.—hydraulic.

NSU 110

FASTEST Prinz yet produced, the 1000 T.T. is powered by a new 1,100 c.c. air-cooled engine with overhead camshaft and five-bearing crankshaft developing 55 h.p. to give a top speed of 94 m.p.h. Externally it is identified by four headlamps joined by a black band. Front brakes are discs. Also new is the type 110, with longer wheelbase, roomier interior, more luggage space and the 1,100 c.c. engine.

CLOSE-UP
Four-cyl.; o.h.c. air-cooled; 72 × 66.6 mm.; 1,085 c.c.; 53 b.h.p.; 8 to 1 comp.; coil ign.; Solex carb.; 4-speed, 16.5, 9.1, 5.82, 4.16 to 1; cen. lvr.; susp. f. and r. ind. coil; 2-door; 4-seat; hyd. brks., disc front opt.; max. 90 m.p.h.; cruise 80; m.p.g. 32-36; whl. base 8ft.; track, f. 4ft. 2⅜in., r. 4ft. 1in.; lgth. 13ft. 1½in.; width 4ft. 11in.; ht. 4ft. 6in.; g.c. 6in.; turng. cir. 32ft. 6in.; kerb wt. 14¼ cwt.; tank 10 gals.; 12-volt.

N.S.U. PRINZ WANKEL

COMPLETING its second year in production with the revolutionary Wankel engine, this smart Bertone-styled convertible is a historical model which has proved practical and economical. With luggage trunks at front and rear, the engine is not easy to find and when rear floor is lifted, the little circular engine is nearly hidden by alternator, carburetter, starter and other accessories, but it's worth looking for.

CLOSE-UP
Wankel rotating-piston engine; 498 c.c.; 50 b.h.p.; 8.6 to 1 comp.; coil ign. Solex carb.; 4-speed, 13.65, 7.87, 5.20, 3.77 to 1; cen. lvr.; susp., f. and r. ind. coil; 2-door; 2-seat; hyd. brks., disc front; max. 96 m.p.h.; cruise 85; m.p.g. 30-35; whl. base 6ft. 8in.; track f. 4ft. 1in., r. 4ft. 0⅝in.; lgth. 11ft. 8⅞in.; width 4ft. 11¾in.; ht. 4ft. 1¾in.; g.c. 6in.; turng. cir. 29ft. 3in.; kerb wt. 13¾ cwt.; tank 7¾ gals.; 12-volt.

£1,150 + £241 p.t. = £1,391

OLDSMOBILE TORONADO

FASTEST front-wheel drive car in the world, the new General Motors Toronado will be watched with interest by engineers everywhere. Its great 7-litre V8 engine is canted sideways and delivers power to the automatic transmission through a silent chain. Long, low, rounded lines make it a rival for the best sporting coupes from Europe but it seats six people.

CLOSE-UP
Eight-cyl.; o.h.v.; 104.8 × 101 mm.; 6,965 c.c.; 385 b.h.p. gross; 10.5 to 1 comp.; coil ign.; four-choke carb.; 3-speed auto.; cen. lvr.; susp., f. ind. torsion bar, r. half-elliptic; 2-door; 6-seat; hyd. servo brks.; max. 120 m.p.h.; cruise 100; m.p.g. 15-17; whl. base 9ft. 11in.; track, f. 5ft. 3⅜in., r. 5ft. 3in.; lgth. 17ft. 7in.; width 6ft. 6½in.; ht. 4ft. 4¾in.; g.c. in.; kerb wt. 40¼ cwt.; tank 20 gals.; 12-volt.

OLDSMOBILE 4-4-2

DISTINCTIVE styling with recessed rear window, air outlets on front wings and deep one-piece bumpers identifies the 1966 version of the high-performance 4-4-2 which has a 6,556 c.c. V.8 engine, equipped with four-choke carburetter to provide a great surge of acceleration away from the traffic lights. This model has the conventional layout of front engine and rear drive.

CLOSE-UP
Eight.-cyl.; o.h.v.; 101.6 · 101 mm.; 6,556 c.c.; 350 b.h.p. gross; 10.25 to 1 comp.; coil ign.; four-choke carb.; 3-speed, 9.16, 5.25, 3.55 to 1; col. lvr., 4-speed or auto. opt.; susp., f. ind. coil, r. coil; 2- or 4-door; 6-seat; hyd. brks., servo opt.; max. 105 m.p.h.; cruise 85; m.p.g. 11-15; whl. base 9ft. 7in.; track f. and r. 4ft. 10in.; lgth. 17ft. 4in.; width 6ft. 1¾in.; ht. 4ft. 5¾in.; g.c. 6in.; turng. cir. 41ft. 4in.; kerb wt. 30½ cwt.; tank 16 gals.; 12-volt.

Abbreviations—g.c.—ground clearance; susp.—suspension; f.—front; r.—rear; comp.—compression; s.v.—side-valves; o.h.v.—overhead valves; o.h.c.—overhead camshaft; hyd.—hydraulic.

37

PANHARD 24 C.T.

LAST surviving model from France's oldest car manufacturer, now completely absorbed by Citroen. This coupe in contemporary style is now available in various versions including a new lower priced one. Power unit is an 848 c.c. air-cooled flat twin driving the front wheels and it delivers between 42 and 50 h.p. according to tune and modification. The faster versions have disc front brakes.

CLOSE-UP

Two-cyl.; o.h.v.; air-cooled; 84.9×75 mm.; 848 c.c.; 50 b.h.p.; 8.3 to 1 comp.; coil ign.; Zenith 2-choke carb.; 4-speed, 16.49, 9.28, 6.15, 4.52 to 1; cen. lvr.; susp., f. ind. transv. leaf, r. torsion bar; 2-door; 2/4 seat; disc. brks.; max. 93 m.p.h.; cruise 85; m.p.g. 34-36; whl. base 7ft. 6in.; track f. and r. 4ft. 3in.; lgth. 14ft.; width 5ft. 4in.; ht. 4ft.; g.c. 6¼in.; turng. cir. 32ft.; kerb wt. 16½ cwt.; tank 9¼ gals.; 12-volt.

£1,197 + £251 p.t. = £1,448

PEUGEOT 204

TRANSVERSE engine, gears in crankcase, front-wheel drive. Sounds like the BMC formula but the execution is different. Open-top light alloy cylinder block, overhead camshaft, light alloy head with hemispherical combustion chambers, all-synchromesh gears are important differences. Suspension is all-independent, by Macpherson coil spring struts at front, and similar struts with light alloy trailing arms at rear. An important new venture from an old-established manufacturer.

CLOSE-UP

Four-cyl.; o.h.c.; 75×64 mm.; 1,130 c.c.; 53 b.h.p.; 8.8 to 1 comp.; coil ign.; Solex carb.; 4-speed, 15.15, 9.25, 6.06, 4.23 to 1; col. lvr.; susp. f. and r. ind. coil; 4-seat; hyd. brks., disc front; max. 86 m.p.h.; cruise 78; m.p.g. 26-30; whl. base 8ft. 6in.; track, f. 4ft. 4in., r. 4ft. 1in.; lgth. 13ft.; width 5ft. 1in.; ht. 4ft. 7in.; g.c. 5½in.; turng. cir. 31ft. 2in.; kerb wt. 16¾ cwt.; tank 9¼ gals.; 12-volt.

PEUGEOT 404

SINCE its debut five years ago this French saloon with the angular Pininfarina styling, canted-over engine and Macpherson front suspension has established itself as a rugged car with a capacity for hard work. The range now includes a station wagon, Super Luxe saloon and cabriolet. Both the latter have high compression fuel injection engines producing 88 h.p. against 70 with a carburetter. A diesel engine is also available.

CLOSE-UP

Four-cyl.; o.h.v.; 84×73 mm.; 1,618 c.c.; 70 b.h.p.; 7.4 to 1 comp.; coil ign.; Solex carb.; 4-speed, 16.80, 9.42, 6.05, 4.2 to 1; col. lvr.; susp., f. ind. coil, r. coil; 4-door; 4/5-seat; hyd. brks.; max. 90 m.p.h.; cruise 75-80; m.p.g. 30; whl. base 8ft. 8½in.; track f. 4ft. 4¾in., r. 4ft. 2¼in.; lgth. 14ft. 6in.; width 5ft. 5½in.; ht. 4ft. 9¼in.; g.c. 6in.; turng. cir. 32ft.; kerb wt. 20½ cwt.; tank 11 gals.; 12-volt.

£903 + £190 p.t. = £1,093

VALIANT

COMPACT, smooth and comfortable car from the Chrysler Group with pleasant styling and good detail finish. Like most of the original compact Americans, it has been developed into a whole range of cars; saloons, hardtop coupes, convertibles and station wagons, with a variety of six-cylinder and V8 engines to meet the needs of economy-minded buyers and those who want performance with moderate dimensions.

CLOSE-UP

Six-cyl.; o.h.v.; 86.3×79.4 mm.; 2,789 c.c.; 100 b.h.p.; 8.5 to 1 comp.; coil ign.; Holley carb.; 3-speed, 10.4, 6.87, 3.23 to 1; col. lvr., 4-speed or auto. opt.; susp., f. ind. torsion bar, r. half-elliptic; 2- or 4-door; 5-seat; hyd. servo brks.; max. 94 m.p.h.; cruise 85; m.p.g. 18-23; whl. base 8ft. 10in.; track, f. 4ft. 7½in., r. 4ft. 7½in.; lgth. 15ft. 8in.; width 5ft. 10½in.; ht. 4ft. 5in.; g.c. 6in.; turng. cir. 37ft.; kerb wt. 24 cwt.; tank 15 gals.; 12-volt.

£1,724 + £331 p.t. = £2,055

Abbreviations—g.c.—ground clearance; susp.—suspension; f.—front; r.—rear; comp.—compression; s.v.—side-valves; o.h.v.—overhead valves; o.h.c.—overhead camshaft; hyd.—hydraulic.

PONTIAC PARISIENNE

MAJOR breakaway from normal American engine design, the new Pontiac overhead camshaft engine is available in two versions; with twin choke carburetter giving 165 h.p. gross or with four-choke carburetter giving 207 h.p. The camshaft is hollow and driven by a rubber belt reinforced with glass fibre. The four-choke carburetter uses two chokes on a light throttle and brings in two more by air valves at full throttle.

CLOSE-UP
Six-cyl.; o.h.c.; 98.4 × 82.5 mm.; 3,769 c.c.; 165 b.h.p. gross; 9 to 1 comp.; coil ign.; Rochester carb.; 3-speed, 9.05, 5.17, 3.08 to 1; auto. opt.; susp., f. ind. coil, r. coil; 2- or 4-door; 5-seat; hyd. brks.; max. 94 m.p.h.; cruise 80; m.p.g. 16-20; whl. base 9ft. 11in.; track, f. 5ft. 2½in., r. 5ft. 3in.; lgth. 17ft. 7in.; width 6ft. 6½in.; ht. 4ft. 7½in.; g.c. 6in.; turng. cir. 46ft.; tank 20 gals.; kerb wt. 34½ cwt.; 12-volt.

£1,840 + £385 p.t. = £2,225

PONTIAC G.T.O.

IN Italian, GTO stands for Gran Turismo Omologato. What it stands for in American remains obscure, but the pattern is clear enough; sheer brute power to give startling tyre-burning acceleration which has made a name for this Pontiac as one of the hottest production cars to come out of America. Four seat belts are standard. Tempest models have driver-controlled vacuum door locks.

CLOSE-UP
Eight-cyl.; o.h.v.; 103 × 95 mm.; 6,375 c.c.; 335 b.h.p. gross; 10.75 to 1 comp.; coil ign.; four-choke Carter carb.; 3-speed, 9.05, 5.18, 3.08 to 1; col. lvr., 4-speed or auto opt.; susp., f. ind. coil, r. coil; 2 or 4-door; 6-seat; hyd. servo brks.; max. 120 m.p.h.; cruise 90; m.p.g. 11-16; whl. base 9ft. 7in.; track f. and r. 4ft. 10in.; lgth. 17ft. 2in.; width 5ft. 11¼in.; ht. 4ft. 5½in.; g.c. 4in.; turng. cir. 43ft. 6in.; kerb wt. 27¾ cwt.; tank 17¾ gals.; 12-volt.

£2,009 + £420 p.t. = £2,429

PORSCHE Type 911

CLEAN-CUT body lines evolved by a grandson of Ferdinand Porsche retain the Porsche character in more practical form. The power unit is a 2-litre flat six in light alloy with chain-driven overhead camshaft to each bank and two twin-choke carburetters. The gearbox has five speeds and trailing-arm rear suspension with transverse torsion bars replaces the former swing axles.

CLOSE-UP
Six-cyl.; o.h.c.; air-cooled; 80 × 66 mm.; 1,991 c.c.; 130 b.h.p.; 9 to 1 comp.; coil ign.; 2 twin choke Solex carbs.; 5-speed, 13.68, 8.36, 5.84, 4.43, 3.35 to 1; cen. lvr.; susp., f. and r. ind. torsion bar; 2-door; 2/4-seat; hyd. disc brks.; max. 130 m.p.h.; cruise 120; m.p.g. 25; whl. base 7ft. 2¾in.; track f. 4ft. 4½in., r. 4ft. 3½in.; lgth. 13ft. 6¾in.; width 5ft. 3in.; ht. 4ft. 4in.; g.c. 6in.; turng. cir. 32ft. 9in.; kerb wt. 21¾ cwt.; tank, 16¼ gals.; 12-volt.

£2,844 + £594 p.t. = £3,438

PORSCHE 912

ABANDONED at last is the historic streamlined shape that made the Porsche name. The more angular, but roomier new body is now used for both four- and six-cylinder models. With it comes the trailing link rear suspension, finally ousting the old swing axles. But still retained are the fine finish, attention to detail and individual character that turn owners into addicts.

CLOSE-UP
Four-cyl.; o.h.v., air-cooled; 82.5 × 74 mm.; 1,582 c.c.; 90 b.h.p.; 9.3 to 1 comp.; coil ign.; 2 Solex carbs.; 5-speed, 13.69, 8.33, 5.83, 4.61, 3.80 to 1; cen. lvr.; susp. f. and r. ind. torsion bar; 2-door; 2/4-seat; disc brks.; max. 110 m.p.h.; cruise 100; m.p.g. 30; whl. base 7ft. 2¾in.; track, f. 4ft. 4½in., r. 4ft. 3½in.; lgth. 13ft. 6¾in.; width 5ft. 3in.; ht. 4ft. 4in.; g.c. 6in.; turng. cir. 32ft. 9in.; kerb wt. 19 cwt.; tank 13½ gals.; 12-volt.

£2,040 + £427 p.t. = £2,467

Abbreviations—g.c.—ground clearance; susp.—suspension; f.—front; r.—rear; comp.—compression; s.v.—side-valves; o.h.v.—overhead valves; o.h.c.—overhead camshaft; hyd.—hydraulic.

RAMBLER CLASSIC SIX

AN American car that is almost a naturalised European since Renault began assembling it for the Common Market. Robust six-cylinder engine, compact but roomy bodywork devoid of short-lived styling gimmicks, self-adjusting brakes and a smooth, effortless top-gear performance give it a strong appeal for motorists who want space and performance at a moderate price. Power steering is optional.

CLOSE-UP
Six-cyl.; o.h.v.; 95.25 × 76.2 mm.; 3,257 c.c.; 128 b.h.p. gross; 8.5 to I comp.; coil ign.; Carter carb.; 3-speed, 8.63, 5.39, 3.31 to I; col. lvr., overdrive or auto. opt.; susp., f. ind. coil, r. coil; 2- or 4-door; 5/6-seat; dual hyd. brks., disc front opt.; max. 95 m.p.h.; cruise 85; m.p.g. 23; whl. base 9ft. 4in.; track, f. 4ft. 10¼in., r. 4ft. 9¾in.; lgth. 16ft. 3in.; width 6ft. 2½in.; ht. 4ft. 6¾in.; g.c. 6in.; turng. cir. 37ft. 3in.; kerb wt. 27 cwt.; tank 15¾ gals.; 12-volt.

RELIANT REBEL

THIS is a popular-priced family car with a glass-fibre, two-door saloon body which has proved to be a winner. Designed by David Ogle Associates, it is compact, robust and manoeuvrable. It has plenty of zing from a water-cooled, four-cylinder light alloy engine and it is cheap on fuel. Reliant's challenge to the big fellows has come off and you see many of these trim models on the road.

CLOSE-UP
Four-cyl.; o.h.v.; 55.88 × 60.96 mm.; 598 c.c.; 27 b.h.p.; 8.5 to I comp.; coil ign.; Solex carb.; 4-speed, 18.67, 10.53, 6.36, 4.38 to I; cen. lvr.; susp., f. ind. coil, r. half-elliptic; 2-door; 4-seat; hyd. brks.; max, 68 m.p.h.; cruise 60; m.p.g. 55; whl. base 7ft. 5in.; track f. 3ft 11⅜in.; r. 3ft. 10⅝in.; lgth 11ft. 6in.; width 4ft. 10in.; ht. 4ft. 7½in.; g.c. 6in.; turng. cir. 29ft.; kerb wt. 10½ cwt.; tank 6 gals.; 6-volt.
£433 + £92 p.t. = £525

RELIANT SCIMITAR

THIS swift, good-looking car has de Normanville overdrive as an optional extra. It is built to seat three people with an occasional fourth and its two-door body is glass fibre on a steel chassis. Plenty of power comes from the Ford engine transmitted through a four-speed and reverse all-synchromesh gearbox. Even its colour schemes make exciting reading. Examples: Bahama yellow, silver streak and Manhattan blue.

CLOSE-UP
Six-cyl.; o.h.v.; 82.6 × 79.5 mm.; 2,553 c.c.; 116 b.h.p.; 8.3 to I comp.; coil ign.; 3 S.U. carbs.; 4-speed, 12.24, 8.56, 5.46, 3.875 to I, de Normanville overdrive opt.; cen. lvr.; susp., f. ind. coil, r. coil; 2-door; 2/3-seat; hyd. brks., disc front; max. 110 m.p.h.; cruise 95; m.p.g. 20-25; whl. base 7ft. 8in.; track f. 4ft. 2¾in.; r. 4ft. 1¾in.; lgth. 13ft. 11¾in.; width 5ft. 2in.; ht. 4ft. 3in.; g.c. 6in.; turng. cir. 33ft.; kerb wt. 21¼ cwt.; tank 20 gals.; 12-volt.
£1,068 + £224 p.t. = £1,292

RENAULT DAUPHINE GORDINI

ONE of the best-looking Renaults, the Dauphine is still going strong after a long career. The Gordini version is the most powerful model, with 845 c.c. engine modified, with the aid of special head, new manifolds and different carburetter to produce 33 h.p. instead of 27. All Dauphines now have disc brakes on all four wheels. The spare wheel lies flat under the nose, forming an auxiliary bumper.

CLOSE-UP
Four-cyl.; o.h.v.; 58 × 80 mm.; 845 c.c.; 34 b.h.p.; 8.5 to I comp.; coil ign.; Solex carb.; 4-speed, 15.84, 9.84, 6.48, 4.51 to I; cen. lvr.; susp., f. and r. ind. coil; 4-door; 4-seat; disc brks.; max. 82 m.p.h.; cruise 70; m.p.g. 36-40; whl. base 7ft. 5½in.; track f. 4ft. 1¼in., r. 4ft. 1in.; lgth. 12ft. 11in.; width 5ft.; ht. 4ft. 6¾in.; g.c. 6in.; turn. cir. 29ft. 10in.; kerb wt. 12¾ cwt.; tank 7 gals.; 12-volt.
£494 + £104 p.t. = £598

RENAULT R4L

FRONT-WHEEL drive and all-independent suspension by long, flexible torsion bars give this versatile utility model its ability to deal lightheartedly with rough roads and stony tracks. Four big doors and a lift-up tail panel make it adaptable as family car or goods carrier. Light construction and simple trim enable it to get a lot of performance out of its willing 845 c.c. engine.

CLOSE-UP

Four-cyl.; o.h.v.; 58×80 mm.; 845 c.c.; 28 b.h.p.; 8 to 1 comp.; coil ign.; Zenith carb.; 3-speed, 15.68, 7.60, 4.28 to 1; dash lvr.; susp., f. and r. ind. torsion bar; 5-door; 4-seat; hyd. brks.; max. 68 m.p.h.; cruise 55; m.p.g. 45-50; whl. base 8ft.; track f. 4ft. $1\frac{1}{4}$in., r. 3ft. $11\frac{1}{2}$in.; lgth. 12ft.; width 4ft. $10\frac{1}{2}$in.; ht. 5ft.; g.c. $6\frac{7}{8}$in.; turng. cir. 31ft.; kerb wt. $12\frac{3}{4}$ cwt.; tank $5\frac{3}{4}$ gals.; 6-volt.

£453 + £96 p.t. = £549

RENAULT 1100

EXTENSIVE re-styling adds new elegance to the medium-range car from France's state-owned car factory and gives it a valuable increase in luggage space. Grouping of head-lamps and auxiliary lamps is new and equipment is improved in detail. A design that originally grew out of the Dauphine, the 1100 has the same basic features of rear engine, coil spring front suspension and swing axles at the rear, and has disc brakes all round.

CLOSE-UP

Four-cyl.; o.h.v.; 70 72 mm.; 1,108 c.c.; 44.5 b.h.p.; 8.5 to 1 comp.; coil ign.; Solex carb.; 4-speed, 14.93, 9.28, 6.11, 4.23 to 1; cen. lvr.; susp. f. and r. ind. coil; 4-door; 4-seat; hyd. disc brks.; max. 83 m.p.h.; cruise 70; m.p.g. 35-39; whl. base 7ft. $5\frac{1}{4}$in.; track, f. 4ft. $1\frac{1}{4}$in., r. 4ft.; lgth. 13ft. $9\frac{1}{2}$in.; width 4ft. $10\frac{1}{2}$in.; ht. 4ft. $6\frac{1}{2}$in.; g.c. $5\frac{3}{8}$in.; turng. cir. 30ft. 6in.; kerb wt. $15\frac{5}{8}$ cwt.; tank $8\frac{1}{2}$ gals.; 12-volt.

£577 + £122 p.t. = £699

RENAULT R16

TREND-SETTING front-drive model from France's largest manufacturer. Saloon-cum-station wagon utility of the R4 with sophisticated style and complete equipment. Seats you can fold away or lift out, lift-up rear door and a pivoted parcel shelf to conceal the contents of the luggage boot. Long torsion bars give sure road grip and a soft ride, cooling system is sealed, brakes are discs.

CLOSE-UP

Four-cyl.; o.h.v.; 76×81 mm.; 1,470 c.c.; 58 b.h.p.; 8.5 to 1 comp.; coil ign.; Solex carb.; 4-speed, 13.6, 8.48, 5.58, 3.88 to 1; col. lvr.; susp. f. and r. ind. torsion bar; 5-door; 5-seat; hyd. brks., disc front; max. 86 m.p.h.; cruise 78; m.p.g. 27-30; whl. base 8ft. $9\frac{1}{2}$in.; track, f. 4ft. $4\frac{5}{8}$in., r. 4ft. $2\frac{7}{8}$in.; lgth. 13ft. $10\frac{1}{2}$in.; width 5ft. $4\frac{5}{8}$in.; ht. 4ft. $9\frac{1}{4}$in.; g.c. $5\frac{7}{8}$in.; turng. cir. 32ft. 8in.; kerb wt. $19\frac{1}{4}$ cwt.; tank 12 gals.; 12-volt.

RILEY ELF

HERE is a splendid little car that has all the agility of the famous Mini models plus a touch of elegance and tradition. It is as much at home in traffic as whizzing along a country road. Refinements like the wood veneer instrument panel housing speedometer, fuel gauge, oil gauge and thermometer lift the nippy Elf into the low-priced luxury class. It continues to sell well in many markets.

CLOSE-UP

Four-cyl.; o.h.v.; 64.58 76.2 mm.; 998 c.c.; 38 b.h.p.; 8.3 to 1 comp.; coil ign.; S.U. carb.; 4-speed, 13.66, 8.18, 5.32, 3.76 to 1; cen. lvr.; susp., f. and r. ind. rubber-hyd.; 2-door; 4-seat; hyd. brks.; max. 75 m.p.h.; cruise 62; m.p.g. 40; whl. base 6ft. 8in.; track f. 3ft. $11\frac{1}{2}$in.; r. 3ft. 10in.; lgth. 10ft. $10\frac{1}{4}$in.; width 4ft. $7\frac{1}{2}$in.; ht. 4ft. 5in.; g.c. $6\frac{1}{2}$in.; turng. cir. 31ft. 7in.; kerb wt. 13 cwt.; tank $5\frac{1}{2}$ gals.; 12-volt.

£493 + £104 p.t. = £597

Abbreviations—g.c.—ground clearance; susp.—suspension; f.—front; r.—rear; comp.—compression; s.v.—side-valves; o.h.v.—overhead valves; o.h.c.—overhead camshaft; hyd.—hydraulic.

RILEY KESTREL

YET another disguise for the BMC's successful front-drive 1100 with the transverse front engine, disc front brakes and Hydrolastic rubber-and-water suspension. Twin carburetters raise the output to 55 h.p. A rev counter recalls the sporting successes that built the Riley name; instrument panel in English walnut veneer. Heater, windscreen washer, headlamp flasher, leather upholstery and wheel rim trim are standard.

CLOSE-UP

Four-cyl.; o.h.v.; 64.58 × 83.72 mm.; 1,098 c.c.; 55 b.h.p.; 8.9 to 1 comp.; coil ign.; 2 S.U. carbs.; 4-speed, 14.99, 8.98, 5.83, 4.13 to 1; cen. lvr.; susp., f. and r. ind. rubber hyd.; 4-door; 4-seat; hyd. brks., disc front; max. 85 m.p.h.; cruise 75; m.p.g. 35-38; whl. base 7ft. 9½in.; track f. 4ft. 3½in., r. 4ft. 2⅞in.; lgth. 12ft. 2¾in.; width 5ft. 0¾in.; ht. 4ft. 4¾in.; g.c. 6in.; turng. cir. 34ft. 9in.; kerb wt. 16⅝ cwt.; tank 8 gals; 12-volt.

£645 + £136 p.t. = £781

ROLLS-ROYCE SILVER SHADOW

RISING to the challenge of swift technical advance, Rolls-Royce re-think The Best Car in the World. Tailored to today's traffic, the Silver Shadow is smaller, roomier, lighter, swifter. A unit structure saves space, all-independent self-levelling suspension gives a better-than-ever ride and triple-safe disc brakes with hydraulic servos complement the improved engine, automatic transmission and power steering.

CLOSE-UP

Eight-cyl.; o.h.v.; 104.1 × 91.4 mm.; 6,230 c.c.; b.h.p. not revealed; 9 to 1 comp.; coil ign.; 2 S.U. carbs.; 4-speed auto., 11.75, 8.1, 4.46, 3.08 to 1; col. lvr.; susp. f. and r. ind. coil, hyd. levelling; 4-door; 5-seat; disc hyd. servo brks.; max. 120 m.p.h.; cruise 100; m.p.g. 13-16; whl. base 9ft. 11½in.; track f. and r. 4ft. 9½in.; lgth. 16ft. 11½in.; width 5ft. 11in.; ht. 4ft. 11¾in.; g.c. 6½in.; turng. cir. 38ft.; kerb wt. 41½ cwt.; tank 24 gals.; 12-volt.

£5,425 + £1,131 p.t. = £6,556

ROLLS-ROYCE PHANTOM V

THE car for crowned heads seen throughout the world. Britain's most plush offering in motoring. Elegant despite its size, it accommodates seven passengers in addition to the chauffeur. And the task of driving this large car slowly in traffic is made remarkably easy with automatic transmission and power-assisted steering. Name any luxury on a car and you'll find this has it. A wonderful ambassador wherever it travels.

CLOSE-UP

Eight-cyl.; o.h.v.; 104.14 × 91.44 mm.; 6,230 c.c.; b.h.p. not revealed; 9 to 1 comp.; coil ign.; 2 S.U. carbs.; 4-speed auto., 14.86, 10.23, 5.64, 3.89 to 1; col. lvr.; susp., f. ind. coil, r. half-elliptic; 4-door; 7-seat; hyd. servo brks.; max. 100 m.p.h.; cruise 85; m.p.g. 12; whl. base 12ft.; track, f. 5ft. 0⅞in., r. 5ft. 4in.; lgth. 19ft. 10in.; width 6ft. 7in.; ht. 5ft. 9in.; g.c. 7½in.; turng. cir. 48ft. 9in.; tank 23 gals.; 12-volt.

£7,875 + £1,642 p.t. = £9,517

ROVER 2000

YOUNG, pace-making car that changed the Rover image, with an interior that set new standards for passenger protection, functional controls and instrument legibility. Four individual seats with reclining front backrests; flexible bins in front to protect the knees. Unique bell-crank front suspension and De Dion rear combine outstanding comfort with fine road holding. All body panels are detachable for easy repair.

CLOSE-UP

Four-cyl.; o.h.c.; 85.7 / 85.7 mm.; 1,978 c.c.; 90 b.h.p.; 9 to 1 comp.; coil ign.; S.U. carb.; 4-speed, 12.83, 7.55, 4.92, 3.54 to 1; cen. lvr.; susp., f. ind. coil, r. de Dion coil; 4-door; 4-seat; disc servo brks.; max. 105 m.p.h.; cruise 95; m.p.g. 28-32; whl. base 8ft. 7⅜in.; track, f. 4ft. 5⅜in., r. 4ft. 4½in.; lgth. 14ft. 10½in.; width 5ft. 6½in.; ht. 4ft. 6⅜in.; g.c. 6½in.; turng. cir. 31ft. 6in.; kerb wt. 24¾ cwt.; tank 12 gals.; 12-volt.

£1,073 + £225 p.t. = £1,298

ROVER 3-LITRE

HEADRESTS for all four occupants with reading lamps for rear passengers recessed in backs of front ones are an option in the re-styled interior of this solidly built Rover. Interior trim is now closer in style to that of the 2000 with revised facia, new more comfortable front seats with adjustable backrests and separate heater controls for rear passengers.

CLOSE-UP

Six-cyl.; o.h. inlet, side exhaust; 77.8×105 mm.; 2,995 c.c.; 121 b.h.p.; 8.75 to 1 comp.; coil ign.; S.U. carb.; 4-speed, 14.52, 8.11, 5.48, 4.3 to 1, de Normanville overdrive; cen. lvr., BW auto. opt.; susp., f. ind. torsion bar, r. half-elliptic; 4-door; 4-seat; hyd. servo brks., disc front; max. 105 m.p.h.; cruise 90; m.p.g. 18-25; whl. base 9ft. 2½in.; track f. 4ft. 7½in., r. 4ft. 8in.; lgth. 15ft. 6½in.; width 5ft. 10in.; ht. 4ft. 11¼in.; g.c. 7¼in.; turng. cir. 40ft.; kerb wt. 32½ cwt.; tank 14 gals.; 12-volt.

£1,412+£296 p.t. = £1,708

ROVER 3-LITRE COUPE

STRICTLY for four, with contoured seats, generous armrests and lowered roof line, the coupe adds a sporting touch to 3-litre comfort and performance. Interior improvements to facia and trim are in line with those on the saloon. Reclining front seats, separate controls for rear compartment heating, tool tray-cum-picnic table, are standard. Adjustable headrests (front have reading lamps for rear) optional.

CLOSE-UP

Six-cyl.; o.h. inlet, side exhaust; 77.8×105 mm.; 2,995 c.c.; 121 b.h.p.; 8.75 to 1 comp.; coil ign.; S.U. carb.; 4-speed, 14.52, 8.11, 5.48, 4.3 to 1; de Normanville overdrive; cen. lvr., BW auto opt.; susp., f. ind. torsion bar, r. half-elliptic; 4-door; 4-seat; hyd. servo brks., disc front; max. 105 m.p.h.; cruise 90; m.p.g. 18-22; whl. base 9ft. 2½in.; track f. 4ft. 7½in., r. 4ft. 8in.; lgth. 15ft. 6½in.; width 5ft. 10in.; ht. 4ft. 8¾in.; g.c. 7¼; turng. cir. 37ft.; kerb wt. 33¼ cwt.; tank 14 gals.; 12-volt.

£1,537+£321 p.t. = £1,858

SAAB 96

TRIPLE-CHOKE carburetter formerly reserved for the sports model, is now a feature of the standard saloon. New inlet manifold, high output ignition coil and higher compression raise output to 42 h.p. A fully synchronised four-speed gearbox and a headlamp flasher are also offered. SAAB durability is further enhanced by improved body rust-proofing and new stainless steel side mouldings and hub caps.

CLOSE-UP

Three-cyl.; two-stroke; 70×72.9 mm.; 841 c.c.; 40 b.h.p.; 8 to 1 comp.; coil ign.; Zenith carb.; 3-speed, 17.19, 8.53, 5.23 to 1; 4-speed opt.; col. lvr.; susp., f. ind. coil, r. coil; 2-door; 4-seat; hyd. brks.; max. 78 m.p.h.; cruise 72; m.p.g. 32-34; whl. base 8ft. 2in.; track f. and r. 4ft.; lgth. 13ft. 8in.; width 5ft. 2in.; ht. 4ft. 10in.; g.c. 7½in.; turng. cir. 36ft.; kerb wt. 16¼ cwt.; tank 8½ gals.; 12-volt.

£602+£127 p.t. = £729

SABRA SPORT

POWERED by a modified Ford Consul engine, the Sabra has striking glass fibre bodywork on a chassis with an unusual form of coil spring front suspension and a still more unusual method of locating the rear axle on Watt links with coil springs. Assembled in Israel, it is a product of technical co-operation with Reliant who supplied the designs and production know-how.

CLOSE-UP

Four-cyl.; o.h.v.; 82.6×79.5 mm.; 1,703 c.c.; 90 b.h.p.; 8.9 to 1 comp.; coil ign.; 2 S.U. carbs.; 4-speed, 9.0, 6.0, 4.37, 3.55 to 1; cen. lvr.; susp., f. ind. coil, r. coil; 2-door; 2-seat; hyd. servo brks., disc front.; max. 105 m.p.h.; cruise 85; m.p.g. 25-32; whl. base 7ft. 6in.; track f. and r. 4ft.; lgth. 13ft. 9in.; width 5ft. 1in.; ht. 4ft. 2in.; g.c. 6¾in.; turng. cir. 31ft.; kerb wt. 15¾ cwt.; tank 8½ gals.; 12-volt.

Abbreviations—g.c.—ground clearance; susp.—suspension; f.—front; r.—rear; comp.—compression; s.v.—side-valves; o.h.v.—overhead valves; o.h.c.—overhead camshaft; hyd.—hydraulic.

43

SIMCA 1000 GLS

SEMI-AUTOMATIC transmission is the latest option on this popular rear-engined family car from a Chrysler-controlled French factory. An automatic clutch, a torque converter and gears selected by a central lever give drive combinations for town, mountain and country motoring. Normal gearbox is four-speed all-synchromesh. Underseal, heater-demister, windscreen washer and headlamp flasher are included in the price.

CLOSE-UP
Four-cyl.; o.h.v.; 68 × 65 mm.; 944 c.c.; 52 b.h.p. gross; 9 to 1 comp.; coil ign.; Solex carb.; 4-speed, 15.51, 9.26, 6.16, 4.21 to 1; cen. lvr.; susp., f. ind. trans. leaf, r. ind. coil; 4-door; 4-seat; hyd. brks.; max. 80 m.p.h.; cruise 70; m.p.g. 35; whl. base 7ft. 4in.; track, f. 4ft. 1¼in., r. 4ft. 0⅝in.; lgth. 12ft. 5in.; width. 4ft. 10in.; ht. 4ft. 6in.; g.c. 6½in.; turng. cir. 28ft.; kerb wt. 14⅝ cwt.; tank 8 gals.; 12-volt.

£561 + £119 p.t. = £680

SIMCA 1300/1500

ONE basic body range with choice of 1,290 c.c. or 1,482 c.c. engines gives Simca wide coverage in the up-to-1½-litre market. Like the 1500, the 1300 now has disc front brakes and the 1500 is now available with Borg Warner 35 automatic transmission. The good looking station wagons with wind-down rear windows are now available with 1300 or 1500 engines.

CLOSE-UP
Four-cyl.; o.h.v.; 74 ⁄ 75 mm.; 1,290 c.c.; 62 b.h.p. gross; or 75.2 × 83 mm., 1,475 c.c.; 81 b.h.p. gross; 8.3/9.3 to 1 comp.; coil ign.; Solex or Weber carb.; 4-speed, 16.22, 9.14, 6.15, 4.45 to 1; cen. lvr.; susp., f. ind. coil, r. coil; 4-door; 4-seat; hyd. brks., disc front on 1500; max. 85/93 m.p.h.; cruise 70-80; m.p.g. 28-32; whl. base 8ft. 3⅓in.; track, f. 4ft. 4in., r. 4ft. 3⅓in.; lgth. 13ft. 11¼in.; width 5ft. 2in.; ht. 4ft. 7¼in.; g.c. 6in.; turng. cir. 32ft.; kerb wt. 19½-20 cwt.; tank 12 gals.; 12-volt.

1300—£661 + £139 p.t. = £800
1500—£760 + £160 p.t. = £920

SINGER CHAMOIS MK II

SMOOTH-RUNNING, quiet and comfortable small car developed from the Hillman Imp, but with superior trim and upholstery, broad-base wheels, braced-tread tyres. Mark II has larger valves in its light alloy overhead camshaft engine; new camshaft, modified head, larger carburetter and new distributor. The heater gives quicker output from cold. Rear seat leg room is increased by a revised backrest, trim is further improved and there are new colour schemes.

CLOSE-UP
Four-cyl.; o.h.c.; 68 ⁄ 60.4 mm.; 875 c.c.; 39 b.h.p.; 10 to 1 comp.; coil ign.; Solex carb.; 4-speed, 16.59, 8.91, 5.70, 4.14 to 1; cen. lvr.; susp. f. and r. ind. coil; 2-door; 4-seat; hyd. brks.; max. 80 m.p.h.; cruise 75; m.p.g. 40; whl. base 6ft. 10in.; track, f. 4ft. 1½in., r. 4ft. 0½in.; lgth. 11ft. 9¼in.; width 5ft. 0¼in.; ht. 4ft. 6½in.; g.c. 5½in.; turng. cir. 30ft.; kerb wt. 14¼ cwt.; tank 6 gals.; 12-volt.

£487 + £103 p.t. = £590

SINGER VOGUE

EQUIPPED with a high performance 91 b.h.p version of the new Rootes 1725 c.c. engine, this popular model is given more power and snappier performance. Other improvements include the introduction of an alternator to save the battery, a redesigned gear lever for the all-synchromesh gearbox, and thief-proof push buttons in the front quarter lights. The car is already known for its lush interior and now they have added an inside light to the luggage boot.

CLOSE-UP
Four-cyl.; o.h.v.; 81.5 × 82.55 mm.; 1,725 c.c.; 81 b.h.p. gross; 8.3 to 1 comp.; coil ign.; Solex carb.; 4-speed, 13.04, 8.32, 5.41, 3.89 to 1; de Normanville overdrive or BW auto. opt.; cen. lvr.; susp., f. ind. coil, r. half-elliptic; 4-door; 4/5-seat; hyd. brks., disc front; max. 90 m.p.h.; cruise 80; m.p.g. 26-32; whl. base 8ft. 5in.; track, f. 4ft. 3¼in., r. 4ft. 0½in.; lgth. 13ft. 9in.; width 5ft. 3in.; ht. 4ft. 10in.; g.c. 5½in.; turng. cir. 36ft.; kerb wt. 21¼ cwt.; tank 10½ gals.; 12-volt.

£740 + £156 p.t. = £896

Abbreviations—g.c.—ground clearance; susp.—suspension; f.—front; r.—rear; comp.—compression; s.v.—side-valves; o.h.v.—overhead valves; o.h.c.—overhead camshaft; hyd.—hydraulic.

SKODA OCTAVIA SUPER

MAXIMUM for your money is the keynote of Czechoslovakia's export drive, provided you don't expect luxury finish too. Heater, radiator blind, full toolkit, wheel discs, adjustable backrests are included in the low price. Tubular backbone chassis carries coil spring front suspension, and swing axles at the rear. Windscreen and rear window are interchangeable. Standard-grade fuel will do.

CLOSE-UP
Four-cyl.; o.h.v.; 72×75 mm.; 1,221 c.c.; 44 b.h.p.; 7.5 to 1 comp.; coil ign.; Jikov carb.; 4-speed, 20.4, 11.8, 7.6, 4.78 to 1; col. lvr.; susp., f. ind. coil, r. ind. transv. leaf; 2-door; 4-seat; hyd. brks.; max. 77 m.p.h.; cruise 65; m.p.g. 35-40; whl. base 7ft. 10½in.; track, f. 3ft. 11⅝in., r. 4ft. 1in.; lgth. 13ft. 4in.; width 5ft. 3in.; ht. 4ft. 8½in.; g.c. 6¾in.; turng. cir. 38ft.; kerb wt. 18¼ cwt.; tank 6½ gals.; 12-volt.

£380 + £80 p.t. = £460

SKODA 1000 MB

CZECH that's easy on your overdraft. Latest model from a nationalised car industry is an economical design with rear engine and all-independent suspension. Reclining front seats, heater, adjustable fresh air inlets, screen washer, full toolkit are provided. Spare wheel, above front bumper is accessible without removing luggage. Fuel filler, engine compartment, luggage trunk, are locked when the car is. All wings are detachable.

CLOSE-UP
Four-cyl.; o.h.v.; 68×68 mm.; 988 c.c.; 40 b.h.p.; 8.3 to 1 comp.; coil ign.; Jikov carb.; 4-speed, 16.87, 9.41, 6.26, 4.26 to 1; cen. lvr.; susp. f. and r. ind. coil; 4-door; 4-seat; hyd. brks.; max. 75 m.p.h.; cruise 68; m.p.g. 36-38; whl. base 7ft. 10½in.; track, f. 4ft. r. 4ft. 1in.; lgth. 13ft. 8⅜in.; width 5ft. 4in.; ht. 4ft. 7½in.; g.c. 6⅛in.; turng. cir. 35 ft.; kerb wt. 15⅝ cwt.; tank 7 gals.; 12-volt.

£479 + £101 p.t. = £580

SUNBEAM ALPINE

EXTRA sparkle for this Sunbeam comes from the 1.7 litre five-bearing twin-camshaft engine which delivers smoother power and more of it. Better trim, footwell ventilation, new instruments, are features of sports tourer and GT coupe. Tourer has better quality hood material, with soft covers, easier to manipulate; coupe has occasional rear seats, two-speed heater fan. Steering wheel and pedals are adjustable.

CLOSE-UP
Four-cyl.; o.h.v.; 81.5×82.55 mm.; 1.725 c.c.; 100 b.h.p. gross; 9.2 to 1 comp.; coil ign.; 2 Stromberg carbs.; 4-speed, 12.14, 7.75, 5.04, 3.89 to 1; cen. lvr.; de Normanville overdrive opt.; susp., f. ind. coil, r. half-elliptic; 2-door; 2-seat; hyd. servo brks., disc front; max. 100 m.p.h.; cruise 85; m.p.g. 25; whl. base 7ft. 2in.; track, f. 4ft. 3¾in., r. 4ft. 0½in.; lgth. 13ft.; width 5ft. 0½in.; ht. 4ft. 4½in.; g.c. 4¼in.; turng. cir. 34ft.; kerb wt. 19½ cwt.; tank 9 gals.; 12-volt.

£725 + £153 p.t. = £878

SUNBEAM RAPIER

THIS graceful sports saloon gets an exhilarating boost in getaways and top speed with the new 1725 c.c. Rootes engine. The fitting of an alternator in place of the conventional dynamo adds an extra touch of refinement. Detailed improvements include self-adjusting rear brakes and new colour and trim schemes. This is the model for the sportsman who also likes to give his family an outing.

CLOSE-UP
Four-cyl.; o.h.v.; 81.5×82.55 mm.; 1,725 c.c.; 91 b.h.p. gross; 9.2 to 1 comp.; coil ign.; Twin-choke Solex carb.; 4-speed, 13.04, 8.32, 5.41, 3.89 to 1; cen. lvr.; de Normanville overdrive opt.; susp., f. ind. coil, r. half elliptic; 2-door; 4-seat; hyd. servo brks.; disc front; max. 95 m.p.h.; cruise 80; m.p.g. 25-30; whl. base 8ft.; track, f. 4ft. 3¾in., r. 4ft. 0½in.; lgth. 13ft. 7½in.; width 5ft. 1in.; ht. 4ft. 9½in.; g.c. 5½in.; turng. cir. 36ft.; kerb wt. 20¾ cwt.; tank 10 gals.; 12-volt.

£750 + £158 p.t. = £908

Abbreviations—g.c.—ground clearance; susp.—suspension; f.—front; r.—rear; comp.—compression; s.v.—side-valves; o.h.v.—overhead valves; o.h.c.—overhead camshaft; hyd.—hydraulic.

SUNBEAM TIGER

QUART into pint-pot exercise successfully concluded with the installation of a 4.2-litre Ford V8 engine where a 1.6-litre four-cylinder sat before. But Rootes engineering didn't stop there. Stronger structure and suspension, new steering, more powerful brakes, tame the Tiger but it's still an exciting creature with a growl that means business. And the price is moderate for this kind of performance.

CLOSE-UP

Eight-cyl.; o.h.v.; 96.5 73 mm.; 4,261 c.c.; 164 b.h.p. gross; 8.8 to 1 comp.; coil ign.; Twin-choke Ford carb.; 4-speed, 6.68, 4.86, 3.71, 2.88 to 1; cen. lvr.; susp., f. ind. coil, r. half-elliptic; 2-door; 2-seat; hyd. servo brks., disc front; max. 118 m.p.h.; cruise 95; m.p.g. 15-20; whl. base 7ft. 2in.; track, f. 4ft. 3½in.; r. 4ft. 0½in.; lgth. 13ft. 2in.; width 5ft. 0½in.; ht. 4ft. 3½in.; g.c. 5in.; turng. cir. 37ft. 9in.; kerb wt. 23⅜ cwt.; tank 11¼ gals.; 12-volt.

£1,195 + £251 p.t. = £1,446

TRIPLEX G.T.S.

RESEARCH into new kinds of glass and ways of fitting it is the object of this light and airy station wagon built for Triplex by David Ogle Associates on a Reliant Scimitar chassis. Glazing is stuck on, not sealed in rubber. It is heat-absorbing but later, glass with energy-reflecting films and photochromatic glass which changes colour in sunlight will be tried.

CLOSE-UP

Six-cyl.; o.h.v.; 83×80 mm.; 2,553 c.c.; 120 b.h.p.; 8.3 to 1 comp.; coil ign.; 3 S.U. carbs.; 4-speed, 12.2, 8.3, 5.45, 3.88 to 1; cen. lvr.; susp. f. and r. ind. coil; 2-door; 4-seat; hyd. brks., disc front; max. 120 m.p.h.; cruise 100; m.p.g. 19-24; whl. base 7ft. 8in.; track f. and r. 4ft. 2in.; lgth. 13ft. 11½in.; width 5ft. 2in.; ht. 4ft. 4in.; g.c. 5in.; turng. cir. 35ft.; kerb wt. 20¾ cwt.; tank 20 gals.; 12-volt.

T.V.R. TRIDENT

LOVELY crackly crisp noises pour from the exhaust pipes as you open up the big Ford V8 engine in the elegant TVR Trident. Styled in Paris by Fiore and built in Italy by Fissore, the body is of aluminium and steel. TVR also build the Griffith competition coupe with Ford engine tuned to give up to 271 b.h.p. and the TVR 1800 with five-bearing MGB engine.

CLOSE-UP

Eight-cyl.; o.h.v.; 101.6×72.9 mm.; 4,727 c.c.; 271 b.h.p. gross; 10 to 1 comp.; coil ign.; Holley carb.; 4-speed, cen. lvr.; susp. f. and r. ind. coil; 2-door; 4-seat; disc brks.; max. 150 m.p.h.; cruise 130; m.p.g. 15-18; whl. base 7ft. 6in.; track, f. 4ft. 6½in., r. 4ft. 7½in.; lgth. 13ft. 4in.; width 5ft. 5½in.; ht. 4ft. 2in.; g.c. 6in.; 12-volt.

TOYOTA CORONA

BUILT by the Toyota Motor Co. in Toyota, Japan, the Corona has an individual angular line and good detail finish. The o.h.v. pushrod four-cylinder engine has three main bearings and the transmission offers a choice between three-speed all-synchromesh with column lever, four-speed box with central lever or Toyoglide automatic with torque-converter and two-speed box. Suspension is conventional; brakes are drums.

CLOSE-UP

Four-cyl.; o.h.v.; 78×78 mm.; 1,490 c.c.; 74 b.h.p. gross; 8 to 1 comp.; coil ign.; Aisan carb.; 4-speed, 13.58, 7.81, 5.18, 3.7 to 1; col. lvr.; susp., f. ind. coil, r. half-elliptic; 4-door; 4-seat; hyd. brks.; max. 83 m.p.h.; cruise 70; m.p.g. 30-35; whl. base 7ft. 11in.; track f. and r. 4ft. 2in.; lgth. 13ft. 4in.; ht. 4ft. 8in.; g.c. 6¾in.; turng. cir. 32ft. 6in.; kerb wt. 18¾ cwt.; tank 9¾ gals.; 12-volt.

Abbreviations—g.c.—ground clearance; susp.—suspension; f.—front; r.—rear; comp.—compression; s.v.—side-valves; o.h.v.—overhead valves; o.h.c.—overhead camshaft; hyd.—hydraulic.

TRIUMPH 2000

AFTER two years of success with the saloon, the range is extended by a station wagon. Six-cylinder smoothness, the ride and road-grip advantages of independent suspension all round, and the clean-cut Michelotti styling have won converts for the biggest of the Triumphs at home and abroad. It is becoming familiar in international rallies. Transmission options include overdrive or Borg Warner automatic.

CLOSE-UP
Six-cyl.; o.h.v.; 74.7 × 76 mm.; 1,998 c.c.; 90 b.h.p.; 8.5 to 1 comp.; coil ign.; 2 Stromberg carbs.; 4-speed, 13.45, 8.61, 5.68, 4.1 to 1; cen. lvr., de Normanville overdrive or BW auto. opt.; susp. f. and r. ind. coil; 4-door; 5-seat; hyd. servo brks., disc front; max. 95 m.p.h.; cruise 80; m.p.g. 24-28; whl. base 8ft. 10in.; track, f. 4ft. 4in., r. 4ft. 2½in.; lgth, 14ft. 7in.; width 5ft. 5in.; ht. 4ft. 8in.; g.c. 5½in.; turng. cir. 33ft.; kerb wt. 22½ cwt.; tank 14 gals.; 12-volt.

£925 + £194 p.t. = £1,119

TRIUMPH HERALD 1200

CONVERTIBLE and coupe, two body styles rare in Britain attract many buyers to the Herald range. There are also saloons and station wagons of course. All have separate chassis, body panels detachable for repair and all-independent suspension. With 8 to 1 compression the 1,147 c.c. engine develops 39 h.p.; with higher compression it delivers 51 h.p. for the 12/50 saloon which also has disc front brakes and folding top.

CLOSE-UP
Four-cyl.; o.h.v.; 69.3 × 76 mm.; 1,147 c.c.; 39 b.h.p.; 8 to 1 comp.; coil ign.; Solex carb.; 4-speed, 15.42, 8.88, 5.75, 4.11 to 1; cen. lvr.; susp., f. ind. coil, r. ind. transv. leaf; 2-door; 4-seat; hyd. brks.; max. 77 m.p.h.; cruise 70; m.p.g. 28-32; whl. base 7ft. 7½in.; track f. and r. 4ft.; lgth. 12ft. 9in.; width 5ft.; ht. 4ft. 4in.; g.c. 6¾in.; turng. cir. 26ft. 3in.; kerb wt. 15½ cwt.; tank 7 gals.; 12-volt.

£489 + £103 p.t. = £592

TRIUMPH 1300

FRONT-WHEEL drive gains another important convert with this clean-cut four-five seater. Four-cylinder engine mounted fore and aft with the four-speed all-synchromesh gearbox below it. Sub frames at front and rear carry the all-independent suspension. Front seats slide, tilt, rise and fall. Steering is adjustable for rake and height. Ventilation is highly developed.

CLOSE-UP
Four-cyl.; o.h.v.; 73.7 × 76 mm.; 1,296 c.c.; 61 b.h.p. gross; 8.5 to 1 comp.; coil ign.; Stromberg carb. 4-speed, 13.97, 8.87, 5.96, 4.37 to 1; cen. lvr.; susp. f. and r. ind. coil; 4-door; 5-seat; hyd. brks., disc front; max. 85 m.p.h.; cruise 75; m.p.g. 30-33; whl. base 8ft. 0⅜in.; track, f. 4ft. 5in., r. 4ft. 4⅝in.; lgth. 12ft. 11in.; width 5ft. 1⅞in.; ht. 4ft. 6in.; g.c. 5⅛in.; turng. cir. 30ft.; kerb wt. 18 cwt.; tank 11¾ gals.; 12-volt.

TRIUMPH T.R.4

A STURDY sports car with detachable roof panel, a steel body, detachable windscreen, winding windows and laminated safety glass. With this goes completely redesigned chassis, immensely strong and a splendid basis for a fast sports car. Nylon bushes and sealed joints on the front suspension reduces maintenance work. Redesigned seats, thick pile carpets and door waist rails make fast driving comfortable.

CLOSE-UP
Four-cyl.; o.h.v.; 86 × 92 mm.; 2,138 c.c.; 104 b.h.p.; 9 to 1 comp.; coil ign.; 2 Stromberg carbs.; 4-speed, 11.61, 7.44, 4.9, 3.7 to 1; cen. lvr. de Normanville overdrive opt.; susp. f. and r. ind. coil; 2-door; 2/3-seat; hyd. brks., disc front; max. 110 m.p.h.; cruise 95; m.p.g. 25; whl. base 7ft. 4in.; track, f. 4ft. 2in., r. 4ft. 1in.; lgth. 12ft. 7in.; width 4ft. 9½in.; ht. 4ft. 2in.; g.c. 6in.; turng. cir. 33ft. 7in.; kerb wt. 21 cwt.; tank 11¾ gals.; 12-volt.

£800 + £168 p.t. = £968

Abbreviations—g.c.—ground clearance; susp.—suspension; f.—front; r.—rear; comp.—compression; s.v.—side-valves; o.h.v.—overhead valves; o.h.c.—overhead camshaft; hyd.—hydraulic.

47

TRIUMPH SPITFIRE MARK 2

NEW points about this nippy little sports car: re-designed seats, a new camshaft and exhaust manifold adding zip performance, and a diaphragm-type clutch requiring less pedal effort. Laycock de Normanville overdrive is an optional extra, as well as wire wheels and competition equipment. An ideal car for the sporty type watching the pennies. Available in both soft top and hard top versions.

CLOSE-UP
Four-cyl.; o.h.v.; 69.3 × 76 mm.; 1,147 c.c.; 67 b.h.p.; 9 to 1 comp.; coil ign.; 2 S.U. carbs.; 4-speed, 15.42, 8.88, 5.74, 4.11 to 1; cen. lvr. de Normanville overdrive opt.; susp., f. ind. coil, r. ind. transv. leaf; 2-door; 2-seat; hyd. brks., disc front; max. 96 m.p.h.; cruise 82; m.p.g. 35-40; whl. base 6ft. 11in.; track, f. 4ft. 1in., r. 4ft.; lgth. 12ft. 1in.; width 4ft. 9in.; ht. 3ft. 11½in.; g.c. 5in.; turng. cir. 24ft.; kerb wt. 14 cwt.; tank 8¼ gals.; 12-volt.

£550 + £116 p.t. = £666

VANDEN PLAS 1100

THIS is the queen of the much-liked British Motor Corporation's 1100 models. It has the grace of a Pininfarina body combined with the ultra-functional interior designed by the brilliant Alec Issigonis. It provides near-sumptuous motoring at very light cost. Apart from a luxury trim this model has hydrolastic suspension and a twin-carburetter transverse engine. It is here to stay for a long time.

CLOSE-UP
Four-cyl.; o.h.v. 64.58 × 83.72 mm.; 1,098 c.c.; 55 b.h.p.; 8.9 to 1 comp.; coil ign.; 2 S.U. carbs.; 4-speed, 14.99, 8.98, 5.83, 4.13 to 1; cen. lvr.; susp. f. and r. ind. rubber-hydraulic; 4-door; 4-seat; hyd. brks., disc front; max. 85 m.p.h.; cruise 75; m.p.g. 35-37; whl. base 7ft. 9½in.; track, f. 4ft. 3½in., r. 4ft. 2⅞in.; lgth. 12ft. 2¾in.; width 5ft. 0⅜in.; ht. 4ft. 4¾in.; g.c. 6in.; turng. cir. 34ft. 9in.; kerb wt. 17¼ cwt.; tank 8 gals.; 12-volt.

£765 + £161 p.t. = £926

VANDEN PLAS PRINCESS R

A SPLENDID example of a mass-producing car manufacturer merging with stately Rolls Royce. The British Motor Corporation supply the body and chassis and Rolls Royce the special 3.9-litre light-alloy, six-cylinder engine. The result is a delightful car which has the good looks of traditional Vanden Plas styling along with a power plant that is silent, functional and a joy to handle.

CLOSE-UP
Six-cyl.; o.h. inlet, s. exhaust; 95.2 × 91.4 mm.; 3,909 c.c.; 175 b.h.p.; 7.8 to 1 comp.; coil ign.; 2 S.U. carbs.; BW 3-speed auto., 7.56, 4.62, 3.15 to 1; col. lvr.; susp., f. ind. coil, r. half-elliptic; 4-door; 5-seat; hyd. servo brks., disc front; max. 106 m.p.h.; cruise 90; m.p.g. 14-17; whl. base 9ft. 2in.; track, f. 4ft. 7in., r. 4ft. 5½in.; lgth. 15ft. 8in.; width 5ft. 8½in.; ht. 4ft. 11in.; g.c. 6in.; turng. cir. 42ft. 5in.; kerb wt. 31⅞ cwt.; tank 16 gals.; 12-volt.

£1,650 + £345 p.t. = £1,995

VAUXHALL VIVA

VIVA SL is the latest, luxurious addition to the Viva range. New grille, side flashes in contrasting colours and new horizontal light clusters distinguish it from other models. Extra padding on a matt silver facia, lockable glove box and large map pockets enhance the interior. Mechanical and trim improvements are made to other Viva models to increase the appeal of this popular economical small car for 1966.

CLOSE-UP
Four-cyl.; o.h.v.; 74.3 × 60.9 mm.; 1,057 c.c.; 44 b.h.p.; 8.5 to 1 comp.; coil ign.; Solex carb.; 4-speed, 15.53, 9.12, 5.79, 4.125 to 1; cen. lvr.; susp., f. ind. transv. leaf, r. half-elliptic; 2-door; 4-seat; hyd. brks., disc opt.; max. 80 m.p.h.; cruise 70; m.p.g. 40-45; whl. base 7ft. 7½in.; track, f. 3ft. 11½in., r. 4ft.; lgth. 12ft. 11in.; width 4ft. 11¾in.; ht. 4ft. 5¾in.; g.c. 5in.; turng. cir. 29ft.; kerb wt. 14 cwt.; tank 7 gals.; 12-volt.

£436 + £102 p.t. = £538

VAUXHALL VICTOR

SLIGHT changes to these well-established favourites include a walnut fascia in place of white metal on the Victor de Luxe version, and a different colour for the dashboard meters on the VX/490. After a chequered beginning these two cars are now brilliant examples of Anglo-American co-operation. Their new bodywork has hit the jackpot. They have plenty of space for passengers and quiet-running engines.

CLOSE-UP

Four-cyl.; o.h.v.; 81.63×76.2 mm.; 1,594 c.c.; 69 b.h.p.; 8.5 to 1 comp.; coil ign.; Zenith carb.; 3-speed, 13.2, 6.74, 4.125 to 1, 4-speed opt.; col. lvr.; susp., f. ind. coil, r. half-elliptic; 4-door; 5-seat; hyd. brks., disc opt.; max. 80 m.p.h.; cruise 70; m.p.g. 28-34; whl. base 8ft. 4in.; track, f. 4ft. 2¾in., r. 4ft. 4⅜in.; lgth. 14ft. 5¼in.; width 5ft. 4in.; ht. 4ft. 8in.; g.c. 7in.; turng. cir. 33ft. 6in.; kerb wt. 19¾ cwt.; tank 10 gals.; 12-volt.

VAUXHALL CRESTA

VELOX has vanished. Vauxhall's new sixes are Cresta and Cresta de luxe with new longer, roomier bodywork. Curved side windows contribute towards an extra 4¼ inches of shoulder room, luggage capacity is nearly doubled and the body is much more rigid. Mechanical parts are basically as before but engine power is raised to 123 h.p. and rear drum brakes are self adjusting. Rear springs are now variable-rate.

CLOSE-UP

Six-cyl.; o.h.v.; 92×82.6 mm.; 3,294 c.c.; 123 b.h.p.; 8.5 to 1 comp.; coil ign.; downdraught carb.; 3-speed, 8.67, 5.14, 3.45 to 1; col. lvr., 4-speed, auto or overdrive opt.; susp., f. ind. coil, r. half-elliptic; 4-door; 6-seat; hyd. servo brks., disc front; max. 102 m.p.h.; cruise 90; m.p.g. 19-23; whl. base 8ft. 11½in.; track, f. 4ft. 7¼in., r. 4ft. 8¼in.; lgth. 15ft. 7⅛in.; width 5ft. 9¾in.; ht. 4ft. 7⅝in.; g.c. 6½in.; turng. cir. 36ft. 6in.; kerb wt. 25 cwt.; tank 15 gals.; 12-volt.

VOLKSWAGEN 1300 DE LUXE

LENGTHENING the stroke raises engine capacity to 1,285 c.c. but the "beetle" body line is still unchanged. Identification points; lighter slotted wheels, flatter hub caps, 1300 emblem on rear panels. Interior improvements include a third defroster vent, combined head lamp dipper, flasher and indicator switch, upholstery covering more of the seat frames. New front suspension with wider-apart trailing arms and sealed ball joints cuts servicing.

CLOSE-UP

Four-cyl.; o.h.v.; air-cooled; 77×69 mm.; 1,285 c.c.; 50 b.h.p. gross; 7.4 to 1 comp.; coil ign.; Solex carb.; 4-speed, 16.63, 9.01, 5.77, 3.89 to 1; cen. lvr.; susp. f. and r. ind. torsion bar; 2-door; 4-seat; hyd. brks.; max. 75 m.p.h.; cruise 75; m.p.g. 33-37; whl. base 7ft. 10½in.; track, f. 4ft. 3⅜in., r. 4ft. 3¼in.; lgth. 13ft. 4¼in.; width 5ft. 0½in.; ht. 4ft. 11in.; g.c. 6in.; turng. cir. 36ft.; kerb wt. 15½ cwt.; tank 8¾ gals.; 6-volt.

VOLKSWAGEN 1600

EXTERNALLY almost unchanged, the saloon and station wagon versions of the VW can now be had with the 1600 engine and disc front brakes as alternative to the 1500 and drums all round. The bigger engine raises top speed by 6 m.p.h. for a loss of about 1½ miles per gallon. Following usual VW policy it is lightly stressed so that it can be driven flat out indefinitely.

CLOSE-UP

Four-cyl.; o.h.v.; air-cooled; 85.8×69 mm.; 1,584 c.c.; 65 b.h.p. gross; 7.7 to 1 comp.; coil ign.; 2 Solex carbs.; 4-speed, 15.7, 8.5, 5.4, 3.7 to 1; cen. lvr.; susp. f. and r. ind. torsion bar; 2-door; 4/5-seat; hyd. brks., disc front; max. 83 m.p.h.; cruise 83; m.p.g. 32-34; whl. base 7ft. 10½in.; track, f. 4ft. 3⅝in., r. 4ft. 5in.; lgth. 13ft. 10⅜in.; width 5ft. 3¼in.; ht. 4ft. 10⅛in.; g.c. 5⅞in.; turng. cir. 36ft. 5in.; kerb wt. 17¼ cwt.; tank 8¾ gals.; 6-volt.

Abbreviations—g.c.—ground clearance; susp.—suspension; f.—front; r.—rear; comp.—compression; s.v.—side-valves; o.h.v.—overhead valves; o.h.c.—overhead camshaft; hyd.—hydraulic.

VOLKSWAGEN 1600 TL

FAST-BACK styling gives a sporting line while conserving a surprising amount of headroom in the rear seats of this latest addition to the VW range. The 1600 c.c. engine gives it a maximum speed of about 87 m.p.h. which is also the cruising speed. Front brakes are discs, front seat backrests are adjustable and detail finish is up to the usual high VW standard.

CLOSE-UP

Four-cyl.; o.h.v.; air-cooled; 85.8×69 mm.; 1,584 c.c.; 65 b.h.p. gross; 7.7 to 1 comp.; coil ign.; 2 Solex carbs.; 4-speed, 15.7, 8.5, 5.4, 3.7 to 1; cen. lvr.; susp. f. and r. ind. torsion bar; 2-door; 4-seat; hyd. brks., disc front; max. 84 m.p.h.; cruise 84; m.p.g. 32-34; whl. base 7ft. 10½in.; track, f. 4ft. 3⅜in., r. 4ft. 5in.; lgth. 13ft. 10⅜in.; width 5ft. 3¼in.; ht. 4ft. 10⅛in.; g.c. 5⅞in.; turng. cir. 36ft. 5in.; kerb wt. 17⅞ cwt.; tank 8¾ gals.; 6-volt.

VOLGA

MADE in Gorky with a big four-cylinder petrol engine of 2½ litres, the Volga is also assembled in Belgium with a British Rover diesel unit. Two body styles, saloon and station wagon, have been refined over the years with better finish and equipment, reflecting rising Soviet living standards. But they still have to stand up to bad roads and poor service and so are heavily built.

CLOSE-UP

Four-cyl.; o.h.v.; 92×92 mm.; 2,445 c.c.; 80 b.h.p.; 7.5 to 1 comp.; coil ign.; K105 carb.; 3-speed, 14.19, 8.07, 4.56 to 1; cen. lvr.; susp., f. ind. coil, r. half elliptic; 4-door; 5-seat; hyd. brks.; max. 78 m.p.h.; cruise 70; m.p.g. 21; whl. base 8ft. 11in.; track, f. 4ft. 7⅜in., r. 4ft. 8¼in.; lgth. 15ft. 7⅜in.; width 5ft. 10½in.; ht. 5ft. 3¼in.; g.c. 8in.; turng. cir. 38ft. 6in.; kerb wt. 28¼ cwt.; tank 13¼ gals.; 12-volt.

VOLVO 131

CHEAPEST Volvo on the British market. But don't be fooled, this is no child's toy but a beautifully made precision machine from Sweden. Engine is simple but robust and performance is smooth and very quiet. Back rest is adjustable and front brakes are Girling discs. Single carburetter is the B18A type. This package of goodies comes in a neat two-door saloon.

CLOSE-UP

Four-cyl.; o.h.v.; 84.1×80 mm.; 1,778 c.c.; 75 b.h.p.; 8.5 to 1 comp.; coil ign.; Zenith carb.; 4-speed, 12.78, 8.2, 5.62, 4.1 to 1; cen. lvr.; susp., f. ind coil, r. coil; 2-door; 4-seat; hyd. brks., disc front; max. 90 m.p.h.; cruise 80; m.p.g. 26-29; whl. base 8ft. 6⅜in.; track f. and r. 4ft. 3⅜in.; lgth. 14ft. 7¼in.; width 5ft. 3⅜in.; ht. 4ft. 11½in.; g.c. 6¼in.; turng. cir. 36ft.; kerb wt. 20¾ cwt.; tank 10 gals.; 12-volt.

£845+£178 p.t.=£1,023

VOLVO P.1800

FIVE years old and still a firm favourite with buyers who want speed and luxury. Volvo's home is Gottenburg but the P.1800 is Birmingham made by Jensen. It cruises at 95 m.p.h. and transports occupants in comfort and safety. Luggage space is good. To cope with severe Scandinavian winters the heater is powerful and the car starts instantly whatever the weather.

CLOSE-UP

Four-cyl.; o.h.v.; 84.14×80 mm.; 1,778 c.c.; 96 b.h.p.; 9.5 to 1 comp.; coil ign.; 2 S.U. carbs.; 4-speed, 14.27, 9.07, 6.3, 4.5 to 1; cen. lvr., overdrive; susp., f. ind. coil, r. coil; 2-door; 2/4-seat; servo brks., disc front; max. 110 m.p.h.; cruise 95; m.p.g. 26-30; whl. base 8ft. 0½in.; track f. and r. 4ft. 3⅜in.; lgth. 14ft. 5¼in.; width 5ft. 7in.; ht. 4ft. 2½in.; g.c. 6in.; turng. cir. 31ft.; kerb wt. 24 cwt.; tank 10 gals.; 12-volt.

£1,500+£314 p.t.=£1,814

Abbreviations—g.c.—ground clearance; susp.—suspension; f.—front; r.—rear; comp.—compression; s.v.—side-valves; o.h.v.—overhead valves; o.h.c.—overhead camshaft; hyd.—hydraulic.

WARTBURG

IMPROVED in several respects for 1966, the Wartburg retains the basic features of three-cylinder two-stroke engine and front wheel drive. Built at the Eisenach factory in East Germany formerly owned by Auto Union, it bears a general resemblance to the DKW, but styling and detail work are quite different. Saloon, coupe, station wagon or camping wagon with sun roof are the models produced.

CLOSE-UP

Three-cyl.; two-stroke; 73.5×78 mm.; 991 c.c.; 45 b.h.p.; 7.5 to 1 comp.; coil ign.; BVF carb.; 4-speed, 15.89, 10.36, 6.15, 4.64 to 1; col. lvr.; susp., f. ind. transv. leaf, r. transv. leaf; 4-door; 4/5-seat; hyd. brks.; max. 77 m.p.h.; cruise 70; m.p.g. 30-32; whl. base 8ft. 0½in.; track f. 3ft. 10⅞in., r. 4ft. 1⅛in.; lgth. 14ft. 1¼in.; width 5ft. 1⅞in.; ht. 4ft. 9in.; g.c. 7¼in.; turng. cir. 37ft.; kerb wt. 18½ cwt.; tank 9⅜ gals.; 6-volt.

£487 + £103 p.t. = £590

WOLSELEY 1100

SOMETHING for everyone seems to be BMC's aim with the front-drive 1100. There are at least thirteen versions, including the two Innocentis assembled in Italy. Wolseley's offering has four doors, twin carburetters, leather upholstery, American walnut veneered facia with strip-trip speedometer and child-proof safety locks. Basic layout includes transverse engine with sealed cooling system, Hydrolastic all-independent suspension and disc front brakes.

CLOSE-UP

Four-cyl.; o.h.v.; 64.58×83.72 mm.; 1,098 c.c.; 55 b.h.p.; 8.9 to 1 comp.; Coil ign.; 2 S.U. carbs.; 4-speed, 14.99, 8.98, 5.83, 4.13 to 1; cen. lvr.; susp., f. and r. ind. rubber-hyd.; 4-door; 4-seat; hyd. brks., disc front; max. 85 m.p.h.; cruise 75; m.p.g. 35-38; whl. base 7ft. 9½in.; track f. 4ft. 3½in.; r. 4ft. 2⅞in.; lgth. 12ft. 2¾in.; width 5ft. 0⅜in.; ht. 4ft. 4¾in.; g.c. 6in.; turng. cir. 34ft. 9in.; kerb wt. 16⅝ cwt.; tank 8 gals.; 12-volt.

£623 + £131 p.t. = £754

WOLSELEY 16/60

BRITISH Motor Corporation's abundant orders for this good-looking car fully support their decision to continue its production. It is powered by the well-proven 1622 c.c. B.M.C. engine which gives this four-to-five-seater adequate urge coupled with a host of interior comforts. Its road behaviour is good-tempered, sound without being flashy. A car that will be with us for some time yet.

CLOSE-UP

Four-cyl.; o.h.v.; 76.2×88.9 mm.; 1,622 c.c.; 61 b.h.p.; 8.3 to 1 comp.; coil ign.; S.U. carb.; 4-speed, 15.64, 9.52, 5.91, 4.3 to 1; cen. lvr., BW auto. opt.; susp., f. ind. coil, r. half-elliptic; 4-door; 4-seat; hyd. brks.; max. 80 m.p.h.; cruise 70; m.p.g. 26-30; whl. base 8ft. 4¼in.; track, f. 4ft. 2⅝in., r. 4ft. 3⅜in.; lgth. 14ft. 6½in.; width 5ft. 3½in.; ht. 4ft. 10⅞in.; g.c. 6¼in.; turng. cir. 37ft.; kerb wt. 22½ cwt.; tank 10 gals.; 12-volt.

£705 + £148 p.t. = £853

WOLSELEY 6/110 MARK II

THIS is the car for the family man or the business executive who likes to cut a dash slightly above the others. It has sound Wolseley styling and comfort and is no new-comer to this market. It has top standards in suspension, braking and a wonderfully docile four-speed gearbox. Luxury includes adjustable backrests for front seats, leather upholstery and a polished wood instrument panel. A well-shaped motor car.

CLOSE-UP

Six-cyl.; o.h.v.; 83.34×88.9 mm.; 2,912 c.c.; 120 b.h.p.; 8.3 to 1 comp.; coil ign.; 2 S.U. carbs.; 4-speed, 10.31, 8.1, 5.11, 3.92 to 1; cen. lvr., BW overdrive or auto. opt.; susp., f. ind. coil, r. half-elliptic; 4-door; 5-seat; hyd. servo brks., disc front; max. 102 m.p.h.; cruise 85; m.p.g. 18-22; whl. base 9ft. 2in.; track, f. 4ft. 7in., r. 4ft. 5¼in.; lgth. 15ft. 8in.; width 5ft. 8½in.; ht. 5ft.; g.c. 6¼in.; turng. cir. 41ft.; kerb wt. 31 cwt.; tank 16 gals.; 12-volt.

£975 + £205 p.t. = £1,180

Abbreviations—g.c.—ground clearance; susp.—suspension; f.—front; r.—rear; comp.—compression; s.v.—side-valves; o.h.v.—overhead valves; o.h.c.—overhead camshaft; hyd.—hydraulic.

STOP! *You have now reached GADGET CORNER and waiting to show you round is DENNIS MAY*

with a little help in passing from the girl in the picture . . .

START with the Liquid Stuff

DINNER starts with soup . . . so let's begin our sampling of the Show's groaning board of accessories and related products with liquid and semi-liquid nosh.

Car cleaning preparations are, as usual, thick on the gallery shelves, and stupefyingly various . . . *Chacun a son goo*, as you might say. New to the British market since last Earls Court is Union Carbide's big range of car cosmetics: these include a potent chromium polish and stuff called Wax Wash, which produces a polish without polishing when you wipe body surfaces gently down after washing.

Package deals often offer shrewd value, and the Car Kit Bargain line recently launched by S. C. Johnson and Sons Ltd. is a case in point; single carton containing a tin of One Step Wax cleaner polish and three helpings of shampoo cost only 6/6—less than some of the individual makings of this four-decker sandwich.

Akin to Union Carbide's Wax Wash is the Wash-N-Polish car shampoo (10d. per large sachet), product of Widney Margolis Ltd. Again, the shine-up is self-inducing—no elbow grease called for. W-N-P leaves a bright protective film behind it which isn't afraid of our climate.

Next up is Clearadex, a screenwash additive evolved after more than two years of research and experiment by Alexander Engineering, the go-faster people. Clearadex gets away from the regular detergent or alcohol bases and is claimed to turn the tables in the war on the rubber dust *cum* unburnt hydrocarbons muck forming typical screen film. 1s. per sachet.

Talking of screen purgation, ask the factors if they can show you a glass cleaning pad that E. H. Howard Ltd. of Ipswich put in circulation a month or two back. One side of this handy little gizmo is nylon-mesh faced, for attacks on frost deposits or dead insects, according to season; the other side is soft, for the finishing rub-up. Price 2s. 6d.

Something else in the same vein is a six-by-four screen cleaner pad by Fownes Gloves Ltd. (3s. 11d.), but in this case oil-dressed chamois

THE GIRL is really only here to point out—which is, in fact, precisely what she is doing—the new Lucas "Dip-Right" Lens Converter for Continental driving. When fitted, the amber lenses automatically convert left-hand dip-beams to right-hand dips, thus pleasing everybody, particularly on-coming Continentals. . . .

takes care of the rough work while an area of unfluffing cotton delivers the *coup de grace*.

For the hole-and-corner work involved in cleaning a car's interior really thoroughly, the mini-sized Anda Featherweight vacuum cleaner is tempting at £4 19s. 6d. (*Thinks*: Christmas present for wife, then borrow it back.) Deal includes 6in. brush, slender nozzle for upholstery, two 12in. tubes, 12ft. of flex; 220-240v. motor . . .

And if it's true, as Gwyn Thomas says, that cleanliness is next to dirtiness, what is next to comfort and smartness in personal motoring gear? That needs thinking about, but meantime a rummage through the Earls Court autumn collections discloses two compelling items bearing the John Surtees brand and marketed by Interior Silent Travel Ltd., Eaton Bray, Dunstable, Beds. The first is a pair of thin and exquisitely supple driving gloves in Abyssinian leather (£2 9s. 11d.), the second a top-quality driving shoe. The latter

features an anti-scuff panel above the heel, elasticated topline for foot freedom. The gloves, by the way, are exactly as worn by John in successful pursuit of his World Champion title.

Talking of wares that are equally suitable for the Grand Prix or a grand spree, Jim Clark, successor to Surtees as motor racing's first gentleman, lends his name to a new lace-on steering wheel glove, the Tarantella GT, marketed by GT Steering Wheel Covers of Walsall. In the current fashion, these gloves are made in leather with foam backing. 27s. 6d. each.

Lacking by-appointment-to-Clark rating but otherwise rather similar are the leather wheel gloves by Conway Car Accessories (Stand 250) and Romac Industries (Stand 187), prices, 35s. and 32s. 6d. respectively. Alternatively, for drivers who don't race or even care to ape those who do, Kumficar of Halifax use nylon

(continued on page 63)

CONTINUING THE GADGET TOUR

moquette, a familiar seat-cover material, for *their* latest wheel glove. (Stand 48.)

Wood-rimmed steering wheels with aluminium alloy skeletons and drilled spokes are practically indispensible wear these days on sports and souped-up cars. As good an example as any perhaps is Styla's, on Stand 78 (£7 10s. 0d.). Two designs—flat and dished. Rim has a three-coat Melamine satin finish.

The enthusiasm, even fanaticism, bred by Mini ownership ensures a constant spate of specialities for these endearing road mice, and here are just a few to run down at the Show:—

Item . . . Wheel spacers to increase track measurement and, with it, stability. The gain is worth having, too, at 2½ins. Gran Turismo Wheels Ltd. are the makers. Price £2 9s. 6d. per pair.

Item . . . Acoustikit sound-proofing sets ("Gone the merry Morris din", like Keats said) for all Mini variants, saloon, wagon, pick-up. Depending on the model, a set comprises anything from 11 to 25 pre-cut pieces of acoustic material. £4 10s. 0d. to £6 15s. 0d. Made by Elflow Developments Co., 386 Astwood Road, Worcester.

Item . . . Rear Vista back window wiper by H. Millar and Co. Ltd., Aston Brook St., Birmingham 6. Cleans inner and outer surfaces simultaneously, is cable-operated by a remote control lever mounted above the driver's window. 4 gns.

Item . . . Steering-column rake adjuster kit. Just the thing if you dislike the Mini's 'flat' wheel attitude. Makers: Cosmic Car Accessories Ltd., Bescot St., Walsall. £1. The holes involved come free—they're there already.

Item . . . Minitable picnic shelf, instantly attachable and detachable. Fits above the facia, serves both front-seat occupants. Made by Brexton Ltd., 5 Grange Rd., Small Heath, Birmingham 10.

Item . . . Eversure hydraulic Mini jack, robust replacement for the rather flimsy piece of hoisting tackle that B.M.C. supply for these cars. The Eversure job (Waterfall Lane, Trading Estate, Old Hill, Staffs.) has a closed height of 22½ins., gives an 11ins. lift.

Item . . . Special suspension dampers for Minis, evolved jointly by Girling and Speedwell, marketed by Speedwell Performance Conversions Ltd., Cornwall Avenue, N.3. These rugged telescopics have Monte Carlo Rally winning know-how built into them. Suit all Minis, with or without lowered suspension.

Now back from the particular to the general . . .

Three new or newish driving mirrors, all of them for outside mounting, will be worth a stop and a look. First comes the Selectaview wing mirror from Armstrong Patents Co. Ltd.,

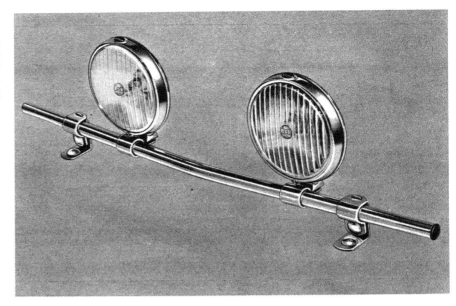

Smart STYLA quartz-iodine lamps, badge-bar mounted, illustrate a growing trend.

Beverley, Yorks.; this one is controllable for angle from the driving seat, via invisible cables, to take care of short-to-tall or *vice versa* changes of driver.

Second is a door pillar mirror, the Overtaker, by Stadium Ltd., 30 Queensway, Enfield, Mddx. Its appointed position, further back than the commoner wing site, gives a bigger image and brings the mirror within wiping and adjusting range without taking the weight off your pants.

On Stand 34 Desmo show what is claimed to be the first all-plastic exterior mirror, incorporating this maker's well-known self-aligning facility. Patented sealing ring makes it shatterproof in the event of crash breakage, a worthwhile safety point.

What catches the eye in the illumination field? Quarz-iodine lamps galore for a start. To take a good example at random, Ceag Ltd. (Stand 385) make a feature of their new Lumax 2000 series of Q-I fog and driving lamps, with the qualities of gimlet penetration and low dazzle factor that international rallymen demand. These give an attractively shallow (2½ins.) profile and polished stainless steel finish. Could be a hit with far-and-fast drivers at 10 gns. per matched pair.

If you will be making for the continent next holidaytime, make for the Joseph Lucas stand (No. 222) right now and sort out the Dip-Right Lens Converter. Fitted to headlamps in minutes, it about-faces the dipping bias from left- to right-hand; lenses are the required amber tint.

(continued on page 64)

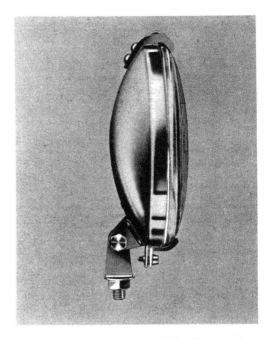

This is another quartz-iodine driving lamp, a slim-line model by CEAG, finished in stainless steel.

with a sort of cartoon-commentary by CHIC...

and ENDING this Guide to Gadgets with a look in the mirror by the man at the wheel . . .

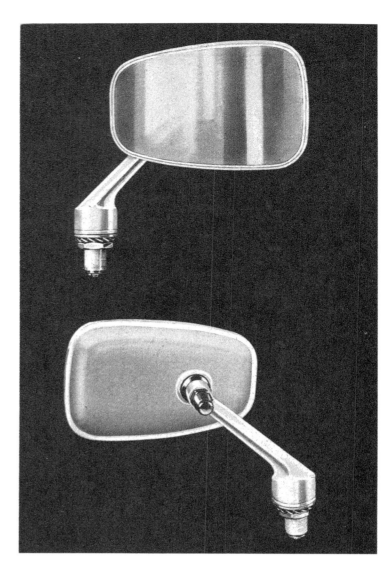

THE WHEEL is leather-gloved, very elegant, by Conway Car Accessories. THE WING-MIRRORS by Desmo are made in acrylic and, being plastic, are shatterproof should you have a shunt.

(from page 63)

Nothing escapes the styling attentions of the Styla stylists—not even a reversing lamp, and why should it? Reversing lamps, like anything else, can look good, bad or indecent, and Styla's new Slimline, chrome plated on brass and designed to fit above or below the bumper, looks good.

Backtracking briefly to quartz-iodine fog lamps, Cibie break all records for diameter/slimness ratio with their *disco volante*-like Type 45, which is 7 inches across and only 1¾in. thick. Cibie chandlery is noted for beam spread and good light emission. £7 15s. 0d. each from Britover (Continental) Ltd., 13 Belsize Lane, N.W.3.

Even in today's affluent society, to judge by the proliferation of anti-theft devices, plenty of people *acquire* cars or their contents (or try to) without actually paying for them. So watch out for:—

. . . 1. The inexpensive Pedalock (Delite Accessories Ltd., Wardrobe Court, E.C.4), which does more than its name implies and locks either a pedal, the gear lever or steering wheel. 19s. 11d.

. . . 2. The more elaborate and harder-to-beat Auto Stop (Top Grade Electronics Ltd., Pump Lane, Hayes, Mddx.—£6 19s. 6d.), which snuffs the ignition and, if monkeyed with, sounds the horn.

. . . 3. The Klik-On (Klik-On Co., 9 Windsor Avenue, Penwortham, Preston—£2 7s. 6d.), which, like the Auto Stop, is purely mechanical and locks the handbrake on.

. . . 4. The Alert Car Alarm (L. F. Brenner Ltd., Stand 402—4 gns.). Pre-Show dope on this one keeps the working principle under L. F. Brenner's hat but does reveal that each A.C.A. is sold with an application form entitling the buyer to twenty-eight days' free use of a hire car if his own is pinched in spite of its Alarm. Shrewd piece of public relations, that.

Finally, a short short-list of goodies picked with a pin and closed eyes:—

Key-Leather's K-L Thermo Start (Stand 277) for a quick fire-up when there's a nip in the morning air: 400w. element connects up to the bottom radiator hose, current comes off the mains supply. And pre-heated coolant water means your heater is ready for business that much earlier, remember. £4 17s. 6d.

Barnacle's car-name crests (Stand 352) for fitting to gear lever knobs—one of the pleasanter prettifying touches to be seen around the galleries. 19s. 6d. each.

Castrol's Surecoat for killing rust prenatally. You spray or brush it on and it leaves a protective film that really does its job. Inexpensive at 17s. 6d. per gallon.

★ ★ ★ ★ ★

P.S. Had any punctures lately? My last was five years ago but if you imagine flats are on the way out, one exhibitor's annual output of tyre patches is *sixty million.* Romac is the name. (Stand 187.)

PLUS a final smile by CHIC

C A R S
OF THE LATE 60'S
BRITISH AND IMPORTED MODELS 1965-1969

MOTOR SHOW REVIEW GUIDE
1966

A - Z
SECTION

Don't take a car for granted

by SIR PATRICK HENNESSY

Sir Patrick Hennessy is President of the Society of Motor Manufacturers and Traders and Chairman of the Ford Motor Company.

¶ TAKE A CAR—any car, but preferably a British car—from this year's International Motor Show and take a long look at it. No doubt you will delight in its sleek looks, enthuse over the uncluttered, comfortable interior and dream of the effortless miles gliding away beneath you. The Motor Show is undoubtedly romantic, exciting and enticing but hidden behind the obvious attractions there is a more serious side.

¶ IN BRITAIN car manufacturers undertake some of the most rigorous research, development and testing programmes in the world. These take place at their own proving grounds, at the Motor Industry Research Association in Warwickshire and on the roads themselves, here and abroad, with the object of producing more roadworthy, more efficient, longer lasting vehicles than ever before.

¶ BRITISH motor manufacturers have always placed the utmost importance upon built-in safety in the form of effective braking, tenacious roadholding and light, precise steering. But with the emphasis, not only on the prevention of accidents but also on the lessening of injury when an accident has occurred, further intensive research is being carried out into the means of minimising the effect of a crash on driver and passengers. Already many of the findings have been incorporated into today's cars and still more will be found in the new models to come.

¶ SOME of these new models will first be shown at Earls Court this year and will, of course, attract the most attention. But even if the appearance of a car differs little from the previous year's model, do not be misled into thinking that there have been few improvements. Virtually every car on show will boast significant changes. Through this extremely valuable guide I hope that you will become aware of this steady technical advance and above all will recognise that the British motor industry is continually striving to create for you a vehicle combining supreme comfort, safety and efficiency.

CLEARLY, there is one outstanding trend at this year's 51st Motor Show. It is the concentration of manufacturers on safety for both driver and passengers, and a tour of the plush corridors at Earls Court shows that this safety-with-comfort keynote has been set by British manufacturers.

At a time when the speed limit for cars in this country is 70 m.p.h. and when that forceful American author Ralph Nader is plaguing the manufacturers in America to produce safer cars, it is gratifying to know that we at home are setting this safety trend.

On scores of stands at this Show devices to make our roads safer have been spearheaded by the British, and in many cases adopted by the foreigners. I mean such safety devices as disc brakes and monocoque body and chassis designed into one piece.

During your tour you will also see the widespread fashion now for padded dashboards, telescopic and yielding steering-wheels and columns, child-safety doorlocks, heated windscreens and heated rear windows and the adoption of seat-belts or their anchoring points—a wise introduction this, since Transport Minister Barbara Castle says they will be compulsory in Britain next year.

Personally I should like to have seen more safety belts provided for rear passengers as well as for the front-seat occupants, as in a crash everybody in the involved cars may be jettisoned through the windscreen with tragic results.

Still on this safety theme, there are new types of tyre which cling to the road more closely. These are due directly to the unlimited resources poured into motor-racing research by British tyre firms, and they are now being followed by overseas tyre manufacturers.

Another major safety device on show is the Dunlop Maxaret braking device which prevents the wheels from locking in the most skiddy conditions.

This year, therefore, owing to the 70 m.p.h. speed limit, the emphasis is not on all-out speed, but on cars which produce the fastest acceleration for quick, safe overtaking, and on those built specifically for a comparatively high cruising speed with comfort.

The car producers have also concentrated on giving car interiors more lush fittings, more seating comfort and more standard equipment, all of which,

It's YOUR safety FIRST

in earlier years, were costly optional extras.

I believe that the 1966 Motor Show, from the salesman's point of view (and surely this is the Show's purpose) will be the toughest since the war. With the national financial squeeze and the drastic tightening up of bank overdrafts, the white-collared, immaculately dressed car salesmen will need all their skill and guile to promote and sell their models.

But the shrinking in the sales demand may not be an entirely bad thing since it must sharpen the ingenuity and inventiveness of car makers—a useful spur towards a fresh business stimulus.

With no fewer than 14 countries exhibiting their cars, enormous competition prevails. There are cars from such off-beat producers as Israel, East Germany and Japan, while Austria is showing here for the first time since the war. Most of them have been holding back their new models for Earls Court, now acknowledged the greatest sales market for motor cars in the world.

Fortunately the Exhibition is also the finest showground of British engineering and automobile design, and allows the whole world to see the genius of our products. At a time of severe financial restriction the timing of the Show could not be better for this country.

In fact I believe that this magnificent assembly of more than 500 car and accessory stands in Hall and Balcony, glittering beneath limitless arc-lights, provides a natural fulcrum to project both Britain's brilliant products and those from foreign manufacturers, who bring the number of motor manufacturers exhibiting to just under 70.

Without hesitation I say that the Motor Show stands alone throughout the year as this country's premier exhibition. On it will be focused the interest of the 12,939,800 motor vehicle owners in this country, in addition to twice this number who travel in them as passengers. In fact there is one vehicle for every 12.8 yards of road here, and the latest model of almost every car will be on show at Earls Court.

It is intended that the Daily Express Motor Show Review should be a guide and an aid to everyone interested in motoring so that they may join in the fun and excitement of this high-spot in the motoring year.

My aim in compiling the review has also been to help the many unable to share the experience of visiting Earls Court. If it is successful in indicating to them the colourful atmosphere and eye-catching diversities of the vast show, my object will have been achieved.

BASIL CARDEW

Daily Express Motoring Reporter & Editor of the Daily Express Motor Show Review

Graham Hill driving in the "Indianapolis"

Just out—the new Vauxhall Viva SL

FOUR
of the reasons why there's
a good
time
coming

Just out—the new Super Cortina

by DAVID BENSON

The new Ford Zephyr

HIGHLIGHT of the past twelve months in the motoring world was, for me, the moment when, ten laps from the end of the fantastic Indianapolis 500 mile race in the USA, three Britons in British built cars were leading the race and had completely demolished the might of American opposition on its home ground.

This was my second visit to the famous 2 and a half mile oval track which has become synonymous with high speed and danger. When I first went there in 1964 I was horrified by the second lap accident that took two lives and my national pride was hurt by the American boasts that European "sporty" drivers weren't tough enough for the track.

But this year the British triumph was so complete that a dispute after the race about who had really won was between two British drivers. Graham Hill was finally adjudged the winner with Jimmy Clark a worthy second. To show that there was no ill feeling between the two men, Jimmy arranged a surprise party for Graham on their return to England.

1966 was also the start of the new Grand Prix formula for 3 litre cars. Although the much vaunted BRM H 16 engine never really got going and the 1965 world champion, Jim Clark, had a hard time even finishing, the season was again a triumph for British engineering talent. When 40-year-old Jack Brabham took the world title for the third time he was backed by British mechanics and largely British effort in the building of his car. Although Jack is basically an Australian and his car was powered by an Australian built Repco engine, he has lived in this country long enough to be considered a local. His chief designer Ron Tauranac was born in this country, emigrated to Australia as a boy and returned to lead the Brabham outfit.

Away from motor racing but still in the sport, January saw the fiasco of the Monte Carlo Rally. British Minis and Ford Cortinas had decisively beaten the opposition only to be disqualified for allegedly having the wrong lights. This theme was carried over to other continental rallies and has given the British works teams considerable food for thought. It is doubtful whether next year there will be quite so many rally teams and so much con-

certed effort put by manufacturers into this class of sport.

High spots for the industry were the introduction of a number of new models despite the credit freeze. In the spring Fords announced their Mark 4 range which completely broke with tradition. Amongst other innovations they placed the spare wheel under the bonnet and left a clear boot, mainly situated between the wheels with the minimum of rear end overhang. The handling and roadholding of the new car was quite outstanding.

Ford followed this up on the eve of the Show with a Cortina, similar in appearance to the Mark 4 and boasting considerably more luxury and a higher standard of finish than the replaced Cortina which had sold over 1 million units—52 per cent going to export.

Vauxhall brought out a bigger, better and completely restyled and engineered Viva in the late Autumn and against the current trend brought about by the freeze, they were able to announce full order books.

Triumph also hit out against Mr Callaghan's restrictive measures by putting a mouth-watering GT 6—basically a Spitfire with the Triumph 2000 engine—on the market. Initial production is earmarked for export but long queues are already forming at home for the first cars released on the British market.

When Mr George Brown opened the 1965 show, the industry was buoyant, it looked forward to a record year. In fact the record was achieved with over 1,200,000 vehicles produced in the twelve months. This year the industry still hopes that it will equal that target despite the Government's credit squeeze, limiting of HP and reduction of credit facilities for traders.

But there is no doubt that the heaviest load in the freeze measures was taken by the motor industry. As one distinguished car maker told me: "We didn't miss a single thing in all the Government's deflationary measures—from selective employment tax to increased fuel tax."

He might have added that the Government also lopped some £14 million off the roads programme—another crippling blow to all motorists and to manufacturers in their efforts to beat down costs caused by congestion and to maintain their export records.

The last 12 months are also infamous for the introduction of the 70 mile an hour speed limit. This measure was brought in after Ministerial panic over a series of multiple crashes on motorways mainly in fog. The remedy bore no relation to the ailment but Mr Tom Fraser was persuaded that it would be a worthwhile experiment.

As it happened the experiment outlived the Minister's term of office.

In December the Prime Minister presented the breathless motoring population with a brand new Minister of Transport—a woman who could not even drive a motor car.

So far the 54-year-old red-head, Mrs Barbara Castle has produced little but words and promises. She has described herself as a good Minister of Transport—without producing supporting evidence.

She HAS produced a great deal of new and restrictive legislation including a controversial Road Safety Bill. She has also suggested separate licences for drivers of automatic cars and called for a ban on the under seventeens who can at present qualify for a motor cycle licence.

She has also extended the 70 limit on the grounds that a greater length of time is needed to prove its worth—although most engineers believe that without an adequate control for comparison the experiment is invalid anyway.

Just where she will lead the motoring community in the future is very difficult to forecast, but anyone who took the gloomy view that more and restrictive legislation was on the way could hardly be blamed.

However, of one thing I am certain, the motor industry which so proudly displays its products at Earls Court over the next two weeks, can take it. It will survive, despite the squeeze, despite the down-beat legislation and despite the gloomy procrastinations of the pundits.

A quick look around Earls Court will show you why.

No other country in the world can boast such a wide choice of model, such an unparalleled record in exports and such a forward thinking programme masterminded by such enthusiastic executives.

JAGUAR
announce two outstanding new models

THE 420 SALOON Jaguar now proudly introduce an important addition to their medium size saloon car range. This impressively styled new 420 model has the compact dimensions of the famous 'S' Type and an entirely new frontal appearance incorporating four headlight system and imposing new radiator grille. With 4.2 litre XK twin carburettor engine, automatic transmission or manual 4 speed all-synchromesh gear box, with or without overdrive, optional power steering, independent suspension all round, 4 wheel disc brakes, alternator and pre-engaged starter, it offers commanding power and the very highest degree of road safety. Its full 5 seater body provides luxurious comfort with finest leather hide upholstery, reclining front seats and variable control heating for front and rear compartments.

THE 420 'G' SALOON For spacious and silent, high-performance motoring, Jaguar now present the new 420 'G' —a luxury saloon with every conceivable refinement and many new interior and exterior styling features. Powered by the advanced design 4.2 litre XK three carburettor engine, with Borg Warner Model 8 automatic transmission or 4 speed all-synchromesh manual gear box, with or without overdrive, and with independent suspension all round, four wheel disc brakes, 'Varamatic' power steering, alternator and pre-engaged starter, the new 420 'G' has a newly designed radiator grille and additional side-mounted continental direction indicators . . . The luxurious five seater interior with variable car temperature control has reclining front seats and is upholstered throughout in Vaumol leather hide. The instrument panel has a padded safety screen rail. A heated backlight, electrically operated windows and Delanair Air Conditioning are available extras.

Stand 138 Earls Court

LONDON SHOWROOMS : 88 PICCADILLY W.1

THE RANGE OF 2·4, 3·4 AND 3·8 MK 2 MODELS, THE 3·4 AND 3·8 'S' MODELS AND THE 4·2 'E' TYPE MODELS CONTINUES FOR 1967

The new Triumph GT6 tops a great triple bill
co-starring the new Vitesse 2-Litre & '67 Triumph 2000s

Triumph GT6 brings Le Mans to Earls Court The GT6 takes its breeding from the Triumph Spitfires that came first and second in their class at Le Mans last year. It puts 95 bhp to work in the key over-taking speeds; 50-70 in 8.5 seconds means you overtake decisively with a reassuring margin. The power is delivered with 2-litre, 6-cylinder smoothness. The handling is *race-proved*. The chassis, independent suspension and front disc brakes are all of the same stamp as the Le Mans winners. Appointments include a leather-covered steering wheel, pile carpet, walnut facia, GT seats.

New Triumph Vitesse 2-Litre offers surprising, not to say startling performance. It weighs the same 18¼ cwt as its predecessor—but now has a 2-litre, 95 bhp engine. A power-to-weight ratio that makes it a very potent machine indeed. 6 cylinders and Leyland engineering take care of the power

smoothly. Vitesse owners are maintained in the usual way—handsomely. The new seats with padded rolls are even more inviting than before. All-independent suspension and front disc brakes make the Vitesse safe and sure-footed as well as volatile. More safety factors: the steering column telescopes on serious impact, the driver is surrounded by padded surfaces.

'67 Triumph 2000s Changes feature interior refine-ments. Both the Saloon and the Estate Car have redesigned seats with *leather* upholstery. A new 'full-flow' heater/ventilation system gives added comfort and safety. The air is cool or warm and always fresh—even with the windows closed. The driver stays alert, the rear window stays clear. Both the saloon and the estate carry five people in comfort, the estate also has a loadspace of

fifty cubic feet, and a loading length of 5 ft. 3¾ ins.

Triumph 1300—'**best small car**' *Autocar* called the new 1300 'the best small car currently available'. Now in volume production, the 1300 earns this title with such refinements as: adjustable steering: full-flow ventilation and heating: 'all-systems-go' instrumentation. No other car is so lavishly equipped for only £835 1s. 10d., tax paid.

Look for the biggest crowd— that's the Triumph stand

With cars like the GT6, interest—and the crowds—centre on the Triumph stand. In addition to the cars above see the Triumph Spitfire Mk 2, Triumph TR4A, and complete Herald range.

STANDARD-TRIUMPH SALES LTD. LONDON
OFFICE AND SHOWROOMS: BERKELEY SQUARE
LONDON W1. TELEPHONE: GROSVENOR 6050

 **TRIUMPH**

Triumph Vitesse 2-Litre, 95 bhp under the bonnet!

'67 Triumph 2000. Leather upholstery, fresh-air heating

Triumph 2000 Estate. Elegant lines—bulky loads

Your easy-to-follow guide to the new cars

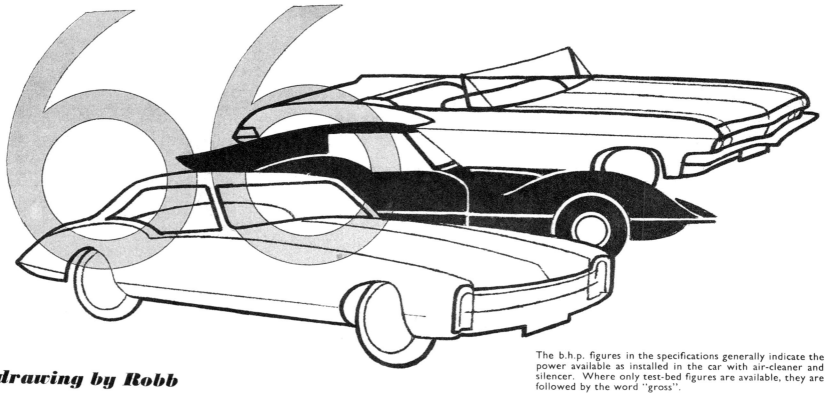

drawing by Robb

The b.h.p. figures in the specifications generally indicate the power available as installed in the car with air-cleaner and silencer. Where only test-bed figures are available, they are followed by the word "gross".

A.C. 428

TRI-NATIONAL fast tourer with body styled by Frua of Italy, chassis by A.C. Cars of England and competition-tested Ford V8 engine from the USA, the AC Convertible offers the best of old and new worlds. High performance with minimum maintenance. Suspension joints are sealed and need no greasing. Folding top retracts under metal cover. Tubular chassis with all-independent suspension like that of the famous Cobra.

CLOSE-UP

Eight-cyl.; o.h.v.; 104.9 × 101.1 mm.; 6,989 c.c.; 345 b.h.p. gross; 10.5 to 1 comp.; Ford 4-choke carb.; 4-speed, 8.21, 5.98, 4.56, 3.54 to 1; cen. lvr. auto. opt.; susp., f. and r. ind. coil; 2-door; 2-seat; disc servo brks.; max. 140 m.p.h.; cruise, 115; m.p.g. 13-18; whl. base, 8ft.; track f. 4ft. 7in.; r. 4ft. 8in.; lgth., 14ft. 6in.; width 5ft. 7in.; ht. 4ft. 3in.; g.c. 5in.; turng. cir., 35ft.; kerb wt. 28 cwt.; tank 17 gals.; 12-volt.

A.C. 289

HOME market equivalent of the race-winning Cobra, with Ford V8 engine of 4.7-litres in British tubular chassis with all-independent anti-dive coil spring suspension. Camber, castor and toe-in of rear wheels are controllable by adjustment and steering swivels require no lubrication. Self-adjusting disc brakes have twin master cylinders. All-synchromesh gearbox, limited slip differential, rack and pinion steering are standard equipment.

CLOSE-UP

Eight-cyl.; o.h.v.; 101.6 × 72.9 mm.; 4,727 c.c.; 280 b.h.p.; 11 to 1 comp.; Holley carb.; 4-speed, 8.36, 6.30, 4.99, 3.54 to 1; cen. lvr.; susp. f. and r. ind. coil; 2-door; 2-seat; disc brks.; max. 150 m.p.h.; cruise 130; m.p.g. 17-20; whl. base 7ft. 6in.; track, f. 4ft. 7in., r. 4ft. 6in.; lgth. 13ft.; width 5ft. 8in.; ht. 4ft. 1in.; g.c. 5in.; turng. cir. 34ft.; kerb wt. 20¾ cwt.; tank 17 gals.; 12-volt.
£2,260 + £519 p.t. = £2,779

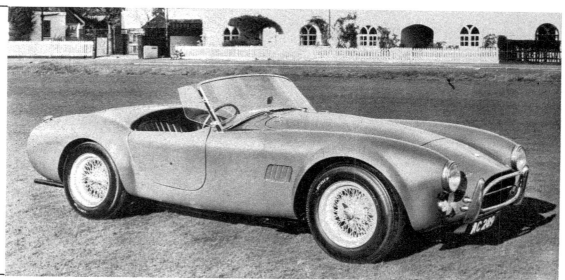

ALFA ROMEO GIULIA DUETTO

IF Romeo had had a car like this, Juliet wouldn't have been left standing on the balcony. Pininfarina's styling gives a longer line for this new convertible. Twin-cam engine with two twin-choke carburetters, five speed all-synchro gearbox, disc brakes and rear axle with radius arms, A-bracket and coil springs, form the recipe for a car the Italians call Sportivissima.

CLOSE-UP

Four-cyl.; o.h.c.; 78 × 82 mm.; 1,570 c.c.; 109 b.h.p.; 9 to 1 comp.; 2 Weber 2-choke carbs.; 5-speed, 15.03, 9.02, 6.16, 4.55, 3.59 to 1; cen. lvr.; susp., f. ind. coil, r. coil; 2-door; 2-seat; disc brks., servo opt.; max 116 m.p.h.; cruise 95 m.p.g. 27-30; whl. base 7ft. 4½in.; track f. 4ft. 3½in.; r. 4ft. 2in.; lgth. 13ft. 11½in.; width 5ft. 4½in.; ht. 4ft. 2¾in.; g.c. 5in.; turng. circ. 34ft. 5in.; kerb wt. 20 cwt.; tank 10 gals.; 12-volt.

£1,540 + £355 p.t. = £1,895

ALFA ROMEO GIULIA SUPER

NOT the most elegant of Alfas, but a fast well-equipped family four-seater with a strong sporting character. Its twin-cam engine is brought to optimum efficiency by two twin-choke Weber carburetters, the gearbox has five speeds, disc brakes all round see to the stopping and precise location of the rear axle on radius arms and a central A-bracket guarantees good road holding.

CLOSE-UP

Four-cyl.; o.h.c.; 78 × 82 mm.; 1,570 c.c.; 98 b.h.p.; 9 to 1 comp.; 2 Weber twin-choke carbs.; 5-speed, 19.8, 15.7, 11.6, 7.9, 4.8 to 1; cen. lvr.; susp., f. ind. coil, r. coil; 4-door; 4-seat; disc servo brks.; max. 107 m.p.h.; cruise 90; m.p.g. 20-25; whl. base 8ft. 2⅛in.; track, f. 4ft. 3¾in., r. 4ft. 2in.; lgth. 13ft. 7in.; width 5ft. 1⅛in.; ht. 4ft. 8⅛in.; g.c. 5⅛in.; turng. cir. 34ft. 6in.; kerb wt. 20⅝ cwt.; tank 10 gals.; 12-volt.

£1,300 + £300 p.t. = £1,600

ALFA ROMEO 2600 SPIDER

CARROZZERIA Touring do the Superleggera Spider body, Bertone do the Sprint coupe and Zagato does the lightweight competition short chassis SZ coupe; a selection to delight enthusiasts. Each has the six-cylinder engine with twin chain-driven overhead camshafts and three twin-choke carburetters driving through an excellent five-speed gearbox. Thoroughbred cars from a state-owned concern which has not forgotten how to make cars for individualists.

CLOSE-UP

Six-cyl.; o.h.c.; 83 × 79.6 mm.; 2,584 c.c.; 145 b.h.p.; 9.1 to 1 comp.; 3 Solex twin-choke carbs.; 5-speed, 15.79, 9.50, 6.47, 4.77, 3.77 to 1; cen. lvr.; susp., f. ind. coil, r. coil; 2-door; 4-seat; hyd. servo brks., disc front; max. 120 m.p.h.; cruise 100; m.p.g. 15-20; whl. base 8ft. 2½in.; track, f. 4ft. 7in., r. 4ft. 6in.; lgth. 14ft. 9½in.; width 5ft. 6½in.; ht. 4ft. 4in.; g.c. 4¾in.; turng. cir. 32ft.; kerb wt. 25¼ cwt.; tank 13¼ gals.; 12-volt.

£2,066 + £475 p.t. = £2,541

AMPHICAR

LIKE a duck, it takes to water. The ideal vehicle for dodging traffic jams; you simply turn to the canals and rivers. German-built, it is powered by a Triumph Herald 1,147 c.c. engine with special 4-speed all-synchromesh gearbox. For motoring on water, drive is transmitted via two propellor shafts housed in tunnels one each side of the engine to two three-bladed nylon propellers.

CLOSE-UP

Four-cyl.; o.h.v.; 69.3 × 76 mm.; 1,147 c.c.; 38 b.h.p.; 8 to 1 comp.; Solex carb.; 4-speed, 21.22, 13.73, 8.26, 4.91 to 1; cen. lvr.; susp. f. and r. ind. coil; 2-door; 4-seat; hyd. brks.; max. 68 m.p.h.; cruise 55; m.p.g. 28; whl. base 7ft.; track, f. 4ft., r. 4ft. 2in.; lgth. 14ft. 3in.; width 5ft. 2in.; ht. 5ft.; g.c. 10in.; turng. cir. 37ft.; kerb wt. 20¾ cwt.; tank 10½ gals.; 12-volt.

£888 + £206 p.t. = £1,094

Abbreviations—g.c.—ground clearance; susp.—suspension; f.—front; r.—rear; comp.—compression; s.v.—side-valves; o.h.v.—overhead valves; o.h.c.—overhead camshaft; hyd.—hydraulic.

61

ALVIS 3-LITRE SERIES III

NOW amalgamated with Rover, Alvis is famed for its military vehicles, but also makes fine cars with saloon and convertible bodies by Park Ward. Choice of engines, with two or three carburetters. 5-speed ZF gearbox is standard. ZF power-assisted steering and Borg Warner automatic transmission are options. Unusual headlamp mounting has four lamps grouped in vertical pairs. Wire wheels are another feature.

CLOSE-UP

Six-cyl.; o.h.v.; 84×90 mm.; 2,993 c.c.; 150 b.h.p.; 8.5 to 1 comp.; 3 S.U. carbs.; 5-speed, 11.38, 6.97, 4.86, 3.77, 3.07 to 1; cen. lvr.; BW auto opt.; susp., f. ind. coil, r. half-elliptic; 2-door; 4-seat; disc servo brks.; max. 112 m.p.h.; cruise 90; m.p.g. 18-22; whl. base 9ft. 3½in.; track f. 4ft. 7½in., r. 4ft. 6½in.; lgth. 15ft. 8½in.; width 5ft. 6in.; ht. 5ft.; g.c. 7in.; turng. cir. 39ft. 6in.; kerb wt. 30½ cwt.; tank 14¼ gals.; 12-volt.

£2,667+£614 p.t. = £3,281

ASTON MARTIN DB6

EXPERIENCE has shown that this sports beauty which telescopes miles into minutes is now at the peak of its performance. While it has more head, body and leg room than any Aston Martin previously built, the structural changes to its body have also paid off handsomely. Magnificent road holding and greater safety at speed stem from the aerodynamic spoiler on the familiar fast-back styling. A thoroughbred car, through and through.

CLOSE-UP

Six-cyl.; o.h.c.; 96×92 mm.; 3,995 c.c.; 282 b.h.p.; 8.75 to 1 comp.; 3 S.U. carbs.; 5-speed, 10.29, 6.64, 4.64, 3.77, 3.14 to 1; cen. lvr., auto opt.; susp. f. ind. coil, r. coil; 2-door; 4-seat; disc servo brks.; max. 150 m.p.h.; cruise 125; m.p.g. 15-18; whl. base 8ft. 5½in.; track f. 4ft. 6in., r. 4ft. 5½in.; lgth. 15ft 2in.; width 5ft. 6in.; ht. 4ft. 5½in.; g.c. 6½in.; turng. cir. 34ft.; kerb wt. 29 cwt.; tank 19 gals.; 12-volt.

£4,135+£949 p.t. = £5,084

ASTON MARTIN VOLANTE

VOLANTE convertible, a dream car for open-air lovers, has revised bodywork on original short chassis. Trim is finest hide with Wilton pile carpets, Sundym glass. Platform chassis and bodyframe are rust-proofed, sound insulated and undersealed. Body panels are light alloy. Adjustable reclining seat backs have new safety locks. Lockable glovebox, sun visors, passenger's grab handle, seat belt attachment points, laminated safety glass windscreen are standard.

CLOSE-UP

Six-cyl.; o.h.c.; 96×92 mm.; 3,995 c.c.; 282 b.h.p.; 8.9 to 1 comp.; 3 S.U. carbs.; 5-speed, 10.18, 6.64, 4.64, 3.77, 3.14 to 1; cen. lvr., auto opt.; susp., f. ind. coil, r. coil; 2-door; 4-seat; disc servo brks.; max. 148 m.p.h.; cruise 120; m.p.g. 15-18; whl. base 8ft. 2in.; track f. 4ft. 6in., r. 4ft. 5½in.; lgth. 15ft.; width 5ft. 6in.; ht. 4ft. 5in.; g.c. 6½in.; turng. cir. 34ft.; kerb wt. 29 cwt.; tank 16 gals.; 12-volt.

£4,135+£949 p.t. = £5,084

AUSTIN MINI

CLASSLESS car that became a cult. Mini-varieties are innumerable and the basic model offers countless improvements to trim and mechanical details. Hydrolastic suspension quells pitch on bumpy roads and one of the world's best automatic transmissions is an extra-cost option. If the standard saloon doesn't fill the bill there are station wagons, vans, pick-ups, mokes, beach cars, man-about-town modifications, convertibles and even caravans.

CLOSE-UP

Four-cyl.; o.h.v.; 63×68.3 mm.; 848 c.c.; 34 b.h.p.; 8.3 to 1 comp.; S.U. carb.; 4-speed, 13.66, 8.18, 5.32, 3.76 to 1; cen. lvr., auto opt.; susp. f. and r. ind. rubber-hyd.; 2-door; 4-seat; hyd. brks.; max. 73 m.p.h.; cruise 60; m.p.g. 32-40; whl. base 6ft. 8in.; track, f. 3ft. 11½in., r. 3ft. 9¾in.; lgth. 10ft.; width 4ft. 7½in.; ht. 4ft. 5in.; g.c. 6½in.; turng. cir. 31ft. 7in.; kerb wt. 11¾ cwt.; tank 5½ gals.; 12-volt.

£388+£90 p.t. = £478

Abbreviations—g.c.—ground clearance; susp.—suspension; f.—front; r.—rear; comp.—compression; s.v.—side-valves; o.h.v.—overhead valves; o.h.c.—overhead camshaft; hyd.—hydraulic.

AUSTIN 1100

SISTER to the Morris 1100, this well-shaped saloon now has automatic drive as alternative to manual four forward gear change. When switched to automatic the car is a honey to drive in traffic and out on the road its novel "water-and-rubber" suspension still makes for happy motoring. Power comes from an east-to-west fitted engine in front, a design that has come to stay.

CLOSE-UP
Four-cyl.; o.h.v.; 64.58×83.72 mm.; 1,098 c.c.; 48 b.h.p.; 8.5 to 1 comp.; S.U. carb.; 4-speed, 14.99, 8.98, 5.83, 4.13 to 1; cen. lvr.; susp. f. and r. ind. rubber-hyd.; 2- or 4-door; 4-seat; hyd. brks., disc front; max. 76 m.p.h.; cruise 60; m.p.g. 34-38; whl. base 7ft. 9½in.; track f. 4ft. 3½in., r. 4ft. 2⅞in.; lgth. 12 ft. 2¾in.; width 5ft. 0⅜in.; ht. 4ft. 5in.; g.c. 5¼in.; turng. cir. 34ft.; kerb wt. 16½ cwt.; tank 8½ gals.; 12-volt.
£507+£118 p.t. = £625

AUSTIN A/110

A car that looks good and behaves well in any circumstances—in town or country. It does its job silently, smoothly and without fuss. A sound work-a-day car for the business man and roomy for the family. Minor improvements keep this long standing favourite well up to date. Note particularly the improvements in suspension, braking and silencing.

CLOSE-UP
Six-cyl.; o.h.v.; 83×89 mm.; 2,912 c.c.; 120 b.h.p.; 8.3 to 1 comp.; 2 S.U. carbs.; 4-speed, 10.31, 8.1, 5.11, 3.91 to 1; cen. lvr. BW overdrive or auto. opt.; susp., f. ind. coil, r. half-elliptic; 4-door; 5/6-seat; servo brks., disc front; max. 102 m.p.h.; cruise 80; m.p.g. 18-23; whl. base 9ft. 2in.; track f. 4ft. 6in., r. 4ft. 5¼in.; lgth. 15ft. 7½in.; width 5ft. 8½in.; ht. 5ft. 0½in.; g.c. 6¼in.; turng. cir. 41ft.; kerb wt. 28½ cwt.; tank 16 gals.; 12-volt.
£890+£206 p.t. = £1,096

AUSTIN HEALEY SPRITE MK IV

ELIXIR of youth in a four-wheeled package, powered by BMC's durable 1,275 c.c. pushrod engine. Latest batch of improvements include new crankshaft and cylinder head for greater power and smoother, quieter performance. Rear suspension is vastly improved since semi-elliptic leaf springs replaced quarter elliptics. There are winding windows and hinged quarter lights. Redesigned facia is more convenient and there's a small parcel shelf.

CLOSE-UP
Four-cyl.; o.h.v.; 70.6×81.3 mm.; 1,275 c.c.; 70 b.h.p.; 9.75 to 1 comp.; 2 S.U. carbs.; 4-speed, 13.5, 8.09, 5.73, 4.22 to 1; cen. lvr.; susp., f. ind. coil, r. half-elliptic; 2-door; 2-seat; hyd. brks., disc front; max. 95 m.p.h.; cruise 80; m.p.g. 26-30; whl. base 6ft. 8in.; track, f. 3ft. 9¾in., r. 3ft. 8¾in.; lgth. 11ft. 5¼in.; width 4ft. 5in.; ht. 4ft. 1¾in.; g.c. 5in.; turng. cir. 32ft.; kerb wt. 14½ cwt.; tank 6 gals.; 12-volt.

AUSTIN HEALEY 3000 MARK III

BIG banger with a hefty six-cylinder engine developed from a car that appeared 14 years ago in lighter form with four cylinders. It was for long a mainstay of the BMC rally team, where its rugged construction kept it winning over rocky Alpine byways. Small rear seats for children, reasonable luggage space and improved weather protection augment its appeal for the sporting family man.

CLOSE-UP
Six-cyl.; o.h.v.; 83.3×88.9 mm.; 2,912 c.c.; 148 b.h.p.; 9 to 1 comp.; 2 S.U. carbs.; 4-speed, 9.34, 7.33, 4.63, 3.54 to 1; cen. lvr., de Normanville overdrive opt.; susp., f. ind. coil, r. half-elliptic; 2-door; 2/3 seat; hyd. servo brks., disc front; max. 120 m.p.h.; cruise 100; m.p.g. 20-23; whl. base 7ft. 7¾in.; track f. 4ft. 0¾in., r. 4ft. 2in.; lgth. 13ft. 1½in.; width 5ft.; ht. 4ft. 2in.; g.c. 4½in.; turng. cir. 35ft.; kerb wt. 23 cwt.; tank 12 gals.; 12-volt.
£915+£211 p.t. = £1,126

AUDI

FRONT wheel drive Volkswagen? Well, you could put it that way, for VW now own Auto Union, makers of the Audi, though Mercedes-Benz designed the unique engine with high-swirl bowl-in-piston combustion and 11.2 to 1 compression. Station wagon is a new alternative to the saloon. Disc front brakes are mounted inboard, bumpers are stainless steel, fan is glass fibre and nylon.

CLOSE-UP

Four-cyl.; o.h.v.; 80 × 84.4 mm.; 1,695 c.c.; 72 b.h.p.; 11.2 to 1 comp.; Solex carb.; 4-speed, 13.22, 7.56, 5.13, 3.76 to 1; col. lvr.; susp., f. ind. torsion bar, r. torsion bar; 2/4-door; 4/5-seat; hyd. brks., disc front; max. 92 m.p.h.; cruise 85; m.p.g. 32-38; whl. base 8ft. 2in.; track, f. 4ft. $4\frac{7}{8}$in., r. 4ft. $4\frac{1}{4}$in.; lgth. 14ft. $0\frac{1}{2}$in.; width 5ft. 4in.; ht. 4ft. 8in.; g.c. $6\frac{1}{4}$in.; turng. cir. 34ft. 9in.; kerb wt. $19\frac{3}{4}$ cwt.; tank $11\frac{3}{8}$ gals.; 12-volt.

£948 + £294 p.t. = £1,242

AUTO UNION DKW F102

HEIR to a long two-stroke tradition that goes back to pre-war DKWs with transverse engines and front wheel drive (Good gracious! perhaps it's not a new idea after all!), today's DKW is a sophisticated machine. Its three-cylinder engine has pump lubrication and closed-circuit cooling system. The gearbox has synchromesh on all speeds, front brakes are discs and no chassis greasing is needed.

CLOSE-UP

Three-cyl.; two-stroke; 81 × 76 mm.; 1,175 c.c.; 60 b.h.p.; 7.5 to 1 comp.; Solex carb.; 4-speed, 14.85, 7.76, 4.79, 3.63 to 1; col. lvr.; susp. f. ind. torsion bar, r. torsion bar; 2 or 4-door; 4-5-seat; hyd. brks., disc front; max. 90 m.p.h.; cruise, 76; m.p.g. 28-30; whl. base, 8ft. $1\frac{5}{8}$in.; track f. 4ft. $4\frac{3}{8}$in., r. 4ft. $4\frac{1}{4}$in.; lgth. 15ft. $6\frac{1}{2}$in.; width 5ft. $3\frac{3}{4}$in.; ht. 4ft. $9\frac{1}{2}$in.; g.c. $5\frac{1}{2}$in.; turng. cir. 38ft. 6in.; kerb wt. 17 cwt.; tank 10 gals.; 6-volt.

£806 + £187 p.t. = £993

BENTLEY T-TYPE

IT is doubtful that greater luxury has ever been incorporated in a sporting type of motor car than in this full-blooded brother of the latest Rolls-Royce. In fact, the only difference between these two world thoroughbreds is the radiator grille. Caviar-and-champagne fitments include all-independent, self-levelling suspension, disc brakes with hydraulic servos, and electrically operated seats that rise and tilt.

CLOSE-UP

Eight-cyl.; o.h.v.; 104.1 × 91.4 mm.; 6,230 c.c.; b.h.p. not revealed; 9 to 1 comp.; 2 S.U. carbs.; 4-speed auto., 11.75, 8.1, 4.46, 3.08 to 1; col. lvr.; susp. f. and r. ind. coil, hyd. levelling; 4-door; 5-seat; disc, hyd. servo brks.; max. 120 m.p.h.; cruise 100; m.p.g. 13-16; whl. base 9ft. $11\frac{1}{2}$in.; track f. and r. 4ft. $9\frac{1}{2}$in.; lgth. 16ft. $11\frac{1}{2}$in.; width 5ft. 11in.; ht. 4ft. $11\frac{3}{4}$in.; g.c. $6\frac{1}{2}$in.; turng. cir. 38ft.; kerb wt. $41\frac{1}{2}$ cwt.; tank 24 gals.; 12-volt.

£5,375 + £1,233 p.t. = £6,608

BMW 1600

COMPACTNESS without contortions. New, light, fast two-door saloon has two-inch shorter wheelbase than the original 1600 with little loss of space. Width is down $4\frac{3}{4}$ in. with loss of only $\frac{3}{4}$ in. inside. 13 in. instead of 14 in. wheels help. Engine, developed from the previous 1600, has bigger 1800 valves, gives 85 h.p. installed. Note adjustable backrests, rear window demister, aerodynamic wiper blades for high speed efficiency, and automatic screen washer.

CLOSE-UP

Four-cyl.; o.h.c.; 71 × 84 mm.; 1,573 c.c.; 85 b.h.p.; 8.6 to 1 comp.; Solex carb.; 4-speed, 15.76, 8.42, 5.51, 4.11 to 1; cen. lvr.; susp., f. and r. ind. coil; 2-door; 4-seat; hyd. brks., disc front; max. 100 m.p.h.; cruise, 85; m.p.g. 27-29; whl. base 8ft. $2\frac{1}{2}$in.; track f. and r. 4ft. 4in.; lgth. 13ft. $10\frac{1}{2}$in.; width 5ft. $2\frac{5}{8}$in.; ht. 4ft. $7\frac{1}{2}$in.; g.c. 6in.; turng. cir. 31ft. 6in.; kerb wt. $18\frac{1}{2}$ cwt.; tank 10 gals.; 6-volt.

Abbreviations—g.c.—ground clearance; susp.—suspension; f.—front; r.—rear; comp.—compression; s.v.—side-valves; o.h.v.—overhead valves; o.h.c.—overhead camshaft; hyd.—hydraulic.

BMW 2000

FIFTIETH anniversary models have been pouring from BMW this year. The 2000 saloon appears in three versions; standard with new body styling featuring rectangular headlamps and horizontal tail lamps, and engine giving 113 h.p. gross; competition TI with twin-carburetter 135 hp. engine in the normal body with circular headlamps and vertical tail lamps; TILUX with 135 hp and the new body. Improved suspension, bigger brake discs, new seats, rear window demisting on all models.

CLOSE-UP
Four-cyl.; o.h.c.; 89 × 80 mm.; 1,990 c.c.; 100 b.h.p.; 8.5 to 1 comp.; Solex carb.; 4-speed, 15.76, 8.42, 5.51, 4.11 to 1; cen. lvr.; susp., f. and r. ind. coil; 4-door; 5-seat; hyd. servo brks., disc front; max. 104 m.p.h.; cruise, 88; m.p.g. 22-26; whl. base 8ft. 4½in.; track f. 4ft. 4in., r. 4ft. 6in.; lgth., 14ft. 11in.; width 5ft. 5in.; ht. 4ft. 8¾in.; g.c. 6½in.; turng. cir. 33ft. 6in.; kerb wt. 21⅞ cwt.; tank, 12 gals.; 12-volt.

£1,445+£332 p.t. = £1,777

BOND EQUIPE G.T. 4S

A sunshine roof is now an optional extra to this nippy, four-seater car that is built for the individualist motorist. It has a Triumph Herald steel chassis, Spitfire Mk 2 engine and a light, glass-fibre body. In fact, it has so many Herald derivations that this model can be serviced by Triumph agents. A smart and distinctive car that has a lot of followers.

CLOSE-UP
Four-cyl.; o.h.v.; 69.3 × 76 mm.; 1,147 c.c.; 67 b.h.p.; 9 to 1 comp.; 2 S.U. carbs.; 4-speed, 15.7, 11.3, 7.3, 4.2 to 1; cen. lvr.; susp., f. ind. coil, r. ind. trans. leaf; 2-door; 2/4-seat; hyd. brks., disc front; max. 85 m.p.h.; cruise 75; m.p.g. 30-35; whl. base 7ft. 7½in.; track, f. 4ft. 1in., r. 4ft. 0½in.; lgth. 13ft. 2¾in.; width 5ft. 0½in.; ht. 4ft. 4½in.; g.c. 6in.; turng. cir. 25ft.; kerb wt. 16 cwt.; tank 10 gals; 12-volt.

£697+£161 p.t. = £858

BRISTOL 409

NOW it will be possible to fit power-steering as an optional extra to this well-shaped car that appeals particularly to the esoteric motorist. The many improvements made to it last year are now paying off and these include better suspension, brakes, and engine-urge. It gives a smooth, effortless ride that is matched by its elegance and beauty. They say once a Bristol owner, always a Bristol owner.

CLOSE-UP
Eight-cyl.; o.h.v.; 99.3 × 84.07 mm.; 5,211 c.c.; 250 b.h.p. gross; 9 to 1 comp.; Carter 4-choke carb.; 3-speed auto, 7.5, 4.5, 3.07 to 1; push button control; susp., f. ind. coil, r. torsion bar; 2-door; 4-seat; disc servo brks.; max. 125 m.p.h.; cruise 100; m.p.g. 18-20; whl. base 9ft. 6in.; track f. 4ft. 6in., r. 4ft. 6½in.; lgth. 16ft. 1½in.; width 5ft. 8in.; ht. 5ft.; g.c. 6½in.; turng. cir. 39ft. 6in.; kerb wt. 32 cwt.; tank 18 gals.; 12-volt.

£4,260+£978 p.t. = £5,238

BUICK RIVIERA

DISC front brakes with servo and dual master cylinders at last give this elegant American coupe stopping power to match the urge of its 360 h.p. V8 engine, while a positive traction differential helps control wheelspin on fast getaways. Automatic cornering and reversing lamps, 4-way hazard warning system and a lane change indicator are among the electrical amenities. Air-conditioning and stereo radio with electric aerial are included.

CLOSE-UP
Eight-cyl.; o.h.v.; 106.4 × 99 mm.; 7,047 c.c.; 360 b.h.p. gross; 10.25 to 1 comp.; Rochester 4-choke carb.; 3-speed auto., 8.01, 4.78, 3.23 to 1; cen. lvr.; susp. f. ind. coil, r. coil; 2-door; 4-seat; hyd. servo brks., disc front; max. 120 m.p.h.; cruise 100; m.p.g. 13-17; whl. base 9ft. 11in.; track, f. 5ft. 3⅛in., r. 5ft. 3in.; lgth. 17ft. 7⅛in.; width 6ft. 7¾in.; ht. 4ft. 6¼in.; g.c. 6in.; kerb wt. 38⅞ cwt.; tank 17½ gals.; 12-volt.

£3,250+£747 p.t. = £3,997

BUICK LE SABRE

PILLARLESS coupe, convertible and saloon are body styles available on this powerful quality car from a famous American factory. Featured in the latest specification are reclining passenger seat, front seat headrests, dual brake master cylinders, retractable safety belts and safety mirror with soft frame and breakaway bracket. The luggage boot lock is remotely controlled, and the twin-speaker radio has an electrically operated aerial.

CLOSE-UP
Eight-cyl.; o.h.v.; 95.25 × 97.8 mm.; 5,572 c.c.; 260 b.h.p. gross; 10.25 to 1 comp.; Rochester 4-choke carb.; 3-speed auto., 7.6, 4.5, 3.07 to 1; col. lvr.; susp. f. ind., r. coil; 2-door; 5-seat; hyd. servo brks.; max. 105 m.p.h.; cruise 90; m.p.g. 14-18; whl. base 10ft. 3in.; track, f. and r. 5ft. 3in.; lgth. 18ft. 1½in.; width 6ft. 8in.; ht. 4ft. 9in.; g.c. 5½in.; turng. cir. 42ft. 3in.; kerb wt. 40 cwt.; tank 21 gals.; 12-volt.

CADILLAC ELDORADO

SENSATIONAL switch by G.M. puts front-wheel drive and disc front brakes onto America's top luxury car. But that's not all. Equipment on this fine five-seater coupe includes Cruise Control motorway speed regulator, air conditioning, seat warmer, stereo radio, automatic level control for the suspension, tilt-and-telescope steering column. Steering, windows and brakes are naturally power operated. Vacuum-operated shutters conceal the headlamps.

CLOSE-UP
Eight-cyl.; o.h.v.; 104.9 × 101.6 mm.; 7,031 c.c.; 340 b.h.p. gross; 10.5 to 1 comp.; Rochester 4-choke carb.; 3-speed auto., 7.96, 4.75, 3.21 to 1; cen. lvr.; susp. f. ind. coil, r. coil with level control; 2-door; 5-seat; hyd. servo brks., disc front; max. 125 m.p.h.; cruise 105; m.p.g. 11-15; whl. base, 10ft.; track f. 5ft. 3½in.; r. 5ft. 3in.; lgth. 18ft. 5in.; width 6ft. 7in.; ht. 4ft. 5½in.; g.c. 5½in.; turng. cir. 43ft. 6in.; kerb wt. 41 cwt.; tank 21 gals.; 12-volt.

CHEVROLET CAMARO

EAGERLY-AWAITED challenger from G.M. to Ford's all-conquering Mustang. Power in plenty on this one from a 5.7-litre V8 engine and a sports-style four-speed transmission with gear lever on centre console. Disc front brakes with dual master cylinder and warning light, plus a limited-slip differential spell safety at speed. The designers were liberal with lights for reversing, under bonnet, in ashtray and luggage compartment.

CLOSE-UP
Eight-cyl.; o.h.v.; 101.6 × 88.4 mm.; 5.736 c.c.; 295 b.h.p. gross; 10.25 to 1 comp.; Rochester 4-choke carb.; 4-speed, 8.8, 6.6, 5.1, 3.5 to 1; cen. lvr.; susp. f. ind. coil, r. half-elliptic; 2-door; 4-seat; hyd. brks., disc front; max. 125 m.p.h.; cruise 100; m.p.g. 15-18; whl. base, 9ft.; track f. 4ft. 11in., r. 4ft. 10⅞in.; lgth. 15ft. 5in.; width 6ft. 6in.; ht. 4ft. 3in.; g.c. 5½in.; turng. cir. 37ft.; kerb wt. 25¾ cwt.; tank 15½ gals.; 12-volt.

CHEVROLET IMPALA

ONE of the world's fastest-selling cars, available in a great range of body styles, engine sizes and transmissions, both manual and automatic. Safety features for 1967 include dual brake master cylinders, safety tyre rims, new door locks, latches and hinges, 4-way emergency flashers, rear window demisters, soft window winders and coat hooks, flexibly framed anti-dazzle mirror with breakaway bracket, energy absorbing instrument panel.

CLOSE-UP
Eight-cyl.; o.h.v.; 98.4 × 76.2 mm.; 4,638 c.c.; 195 b.h.p. gross; 9.25 to 1 comp.; Rochester 2-choke carb.; 2-speed auto., 6.11, 3.36 to 1; col. lvr.; susp., f. ind. coil, r. coil; 2 or 4-door; 6-seat; hyd. servo brks.; max. 108 m.p.h.; cruise 90; m.p.g. 15-18; whl. base 9ft. 11in.; track, f. 5ft. 2½in., r. 5ft. 2⅜in.; lgth. 17ft. 9½in.; width 6ft. 7½in.; ht. 4ft. 7½in.; g.c. 7½in.; turng. cir. 40ft. 9in.; kerb wt. 33¾ cwt.; tank 20 gals.; 12-volt.

Abbreviations—g.c.—ground clearance; susp.—suspension; f.—front; r.—rear; comp.—compression; s.v.—side-valves; o.h.v.—overhead valves; o.h.c.—overhead camshaft; hyd.—hydraulic.

CHRYSLER NEW YORKER

EXTERNAL evidence that you've made the grade. A prestige model from one of America's big three, with the new safety features that are mandatory for 1967, including twin circuit braking system and energy-absorbing steering column. Servo brakes, power steering are standard and the options include electric operation for seat adjustment and side windows plus full air conditioning. Choice of bodies includes saloon and hardtop coupes.

CLOSE-UP
Eight-cyl.; o.h.v.; 109.7×95 mm.; 7,206 c.c.; 350 b.h.p. gross; 10 to 1 comp.; Carter 4-choke carb.; 3-speed auto, 6.86, 4.21, 2.76 to 1; col. lvr.; susp., f. ind. torsion bar, r. half-elliptic; 2 or 4-door; 6-seat; hyd. brks.; max. 120 m.p.h.; cruise 95; m.p.g. 12; whl. base 10ft. 4in.; track, f. 5ft. 2in., r. 5ft. 0¾in.; lgth. 18ft. 3in.; width 6ft. 7½in.; ht. 4ft. 7¾in.; g.c. 6in.; turng. cir. 44ft.; kerb wt. 38½ cwt.; tank 20 gals.; 12-volt.

CHRYSLER VALIANT

ORIGINALLY one of the "compact" Americans, the Valiant now has a long lean line like the larger Plymouths. Modifications to chassis and interior reflect the growing American preoccupation with safety. The Valiant range includes saloons, station wagons, convertibles and coupes with engines ranging from 2.8-litre six to 4.5-litre V8. Transmission options include three- or four-speed gearbox, auto transmission, self-locking differential.

CLOSE-UP
Six-cyl.; o.h.v.; 86.3×79.4 mm.; 2,789 c.c.; 100 b.h.p. gross; 8.5 to 1 comp.; Ball & Ball carb.; 3-speed, 10.4, 6.87, 3.23 to 1; col. lvr., 4-speed or auto. opt.; susp., f. ind. torsion bar, r. half-elliptic; 2- or 4-door; 5-seat; hyd. servo brks.; max. 94 m.p.h.; cruise 85; m.p.g. 17-22; whl. base 8ft. 10in.; track, f. 4ft. 7⅞in., r. 4ft. 7½in.; lgth. 15ft. 8in.; width 5ft. 10½in.; ht. 4ft. 5in.; g.c. 6in.; turng. cir. 37ft.; kerb wt. 24 cwt.; tank 15 gals.; 12-volt.

£1,724 + £397 p.t. = £2,121

CITROEN DS 21

STILL unbeatable for style and advanced mechanical design, the 11-year-old DS now has a five-bearing oversquare engine, new all-synchro gearbox with servo shift, improved brakes and shock absorbers. Automatic clutch and power steering are standard. Citroen pioneered disc brakes on family cars and self-levelling hydraulic-pneumatic suspension. Front-wheel drive, of course, a feature of all Citroens for over thirty years.

CLOSE-UP
Four-cyl.; o.h.v.; 90×85.5 mm.; 2,175 c.c.; 100 b.h.p.; 8.75 to 1 comp.; Weber twin-choke carb.; 4-speed, 14.22, 8.49, 5.56, 3.72 to 1; dash lvr.; susp. f. and r. ind. hyd.-pneu.; 4-door; 5/6-seat; hyd. servo brks., disc front; max. 109 m.p.h.; cruise 95; m.p.g. 25-30; whl. base 10ft. 3in.; track, f. 4ft. 11in., r. 4ft. 3¼in.; lgth. 15ft. 10in.; width 5ft. 10½in.; ht. 4ft. 9⅝in.; g.c. 5⅜in.; turng. cir. 36ft.; kerb wt. 25 cwt.; tank 14 gals.; 12-volt.

£1,487 + £342 p.t. = £1,829

CITROEN SAFARI 21

CITROEN'S seven-seater utility model is available in two forms; Safari 19 with the new 1,985 c.c. five-bearing engine plus the normal clutch and gearbox of the DS 19 saloon, or Safari 21, with the 2,175 c.c. five-bearing engine, automatic clutch, hydraulic gear control and power steering of the DS 21. Both have the self-levelling hydraulic-pneumatic suspension which set the motoring world on its ears plus inboard disc brakes at the front.

CLOSE-UP
Four-cyl.; o.h.v.; 90×85.5 mm.; 2,175 c.c.; 100 b.h.p.; 8.75 to 1 comp.; Weber twin-choke carb.; 4-speed, 14.22, 8.49, 5.56, 3.72 to 1; dash lvr.; susp.; f. and r. ind. hyd. pneu.; 5-door; 7-seat; hyd. servo brks., disc front; max. 102 m.p.h.; cruise 90; m.p.g. 24-28; whl. base 10ft. 3in.; track f. 4ft. 11in., r. 4ft. 3¼in.; lgth. 16ft. 4½in.; width 5ft. 10½in.; ht. 5ft. 0½in.; g.c. 5⅜in.; turng. cir., 36ft.; kerb wt. 27¼ cwt.; tank 14 gals.; 12-volt.

£1,569 + £361 p.t. = £1,930

Abbreviations—g.c.—ground clearance; susp.—suspension; f.—front; r.—rear; comp.—compression; s.v.—side-valves; o.h.v.—overhead valves; o.h.c.—overhead camshaft; hyd.—hydraulic.

67

DAF DAFFODIL

BELT-DRIVEN baby from the land of the bulb fields, the Dutch DAF has the unique automatic transmission that has even stood the test of single-seater racing. Recent improvements include deeper grille, less sloping bonnet, redesigned lamps, rear quarter extractor vents. Features for British market include walnut facia, fitted carpets, parcel shelf. Production continues alongside the new bigger Michelotti-styled 44.

CLOSE-UP

Two-cyl.; o.h.v. air cooled; 85.5×65 mm.; 746 c.c.; 30 b.h.p.; 7.5 to 1 comp.; Solex carb.; auto. belt drive 16.4 to 3.9 to 1; cen. lvr.; susp., f. ind. trans. leaf, r. ind. coil; 2-door; 4-seat; hyd. brks.; max. 65 m.p.h.; cruise 65; m.p.g. 38-48; whl. base 6ft. 8½in.; track f. and r. 3ft. 10½in.; lgth. 11ft. 10½in.; width 4ft. 9in.; ht. 4ft. 6¼in.; g.c. 6¾in.; turng. cir. 31ft.; kerb wt. 13¼ cwt.; tank, 7 galls.; 6-volt.

£495+£116 p.t. = £611

DAF 44

DAF announces a more powerful car to partner the Daffodil with engine increased to 844 c.c. and body styled by Michelotti. Experience on Formula 3 racing cars, an American army airborne truck, American gas company vans and Swedish postal vans has shown that DAF's unique rubber-belt automatic transmission is now ready for larger cars.

CLOSE-UP

Two-cyl.; o.h.v. air-cooled; 85.5×73.5 mm.; 844 c.c.; 40 b.h.p. gross; 7.5 to 1 comp.; Solex carb.; auto. belt drive 15.44 to 3.87 to 1; cen. lvr.; susp., f. ind. transv. leaf, r. ind. coil; 2-door; 4-seat; hyd. brks.; max. 76 m.p.h.; cruise, 76; m.p.g. 36-43; whl. base, 7ft. 4⅛in.; track f. 4ft. 2½in.; r. 4ft. 1¼in.; lgth., 12ft. 7½in.; width, 5ft. 0½in.; ht. 4ft. 6¾in.; g.c. 6¾in.; turng. cir., 30ft.; kerb wt., 14¼ cwt.; tank, 8¾ gals.; 6-volt.

DAIHATSU COMPAGNO 1000

NIPPY Nippon family car sold here in well equipped De luxe form with white-wall tyres, twin fog lamps, twin wing mirrors, reclining backrests for the front seats, a clock and radio. Layout is conventional; water-cooled four-cylinder pushrod engine at front, all-synchro four-speed box, semi-elliptic rear springs, drum brakes. Compagno Spider is a four-seater convertible with high compression 65 h.p. engine.

CLOSE-UP

Four-cyl.; o.h.v.; 68×66 mm.; 958 c.c.; 55 b.h.p. gross; 9 to 1 comp.; Mikuni carb.; 4-speed, 16.74, 10.6, 6.73, 4.55 to 1.; col. or cen. lvr.; susp., f. ind. torsion bar, r. half-elliptic; 2-door; 4-seat; hyd. brks.; max. 80 m.p.h.; cruise, 70; m.p.g. 30-33; whl. base, 7 ft. 5⅜in.; track f. 3ft. 10¾in., r. 3ft. 10in.; lgth., 12ft. 8⅜in.; width 4ft. 8⅞in.; ht. 4ft. 7½in.; g.c. 6½in.; turng. cir. 30ft. 3in.; kerb wt. 16 cwt.; tank 9 gals.; 12-volt.

£658+£155 p.t. = £813

DAIMLER SOVEREIGN

OLD Gottlieb wouldn't recognise it but he might not take it too badly to find Jaguar's twin-cam six-cylinder engine lurking behind the finned grille. Little of recent Daimler design is left beyond name plates and detail fittings, but the smooth, quiet surge of power through the automatic transmission and the luxuriously finished interior give the kind of motoring Daimler drivers expect.

CLOSE-UP

Six-cyl.; o.h.c.; 92×106 mm.; 4,235 c.c.; 255 b.h.p. gross; 8 to 1 comp.; 2 S.U. carbs.; 4-speed, 11.46, 7.44, 5.0, 3.77 to 1. with L de N overdrive; cen. lvr. B.W. auto. opt.; susp., f. and r. ind. coil; 4-door; 5-seat; disc servo brks.; max. 120 m.p.h.; cruise 95; m.p.g. 15-19; whl. base 8ft. 11¾in.; track f. 4ft. 7¼in.; r. 4ft. 6¼in.; lgth. 15ft. 7¾in.; width 5ft. 6¾in.; ht. 4ft. 6½in.; g.c. 7in.; turng. cir. 33ft. 6in.; kerb wt. 31½ cwt.; tank 14 gals.; 12-volt.

£1,724+£397 p.t. = £2,121

DAIMLER LIMOUSINE

THIS is one of the first cars to be merged with the giant British Motor Corporation, where it should hold its place as an outstanding example of power and dignity. It has traditional lines and sumptuous comfort for the man who wants his motoring on an impressive scale. Daimler is a long-established name in Britain and this smooth-lined, majestic car fully adds to its lustre.

CLOSE-UP
Eight-cyl.; o.h.v.; 95.25 / 80.01 mm.; 4,561 c.c.; 220 b.h.p. gross; 8 to 1 comp.; 2 S.U. carbs.; 3-speed, auto. 8.7, 5.4, 3.77 to 1; col. lvr.; susp., f. ind. coil, r. half-elliptic; 4-door; 8-seat; disc servo brks.; max. 110 m.p.h.; cruise 90; m.p.g. 17-20; whl. base 11ft. 6in.; track f. and r. 4ft. 9in.; lgth. 18ft. 10in.; width 6ft. 1¼in.; ht. 5ft. 5½in.; g.c. 7in.; turng. cir. 44ft.; kerb wt. 40 cwt.; tank 16 gals.; 12-volt.

£2,893 + £664 p.t. = £3,557

DODGE POLARA

PRESTIGE model of the Dodge range, with choice of four V8 engines ranging from 5.2 to 7.2-litres. All the amenities that make American motoring so quiet and effortless; automatic transmission with three speeds and torque converter, power steering and now disc front brakes, providing stopping capacity to match the power output. Four headlamps of course, seat belts for all occupants and several new safety ideas for 1967.

CLOSE-UP
Eight-cyl.; o.h.v.; 99.3 × 84.1 mm.; 5,210 c.c.; 230 b.h.p. gross; 9 to 1 comp.; Stromberg 2-choke carb.; 3-speed auto. 7.9, 4.68, 3.23 to 1; col. lvr.; susp., f. ind. torsion bar, half-elliptic; 2 or 4-door; 6-seat; hyd. servo brks., disc front; max. 108 m.p.h.; cruise 85; m.p.g. 12-15; whl. base 10ft. 1in.; track f. 5ft. 0¾in.; r. 4ft. 11¼in.; lgth. 17ft. 8in.; width 6ft. 6¼in.; ht. 4ft. 7in.; g.c. 5⅓in.; turng. cir. 46ft. 3in.; kerb wt. 35½ cwt.; tank 20 gals.; 12-volt.

£2,155 + £496 p.t. = £2,651

ELVA T-TYPE

NOW built by Trojan, the Elva comes in two versions, designed for speed, controllability and comfort. Choice of MGB or Ford Cortina engines and coupe or convertible coachwork. Bodies are in glass fibre on a rigid box-section chassis with independent suspension all round by coil springs and double wishbones. Twin brake master cylinders, now coming into prominence, have been an Elva feature for some time.

CLOSE-UP
Four-cyl.; o.h.v.; 80.3 × 89 mm.; 1,798 c.c.; 98 b.h.p. gross; 8.8 to 1 comp.; 2 S.U. carbs.; 4-speed, 14.2, 8.66, 5.37, 3.91 to 1; cen. lvr.; susp. f. and r. ind. coil; 2-door; 2-seat; hyd. brks., disc front; max. 110 m.p.h.; cruise 95; m.p.g. 28; whl. base 7ft. 6in.; track f. 4ft. 2¼in., r. 4ft. 1in.; lgth. 12ft. 5½in.; width 5ft. 1in.; ht. 3ft. 9½in.; g.c. 6in.; turng. cir. 25ft.; kerb wt. 15½ cwt.; tank 9 gals.; 12-volt.

£897 + £207 p.t. = £1,104

FERRARI 275 GTB

ROAD-GOING coupe based on Ferrari's matchless experience in winning 18 World Championship titles and 4,000 motor races. Chassis with all-independent suspension, powered by a magnificent V.12 overhead camshaft engine (choice of six single carburetters or three with twin chokes), Scaglietti did the Berlinetta body, Pininfarina the Spider. The five-speed gearbox is at the rear in unit with the limited-slip differential.

CLOSE-UP
Twelve-cyl.; o.h.c.; 77 × 58.8 mm.; 3,286 c.c.; 275 b.h.p.; 9.2 to 1 comp.; 3 Weber 2-choke carbs.; 5-speed, 10.9, 6.99, 5.18, 4.12, 3.43 to 1; cen. lvr.; susp. f. and r. ind. coil; 2-door; 2-seat; disc servo brks.; max. 160 m.p.h.; cruise 130; m.p.g. 15-20; whl. base 7ft. 10½in.; track, f. 4ft. 7½in., r. 4ft. 7⅜in.; lgth. 14ft. 3⅜in.; width 5ft. 6⅜in.; ht. 4ft. 5½in.; g.c. 4¾in.; turng. cir. 46ft.; kerb wt. 22 cwt.; tank 20¾ gals.; 12-volt.

£4,900 + £1,180 p.t. = £6,080

Abbreviations—g.c.—ground clearance; susp.—suspension; f.—front; r.—rear; comp.—compression; s.v.—side-valves; o.h.v.—overhead valves; o.h.c.—overhead camshaft; hyd.—hydraulic.

FERRARI 330 GT

AIM that long, lean snout for the open spaces to learn what real motoring is about. The pleasure of playing tunes on that five-speed gearbox, the crisp response of that 4-litre V-12 engine and the impeccable lines of the Pininfarina body work explain why the rich and famous make the pilgrimage to Maranello. GT coupe has two occasional seats in rear; short-chassis GTC is strictly for two.

CLOSE-UP

Twelve-cyl.; o.h.c.; 77 × 71 mm.; 3,967 c.c.; 300 b.h.p.; 8.8 to 1 comp.; 3 Weber 2-choke carbs.; 5-speed, 10.78, 7.22, 5.34, 4.25, 3.39 to 1; cen. lvr.; susp., f. ind. coil, r. half-elliptic; 2-door; 2-seat; disc servo brks.; max. 152 m.p.h.; cruise 130; m.p.g. 12-16; whl. base 8ft. 8⅜in.; track f. 4ft. 7¼in.; r. 4ft. 6¾in.; lgth. 15ft. 10½.; width 5ft. 7½in.; ht. 4ft. 5¾in.; g.c. 4¾in.; turng. cir. 49ft.; kerb wt. 27¼ cwt.; tank 19¾ gals.; 12-volt.

£5,350 + £1,289 p.t. = £6,639

FIAT 500

TOWN cars are not just for tomorrow. Fiat makes them today. Excellent parkability, small thirst, nippy in town traffic or crowded main roads. Freeze-proof, air-cooled engine. Front hinged doors, a deeper windscreen and larger diaphragm clutch were among recent improvements. Folding sun-roof is standard equipment. Fuel capacity recently increased to five gallons with new tank leaving more luggage space under the bonnet.

CLOSE-UP

Two-cyl.; o.h.v.; air cooled; 67.4 × 70 mm.; 499 c.c.; 18 b.h.p.; 7.1 to 1 comp.; Weber carb.; 4-speed, 18.96, 10.59, 6.66, 4.48 to 1; cen. lvr.; susp., f. ind. transv. leaf, r. ind. coil; 2-door; 2/4-seat; hyd. brks.; max. 60 m.p.h.; cruise 55; m.p.g. 55; whl. base 6ft. 0½in.; track f. 3ft. 8⅓in., r. 3ft. 8½in.; lgth. 9ft. 9in.; width 4ft. 4in.; ht. 4ft. 4⅓in.; g.c. 5in.; turng. cir. 28ft. 6in.; kerb wt. 10¼ cwt.; tank 4½ gals.; 12-volt.

£338 + £79 p.t. = £417

FIAT 850 SPIDER

LOW-BUILT lean-lined convertible by Bertone with mechanical parts similar to the 850 coupe but with extra engine power and an astonishing capacity for high revs. Well finished interior and surprisingly good luggage space. A hard top is an optional extra. Like the much admired Coupe, Spider has disc front brakes. A versatile sports car that slips through traffic and can cover long distances quickly.

CLOSE-UP

Four-cyl.; o.h.v.; 65 × 63.5 mm.; 843 c.c.; 49 b.h.p.; 9.3 to 1 comp.; Weber 2-choke carb.; 4-speed, 17.72, 10.02, 6.87, 4.69 to 1; cen. lvr.; susp., f. ind. transv. leaf, r. ind. coil; 2-door; 4-seat; hyd. brks., disc front; max. 90 m.p.h.; cruise 70; m.p.g. 35-40; whl. base 6ft. 7¾in.; track f. 3ft. 9⅛in., r. 3ft. 11⅝in.; lgth. 12ft. 4¾in.; width 4ft. 11in.; ht. 4ft; g.c. 5¼in.; turng. cir. 34ft. 2in.; kerb wt. 14¾ cwt.; tank 6½ gals.; 12-volt.

£826 + £191 p.t. = £1,017

FIAT 1100 R

TWO million buyers in 13 years spelled success for the previous version; now this ever-popular Fiat is redesigned with new front and tail, disc front brakes, improved suspension, smaller wheels, fatter tyres. Engine, brought back from 1,221 c.c. to the original 1,089, maintains performance with new manifolds, and twin-choke carburetter. Driving position is improved, gear lever is now central, grease points are reduced to two.

Four-cyl.; o.h.v.; 68 × 75 mm.; 1,089 c.c.; 48 b.h.p.; 8.1 to 1 comp.; Solex 2-choke carb.; 4-speed, 16.59, 10.23, 6.75, 4.3 to 1; cen. lvr.; susp., f. ind. coil, r. half-elliptic; 4-door; 4-seat; hyd. brks., disc front; max. 80 m.p.h.; cruise 70; m.p.g. 29-34; whl. base 7ft. 8⅜in.; track, f. 4ft. 0½in., r. 3ft. 11⅜in.; lgth 13ft. 0½in.; width 4ft. 9⅛in.; ht. 4ft. 8½in.; g.c. 5⅛in.; turng. cir. 34ft. 9in.; kerb wt. 16¾ cwt.; tank 8¼ gals.; 12-volt.

Abbreviations—g.c.—ground clearance; susp.—suspension; f.—front; r.—rear; comp.—compression; s.v.—side-valves; o.h.v.—overhead valves; o.h.c.—overhead camshaft; hyd.—hydraulic.

FIAT 124

BALANCED blend of good things to tap the growing market between Fiat's 1100 and 1500. Compact five-seater body, smooth but punchy 1,197 c.c. engine with dual carburetter and five bearings. All-synchromesh gearbox, disc brakes on all wheels, safety locks, front hinged bonnet. Coil spring front suspension, longitudinal and transverse radius arms to locate the rear axle. No greasing points to worry about. Well equipped, fast, economical family car.

CLOSE-UP

Four-cyl.; o.h.v.; 73 × 71.5 mm.; 1,197 c.c.; 60 b.h.p.; 8.8 to 1 comp.; Solex 2-choke carb.; 4-speed, 16.12, 9.89, 6.51, 4.3 to 1; cen. lvr.; susp. f. ind. coil, r. coil; 4-door; 4/5-seat; disc brks.; max 90 m.p.h.; cruise 80; m.p.g. 27-32; whl. base 7ft. 11¼in.; track f. 4ft. 4¾in.; r. 4ft. 3¼in.; lgth. 13 ft. 2⅜in.; width 5ft.; ht. 4ft. 5⅝in.; g.c. 4¾in.; turng. cir. 35ft.; kerb wt. 16⅛ cwt; tank 8½ gals.; 12-volt.

FORD ANGLIA

FORD'S veteran low-priced, cheap-running family car is now hitting the million mark in cars sold. It continues to suit almost every type of motorist from the family man to the better-off wife who keeps a second car for the children's schools and shopping. There is a choice of engines, either 997 c.c. or 1,198 c.c., and a practical station wagon version.

CLOSE-UP

Four-cyl.; o.h.v.; 80.96 × 48.41 mm.; 997 c.c.; 37 b.h.p.; 8.9 to 1 comp.; Super: 80.96 × 58.17 mm.; 1,198 c.c.; 48 b.h.p.; 8.7 to 1 comp.; Solex carb.; 4-speed, 16.99, 9.88, 5.83, 4.125 to 1; Super: 14.61, 9.88, 5.83, 4.125 to 1; cen. lvr.; susp., f. ind. coil, r. half-elliptic; 2-door; 4-seat; hyd. brks.; max. 75 m.p.h.; cruise 65; Super: 80 and 70; m.p.g. 35-40; whl. base 7ft. 6½in.; track, f. 3ft. 10in., r. 3ft. 9¾in.; lgth. 12ft. 10in.; width 4ft. 9½in.; ht. 4ft. 9½in.; g.c. 6½in.; turng. cir. 32ft.; kerb wt. 15 cwt.; Super: 15¼ cwt.; tank 7 gals.; 12-volt.

Anglia: £410+£94 p.t. = £504
Super 1200: £500+£115 p.t. = £615

FORD CORSAIR GT

V4 engine of 2-litres gives power in reserve in the hottest version of the Corsair, which is available as saloon or estate car. Instruments include tachometer, oil pressure gauge, engine thermometer. Note the bucket front seats, Aeroflow ventilation, pile carpets and centre console. Fold-away rear seat on the estate car releases 60 cubic feet of carrying capacity and the lift-up tail panel is counterbalanced.

CLOSE-UP

Four-cyl.; o.h.v.; 93.7 × 72.4 mm.; 1,996 c.c.; 88 b.h.p.; 8.9 to 1 comp.; Zenith carb.; 4-speed, 13.38, 9.05, 5.33, 3.78 to 1; cen. lvr.; susp., f. ind. coil, r. half-elliptic; 4-door; 5-seat; hyd. servo brks., disc front; max. 95 m.p.h.; cruise 85; m.p.g. 23-26; whl. base 8ft. 5in.; track, f. 4ft. 2½in., r. 4ft. 1½in.; lgth. 14ft. 8⅜in.; width 5ft. 3¼in.; ht. 4ft. 9in.; g.c. 6¼in.; turng. cir. 35ft. 9in.; kerb wt. 19½ cwt.; tank 10 gals.; 12-volt.

£755+£173 p.t. = £928

FORD CORTINA

RADICALLY different styling brings Ford's major money-spinner into line with the new Zephyrs and Zodiacs. More power boosts performance and flexibility, improved brakes and suspension extend safety margins and enhance the comfort. Detail design and equipment reveals the activity of Ford's new safety engineering section. One of the show's most important newcomers, it will appear with many variations in home and export markets.

CLOSE-UP

Four-cyl.; o.h.v.; 63 × 80.9 mm.; 1,300 c.c.; 53.5 b.h.p.; 9 to 1 comp.; Ford carb.; 4-speed, 14.61, 9.88, 5.82, 4.12 to 1; cen. lvr.; susp. f. ind. coil, r. half-elliptic; 2 or 4-door; 4-seat; hyd. brks., disc front; max. 75 m.p.h.; cruise, 65; m.p.g. 34-37; whl. base 8ft. 2¼in.; track f. 4ft. 4¼in.; r. 4ft. 3in.; lgth. 14ft.; width 5ft. 4⅞in.; ht. 4ft. 6¼in.; g.c. 6¼in.; turng. cir., 30ft.; kerb wt. 17 cwt.; tank 10 gals.; 12-volt.

Abbreviations—g.c.—ground clearance; susp.—suspension; f.—front; r.—rear; comp.—compression; s.v.—side-valves; o.h.v.—overhead valves; o.h.c.—overhead camshaft; hyd.—hydraulic.

FORD ZEPHYR FOUR

LONGER, wider, higher, more powerful than the Mark III, Ford's big four-cylinder has a compact V-type instead of an in-line engine. It's the economical one of the new big cars, but OK for fast cruising, with power for safe overtaking. Servo-assisted disc brakes are self adjusting. Automatic choke and crankcase emission control are standard, to eliminate engine oil-fumes and keep engine compartment clean.

CLOSE-UP

Four-cyl.; o.h.v.; 93.7 × 72.4 mm.; 1,996 c.c.; 88 b.h.p.; 8.9 to 1 comp.; Zenith carb.; 4-speed, 16.32, 8.71, 5.57, 3.7 to 1.; col. lvr.; susp., f. and r. ind. coil; 4-door; 5/6-seat; disc servo brks.; max. 88 m.p.h.; cruise 74; m.p.g. 23-26; whl. base 9ft. 7in.; track f. 4ft. 9in.; r. 4ft. 10in.; lgth. 15ft. 5in.; width, 5ft. 11¼in.; ht. 4ft. 10½in.; g.c. 6in.; turng. circ. 36ft.; kerb wt. 24¼ cwt.; tank 15 gals.; 12-volt.

£772 + £177 p.t. = £949

FORD ZEPHYR SIX

THREE years' development went into this hefty new Ford with Britain's first V6 engine. Spare wheel in front of engine leaves extra luggage space in rear. Choice of transmissions, with four-speed all-synchromesh manual, overdrive or automatic. Front suspension has MacPherson-type struts with stabiliser bar. Rear suspension is new-style independent with swinging-link wishbones. Safety features include anchorages for inertia-reel harness.

CLOSE-UP

Six-cyl.; o.h.v.; 93.7 × 60.3 mm.; 2,495 c.c.; 112 b.h.p.; 9 to 1 comp.; Zenith carb.; 4-speed, 12.33, 8.63, 5.51, 3.9 to 1.; col. lvr. cen. opt.; L de N overdrive or Ford auto. opt.; susp., f. and r. ind. coil; 4-door; 5/6-seat; disc servo brks.; max. 96 m.p.h.; cruise, 85; m.p.g. 18-25; whl. base 9ft. 7in.; track f. 4ft. 9in.; r. 4ft. 10 lgth. 15ft. 5in.; width 5ft. 11¼in.; ht. 4ft. 10½in.; g.c. 6in.; turng. circ. 38ft. 8in.; kerb wt. 25¾ cwt.; tank 15 gals.; 12-volt.

£832 + £191 p.t. = £1,023

FORD ZODIAC

RISE-AND-FALL steering column, adjustable backrests, clash-proof pre-engaged starter, sealed-for-life chassis bearings are offered on Dagenham's plushiest Ford. Twin-choke carburetter and bowl-in-piston combustion chambers appear on a V6 engine bigger than the Zephyr's. There are four headlamps, electric windscreen washers and a high-charge alternator. Choice of 13 acrylic enamel body colours. Self-adjusting servo brakes, nylon speed tyres.

CLOSE-UP

Six-cyl.; o.h.v.; 93.6 × 72.4 mm.; 2,994 c.c.; 128 b.h.p.; 8.9 to 1 comp.; Weber 2-choke carb.; 4-speed, 11.7, 8.19, 5.22, 3.7 to 1; cen. lvr., Laycock overdrive or Ford auto. opt.; susp. f. and r. ind. coil; 4-door; 5-6-seat; disc servo brks.; max. 102 m.p.h.; cruise 88; m.p.g. 17-24; whl. base 9ft. 7in.; track f. 4ft. 9in.; r. 4ft. 10in.; lgth. 15ft. 6in. width 5ft. 11¼in.; ht. 4ft. 10½in.; g.c. 6in.; turng. circ. 38ft. 8in.; kerb wt. 25⅞ cwt.; tank 15 gals.; 12-volt.

£1,010 + £231 p.t. = £1,241

FORD TAUNUS 15M

NOW available with right-hand driving position, Germany's front-wheel-drive Ford is based on the Cardinal, designed in Detroit but never produced there. V4 engine, transverse leaf spring front suspension and recirculating-ball steering are bolted unconventionally together. Automatic choke, heater, laminated windscreen are standard. Body styles include two-door and four-door saloons, coupe and station wagon, with 1.3 or 1.5-litre engines.

CLOSE-UP

Four-cyl.; o.h.v.; 90 × 58.8 mm.; 1,498 c.c.; 50 b.h.p.; 8 to 1 comp.; Solex carb. 4-speed, 12.14, 8.29, 5.26, 3.56 to 1.; col. lvr.; susp., f. ind. transv. leaf, r. half-elliptic; 2 or 4-door; 4/5-seat; disc front; hyd. brks., disc front; max. 80 m.p.h.; cruise 68; m.p.g. 33-36; whl. base, 8ft. 3½in.; track f. and r. 4ft.; lgth. 14ft. 2in.; width 5ft. 3¼in.; ht. 4ft. 6½in.; g.c. 6⅛in.; turng. circ. 37ft. 9in.; kerb wt. 17½ cwt.; tank, 8⅞ gals.; 6-volt.

Abbreviations—g.c.—ground clearance; susp.—suspension; f.—front; r.—rear; comp.—compression; s.v.—side-valves; o.h.v.—overhead valves; o.h.c.—overhead camshaft; hyd.—hydraulic.

FORD MUSTANG

HISTORY was made when this family sporting car toppled popular saloons in America's top-seller lists. Now the imitators are pouring in, but the original is further developed for 1967. Choice of two engines; straight six or V8 in a variety of sizes and powers up to the lightweight 370 h.p. Shelby racer. Disc front brakes optional on V8. Available as 2-door hardtop or cabriolet.

CLOSE-UP
Eight-cyl.; o.h.v.; 101.6×72.9 mm.; 4,728 c.c.; 200 b.h.p. gross; 9.2 to 1 comp.; Ford 2-choke carb.; 3-speed, 7.8, 4.7, 2.8 to 1; cen. lvr., four-speed or auto. opt.; susp., f. ind. coil, r. half-elliptic; 2-door; 4-seat; hyd. brks., servo and disc opt.; max. 118 m.p.h.; cruise 98; m.p.g. 14-17; whl. base 9ft.; track f. and r. 4ft. 8in.; lgth. 15ft. 1½in.; width 5ft. 8½in.; ht. 4ft. 3in.; g.c. 6in.; turng. cir. 40ft.; kerb wt. 25½ cwt.; tank 16 gals.; 12-volt.

£1,883+£433 p.t. = £2,316

FORD G.T.

SPACE capsule on wheels with the prestige of a Le Mans win. It was the 200 m.p.h. 7-litre version that won, but the production 4.7-litre runs up to 150 or so. Getting in is quite a trick. Luggage space is limited to two biscuit boxes in the engine compartment, but you don't buy this sort of car to take auntie out to tea.

CLOSE-UP
Eight-cyl.; o.h.v.; 101.6×72.9 mm.; 4,736 c.c.; 380 b.h.p. gross; 10 to 1 comp.; 4 Weber carbs.; 5-speed, 10.21, 6.20, 4.60, 4.05, 3.59 to 1; cen. lvr.; susp. f. and r. ind. coil; 2-door; 2-seat; disc brks.; max. 160 m.p.h.; cruise 130; m.p.g. 11-13; whl. base 7ft. 11in.; track f. and r. 4ft. 7in.; lgth. 13ft. 4in.; width 5ft. 10in.; ht. 3ft. 4½in.; g.c. 4in.; kerb wt. 17⅞ cwt.; tank 30 gals.; 12-volt.

£5,500+£1,262 p.t. = £6,762

GILBERN

SPORTS Coupe from the Land of Song. Well finished and Welsh, the Gilbern has a glass fibre body on steel tube semi-space frame. Wishbones and coil springs for front suspension; rigid rear axle with radius arms, coil springs and Panhard rod. Disc front brakes. Choice of two engines; MGB 1.8-litre or Ford V4 2-litre. Available as complete car or kit for tax-free assembly.

CLOSE-UP
Four-cyl.; o.h.v.; 80.26×88.9 mm.; 1,798 c.c.; 95 b.h.p. gross; 8.9 to 1 comp.; 2 S.U. carbs.; 4-speed, 14.21, 8.66, 5.37, 3.91 to 1; cen. lvr., de Normanville overdrive opt.; susp., f. ind. coil, r. coil; 2-door; 2/4-seat; hyd. brks.; disc front; max. 104 m.p.h.; cruise 90; m.p.g. 24-30; whl. base 7ft. 8in.; track f. and r. 4ft. 1½in.; lgth. 12ft. 10½in.; width 5ft. 0¾in.; ht. 4ft. 5¼in.; g.c. 6in.; turng. cir. 30ft. 6in.; kerb wt. 17⅛ cwt.; tank 9¼ gals.; 12-volt.

£1,115+£255 p.t. = £1,370

HILLMAN IMP DE LUXE

AS the original Imp with its simple trim faded away, faster, more luxurious versions have proliferated. Imp de luxe, Super Imp and Chamois. Now comes the Sports Chamois and the Sunbeam Imp with 51 b.h.p. engines and servo brakes. For competition drivers there's the made-to-order Rally Imp with twin carburetter engine of 998 c.c. producing 60 b.h.p., bigger brakes, servo operated, and option of a larger fuel tank.

CLOSE-UP
Four-cyl.; o.h.c.; 68×60.4 mm.; 875 c.c.; 39 b.h.p.; 10 to 1 comp.; Solex carb.; 4-speed, 16.59, 8.91, 5.70, 4.14 to 1; cen. lvr.; susp., f. and r. ind. coil; 2-door; 4-seat; hyd. brks.; max. 80 m.p.h.; cruise 75; m.p.g. 40; whl. base 6ft. 10in.; track, f. 4ft. 1½in., r. 4ft. 0½in.; lgth. 11ft. 9in.; width 5ft. 0½in.; ht. 4ft. 6½in.; g.c. 6¼in.; turng. cir. 30ft. 6in.; kerb wt. 14¼ cwt.; tank 6 gals.; 12-volt.

£445+£104 p.t. = £549

Abbreviations—g.c.—ground clearance; susp.—suspension; f.—front; r.—rear; comp.—compression; s.v.—side-valves; o.h.v.—overhead valves; o.h.c.—overhead camshaft; hyd.—hydraulic.

HILLMAN MINX DE LUXE

ONE of the lowest-priced cars in Britain to offer the extra urge of an over-1700 c.c. engine. Another driver gimmick is an optional luxury of Borg-Warner fully automatic transmission. Suitable for the family man or business man who leaves his car at home for his wife to drive. Many rate the Minx de Luxe as the best car in the Rootes range

CLOSE-UP

Four-cyl.; o.h.v.; 81.5×82.5 mm.; 1,725 c.c.; 58 b.h.p.; 8.4 to 1 comp.; Zenith carb.; 4-speed, 13.04, 8.32, 5.41, 3.89 to 1; cen. lvr.; susp.; f. ind. coil, r. half-elliptic; 4-door; 4/5-seat; hyd brks., disc front; max. 84 m.p.h.; cruise 75; m.p.g. 29-34; whl. base 8ft. 5in.; track f. 4ft. 3¾in., r. 4ft. 0½in.; lgth. 13ft. 10½in.; width 5ft. 3¾in.; ht. 4ft. 10in.; g.c. 5½in.; turng. circ. 36 ft.; kerb wt. 21 cwt.; tank 10½ gals.; 12-volt.

£545 + £115 p.t. = £660

HILLMAN HUNTER

SPRIGHTLY successor to the Super Minx. Paring off pounds with no loss of strength, the new body structure permits a higher power to weight ratio and higher gearing which brings dividends in low fuel consumption and effortless high speed cruising. Strut-type front suspension and disc front brakes. Semi-elliptic rear suspension. Canted-over engine with new head and manifolds. New safety interior with minimum projections.

CLOSE-UP

Four-cyl.; o.h.v.; 81.5×82.5 mm.; 1,725 c.c.; 80 b.h.p.; 9.2 to 1 comp.; Stromberg carb.; 4-speed, 12.41, 7.92, 5.15, 3.7 to 1; cen. lvr.; susp., f. ind coil, r. half-elliptic; 4-door; 4/5-seat; hyd. brks., disc front; max. 88 m.p.h.; cruise 75; m.p.g. 28-34; whl. base 8ft. 2½in.; track, f. and r. 4ft. 4in.; lgth. 14ft. 1½in.; width 5ft. 3½in.; ht. 4ft. 8in.; g.c. 6¾in.; turng. cir. 33ft. 6in.; kerb wt. 17½ cwt.; tank 10 gals.; 12-volt.

HINO CONTESSA 1300

JAPANESE countess with strong Italian accent. Michelotti did the styling for this smart, compact four-door saloon which has rear engine, all-synchromesh four speed gearbox. Also seen in its two-door coupe form with twin-carburetter engine tuned to give 65 b.h.p. It's not surprising that Hino's mechanical layout recalls rear-engined Renaults. They used to make them under licence. But the design is strictly Hino's own.

CLOSE-UP

Four-cyl.; o.h.v.; 71×79 mm.; 1,251 c.c.; 55 b.h.p.; 8.5 to 1 comp.; Hitachi twin-choke carb.; 3-speed, 14.17, 7.68, 4.27 to 1; cen. lvr., 4-speed opt.; susp., f. ind. torsion bar, r. ind. coil; 4-door; 4-seat; hyd. brks.; max. 80 m.p.h.; cruise 65; m.p.g. 33; whl. base 7ft. 5⅜in.; track, f. 4ft. 0⅝in., r. 4ft.; lgth. 13ft. 7⅞in.; width 5ft. 0¼in.; ht. 4ft. 6¾in.; g.c. 6¾in.; turng. cir. 30ft. 2in.; kerb wt. 18¼ cwt.; tank 7 gals.; 12-volt.

HONDA

WORLD famous for race winning motorcycles, Honda now invades the car market with small sports cars of highly individual design. Inclined twin-cam four-carburetter engine in light alloy at front. Final drive to rear wheels by rigid axle on coil springs with radius arms and Panhard rod. Coupe and convertible bodies with neat, clean lines. Space behind the front seats for children or luggage.

CLOSE-UP

Four-cyl.; o.h.c.; 60×70 mm.; 791 c.c.; 70 b.h.p.; 9.2 to 1 comp.; Two 2-choke Keihin carbs.; 4-speeds, 18.86, 11.69, 7.60, 5.39 to 1; cen. lvr.; susp. f. ind. torsion bar, r. coil; 2-door; 2-seat; hyd brks., disc front; max. 100 m.p.h.; cruise 84; m.p.g. 34-38; whl. base, 6ft. 7in.; track f. 3ft., 9½in. r. 3ft. 8¾in.; lgth. 10ft 11¼in.; width. 4ft. 7¼in.; ht. 3ft 11¾in.; g.c. 6¼in.; turng. cir. 30 ft 2in.; kerb wt. 14 cwt.; tank 7¾ gals.; 12-volt.

Abbreviations—g.c.—ground clearance; susp.—suspension; f.—front; r.—rear; comp.—compression; s.v.—side-valves; o.h.v.—overhead valves; o.h.c.—overhead camshaft; hyd.—hydraulic.

HUMBER HAWK

FAMILY men and business men in the better-off income brackets go for this outstanding product from the Rootes Group. It has good traditional looks, lush comfort inside and on the road it motors quietly and smoothly. Plenty of room for the family, good luggage space and absolute reliability are bull points for this car which continues to sell well in many markets.

CLOSE-UP
Four-cyl.; o.h.v.; 81×110 mm.; 2,267 c.c.; 73 b.h.p.; 7.5 to 1 comp.; Zenith carb.; 4-speed, 14.13, 9.04, 5.88, 4.22 to 1; de Normanville overdrive or auto opt.; col. lvr.; susp., f. ind. coil, r. half-elliptic; 4-door; 6-seat; servo brks., disc front; max. 85 m.p.h.; cruise 70-75; m.p.g. 20-25; whl. base 9ft. 2in.; track, f. 4ft. 9in., r. 4ft. 7½in.; lgth. 15ft. 4¾in.; width 5ft. 9½in.; ht. 4ft. 11½in.; g.c. 7in.; turng. cir. 38ft.; kerb wt. 28¾ cwt.; tank 16 gals.; 12-volt.

£960+£222 p.t. = £1,182

HUMBER IMPERIAL

ONE of the most expensively equipped cars in the wide Rootes range, the Imperial supplies a host of luxuries both for driver and passengers at a very reasonable cost. For the driver there is power-assisted steering, power-assisted brakes (discs in front), adjustable rear dampers and automatic transmission. For the passengers: occasional tables, cigar lighters in armrests, reading lamps, speakers at front and rear—the lot.

CLOSE-UP
Six-cyl.; o.h.v.; 87.3×82.6 mm.; 2,965 c.c.; 128 b.h.p.; 8 to 1 comp.; 2 Zenith carbs.; 3-speed auto., 9.75, 6.04, 4.22 to 1; col. lvr.; susp., f. ind. coil, r. half-elliptic; 4-door; 5/6-seat; hyd. servo brks., disc front; max. 100 m.p.h.; cruise 90; m.p.g. 16-20; whl. base 9ft. 2in.; track f. 4ft. 8¾in., r. 4ft. 7½in.; lgth. 15ft. 7½in.; width 5ft. 10¼in.; ht. 5ft.; g.c. 7in.; turng. cir. 39ft.; kerb wt. 32¾ cwt.; tank 16 gals.; 12-volt.

£1,565+£361 p.t. = £1,926

ISO GRIFO GL 365

SUPERB 160 m.p.h. Grand Touring two-seater with docile 365 h.p. Corvette V8 engine in an Italian chassis clad in shapely steel by Bertone. Cast alloy wheels and limited slip differential are standard. Centre console carries controls for two-speed wipers and washer, rear window demister, electric window winders. A car that overtakes quick as thought and hits the hundred from rest in just over 16 seconds.

CLOSE-UP
Eight-cyl.; o.h.v.; 101.6×82.6 mm.; 5,359 c.c.; 365 b.h.p. gross; 11 to 1 comp.; four-choke Holley carb.; 4-speed, 7.79, 5.89, 4.63, 3.07 to 1; cen. lvr.; susp., f. ind. coil, r. De Dion coil; 2-door; 2-seat; disc servo brks.; max. 160 m.p.h.; cruise, 130; m.p.g. 14-17; whl. base, 8ft. 2½in.; track f. and r. 4ft. 7½in.; lgth., 14ft 6¾in.; width 5 ft. 9½in.; ht. 3ft. 11in.; g.c. 4½in.; turng. cir., 41ft.; kerb wt. 28⅜ cwt.; tank 22 gals.; 12-volt.

£4,917+£1,136 p.t. = £6,053

JAGUAR 2.4 LITRE MARK 2

THIS speedy, sporty saloon continues to be one of the most popular on the road. It appeals specially to the motorist who wants a lot of motor car for his money, coupled with efficient design and robust performance. With the Jag. 2.4 model he gets all this, and something more—a smooth, sure ride. Latest model, minus fog lamps, and with high grade synthetic upholstery instead of leather, scores the year's most dramatic price reduction.

CLOSE-UP
Six-cyl.; o.h.c.; 83×76.5 mm.; 2,483 c.c.; 120 b.h.p. gross; 8 to 1 comp.; 2 Solex carbs.; 4-speed, 14.42, 7.94, 5.48, 4.27 to 1; cen. lvr., de Normanville overdrive or BW auto. opt.; susp., f. ind. coil, r. cantilever leaf; 4-door; 5-seat; servo disc brks.; max. 105 m.p.h.; cruise 75-80; m.p.g. 23; whl. base 8ft. 11⅜in.; track, f. 4ft. 7in., r. 4ft. 5⅜in.; lgth 15ft. 0¾in.; width 5ft. 6¾in.; ht. 4ft. 9½in.; g.c. 7in.; turng. cir. 33ft. 6in.; kerb wt. 28½ cwt.; tank 12 gals.; 12-volt.

£1,090+£251 p.t. = £1,341

Abbreviations—g.c.—ground clearance; susp.—suspension; f.—front; r.—rear; comp.—compression; s.v.—side-valves; o.h.v.—overhead valves; o.h.c.—overhead camshaft; hyd.—hydraulic.

75

JAGUAR 420

SUCCESSOR to the S-type, re-styled inside and out. Step-up from 3.8 to 4.2 litres boosts power and flexibility on a car that was already mighty fast. Other improvements add to the pleasures of gracious living, Jaguar-style amid finest leather, quality carpets, polished veneers. Roadholding and riding comfort among the best there are. Still more powerful disc brakes give confidence. Power steering is improved.

CLOSE-UP

Six-cyl.; o.h.c.; 92.1×106 mm.; 4,235 c.c.; 255 b.h.p. gross; 8 to 1 comp.; 2 S.U. carbs.; 4-speed, 10.76, 6.98, 4.7, 3.54 to 1; cen. lvr.; susp. f. and r. ind. coil; 4-door; 5-seat; disc servo brks.; max. 120 m.p.h; cruise 100; m.p.g. 16-19; whl. base 8ft. 11⅜in.; track f. 4ft. 7¼in., r. 4ft. 6¼in.; lgth. 15 ft. 7¾in.; width 5 ft. 6¾in.; ht. 4ft. 6½in.; g.c. 7in.; turng. cir. 39ft.; kerb wt. 32⅝ cwt.; tank, 14 gals.; 12-volt.

£1,569 + £361 p.t. = £1,930

JAGUAR E-TYPE 2+2

NO need to send the children to boarding kennels; take them with you on high-speed holidays in the new family 2+2 E-Type. Higher roof line, wider doors, extra elbow room, and ample legroom for tall drivers make it a more convenient car all round. Interior is revised with lockable glove box, full width parcel shelf and Borg Warner automatic transmission is a new option. Two-seater still available for the fancy free.

CLOSE-UP

Six-cyl.; o.h.c.; 92.1×106 mm.; 4,235 c.c.; 265 b.h.p. gross; 9 to 1 comp.; 3 S.U. carbs.; 4-speed, 9.33, 7.29, 4.08, 3.07 to 1; cen. lvr., auto. opt.; susp. f. torsion bar, r. ind. coil; 2-door; 2-4-seat; disc servo brks.; max. 140 m.p.h.; cruise, 115; m.p.g. 18-20; whl. base 8ft. 9in.; track f. and r.4ft. 2in.; lgth. 15ft. 4¾in.; width 5ft. 5¼in.; ht. 4ft. 2⅛in.; g.c. 5in.; turng. cir. 41ft.; kerb wt. 27¾ cwt.; tank 14 gals.; 12-volt.

£1,857 + £427 p.t. = £2,284

JAGUAR 420 G

CHANGES both inside and out are made to this spacious and elegant car. Externally: a revised and bolder radiator grille, and a chromium flash down each side. Interior additions include a padded screen rail above the instrument panel; the instrument panel is now inset in a padded surround; the clock is better positioned to be read by passengers; and the two front seats are given greater lateral stability.

CLOSE-UP

Six-cyl.; o.h.c.; 92×106 mm.; 4,235 c.c.; 255 b.h.p. gross; 8 to 1 comp.; 3 S.U. carbs.; 4-speed 10.76, 6.98, 4.70, 3.54 to 1; cen. lvr.; overdrive or BW auto. opt.; susp. f. and r. ind. coil; 4-door; 5-seat; disc servo brks.; max. 120 m.p.h.; cruise 100; m.p.g. 15-20; whl. base 10ft.; track f. and r. 4ft. 10in.; lgth. 16ft. 10in.; width 6ft. 4¼in.; ht. 4ft. 6½in.; g.c. 5½in.; turng. cir. 38ft. 8in.; kerb wt. 37¼ cwt.; tank 20 gals.; 12-volt.

£1,819 + £419 p.t. = £2,238

JENSEN FF

GONE is the barnacle-encrusted styling of the past. Jensen's revolutionary four-wheel-drive car now has uncluttered lines to match its advanced technical conception and bodies are in steel instead of glass fibre. Inherent safety of the Ferguson four-wheel-drive system is matched by the Maxaret braking control to give maximum stopping power on slippery roads without fear of locking wheels and skidding.

CLOSE-UP

Eight-cyl.; o.h.v.; 108×86 mm.; 6,276 c.c.; 330 b.h.p.; 10 to 1 comp.; Carter 4-choke carb.; 3-speed auto., 7.5, 4.44, 3.07 to 1; col. lvr.; susp. f. ind. coil, r. half-elliptic; 2-door; 4-seat; disc servo brks. with Maxaret; max. 130 m.p.h.; cruise 110; m.p.g. 15-17; whl. base 9ft. 1in.; track f. and r. 4ft. 8½in.; lgth. 15ft. 1in.; width 5ft. 7½in.; ht. 4ft. 7in.; g.c. 5in.; turng. cir. 39ft.; kerb wt. 34 cwt.; tank 16 gals.; 12-volt.

£4,343 + £996 p.t. = £5,339

JENSEN INTERCEPTOR

FROM prototype convertible to production coupe the Interceptor has changed considerably; bigger engine, revised body lines, automatic transmission instead of manual gearbox, normal rear axle instead of de Dion. Power in plenty comes from the 6.3-litre Chrysler V8 engine, the disc brakes are servo-assisted and shock absorbers are driver-controlled. With modern body lines allied to terrific performance, Jensen should reap its reward in exports.

CLOSE-UP

Eight-cyl.; o.h.v.; 108×86 mm.; 6,276 c.c.; 330 b.h.p.; 10 to 1 comp.; Carter 4-choke carb.; 3-speed auto.; 7.5, 4.44, 3.07 to 1; col. lvr.; susp., f. ind. coil, r. half-elliptic; 2-door; 4-seat; disc servo brks.; max. 132 m.p.h.; cruise 110; m.p.g. 15-18; whl. base 8ft. 9in.; track f. 4ft. 7⅞in., r. 4ft. 8⅞in.; lgth. 15 ft. 9in.; width 5ft. 9in.; ht. 4ft. 5in.; g.c. 5½in.; turng. cir. 38ft.; kerb wt. 31¼ cwt.; tank 16 gals.; 12-volt.

£3,043 + £699 p.t. = £3,742

LAMBORGHINI 400 GT

THE driving you dream about, from a millionaire manufacturer already successful in tractors and central heating. His superb V-12 engine has four overhead camshafts. First model was the 3.5-litre 3-seater, followed by the 4-litre 2+2, both bodied by Carrozzeria Touring. Now the fantastic 400 Miura is added with engine transversely mounted at the rear. The competition version has 425 h.p. Bodies for these are by Bertone.

CLOSE-UP

Twelve-cyl.; o.h.c.; 82×62 mm.; 3,930 c.c.; 325 b.h.p.; 9 to 1 comp.; 6 twin-choke Weber carbs.; 5-speed, 9.5, 6.54, 4.62, 3.77, 3.07 to 1; cen. lvr.; susp., f. and r. ind. coil; 2-door; 2/4-seat; disc servo brks.; max. 160 m.p.h.; cruise, 135; m.p.g. 14-17; whl. base, 8ft. 4¾in.; track f. and r. 4ft. 6⅜in.; lgth., 15ft. 2⅝in.; width 5ft. 7⅞in.; ht. 4ft. 2in.; g.c. 5in.; turng. cir. 37ft. 8in.; kerb wt. 25½ cwt.; tank 17 gals.; 12-volt.

LANCIA FLAMINIA COUPE

SIX years of production have confirmed the qualities of the largest Lancia with its front-mounted pioneer V6 engine, rear-mounted gearbox and de Dion axle. Among the body styles is the beautiful 140 h.p. Pininfarina coupe. Other models include the handsome four-door saloon, the 150 h.p. Superleggera coupe and convertible and the lightweight Zagato coupe with three twin-choke Weber carburetters.

CLOSE-UP

Six-cyl.; o.h.v.; 85×81.5 mm.; 2,775 c.c.; 139 b.h.p.; 9 to 1 comp.; Solex 3-choke carb.; 4-speed, 12.1, 8.1, 5.6, 3.9 to 1; cen. lvr.; susp., f. ind. coil, r. de Dion half-elliptic; 2-door; 4-seat; disc servo brks.; max. 112 m.p.h.; cruise 90; m.p.g. 24-26; whl. base 9ft.; track f. and r. 4ft. 5¾in.; lgth. 15ft. 4¼in.; width 5ft. 8½in.; ht. 4ft. 8in.; g.c. 5in.; turng. cir. 40ft.; kerb wt. 30¼ cwt.; tank 12¾ gals.; 12-volt.

£2,431 + £559 p.t. = £2,990

LANCIA FULVIA

CUTE and quick, the little Fulvia has canted-over V4 engine in light alloy, with overhead camshafts. Front-wheel drive, as on all Lancias designed by Dr. Fessia. Engine, transmission, suspension and steering are all carried on a sub frame. Equipment includes dipping mirror, vanity mirror, red warning lamps in rear door edges, grab handles, four headlamps. Coupes have 1,216 c.c. engines giving 80 or 88 h.p.

CLOSE-UP

Four-cyl.; o.h.c.; 72×67 mm.; 1,091 c.c.; 58 b.h.p.; 7.8 to 1 comp.; Solex carb.; 4-speed, 21.18, 12.16, 7.36, 4.78 to 1; cen. lvr.; susp., f. ind. trans. leaf, r. half-elliptic; 4-door; 4-seat; disc brks.; max. 85 m.p.h.; cruise 75; m.p.g. 28-34; whl. base 8ft. 1½in.; track, f. 4ft. 3¼in., r. 4ft. 2½in.; lgth. 13ft. 7in.; width 5ft. 1¼in.; ht. 4ft. 7in.; g.c. 5in.; turng. cir. 37ft.; kerb wt. 19½ cwt.; tank 8⅓ gals.; 12-volt.

£1,140 + £263 p.t. = £1,403

Abbreviations—g.c.—ground clearance; susp.—suspension; f.—front; r.—rear; comp.—compression; s.v.—side-valves; o.h.v.—overhead valves; o.h.c.—overhead camshaft; hyd.—hydraulic.

LANCIA FLAVIA

VIGNALE makes the body for the elegant short-wheelbase convertible, but Flavias come in many styles. There's a Pininfarina coupe, a Zagato Supersport and of course the four-door Berlina. The Zagato is a Coupe des Alpes winner. Lancia now offer petrol injection on the 1.8-litre flat-four light alloy engine which drives the front wheels. Electric clock, powerful ventilation and heating system, rear window defroster are included.

CLOSE-UP

Four-cyl.; o.h.v.; 88×74 mm.; 1,800 c.c.; 92 b.h.p.; 9 to 1 comp.; Solex carb.; 4-speed, 13.65, 8.08, 5.7, 4.1 to 1; col. lvr.; susp., f. ind. trans. leaf, r. half-elliptic; 2/4-door; 5-seat; disc servo brks.; max. 102 m.p.h.; cruise 85; m.p.g. 26-32; whl. base 8ft. 8½in.; track f. 4ft. 3½in., r. 4ft. 2⅜in.; lgth. 15ft. 0½in.; width 5ft. 3½in.; ht. 4ft. 11in.; g.c. 5in.; turng. cir. 36ft.; kerb wt. 24 cwt.; tank 10½ gals.; 12-volt.

£1,402+£323 p.t. = £1,725

LOTUS ELAN S2

ROAD car with racing car road-holding, in coupe or convertible form. Redesign of the convertible has brought more comfort and greater luggage space. Doors now have electrically controlled windows operating in fixed frames and hood stowage is neater. Other changes mean extra strength in the body, reduced maintenance. Body is in glass fibre on a backbone chassis with all-independent suspension.

CLOSE-UP

Four-cyl.; o.h.c.; 82.6×72.75 mm.; 1,558 c.c.; 105 b.h.p.; 9.5 to 1 comp.; 2 twin-choke Weber carbs.; 4-speed 9.76, 6.4, 4.8, 3.9 to 1; cen. lvr.; susp. f. and r. ind. coil; 2-door; 2/3-seat; disc brks.; max. 125 m.p.h.; cruise 100; m.p.g. 30; whl. base 7ft.; track f. and r. 3ft. 11in.; lgth. 12ft. 1½in.; width 4ft. 8in.; ht. 3ft. 5in.; g.c. 6in.; turng. cir. 31ft.; kerb wt. 13¼ cwt.; tank 10 gals.; 12-volt.

£1,262+£290 p.t. = £1,552

MARCOS 1800 L

FROM the splinter group in Bradford-on-Avon, a wooden chassis and plastic body make the light, lithe Marcos unique. The Volvo engine is modified with twin Stromberg carburetters. Choose between 1800 L with live rear axle and 1800 IRS with independent rear suspension. Body lines were recently improved and refined with rear spoiler, bonnet vents, ventilated rear window. Equipment includes overdrive and Pirelli Cinturato tyres.

CLOSE-UP

Four-cyl.; o.h.v.; 84×80 mm.; 1,778 c.c.; 114 b.h.p. gross; 10 to 1 comp.; 2 Stromberg carbs.; 4-speed; 12.24, 7.78, 5.32, 3.91 to 1; cen. lvr., de Normanville overdrive opt.; susp., f. ind. coil, r. half-elliptic; 2-door; 2-seat; hyd. brks., disc front; max. 115 m.p.h.; cruise 95; m.p.g. 22-30; whl. base 7ft. 5½in.; track, f. 4ft. 0¾in., r. 4ft. 3in.; lgth. 13ft. 4¼in.; width 5ft. 2½in.; ht. 3ft. 6½in.; g.c. 4¼in.; turng. cir. 29ft. 6in.; kerb wt. 18¾ cwt.; tank 12 gals.; 12-volt.

£1,310+£301 p.t. = £1,611

MASERATI MISTRALE

MILLIONAIRE motoring by Maserati. Six-cylinder speedsters with convertible or coupe coachwork by Italy's top names. Twin-cam engine has Lucas fuel injection and comes in three sizes; 3.5-litre 235 h.p., 3.7-litre 245 h.p. and 4-litre 255 h.p. The 5-speed gearbox is naturally all-synchromesh. Sebring coupe has electrically operated windows. Automatic transmission can be fitted to all cars and convertible has a snug hard top as option.

CLOSE-UP

Six-cyl.; o.h.c.; 86×106 mm.; 3,692 c.c.; 240 b.h.p.; 8.8 to 1 comp.; Lucas injection; 5-speed, 11.38, 6.97, 4.86, 3.77, 3.2 to 1; cen. lvr.; susp., f. ind. coil, r. half-elliptic; 2-door; 2-seat; disc servo brks.; max. 155 m.p.h.; cruise 130; m.p.g. 17-20; whl. base 7ft. 10½in.; track, f. 4ft. 6½in., r. 4ft. 5⅜in.; lgth. 14ft. 7in.; width 5ft. 5⅜in.; ht. 4ft. 2in.; g.c. 5⅛in.; turng. cir. 38ft.; kerb wt. 25 cwt.; tank 16 gals.; 12-volt.

£4,705+£1,079 p.t. = £5,784

Abbreviations—g.c.—ground clearance; susp.—suspension; f.—front; r.—rear; comp.—compression; s.v.—side-valves; o.h.v.—overhead valves; o.h.c.—overhead camshaft; hyd.—hydraulic.

MASERATI V8 QUATTROPORTE

MAGNIFICENTLY maintaining the traditions of the Trident, this fast but roomy luxury model, with V8 four-camshaft engine and five-speed gearbox shows several changes for 1967. Twin pairs of circular headlamps replace the rectangular ones, permitting use of super-power iodine vapour projectors. Air conditioning is now provided and air ducts along the centre tunnel supply the rear compartment. Interior trim is revised, with mahogany facia.

CLOSE-UP
Eight-cyl.; o.h.c.; 88×85 mm.; 4,136 c.c.; 255 b.h.p.; 8.5 to 1 comp.; 4 Weber carbs.; 5-speed, 9.66, 6.22, 4.35, 3.54, 3.0 to 1; cen. lvr.; BW auto. opt.; susp., f. ind. coil, r. de Dion coil; 4-door; 5-seat; disc servo brks.; max. 143 m.p.h.; cruise 110; m.p.g. 17-18; whl. base 8ft. 10½in.; track, f. 4ft. 6¾in. r. 4ft. 7¹⁄₁₆in.; lgth. 16ft. 5in.; width 5ft. 6½in.; ht. 4ft. 5½in.; g.c. 7in.; turng. cir. 42ft. 9in.; kerb wt. 33½ cwt.; tank 20 gals.; 12-volt.

£4,953+£1,136 p.t. = £6,089

MERCEDES BENZ 230 SL

CYNOSURE of admiring eyes at any sporting get-together, the 230 SL embodies the essence of Daimler-Benz experience in fast car design. Fuel-injection light alloy engine, choice of manual or automatic transmission, and option of an outstanding power steering unit. Rear suspension has low-pivot swing axles with compensator spring. Two body styles, a beautifully equipped convertible roadster and the memorable coupe with the "pagoda" roof line.

CLOSE-UP
Six-cyl.; o.h.c.; 82×72 mm.; 2,306 c.c.; 150 b.h.p.; 9.3 to 1 comp.; Bosch injection; 4-speed, 16.57, 8.55, 5.32, 3.75 to 1; cen. lvr., auto. opt.; susp. f. and r. ind. coil; 2-door; 2-seat; hyd. servo brks., disc front; max. 125 m.p.h.; cruise 110; m.p.g. 20-24; whl. base 7ft. 10½in.; track, f. and r. 4ft. 10½in.; lgth. 14ft. 1½in.; width 5ft. 9¼in.; ht. 4ft. 3½in.; g.c. 5in.; turng. cir. 33ft. 4in.; kerb wt. 25½ cwt.; tank 14½ gals.; 12-volt.

£2,968+£682 p.t. = £3,650

MERCEDES BENZ 250 SE

FINLESS and faster, this fine car with the lower, sleeker silhouette has been an instant success. Compared with previous models power is up, the roof is flatter and lower but the windscreen is larger. Disc brakes are fitted all round with improved suspension using a hydro-pneumatic compensating spring on the rear swing axles which pumps itself up to compensate for extra heavy loads.

CLOSE-UP
Six-cyl.; o.h.c.; 82×78.8 mm.; 2,496 c.c.; 150 b.h.p.; 9.3 to 1 comp.; Bosch injection; 4-speed, 15.88, 8.74, 5.49, 3.92 to 1; cen. or col. lvr., auto opt.; susp. f. and r. ind. coil, hyd.-pneu. levelling; 4-door; 5-seat; disc servo brks.; max. 118 m.p.h.; cruise 100; m.p.g. 18-28; whl. base 9ft. 0½in.; track, f. 4ft. 10½in., r. 4ft. 10⅜in.; g.c. 6in.; turng. cir. 37ft.; kerb wt. 29½ cwt.; tank 18 gals.; 12-volt.

£2,480+£570 p.t. = £3,050

MERCEDES BENZ 300 SEL

SALIENT features of the fabulous 600 in a six-cylinder fuel-injection car of more convenient size and price. Automatic transmission, power steering, and self-levelling air suspension, central servo locking system for all doors, electrically heated rear window, electrically operated sliding roof. The safety steering wheel has a padded hub, instruments are in a shock absorbing safety frame, control knobs are in resilient material.

CLOSE-UP
Six-cyl.; o.h.c.; 85×88 mm.; 2,996 c.c.; 170 b.h.p.; 8.8 to 1 comp.; Bosch injection; 4-speed auto., 15.6, 9.87, 6.19, 3.92 to 1; col. lvr.; susp. f. and r. ind. pneu.; 4-door; 6-seat; disc servo brks.; max. 120 m.p.h.; cruise 100; m.p.g. 20-22; whl. base 9ft. 4½in.; track, f. 4ft. 10½in., r. 4ft. 10⅜in.; lgth. 16ft. 4⅞in.; width 5ft. 11¼in.; ht. 4ft. 7⅞in.; g.c. 6⅞in.; turng. cir. 39ft. 6in.; kerb wt. 33 cwt.; tank 18 gals.; 12-volt.

£4,690+£1,077 p.t. = £5,767

Abbreviations—g.c.—ground clearance; susp.—suspension; f.—front; r.—rear; comp.—compression; s.v.—side-valves; o.h.v.—overhead valves; o.h.c.—overhead camshaft; hyd.—hydraulic.

MERCEDES BENZ 600 PULLMAN

PRESS-BUTTON luxury in a twenty-foot lounge on wheels. Glass division and windows rise and fall at a touch. Servos lock doors, trunk and fuel filler. Other buttons set seat sliding, raise and lower it or change backrest angle. Rearward-facing chairs adjoin cocktail console containing radio with self-erecting aerial. Heater system maintains pre-set temperature by electronic control. Air-conditioning with refrigerator is available.

CLOSE-UP

Eight-cyl.; o.h.c.; 103.1×95 mm.; 6,329 c.c.; 245 b.h.p. 9.0 to 1 comp.; Bosch injection; 4-speed auto., 12.85, 8.14, 5.10, 3.23 to 1; col. lvr.; susp., f. and r. ind.: pneu.; 6-door; 7/8-seat; disc compressed air servo brks.; max. 125 m.p.h.; cruise 100; m.p.g. 18; whl. base 12ft. 9½in.; track f. 5ft. 2½in., r. 5ft. 2in.; lgth. 20ft. 6in.; width 6ft. 6¾in.; ht. 4ft. 11½in.; g.c. 8in.; turng. cir. 47ft. 9in.; kerb wt. 51¾ cwt.; tank 24½ gals.; 12-volt.

£8,270+£1,896 p.t. = £10,166

MERCURY COUGAR

MUSCLING in on the Mustang's phenomenal success, Ford's Mercury division offers a similar model with the 4.7-litre V8 engine as starting point in the power department. Where compact saloons withered under the aura of austerity these compact coupes and convertibles with the sporting lines are sweeping the States. Usual options, of course; automatic transmission, power-assisted brakes. Headlamps are covered when not in use.

CLOSE-UP

Eight-cyl.; o.h.v.; 101.6×72.89 mm.; 4,727 c.c.; 220 b.h.p. gross; 9 to 1 comp.; Ford 4-choke carb.; 3-speed 8.28, 5.07, 3 to 1; cen. lvr. 4-speed or auto. opt.; susp., f. ind. coil, r. half-elliptic; 2-door; 2/4-seat; hyd. servo brks.; max. 118 m.p.h.; cruise 90; m.p.g. 13-17; whl. base 9ft. 5in.; track f. and r. 4ft. 10in.; lgth. 15ft. 8⅝in.; width 5ft. 10¼in.; ht. 4ft. 4in.; g.c. 6in.; turng. cir. 40ft. 6in.; kerb wt. 25½ cwt.; tank 17 gals.; 12-volt.

MG 1100

THIS car is a sporting version of the brilliant series of 1100 c.c. models from the British Motor Corporation. It has the distinctive M.G. front and stepped-up power from the crosswise fitted front engine. At speed the car rides smoothly with the compensating Hydrolastic rubber-and-water suspension. Its popularity is gathering momentum, and for a very good reason.

CLOSE-UP

Four-cyl.; o.h.v.; 64.6×83.7 mm.; 1,098 c.c.; 55 b.h.p. 8.9 to 1 comp.; 2 S.U. carbs; 4-speed, 14.99, 8.98, 5.83, 4.13 to 1; cen. lvr.; susp., f. and r. ind. rubber-hyd.; 4-door.; 4-seat; hyd. brks. disc front; max. 84 m.p.h.; cruise, 75; m.p.g. 25-30; whl. base. 7ft. 9½in.; track f. 4ft. 3½in., r. 4ft. 3in.; lgth., 12ft. 2¾in.; width 5ft. 0½in.; ht. 4ft. 5in.; g.c. 6½in.; turng. cir., 34ft. 9in.; kerb wt., 16½ cwt.; tank, 8 gals.; 12-volt.

£613+£142 p.t. = £755

M.G. MGB

SAFETY Fast with trustworthy handling, steering and braking. The GT coupe has proved a winner from the start; the convertible is still available for open air enthusiasts. Strong five-bearing engine and straightforward chassis design ensure reliable performance. Bucket seats give good support for untiring long journeys. Headlamp flasher combined with finger-tip indicator switch is optional. Laycock de Normanville overdrive is also available.

CLOSE-UP

Four-cyl.; o.h.v.; 80.26×89 mm.; 1,798 c.c.; 95 b.h.p. gross; 8.9 to 1 comp.; 2 S.U. carbs.; 4-speed, 14.21, 8.66, 5.37, 3.91 to 1; cen. lvr., de Normanville overdrive opt.; susp., f. ind. coil, r. half-elliptic; 2-door; 2/3 seat; hyd. brks., disc front; max. 108 m.p.h.; cruise 85; m.p.g. 26-28; whl. base 7ft. 7in.; track, f. 4ft. 1in., r. 4ft. 1¼in.; lgth. 12ft. 9¼in.; width 4ft. 11¾in.; ht. 4ft. 1⅜in.; g.c. 5in.; turng. cir. 32ft. 10in.; kerb wt. 18⅛ cwt.; tank 10 gals.; 12-volt.

£706+£164 p.t. = £870

Abbreviations—g.c.—ground clearance; susp.—suspension; f.—front; r.—rear; comp.—compression; s.v.—side-valves; o.h.v.—overhead valves; o.h.c.—overhead camshaft; hyd.—hydraulic.

M.G. MIDGET

MINI Coopers outperforming MG Midgets? The idea was anathema to Abingdon old-timers, so the Midget gets the wherewithal to defend itself; a 1,275 c.c. power unit of its own with appropriate improvements all round. Coming only two years after engine size was lifted to 1,098 c.c. this emphasises the pace at which performance is escalating. Speed limits don't stop it; they put a premium on fierce acceleration.

CLOSE-UP
Four-cyl.; o.h.v.; 70.6 × 81.3 mm.; 1,275 c.c.; 75 b.h.p.; 9.75 to 1 comp.; 2 S.U. carbs.; 4-speed, 13.5, 8.09, 5.73, 4.22 to 1; cen. lvr.; susp., f. ind. coil, r. half-elliptic; 2-door; 2-seat; hyd. brks., disc front; max. 98 m.p.h.; cruise 80; m.p.g. 27-30; whl. base 6ft. 8in.; track, f. 3ft. 9¾in., r. 3ft. 8¾in.; lgth. 11ft. 5¼in.; width 4ft. 5in.; ht. 4ft. 1¾in.; g.c. 5in.; turng. cir 32ft.; kerb wt. 14¼ cwt.; tank 6 gals.; 12-volt.

MORGAN PLUS 4 2-SEATER

THIS splendid sports car is for those who like individualist motoring. They will find the Plus Four two-seater is now given a lower bonnet line. There is also a reduction in the overall height of the car. This adds up to a more compact and smooth-lined sports model that has already proved its worth in highly competitive events. Just the job for a young couple or the bachelor type of motorist.

CLOSE-UP
Four-cyl.; o.h.v.; 86 × 92 mm.; 2,138 c.c.; 100 b.h.p.; 9 to 1 comp.; 2 Stromberg carbs.; 4-speed, 11.08, 6.5, 4.49, 3.73 to 1; cen. lvr.; susp., f. ind. coil, r. half-elliptic; 2-door; 2-seat; hyd. brks., disc front; max. 110 m.p.h.; cruise 95; m.p.g. 25-28; whl. base 8ft.; track f. 3ft. 11in., r. 4ft. 1in.; lgth. 12ft.; width 4ft. 8in.; ht. 4ft. 4in.; g.c. 6½in.; turng. cir 33ft. 9in.; kerb wt. 17 cwt.; tank 8½ gals.; 12-volt.
£715 + £165 p.t. = £880

MORRIS MINI COOPER S

FURY and resentment are aroused by the Mini Cooper among the old brigade who have paid far more money for far less in the way of performance and road holding. With its hefty 1,275 c.c. twin-carburetter engine, the S is the rally man's choice but many people settle for the 998 c.c. model which looks good value at around £200 less; it's cheaper than an Automatic 850 Mini.

CLOSE-UP
Four-cyl.; o.h.v.; 70.64 × 81.33 mm.; 1,275 c.c.; 75 b.h.p.; 9.75 to 1 comp.; 2 S.U. carbs.; 4-speed, 11.02, 6.6, 4.67, 3.44 to 1; cen. lvr.; susp. f. and r. ind. rubber-hydraulic; 2-door; 4-seat; hyd. servo brks., disc front; max. 95 m.p.h.; cruise 85; m.p.g. 28-32; whl. base 6ft. 8in.; track, f. 4ft. 0⅞in., r. 3ft. 11⅞in.; lgth. 10ft.; width 4ft. 7½in.; ht. 4ft. 5in.; g.c. 6in.; turng. cir. 32ft. 10in.; kerb wt. 13 cwt.; tank 5½ gals.; 12-volt.
£642 + £150 p.t. = £792

MORRIS MINOR 1000

EVEN Alec Issigonis when he designed this car more than 14 years back could scarce have believed it would retain its popularity for so long. But still the public come for it and the model remains a best-seller. Reason: it is well proportioned, cheap to run and it has a heart of gold. A winner if ever there was one.

CLOSE-UP
Four-cyl.; o.h.v.; 64.6 × 83.7 mm.; 1,098 c.c.; 48 b.h.p.; 8.5 to 1 comp.; S.U. carb.; 4-speed, 15.27, 9.16, 5.96, 4.22 to 1; cen. lvr.; susp., f. ind. torsion bar, r. half-elliptic; 2- or 4-door; 4-seat; hyd. brks.; max. 75 m.p.h.; cruise 55; m.p.g. 36-48; whl. base 7ft. 2in.; track f. 4ft. 2¾in., r. 4ft. 2¼in.; lgth. 12ft. 4in.; width 5ft.; ht. 5ft.; g.c. 6¾in.; turng. cir. 33ft.; kerb wt. 15¼ cwt.; tank 6½ gals.; 12-volt.
£426 + £99 p.t. = £525

Abbreviations—g.c.—ground clearance; susp.—suspension; f.—front; r.—rear; comp.—compression; s.v.—side-valves; o.h.v.—overhead valves; o.h.c.—overhead camshaft; hyd.—hydraulic.

81

MORRIS 1100

SUCCESSFUL front-drive family car now available with Automotive-Products automatic transmission or a normal 4-speed gearbox. Hydrolastic suspension, disc front brakes. Combined indicator and headlamp flasher switch. Improvements to heater give better air distribution throughout car. Good boot, generous interior space for packages, shelf stretching full width of facia, glove box, door boxes. Range includes two-door and four-door saloons and Countryman station wagon.

CLOSE-UP
Four-cyl.; o.h.v.; 64.58×83.72 mm.; 1,098 c.c.; 48 b.h.p.; 8.5 to 1 comp.; S.U. carb.; 4-speed, 14.99, 8.98, 5.83, 4.13 to 1; cen. lvr. auto. opt.; susp. f. and r. ind. rubber-hyd.; 2- or 4-door; 4-seat; hyd. brks., disc front; max. 76 m.p.h.; cruise 60; m.p.g. 34-38; whl. base 7ft. 9½in.; track f. 4ft. 3½in., r. 4ft. 2⅞in.; lgth. 12ft. 2¾in.; width 5ft. 0¾in.; ht. 4ft. 5in.; g.c. 5¼in.; turng. cir. 34ft.; kerb wt. 16½ cwt.; tank 8½ gals.; 12-volt.

£532+£123 p.t. = £655

MORRIS 1800

MEDIUM-SIZED model with big-car interior, thanks to transverse engine and front wheel drive. Suspension is the famous Hydrolastic to give a smooth pitch-free ride over the roughest roads. Spare wheel lies in a tray below the roomy boot. Ventilation grilles on facia give cool head and warm feet. Only one point to grease, and service is needed only at 6,000-mile intervals.

CLOSE-UP
Four-cyl.; o.h.v.; 80.26×88.9 mm.; 1,798 c.c.; 84 b.h.p.; 8.2 to 1 comp.; S.U. carb.; 4-speed, 13.78, 9.28, 5.79, 4.19 to 1; cen. lvr.; susp., f. and r. ind. rubber hydraulic; 4-door; 5-seat; hyd. servo brks., disc front; max. 90 m.p.h.; cruise 80; m.p.g. 24-28; whl. base 8ft. 10in.; track f. 4ft. 8⅛in., r. 4ft. 7½in.; lgth. 13ft. 8⅛in.; width 5ft. 7in.; ht. 4ft. 7½in.; g.c. 6¼in.; turng. cir. 38ft. 6in.; kerb wt. 22¾ cwt.; tank 10¾ gals.; 12-volt.

£688+£160 p.t. = £848

MOSKVITCH

FROM the land of Vodka and caviare comes this bread-and butter car with jam at no extra cost. Cheapest 1300 c.c. model on the British market and look at what you get for the money. Heater, demister, radio and aerial, mechanical radiator shutters, towing hooks, fully reclining seats that form a camping bed, coat hooks, glove box, cigar lighter, mud flaps, twin reversing lights, spare paint, polish and cleaning kit.

CLOSE-UP
Four-cyl.; o.h.v.; 76×75 mm.; 1,357 c.c.; 60 b.h.p. gross; 7 to 1 comp.; K-59 carb.; 4-speed, 17.34, 10.19, 6.60, 4.55 to 1; col. lvr.; susp., f. ind. coil, r. half-elliptic; 4-door; 4-seat; hyd. brks.; max. 72 m.p.h.; cruise 60; m.p.g. 35; whl. base 7ft. 9in.; track f. and r. 4ft.; lgth. 13ft. 4in.; width 5ft. 1in.; ht. 5ft. 1½in.; g.c. 7½in.; turng. cir. 39¾ft.; kerb wt. 18 cwt; tank 7¾ gals.; 12-volt.

£551+£128 p.t. = £679

NSU 1000L

NIMBLE economical family model with light alloy o.h.c. engine mounted crosswise at the rear. Runs happily on regular grade fuel. Spare wheel and luggage go in the nose; the rear backrest is removable to increase cargo capacity. Anti-theft steering lock, choke reminder light are standard. Don't miss the 1000 TT, fastest Prinz of all, with 60 h.p. engine giving a 93 m.p.h. maximum. It is distinguished by four headlamps.

CLOSE-UP
Four-cyl.; o.h.c. air-cooled; 69×66.6 mm.; 996 c.c.; 43 b.h.p.; 7.7. to 1 comp.; Solex carb.; 4-speed, 16.44, 8.97, 5.86, 4.12 to 1; cen. lvr.; susp. f. and r. ind. coil; 2-door; 4-seat; hyd. brks., disc front; max. 80 m.p.h.; cruise 79; m.p.g. 33; whl. base, 7ft. 4½in.; track f. 4ft. 1½in., r. 4ft. 0⅝in.; lgth. 12ft. 5⅛in.; width 4ft. 10½in.; ht. 4ft. 5¾in.; g.c. 7½in.; turng. cir. 26ft. 7in.; kerb wt. 12¾ cwt.; tank 8 gals.; 6-volt.

£578+£134 p.t. = £712

NSU 110

BIGGEST NSU built so far, the 110 has a transverse air-cooled four-cylinder engine at the rear, freeing the long nose for luggage. A longer wheelbase than on previous models gives increased interior space. The overhead camshaft five-bearing engine is combined with gearbox and differential. NSU are also developing a twin-rotor Wankel engine following successful experience with the single rotor type in the Prinz convertible.

CLOSE-UP
Four-cyl.; o.h.c. air-cooled; 72×66.6 mm.; 1,085 c.c.; 53 b.h.p.; 8 to 1 comp.; Solex carb.; 4-speed, 16, 10.4, 6.7, 3.8 to 1; cen. lvr.; susp. f. and r. ind. coil; 2-door; 4-seat; hyd. brks., disc front; max. 88 m.p.h.; cruise 80; m.p.g. 25-32; whl. base 8ft. 0½in.; track, f. 4ft. 2½in., r. 4ft. 0½in.; lgth. 13ft. 1½in.; width 4ft. 11in.; ht. 4ft. 6in.; g.c. 7½in.; turng. cir. 29ft. 6in.; kerb wt. 13¾ cwt.; tank 10 gals.; 12-volt.

£636 + £147 p.t. = £783

OLDSMOBILE TORONADO

DETROIT'S wind-of-change car that seems to be setting the States on a front-drive course. Stopping power now improved with disc front brakes, servo assisted. The V8 engine drives by chain to an automatic transmission placed alongside. Rear suspension has single-leaf springs with four shock-absorbers. Steering is power-assisted, brakes have dual master cylinders, front seats are electrically adjusted six ways.

CLOSE-UP
Eight-cyl.; o.h.v.; 104.8×101 mm.; 6,965 c.c.; 385 b.h.p. gross; 10.5 to 1 comp.; Rochester four-choke carb.; 3-speed auto, 7.96, 4.75, 3.21 to 1; cen. lvr.; susp., f. ind. torsion bar, r. half-elliptic; 2-door; 6-seat; hyd. servo brks., disc front; max. 130 m.p.h.; cruise 100; m.p.g. 10-15; whl. base 9ft. 11in.; track, f. 5ft. 3½in., r. 5ft. 3in.; lgth. 17ft. 7in.; width 6ft. 6½in.; ht. 4ft. 4¾in.; g.c. 6in.; turng. cir. 43ft.; kerb wt. 40¼ cwt.; tank 21 gals.; 12-volt.

£3,600 + £827 p.t. = £4,427

OLDSMOBILE CUTLASS

TYPICAL of the luxury available to the American motorist at little over half the British tax-paid prices, the latest Oldsmobile has adjustable tilt-and-telescopic steering column, power-operated steering and windows, four-way electric front seat adjustment, vacuum-operated luggage boot lock. 1967 safety features include disc front brakes, twin master cylinders and warning light, safety door locks and hinges, anti-spin locking differential.

CLOSE-UP
Eight-cyl.; o.h.v.; 100×85.9 mm.; 5,408 c.c.; 320 b.h.p. gross; 10.25 to 1 comp.; Rochester 4-choke carb.; 3-speed, 9.16, 5.25, 3.55 to 1; col lvr. 4-speed or auto opt.; susp., f. ind. coil, r. coil; 2- or 4-door; 6-seat; hyd. servo brks. disc front; max. 105 m.p.h.; cruise 85; m.p.g. 12-16; whl. base 9ft. 7in.; track f. 4ft. 10in., r. 4ft. 11in.; lgth., 17ft. 2in.; width, 6ft. 4in.; ht. 4ft. 6⅜in.; g.c. 6in.; turng. cir. 41ft.; kerb wt., 30 cwt.; tank 16⅝ gals.; 12-volt.

PEUGEOT 204

FAMILY car from a family firm. The 204 is their latest, with transverse light alloy five-bearing engine driving the front wheels. Suspension all-independent; disc brakes at front. Four doors and seats for five with good interior space and lots of room for luggage. Simple and practical interior finish. There's a station wagon too for those who want even more carrying capacity.

CLOSE-UP
Four-cyl.; o.h.c.; 75×64 mm.; 1,130 c.c.; 53 b.h.p.; 8.8 to 1 comp.; Solex carb.; 4-speed, 15.15, 9.25, 6.06, 4.23 to 1; col. lvr.; susp. f. and r. ind. coil; 4-door; 4-seat; hyd. brks., disc front; max. 86 m.p.h.; cruise 78; m.p.g. 26-30; whl. base 8ft. 6in.; track, f. 4ft. 4in., r. 4ft. 1in.; lgth. 13ft.; width 5ft. 1in.; ht. 4ft. 7in.; g.c. 5½in.; turng. cir. 31ft. 2in.; kerb wt. 16¾ cwt.; tank 9¼ gals.; 12-volt.

£798 + £185 p.t. = £983

Abbreviations—g.c.—ground clearance; susp.—suspension; f.—front; r.—rear; comp.—compression; s.v.—side-valves; o.h.v.—overhead valves; o.h.c.—overhead camshaft; hyd.—hydraulic.

83

PEUGEOT 404

SINCE the 404 saloon was introduced in 1960 it has been joined by convertible, station wagon and a coupe styled by Pininfarina with fuel-injection engine. The excellent ZF automatic transmission with torque converter and three-speed planetary gearbox is now offered with the fuel-injection engine on the Super Luxe saloon. A hollow front armrest for stowage of small packages, leather upholstery and sun roof are also provided.

CLOSE-UP

Four-cyl.; o.h.v.; 84×73 mm.; 1,618 c.c.; 70 b.h.p.; 7.4 to 1 comp.; Solex carb.; 4-speed, 16.80, 9.42, 6.05, 4.2 to 1; col. lvr.; susp., f. ind. coil, r. coil 4-door; 4/5-seat; hyd. brks.; max. 90 m.p.h.; cruise 75-80; m.p.g. 30; whl. base 8ft. 8½in.; track f. 4ft. 4¾in., r. 4ft. 2¼in.; lgth. 14ft. 6in.; width 5ft. 5¼in.; ht. 4ft. 9¼in.; g.c. 6in.; turng. cir. 32ft.; kerb wt. 20½ cwt.; tank 11 gals.; 12-volt.

£903 + £209 p.t. = £1,112

PLYMOUTH BARRACUDA

ONE of America's greatest makes, the Plymouth division of Chrysler produces a vast selection of cars. Valiant has six-cylinder engines of 2.8- or 3.7-litres or V8s of 4.5-litres. Barracuda is a fast sports hardtop with disc front brakes. The rest would fill pages of this review, up to the prestige-and-performance Fury V8 of over 7-litres. The accent is on new safety features for 1967.

CLOSE-UP

Eight-cyl.; o.h.v.; 92×84 mm.; 4,475 c.c.; 235 b.h.p. gross; 10.5 to 1 comp.; Carter 4-choke carb.; 4-speed, 7.79, 5.59, 4.07, 2.93 to 1; cen. lvr. auto opt.; susp. f. ind. coil, r. half-elliptic; 2-door; 5-seat; hyd. servo brks., disc front; max 120 m.p.h.; cruise 100; m.p.g. 14-18; whl. base 8ft. 9½in.; track f. 4ft. 7½in.; r. 4ft. 7½in.; lgth. 15ft. 8½in.; width 5ft. 10in.; ht. 4ft. 5½in.; g.c. 5⅜in.; turng. cir. 39ft. 8in.; kerb wt. 27¼ cwt.; tank 15 gals; 12-volt.

£1,870 + £430 p.t. = £2,300

PONTIAC PARISIENNE

REFLECTING the current North American safety trend, the Canada-built right-hand drive Parisienne has energy-absorbing steering column and instrument panel, rear window demister, dual brake master cylinders, two-speed wipers and washers, outside mirror and four-way emergency flasher to give warning if the car is immobilised in heavy traffic. Brakes and steering are power-assisted and the transmission is automatic.

CLOSE-UP

Eight-cyl.; o.h.c.; 98.4×76.2 mm.; 4,638 c.c.; 195 b.h.p. gross; 9.25 to 1 comp.; Rochester 2-choke carb.; 2-speed auto., 5.6, 3.08 to 1; col. lvr.; susp. f. ind. coil, r. coil; 2- or 4-door; 5-seat; hyd. servo brks.; max. 100 m.p.h.; cruise 85; m.p.g. 16-18; whl. base 9ft. 11in.; track. f. 5ft. 2½in., r. 5ft. 2⅜in.; lgth. 17ft. 10½in.; width 6ft. 7½in.; ht. 4ft. 6½in.; g.c. 6in.; turng. cir. 40ft. 9in.; tank 20 gals.; kerb wt. 34 cwt.; 12-volt.

£2,140 + £492 p.t. = £2,632

PONTIAC G.T.O.

PONTIAC'S hot one with an engine giving 335 h.p. on the test bed. Four-choke carburetter, dual exhausts, special springs and dampers, and limited-slip differential are among the performance goodies. Tilting steering wheel, head rests, remote control outside mirror, electric window lifts and on the convertible an electrically operated folding top add to luxury and comfort. Servo steering and servo brakes ensure effortless driving.

CLOSE-UP

Eight-cyl.; o.h.v.; 104.6×95 mm.; 6,556 c.c.; 335 b.h.p. gross; 10.75 to 1 comp.; Carter·four-choke carb.; 3-speed auto., 9.05, 5.18, 3.08 to 1; cen. lvr.; susp., f. ind. coil, r. coil; 2 or 4-door; 6-seat; hyd. servo brks.; max. 120 m.p.h.; cruise 90; m.p.g. 11-16; whl. base 9ft. 7in.; track f. 4ft. 10in., r. 4ft. 11in.; lgth. 17ft. 2½in.; width 6ft. 2¼in.; ht. 4ft. 5¾in.; g.c. 4in.; turng. cir. 40ft. 11in.; kerb wt. 28 cwt.; tank 18 gals.; 12-volt.

£2,670 + £614 p.t. = £3,284

PORSCHE 911S

STAR of the Stuttgart stable is the new 911S which has a big boost in power, improved parking brake and new light alloy wheels in contemporary style. Its flat-six 2-litre engine has compression raised to 9.8 to 1 and two triple-choke Weber carburetters to produce 160 h.p., probably the highest output per litre from all air-cooled production engines except for the competition Carrera. Gearbox has five speeds.

CLOSE-UP

Six-cyl.; o.h.c.; air-cooled; 80×66 mm., 1,991 c.c.; 160 b.h.p.; 9.8 to 1 comp.; 2 triple-choke Weber carbs.; 5-speed, 13.68, 8.37, 5.84, 4.61, 3.51 to 1; cen. lvr.; susp., f. and r. ind. torsion bar; 2-door; 2/4-seat; hyd. disc brks.; max. 140 m.p.h.; cruise 120; m.p.g. 23-25; whl. base 7ft. 2¼in.; track f. 4ft. 4½in., r. 4ft. 3¼in.; lgth. 13ft. 6¼in.; width 5ft. 3in.; ht. 4ft. 4in.; g.c. 6in.; turng. cir. 32ft. 9in.; kerb wt. 21¾ cwt.; tank, 16¼ gals.; 12-volt.

£2,892+£664 p.t. = £3,556

PORSCHE 912

LIKE the sixes, the four-cylinder Porsches are now available with coupe bodywork or the new Targa convertible with built-in roll bar and fixed rear window. Latest improvements include new engine mountings, revised transmission ratios, more powerful horn, better door locks and different carpets. Finish shows the usual Porsche eye for detail and the cranked steering column is a good safety feature.

CLOSE-UP

Four-cyl.; o.h.v.; air-cooled; 82.5×74 mm.; 1,582 c.c.; 90 b.h.p.; 9.3 to 1 comp.; 2 Solex carbs.; 5-speed, 13.68, 8.37, 5.84, 4.61, 3.51 to 1; cen. lvr.; susp. f. and r. ind. torsion bar; 2-door; 2/4-seat; disc brks.; max. 110 m.p.h.; cruise 100; m.p.g. 30; whl. base 7ft. 2¼in.; track, f. 4ft. 4½in., r. 4ft. 3¼in.; lgth. 13ft. 6¼in.; width 5ft. 3in.; ht. 4ft. 4in.; g.c. 6in.; turng. cir. 32ft. 9in.; kerb wt. 19 cwt.; tank 13½ gals.; 12-volt.

£1,972+£456 p.t. = £2,428

RAMBLER 770

LAST of America's "independents" since Studebaker faded out, American Motors produce cars with European appeal; styling doesn't "date" too quickly and disc front brakes are standard. Engine is either 6-cylinder with manual or automatic gearbox or V8 with automatic. Range includes saloon, two-door convertible or station wagon. All models have seat belts for extra safety. The convertible is offered with electrically operated hood.

CLOSE-UP

Eight-cyl.; o.h.v.; 95.25×82.6 mm.; 4,704 c.c.; 198 b.h.p. gross; 8.7 to 1 comp.; Holley 2-choke carb.; 3-speed auto, 8.63, 5.39, 3.31 to 1; col. lvr.; susp., f. ind. coil, r. coil; 2- or 4-door; 5/6-seat; hyd. servo brks.; disc front.; max. 104 m.p.h.; cruise 85; m.p.g. 14-18; whl. base 9ft. 4in.; track, f. 4ft. 10½in., r. 4ft. 9½in.; lgth. 16ft. 3in.; width 6ft. 2½in.; ht. 4ft. 6⅜in.; g.c. 6in.; turng. cir. 39ft. 11in.; kerb wt. 31¾ cwt.; tank 15¾ gals.; 12-volt.

£1,726+£397 p.t. = £2,123

RELIANT REBEL

A splendid example of a popular-priced family car produced by one of the smaller fry. It has a glass-fibre, two-door saloon body and a water-cooled, four-cylinder light alloy engine, the two matching up to give first-class power/weight ratio. Result: A nippy car in town and a robust little model on the open road. Reliant's challenge to the big boys has paid off well.

CLOSE-UP

Four-cyl.; o.h.v.; 55.88×60.96 mm.; 598 c.c.; 27 b.h.p.; 8.5 to 1 comp.; Solex carb.; 4-speed, 18.67, 10.53, 6.36, 4.38 to 1; cen. lvr.; susp., f. ind. coil, r. half-elliptic; 2-door; 4-seat; hyd. brks.; max. 68 m.p.h.; cruise 60; m.p.g. 55; whl. base 7ft. 5in.; track f. 3ft. 11⅝in.; r. 3ft. 10⅝in.; lgth 11ft. 6in.; width 4ft. 10in.; ht. 4ft. 7½in.; g.c. 6in.; turng. cir. 29ft.; kerb wt. 10½ cwt.; tank 6 gals.; 6-volt.

£433+£101 p.t. = £534

Abbreviations—g.c.—ground clearance; susp.—suspension; f.—front; r.—rear; comp.—compression; s.v.—side-valves; o.h.v.—overhead valves; o.h.c.—overhead camshaft; hyd.—hydraulic.

85

RELIANT SCIMITAR

CUTTING itself a slice of the sports car market, the sharp Ogle-styled Scimitar offers high performance and exclusive lines at moderate cost. Reliant-tuned Ford Zodiac engine drives through normal gearbox with overdrive as optional extra. Body is glass fibre with steel reinforcements. New rear suspension gives improved ride and road-holding. Electrically operated sliding roof is optional. Opening boot or bonnet activates automatic lights.

CLOSE-UP
Six-cyl.; o.h.v.; 93.6 × 72.4 mm.; 2,944 c.c.; 130 b.h.p.; 9 to 1 comp.; 3 S.U. carbs.; 4-speed, 12.24, 8.56, 5.46, 3.875 to 1, de Normanville overdrive opt.; cen. lvr.; susp., f. ind. coil, r. coil; 2-door; 2/3-seat; hyd. brks.; disc front; max. 110 m.p.h.; cruise 95; m.p.g. 20-25; whl. base 7ft. 8in.; track f. 4ft. 2¾in.; r. 4ft. 1¾in.; lgth. 13ft. 11½in.; width 5ft. 2in.; ht. 4ft. 3in.; g.c. 6in.; turng. cir. 33ft.; kerb wt. 21¼ cwt.; tank 20 gals.; 12-volt.

£1,068 + £246 p.t. = £1,314

RENAULT 4

CROSS country, camping or church on Sundays; it's all the same to Renault's versatile utility model with the supple torsion bar suspension, front wheel drive and fully opening rear panel. More luxurious seats and door trim, new steering wheel and instrument panel, redesigned controls, feature on the 1967 models. Front brake drums are bigger and wider, the handbrake is improved, and suspension modified in detail.

CLOSE-UP
Four-cyl.; o.h.v.; 58 × 80 mm.; 845 c.c.; 28 b.h.p.; 8 to 1 comp.; Zenith carb.; 3-speed, 15.68, 7.60, 4.28 to 1; dash lvr.; susp., f. and r. ind: torsion bar; 5-door; 4-seat; hyd. brks.; max. 68 m.p.h.; cruise 55; m.p.g. 45-50; whl. base 8ft.; track f. 4ft. 1¼in., r. 3ft. 11½in.; lgth. 12ft.; width 4ft. 10½in.; ht. 5ft.; g.c. 6⅞in.; turng. cir. 31ft.; kerb wt. 12¾ cwt.; tank 5¾ gals.; 6-volt.

£441 + £103 p.t. = £544

RENAULT DAUPHINE GORDINI

HOTTEST of the Dauphines, with special head and manifolds developed by Gordini pushing output up to 33 h.p. against the normal 27.5. Like all Dauphines it now has disc brakes all round. The skill of Amedee Gordini has also been applied to the R8 in a new version with the short nosed body and an engine enlarged to 1,255 c.c. with two twin-choke Weber carburetters giving over 100 h.p.

CLOSE-UP
Four-cyl.; o.h.v.; 58 × 80 mm.; 845 c.c.; 33 b.h.p.; 8.5 to 1 comp.; Solex carb.; 4-speed, 15.84, 9.84, 6.48, 4.51 to 1; cen. lvr.; susp., f. and r. ind. coil; 4-door; 4-seat; disc brks.; max. 82 m.p.h.; cruise 70; m.p.g. 36-40; whl. base 7ft. 5½in.; track f. 4ft. 1½in., r. 4ft.; lgth. 12ft. 11in.; width 5ft.; ht. 4ft. 6¾in.; g.c. 6in.; turn. cir. 29ft. 10in.; kerb wt. 12¾ cwt.; tank 7 gals.; 12-volt.

£461 + £107 p.t. = £568

RENAULT 1100

HEIGHT adjustment for seats that were already among the best in the business adds to the appeal of a car that has had a big boost in popularity since it acquired its longer nose and larger luggage space. A semi-automatic transmission is now available as alternative to the four-speed fully synchronised manual box. The engine has replaceable cylinder liners and all wheels have disc brakes.

CLOSE-UP
Four-cyl.; o.h.v.; 70 × 72 mm.; 1,108 c.c.; 44.5 b.h.p.; 8.5 to 1 comp.; coil ign.; Solex carb.; 4-speed, 14.93, 9.28, 6.11, 4.23 to 1; cen. lvr.; auto. opt.; susp. f. and r. ind. coil; 4-door; 4-seat; hyd. disc brks.; max. 83 m.p.h.; cruise 70; m.p.g. 35-39; whl. base 7ft. 5½in.; track, f. 4ft. 1¾in., r. 4ft.; lgth. 13ft. 9½in.; width 4ft. 10½in.; ht. 4ft. 7½in.; g.c. 5¾in.; turng. cir. 30ft. 6in.; kerb wt. 15⅝ cwt.; tank 8½ gals.; 12-volt.

£567 + £132 p.t. = £699

Abbreviations—g.c.—ground clearance; susp.—suspension; f.—front; r.—rear; comp.—compression; s.v.—side-valves; o.h.v.—overhead valves; o.h.c.—overhead camshaft; hyd.—hydraulic.

RENAULT 16

VISIBLE improvements to this versatile front-drive family car include a more luxurious interior and redesigned heater system to provide cool head and warm feet. The new instrument panel has a warning lamp for worn brake pads. Seats are adjustable for height. Invisible improvements include automatic choke, better exhaust system, new bearings for steering rack and rear suspension arms, better first gear synchromesh.

CLOSE-UP

Four-cyl.; o.h.v.; 76 × 81 mm.; 1,470 c.c.; 58 b.h.p.; 8.5 to 1 comp.; Solex carb.; 4-speed, 13.6, 8.48, 5.58, 3.88 to 1; col. lvr.; susp. f. and r. ind. torsion bar; 5-door; 5-seat; hyd. brks., disc front; max. 86 m.p.h.; cruise 78; m.p.g. 27-30; whl. base 8ft. 9½in.; track, f. 4ft. 4¾in., r. 4ft. 2⅜in.; lgth. 13ft. 10½in.; width 5ft. 4⅜in.; ht. 4ft. 9½in.; g.c. 5⅞in.; turng. cir. 32ft. 8in.; kerb wt. 19¼ cwt.; tank 12 gals.; 12-volt.

£705 + £163 p.t. = £868

RILEY ELF Mark II

A better-looking version of a very popular range of cars. Extra comforts that have been fitted include winding-up windows and ventilation louvres in the dashboard. Then there are concealed door hinges and a remote-control gear box. With existing refinements this snappy Elf really comes into the low-price luxury class. And it is as happy in traffic as on a motorway.

CLOSE-UP

Four-cyl.; o.h.v.; 64.58 × 76.2 mm.; 998 c.c.; 38 b.h.p.; 8.3 to 1 comp.; S.U. carb.; 4-speed, 13.66, 8.18, 5.32, 3.76 to 1; cen. lvr.; susp., f. and r. ind. rubber-hyd.; 2-door; 4-seat; hyd. brks.; max. 75 m.p.h.; cruise 62; m.p.g. 40; whl. base 6ft. 8in.; track f. 3ft. 11½in.; r. 3ft. 10in.; lgth. 10ft. 10½in.; width 4ft. 7½in.; ht. 4ft. 5in.; g.c. 6⅛in.; turng. cir. 31ft. 7in.; kerb wt. 13 cwt.; tank 5½ gals.; 12-volt.

£493 + £114 p.t. = £607

RILEY KESTREL

SWOOPING in to capture its slice of the 1100 market, the Kestrel is one of the most luxurious of the BMC front-drive series. It has Hydrolastic suspension for comfort and safe handling, a twin-carburetter engine for performance and disc front brakes. Facia is wood veneered, the mirror is rimmed in plastic and top and bottom of facia are padded with safety in mind.

CLOSE-UP

Four-cyl.; o.h.v.; 64.58 × 83.72 mm.; 1,098 c.c.; 55 b.h.p.; 8.9 to 1 comp.; 2 S.U. carbs; 4-speed, 14.99, 8.98, 5.83, 4.13 to 1; cen. lvr.; susp., f. and r. ind. rubber hyd.; 4-door; 4-seat; hyd. brks., disc front; max. 85 m.p.h.; cruise 75; m.p.g. 35-38; whl. base 7ft. 9½in.; track f. 4ft. 3½in., r. 4ft. 2⅝in.; lgth. 12ft. 2¾in.; width 5ft. 0⅝in.; ht. 4ft. 4¾in.; g.c. 6in.; turng. cir. 34ft. 9in.; kerb wt. 16⅝ cwt.; tank 8 gals; 12-volt.

£645 + £150 p.t. = £795

ROLLS-ROYCE SILVER SHADOW

SINCE the brilliant new saloon with unit structure, triple-safe braking system and all-independent suspension with automatic height control appeared last year, Rolls-Royce have followed up with a platform chassis for coachbuilders. First to take advantage were H. J. Mulliner, the Rolls-Royce subsidiary, and James Young, a member of the Jack Barclay group, who produce two-door saloon models for R-R and Bentley versions.

CLOSE-UP

Eight-cyl.; o.h.v.; 104.1 × 91.4 mm.; 6,230 c.c.; b.h.p. not revealed; 9 to 1 comp.; 2 S.U. carbs.; 4-speed auto., 11.75, 8.1, 4.46, 3.08 to 1; col. lvr.; susp. f. and r. ind. coil, hyd. levelling; 2/4-door; 5-seat; disc hyd. servo brks.; max. 120 m.p.h.; cruise 100; m.p.g. 13-16; whl. base 9ft. 11½in.; track f. and r. 4ft. 9½in.; lgth. 16ft. 11½in.; width 5ft. 11in.; ht. 4ft. 11¾in.; g.c. 6½in.; turng. cir. 38ft.; kerb wt. 41 cwt.; tank 24 gals.; 12-volt.

£5,425 + £1,245 p.t. = £6,670

Abbreviations—g.c.—ground clearance; susp.—suspension; f.—front; r.—rear; comp.—compression; s.v.—side-valves; o.h.v.—overhead valves; o.h.c.—overhead camshaft; hyd.—hydraulic.

87

ROLLS-ROYCE PHANTOM V

SOVEREIGNS and sheiks, democrats and demagogues; they all turn to the Phantom V as the car combining unmatched prestige with the luxury that can only be achieved by long experience and unhurried craftsmanship. Behind the electrically operated division, occupants can relax in air-conditioned comfort with the mirror-lined cocktail cabinet containing cut-glass goblets. Companions at the sides contain baubles like pigskin cigarette case, notebook.

CLOSE-UP

Eight-cyl.; o.h.v.; 104.14×91.44 mm.; 6,230 c.c.; b.h.p. not revealed; 9 to 1 comp.; 2 S.U. carbs.; 4-speed auto., 14.86, 10.23, 5.64, 3.89 to 1; col. lvr.; susp., f. ind. coil, r. half-elliptic; 4-door; 7-seat; hyd. servo brks.; max. 100 m.p.h.; cruise 85; m.p.g. 12; whl. base 12ft.; track, f. 5ft. 0⅞in., r. 5ft. 4in.; lgth. 19ft. 10in.; width 6ft. 7in.; ht. 5ft. 9in.; g.c. 7¼in.; turng. cir. 48ft. 9in.; kerb wt. 50 cwt.; tank 23 gals.; 12-volt.

£8,700＋£1,995 p.t. = £10,695

ROVER 2000 TC

AWARDED an A.A. gold medal for the safety features in its design, the 2000 is now offered with automatic transmission. The 2000 TC twin-carburetter model, previously reserved for export is now available at home. New cylinder head and manifolds help boost power to 107 h.p. Closed-circuit cooling, an oil cooler and bigger starter are additional innovations and there are several internal improvements.

CLOSE-UP

Four-cyl.; o.h.c.; 85.7×85.7 mm.; 1,978 c.c.; 107 b.h.p.; 9 to 1 comp.; coil ign.; 2 S.U. carbs.; 4-speed, 12.83, 7.55, 4.92, 3.54 to 1; cen. lvr.; susp., f. ind. coil, r. de Dion coil; 4-door; 4-seat; disc servo brks.; max. 110 m.p.h.; cruise 98; m.p.g. 28-32; whl. base 8ft. 7⅞in.; track, f. 4ft. 5⅜in., r. 4ft. 4½in.; lgth. 14ft. 10½in.; width 5ft. 6¼in.; ht. 4ft. 6¾in.; g.c. 6½in.; turng. cir. 31ft. 6in.; kerb wt. 24¾ cwt.; tank 12 gals.; 12-volt.

£1,150＋£265 p.t. = £1,415

ROVER 3-LITRE MK II

THIS is the car for the connoisseur motorist who wants to do his driving in a distinctive "hand built" model. It has a distinctive upper class theme in body line, interior lush comfort, and engine reliability. Doctors and other members of the professions are particularly attracted to the 3-litre Rover, which continues to sell well. Much improved with minor 2000 model modifications.

CLOSE-UP

Six-cyl.; o.h. inlet, side exhaust; 77.8×105 mm.; 2,995 c.c.; 121 b.h.p.; 8.75 to 1 comp.; S.U. carb.; 4-speed, 14.52, 8.11, 5.48, 4.3 to 1, de Normanville overdrive; cen. lvr., BW auto. opt.; susp., f. ind. torsion bar, r. half-elliptic; 4-door; 4-seat; hyd. servo brks., disc front; max. 105 m.p.h.; cruise 90; m.p.g. 18-25; whl. base 9ft. 2½in.; track f. 4ft. 7¼in., r. 4ft. 8in.; lgth. 15ft. 6½in.; width 5ft. 10in.; ht. 4ft. 11¼in.; g.c. 7¼in.; turng. cir. 40ft.; kerb wt. 32½ cwt.; tank 14 gals.; 12-volt.

£1,520＋£350 p.t. = £1,870

ROVER 3-LITRE COUPE

INTERIOR appointments redesigned in line with those on the 2000 have increased the attraction of this comfortable and luxurious four-seater with the sporting lines. Reclining front seats with drop-down backrests, tool tray, picnic tables and separate heater controls for rear-seat passengers are standard. Front-seat headrests containing reading lamps for rear-seat passengers, and BW automatic transmission are optional extras.

CLOSE-UP

Six-cyl.; o.h. inlet, side exhaust; 77.8×105 mm.; 2,995 c.c.; 120 b.h.p.; 8.75 to 1 comp.; S.U. carb.; 4-speed, 14.52, 8.11, 5.48, 4.3 to 1; de Normanville overdrive; cen. lvr., BW auto opt.; susp., f. ind. torsion bar, r. half-elliptic; 4-door; 4-seat; hyd. servo brks., disc front; max. 105 m.p.h.; cruise 90; m.p.g. 18-22; whl. base 9ft. 2½in.; track f. 4ft. 7¼in., r. 4ft. 8in.; lgth. 15ft. 6½in.; width 5ft. 10in.; ht. 4ft. 9⅞in.; g.c. 7¼.; turng. cir. 40ft.; kerb wt. 33¼ cwt.; tank 14 gals.; 12-volt.

£1,600＋£369 p.t. = £1,969

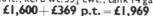

SAAB V4

TWO-STROKE enthusiasts praise the engine's simplicity, economy, durability; detractors dwell on its high consumption at high speeds, poor torque and irregular running at low speeds. Whichever school you support, Saab now has something for you, offering the Ford Taunus 12M TS V4 sports engine of 1,498 c.c. as alternative to the three-cylinder two-stroke of 841 c.c. A free-wheel is retained on the four-stroke model.

CLOSE-UP
Four-cyl.; o.h.v.; 90 × 58.9 mm.; 1,498 c.c.; 65 b.h.p.; 9 to 1 comp.; Solex carb.; 4-speed, 16.98, 10.19, 6.34, 4.09 to 1; col. lvr.; susp., f. ind. coil, r. coil; 2-door; 4-seat; hyd brks., disc front; max. 94 m.p.h.; cruise, 85; m.p.g. 30-33; whl. base, 8ft. 2in.; track f. and r. 4ft.; lgth., 13ft. 8in.; width 5ft. 2in.; ht. 4ft. 10in.; g.c. 7in.; turng. circ. 36ft.; kerb wt., 18½ cwt.; tank, 8¾ gals.; 12-volt.

SABRA SUSSITA

FROM sundrenched Israel comes the Sabra Sussita, designed in England by Reliant Engineering and built in Haifa with many British components, including a Ford Anglia engine. It's a solidly built all-purpose car. Body is in plastic mounted on separate box section steel chassis frame. There's also the Carmel, a two-door saloon version. Backrests are adjustable in six positions and disc brakes are fitted to front wheels.

CLOSE-UP
Four-cyl.; o.h.v.; 80.9 × 58 mm.; 1,198 c.c.; 47 b.h.p.; 7.5 to 1 comp.; Solex carb.; 4-speed, 13.8, 9.32, 5.5, 3.9 to 1.; cen. lvr.; susp., f. ind. coil, r. half-elliptic; 3-door; 5-seat; hyd. brks., disc front; max. 82 m.p.h.; cruise 70; m.p.g. 30; whl. base 7ft. 6½in.; track f. 4ft. 2¾in., r. 4ft. 1½in.; lgth. 13ft. 1½in.; width 5ft. 3⅜in.; ht. 4ft. 9⅞in.; g.c. 7¾in.; turng. cir. 28ft.; kerb wt. 16½ cwt.; tank 7½ gals.; 12-volt.

SIMCA 1000 LS

ROOMY rear-engined small saloon from an ultra-modern Paris factory which produces it in various stages of luxury. A semi-automatic transmission consisting of automatic clutch and torque converter plus three-speed box is now offered at £128, including tax. Normal gearbox has four speeds, all synchronised. There is also a Bertone-designed coupe with disc brakes in left-hand drive only.

CLOSE-UP
Four-cyl.; o.h.v.; 68 × 65 mm.; 944 c.c.; 52 b.h.p. gross; 9 to 1 comp.; Solex carb.; 4-speed, 15.51, 9.26, 6.16, 4.21 to 1; cen. lvr.; susp., f. ind. trans. leaf, r. ind. coil; 4-door; 4-seat; hyd. brks.; max. 80 m.p.h.; cruise 70; m.p.g. 35; whl. base 7ft. 3¾in.; track, f. 4ft. 1¼in., r. 4ft. 0⅜in.; lgth. 12ft. 5in.; width 4ft. 10in.; ht. 4ft. 4½in.; g.c. 6½in.; turng. cir. 29ft.; kerb wt. 14⅝ cwt.; tank 8 gals.; 12-volt.

£519 + £121 p.t. = £640

SIMCA 1301/1501

LONGER lines, with roomier boot and new frontal appearance, distinguish the latest versions of these popular family cars from a Chrysler-controlled French factory. Choice of two engine sizes, three body styles and manual or automatic transmission. Interiors are revised with new instrument panel and new heater with air extractors in the rear quarters.

CLOSE-UP
Four-cyl.; o.h.v.; 74 × 75 mm.; 1,290 c.c.; 62 b.h.p. gross; or 75.2 × 83 mm.; 1,475 c.c.; 81 b.h.p. gross; 8.3/9.3 to 1 comp.; Solex or Weber carb.; 4-speed, 16.22, 9.14, 6.15, 4.45 to 1; cen. lvr.; susp., f. ind. coil, r. coil; 4-door; 4-seat; hyd. brks., disc front on 1501; max. 85/93 m.p.h.; cruise 70-80; m.p.g. 28-32; whl. base 8ft. 3⅛in.; track, f. 4ft. 4in., r. 4ft. 3⅛in.; lgth. 14ft. 7¼in.; width 5ft. 2in.; ht. 4ft. 7¼in.; g.c. 6in.; turng. cir. 32ft.; kerb wt. 19¾-20¼ cwt.; tank 12 gals.; 12-volt.

1301LS £698 + £162 p.t. = £860
1501GL £798 + £185 p.t. = £983

Abbreviations—g.c.—ground clearance; susp.—suspension; f.—front; r.—rear; comp.—compression; s.v.—side-valves; o.h.v.—overhead valves; o.h.c.—overhead camshaft; hyd.—hydraulic.

89

SINGER CHAMOIS Mk II

SMALL quality car of great charm. Ideal for shopping, with its large lift-up rear window. Tireless light alloy engine acquired larger valves and carburetter, new camshaft and modified distributor in Mark II form. Heater output was improved, rear seat legroom was increased. Rear backrest folds down to carry luggage that won't go in the front trunk. Wood facia and door cappings, lockable glove box, add quality touches.

CLOSE-UP

Four-cyl.; o.h.c.; 68×60.4 mm.; 875 c.c.; 39 b.h.p.; 10 to 1 comp.; Solex carb.; 4-speed, 16.59, 8.91, 5.70, 4.14 to 1; cen. lvr.; susp. f. and r. ind. coil; 2-door; 4-seat; hyd. brks.; max. 80 m.p.h.; cruise 75; m.p.g. 40; whl. base 6ft. 10in.; track, f. 4ft. 1½in., r. 4ft. 0½in.; lgth. 11ft. 9¾in.; width 5ft. 0½in.; ht. 4ft. 6½in.; g.c. 5½in.; turng. cir. 30ft.; kerb wt. 14¼ cwt.; tank 6 gals.; 12-volt.

£487+£113 p.t. = £600

SINGER GAZELLE

SMART styling go with smooth, reliable and economical performance to make this car extremely popular with motorists who want a little luxury at the right price. Like all the Rootes Group products, there is an accent on interior refinement including polished walnut veneer dashboard and fully reclining individual front seats. This year you will note there are additions to this luxury treatment.

CLOSE-UP

Four-cyl.; o.h.v.; 81.5×82.5 mm.; 1,725 c.c.; 65 b.h.p. 8.4 to 1 comp.; Zenith carb.; 4-speed, 13, 8.32, 5.41, 3.89 to 1.; cen. lvr., de Normanville overdrive or BW. auto opt.; susp. f. ind coil, r. half-elliptic; 4-door; 4/5-seat; hyd. brks., disc front; max 82 m.p.h.; cruise, 70; m.p.g. 28-33; whl. base, 8ft.; track f. 4ft. 3¾in.; r. 4ft. 2¾in.; lgth., 13ft. 8½in.; width 5ft. 0¾in.; ht. 4ft. 10in.; g.c. 5½in.; turng. cir. 36ft.; kerb wt. 20 cwt.; tank 10 gals.; 12-volt.

£625+£144 p.t. = £769

SINGER VOGUE

LITHE, light and lively newcomer to the Singer range, with four-door body designed for easy access and maximum vision. The high-power version of the five-bearing 1,725 c.c. engine is canted over to give a low bonnet line and has new manifolds. Front brakes are discs, safety was specially studied in steering layout and interior appointments. Strut-type front suspension gives better-than-ever road-holding.

CLOSE-UP

Four-cyl.; o.h.v.; 81.5×82.5 mm.; 1,725 c.c.; 80 b.h.p.; 9.2 to 1 comp.; Stromberg carb.; 4-speed, 12.41, 7.92, 5.15, 3.7 to 1; cen. lvr., L de N. overdrive or BW. auto. opt.; susp., f. ind. coil, r. half-elliptic; 4-door; 4/5-seat; hyd. brks., disc front; max. 88 m.p.h.; cruise 75; m.p.g. 28-34; whl. base 8ft. 2½in.; track, f. and r. 4ft. 4in.; lgth. 14ft. 1¾in.; width 5ft. 3½in.; ht. 4ft. 8in.; g.c. 6¾in.; turng. cir. 33ft. 6in.; kerb wt. 17⅝ cwt.; tank 10 gals.; 12-volt.

SKODA OCTAVIA COMBI

CZECH mate to the rear-engined 1000MB, the Octavia Combi has front engine, rear drive and all-independent suspension, such as Skoda were using over 30 years ago. Equipment is exceptional at the price; heater-demister, reclining seats, screen washer, under-bonnet lamp, fuel reserve, under-body sealing and many other details. Not a concours d'elegance winner, but a strong, practical car built for hard work.

CLOSE-UP

Four-cyl.; o.h.v.; 72×75 mm.; 1,221 c.c.; 44 b.h.p.; 7.5 to 1 comp.; Jikov carb.; 4-speed, 20.4, 11.8, 7.2, 4.78 to 1; col. lvr.; susp., f. ind. coil, r. ind. transv. leaf; 3-door; 4-seat; hyd. brks.; max. 77 m.p.h.; cruise 65; m.p.g. 35-40; whl. base 7ft. 10½in.; track, f. 3ft. 11⅝in., r. 3ft. 13ft. 4in.; lgth. 13ft. 4in.; width 5ft. 3in.; ht. 4ft. 8¼in.; g.c. 6¾in.; turng. cir. 38ft.; kerb wt. 18¼ cwt.; tank 6½ gals.; 12-volt.

£495+£116 p.t. = £611

Abbreviations—g.c.—ground clearance; susp.—suspension; f.—front; r.—rear; comp.—compression; s.v.—side-valves; o.h.v.—overhead valves; o.h.c.—overhead camshaft; hyd.—hydraulic.

SKODA 1000 MB

COMMUNIST concessions to consumer preference are beginning in the car field, as Skoda show by offering a two-door coupe, the 1000 MBX with extra power as an alternative to the four-door 1000 MB saloon. Equipment includes automatic choke, radiator blind, reclining front seats, heater, parking lights, remote control locks for bonnet, boot and fuel filler. Spare wheel above front bumper, helps absorb impacts.

CLOSE-UP
Four-cyl.; o.h.v.; 68×68 mm.; 988 c.c.; 48 b.h.p. gross; 8.3 to 1 comp.; Jikov carb.; 4-speed, 16.87, 9.41, 6.26, 4.26 to 1; cen. lvr.; susp. f. and r. ind. coil; 4-door; 4-seat; hyd. brks.; max. 75 m.p.h.; cruise 68; m.p.g. 36-38; whl. base 7ft. 10½in.; track, f. 4ft. 2⅜in., r. 4ft. 1in.; lgth. 13ft. 8¾in.; width 5ft. 4in.; ht. 4ft. 7in.; g.c. 6½in.; turng. cir. 35ft.; kerb wt. 15⅝ cwt.; tank 7 gals.; 12-volt.

£479+£111 p.t. = £590

SUNBEAM ALPINE

THIS is the car for getting about quickly and stylishly. Its extra urge comes from the now well-proven 1.7-litre five-bearing overhead valve engine tuned to sports car performance. Nothing has been spared to give driver and passenger comfortable motoring with sensible outside trappings. It is lighter than its brother-car the Rapier, and has just that much more sparkle on the road.

CLOSE-UP
Four-cyl.; o.h.v.; 81.5×82.55 mm.; 1,725 c.c.; 91 b.h.p.; 9.2 to 1 comp.; 2 Stromberg carbs.; 4-speed, 12.14, 7.75, 5.04, 3.89 to 1; cen. lvr.; de Normanville overdrive opt.; susp., f. ind. coil, r. half-elliptic; 2-door; 2-seat; hyd. servo brks., disc front; max. 100 m.p.h.; cruise 85; m.p.g. 25; whl. base 7ft. 2in.; track, f. 4ft. 3¾in., r. 4ft. 0½in.; lgth. 13ft.; width 5ft. 0½in.; ht. 4ft. 4½in.; g.c. 4½in.; turng. cir. 34ft.; kerb wt. 19½ cwt.; tank 9 gals.; 12-volt.

£725+£168 p.t. = £893

SUNBEAM RAPIER

ROOTES have always prided themselves on the sporty appearance of their motor cars—the Rapier being the classic example of their theme. It gives this kind of sporting performance and it has good interior fittings usually associated with the family-type car. The robust 1,725 c.c. engine has plenty of power to cope with these extra-weight refinements and give yo first-class motoring.

CLOSE-UP
Four-cyl.; o.h.v.; 81.5×82.55 mm.; 1,725 c.c.; 84 b.h.p.; 9.2 to 1 comp.; Solex carb. twin-choke; 4-speed, 13.04, 8.32, 5.41, 3.89 to 1; cen. lvr.; de Normanville overdrive opt.; susp., f. ind. coil, r. half-elliptic; 2-door; 4-seat; hyd. servo brks., disc front; max. 95 m.p.h.; cruise 80; m.p.g. 25-30; whl. base 8ft.; track, f. 4ft. 3¾in., r. 4ft. 0½in.; lgth. 13ft. 7¼in.; width 5ft. 1in.; ht. 4ft. 9½in.; g.c. 5¾in.; turng. cir. 36ft.; kerb wt. 20¾ cwt.; tank 10 gals.; 12-volt.

£750+£174 p.t. = £924

SUNBEAM TIGER

TIGER that takes off as if its tail was on fire. Effortless cruising at 100 is achieved after top-gear acceleration that makes automatic transmissions seem superfluous. Servo brakes, discs in front, provide the stopping power. Spot the Tiger by the bright side stripes and twin exhaust pipes. Don't miss Sunbeam's new Sports Imp. Twin-carburetter 51 h.p. engine gives a 90 m.p.h. maximum; brakes are servo-assisted.

CLOSE-UP
Eight-cyl.; o.h.v.; 96.5×73 mm.; 4,261 c.c.; 164 b.h.p. gross; 8.8 to 1 comp.; Ford 2-choke carb.; 4-speed, 6.68, 4.86, 3.71, 2.88 to 1; cen. lvr.; susp., f. ind. coil, r. half-elliptic; 2-door; 2-seat; hyd. servo brks., disc front; max. 118 m.p.h.; cruise 95; m.p.g. 15-20; whl. base 7ft. 2in.; track f. 4ft. 3¾in., r. 4ft. 0½in.; lgth. 13ft. 2in.; width 5ft. 0½in.; ht. 4ft. 3½in.; g.c. 5in.; turng. cir. 37ft. 9in.; kerb wt. 23⅝ cwt.; tank 11¾ gals.; 12-volt.

£1,195+£276 p.t. = £1,471

Abbreviations—g.c.—ground clearance; susp.—suspension; f.—front; r.—rear; comp.—compression; s.v.—side-valves; o.h.v.—overhead valves; o.h.c.—overhead camshaft; hyd.—hydraulic.

91

TOYOTA CORONA

SHIPLOADS of Coronas have been building a reputation as well-made easy-to-drive family cars. With four-cylinder water cooled engine, coil springs at front, semi-elliptics at rear and self-adjusting drum brakes, design is straightforward. Repeater direction signals on front wings and two-speed wipers are included. Transparent battery, fuse box, brake and clutch reservoirs and a window in the carburetter speed routine inspection.

CLOSE-UP
Four-cyl.; o.h.v.; 78×78 mm.; 1,490 c.c.; 70 b.h.p.; 8 to 1 comp.; Aisan carb.; 4-speed, 13.58, 7.81, 5.18, 3.7 to 1; col. lvr.; susp., f. ind. coil, r. half-elliptic; 4-door; 4-seat; hyd. brks.; max. 86 m.p.h.; cruise 70; m.p.g. 28-35; whl. base 7ft. 11in.; track f. and r. 4ft. 2in.; lgth. 13ft. 4in.; width 5ft. 0¾in.; ht. 4ft. 8in.; g.c. 6¾in.; turng. cir. 32ft. 6in.; kerb wt. 19 cwt.; tank 9¾ gals.; 12-volt.

£642+£149 p.t. = £791

TOYOTA 1600S

TOYOTA 1600S is a debonair sports coupe which is going to find friends fast. Its 1.6-litre twin carburetter engine, all-synchronised gearbox and disc front brakes make it a slick performer in the 100 m.p.h. range. Equipment includes dual exhausts, four headlamps, rev. counter, reclining seats and an anti-glare tinted screen is available. It also has an automatic station-seeking radio as standard.

CLOSE-UP
Four-cyl.; o.h.v.; 80.5×78 mm.; 1,587 c.c.; 90 b.h.p. gross; 9.2 to 1 comp.; 2 S.U. carbs.; 4-speed, 15.08, 8.67, 5.75, 4.11 to 1; cen. lvr.; susp. f. ind. coil, r. half-elliptic; 2-door; 4-seat; hyd. brks., disc front; max. 100 m.p.h.; cruise 85; m.p.g. 26-30; whl. base, 7ft. 11in; track f. and r. 4ft. 2in.; lgth. 13ft. 4in.; width 5ft. 1⅝in.; ht. 4ft. 6⅛in.; g.c. 7in.; turng. cir. 32ft. 6in.; kerb wt. 18¼ cwt.; tank 9⅞ gals.; 12-volt.

£875+£326 p.t. = £1,201

TRIUMPH HERALD

THIS is just the job for the owner who wants low-priced, high-efficiency fresh air motoring. Like all the Herald models, the convertible has independent suspension all round, and a separate chassis. Body panels are detachable for easy repair, and the car has a tight steering lock similar to that of a London taxi. Backed by the engineering genius of Leyland, this model is outstanding.

CLOSE-UP
Four-cyl.; o.h.v.; 69.3×76 mm.; 1,147 c.c.; 39 b.h.p.; 8 to 1 comp.; Solex carb.; 4-speed, 15.42, 8.88, 5.75, 4.11 to 1; cen. lvr.; susp., f. ind. coil, r. ind. transv. leaf; 2-door; 4-seat; hyd. brks.; max. 77 m.p.h.; cruise 70; m.p.g. 28-32; whl. base 7ft. 7½in.; track f. and r. 4ft.; lgth. 12ft. 9in.; width 5ft.; ht. 4ft. 4in.; g.c. 6¾in.; turning cir. 26ft. 3in.; kerb wt. 15½ cwt.; tank 7 gals.; 12-volt.

£509+£119 p.t. = £628

TRIUMPH 1300

SUCCESSFUL breakaway into front-drive by Harry Webster and the Standard-Triumph design team gives the 1300 exceptional space and performance in a compact size. Gears and differential are directly under the engine; suspension is all-independent. Thoughtfully planned equipment includes fold-away window winders and an eight-light monitor to give warnings on choke, handbrake, fuel level, indicators, ignition, oil pressure, water temperature and headlamps.

CLOSE-UP
Four-cyl.; o.h.v.; 73.7×76 mm.; 1,296 c.c.; 60 b.h.p. gross; 8.5 to 1 comp.; Stromberg carb.; 4-speed, 13.97, 8.87, 5.96, 4.37 to 1; cen. lvr.; susp. f. and r. ind. coil; 4-door; 5-seat; hyd. brks., disc front; max. 85 m.p.h.; cruise 75; m.p.g. 30-33; whl. base 8ft. 0⅞in.; track, f. 4ft. 5in., r. 4ft. 4½in.; lgth. 12ft. 11in.; width 5ft. 1¾in.; ht. 4ft. 6in.; g.c. 5½in.; turng. cir. 30ft.; kerb wt. 18 cwt.; tank 11¾ gals.; 12-volt.

£678+£157 p.t. = £835

Abbreviations—g.c.—ground clearance; susp.—suspension; f.—front; r.—rear; comp.—compression; s.v.—side-valves; o.h.v.—overhead valves; o.h.c.—overhead camshaft; hyd.—hydraulic

TRIUMPH GT6

SPITFIRE compactness with six-cylinder smoothness and nearly 30 extra horsepower make this new coupe a formidable recruit to the sporting scene. Twin-carburetter 2-litre engine provides 95 h.p. to take it well over 100 m.p.h. with a 0-60 time of a fraction over 11 seconds. Anti-fume breather system, no-loss cooling, all-synchromesh gearbox and telescopic steering column are items of interest.

CLOSE-UP
Six-cyl.; o.h.v.; 74.7×76 mm.; 1,998 c.c.; 95 b.h.p.; 9.5 to 1 comp.; 2 Stromberg carbs.; 4-speed, 8.66, 5.82, 4.11, 3.27 to 1; cen. lvr. Laycock de Normanville overdrive opt.; susp., f. ind. coil, r. ind. transv. leaf; 2-door; 2-seat; hyd. brks. disc front; max. 107 m.p.h.; cruise, 85; m.p.g. 28; whl. base, 6ft. 11in.; track f. 4ft. 1in., r. 4ft. 1in.; lgth. 12ft. 1in.; width 4ft. 9in.; ht. 3ft. 11in.; g.c. 4in.; turng. cir. 25ft. 3in.; kerb wt. 17 cwt.; tank 9¾ gals.; 12-volt.

£800 + £185 p.t. = £985

TRIUMPH VITESSE 2-LITRE

REJUVENATED by a larger engine, the Vitesse now lives up to its name with a 100 m.p.h. maximum and real acceleration. Synchromesh first gear and closed-circuit cooling, driving seat adjustable for height and slope, polished wheel trim rings, are standard. Leather upholstery, sun roof, Laycock de Normanville overdrive on third and top gears are among the options. A car for fussless fast cruising.

CLOSE-UP
Six-cyl.; o.h.v.; 74.7×76 mm.; 1,998 c.c.; 95 b.h.p.; 9.5 to 1 comp.; 2 Stromberg carbs.; 4-speed, 10.31, 6.92, 4.86, 3.89 to 1; cen. lvr.; susp., f. ind. coil, r. ind. transv. leaf; 2-door; 4-seat; hyd. brks. disc front; max. 100 m.p.h.; cruise, 80; m.p.g. 28-30; whl. base, 7ft. 7½in.; track f. 4ft. 1in., r. 4ft.; lgth., 12ft. 9in.; width 5ft.; ht. 4ft. 4½in.; g.c. 6¾in.; turng. cir. 25ft.; kerb wt. 18½ cwt.; tank 8¼ gals.; 12-volt.

£681 + £158 p.t. = £839

TRIUMPH TR4A

SINCE this swift, purposeful sports car was redesigned it has been a best-seller throughout the world. It has a sturdy, well-balanced, engine and a low, wind-cheating body in the best sports car tradition. Specially comfort-designed seats, winding windows, thick pile carpets and door waist rails give the fast driver a cossetted ride. A sports car with a high reputation thoroughly deserved.

CLOSE-UP
Four-cyl.; o.h.v.; 86×92 mm.; 2,138 c.c.; 104 b.h.p.; 9 to 1 comp.; 2 Stromberg carbs.; 4-speed, 11.61, 7.44, 4.9, 3.7 to 1; cen. lvr. de Normanville overdrive opt.; susp., f. and r. ind. coil; 2-door; 2/3-seat; hyd. brks., disc front; max. 110 m.p.h.; cruise 95; m.p.g. 25-27; whl. base 7ft. 4in.; track, f. 4ft. 2in., r. 4ft. 1in.; lgth. 12ft. 7in.; width 4ft. 9½in.; ht. 4ft. 2in.; g.c. 6in.; turng. cir. 33ft. 7in.; kerb wt. 21 cwt.; tank 11¾ gals.; 12-volt.

£800 + £185 p.t. = £985

TRIUMPH 2000

SALOON or station wagon with four-speed all-synchromesh gearbox, plus options of overdrive on third and top gears or automatic transmission cater for a wide range of requirements in the 2-litre class. Smooth-running six-cylinder twin-carburetter engine, all-independent suspension, leather upholstery pierced to "breathe" and improved ventilation with extraction of stale air are features of a popular quality car.

CLOSE-UP
Six-cyl.; o.h.v.; 74.7×76 mm.; 1,998 c.c.; 90 b.h.p.; 9 to 1 comp.; 2 Stromberg carbs.; 4-speed, 13.45, 8.61, 5.68, 4.1 to 1; cen. lvr. Laycock de Normanville overdrive or BW auto. opt.; susp., f. and r. ind. coil; 4-door; 5-seat; servo brks., disc front; max. 95 m.p.h.; cruise 80; m.p.g. 24-28; whl. base 8ft. 10in.; track f. 4ft. 4in., r. 4ft. 2⅜in.; lgth. 14ft. 5¾in.; width 5ft. 5in.; ht. 4ft. 8in.; g.c. 6in.; turng. cir. 32ft.; kerb wt. 23 cwt.; tank 14 gals.; 12-volt.

£973 + £224 p.t. = £1,197

Abbreviations—g.c.—ground clearance; susp.—suspension; f.—front; r.—rear; comp.—compression; s.v.—side-valves; o.h.v.—overhead valves; o.h.c.—overhead camshaft; hyd.—hydraulic.

93

VANDEN PLAS 1100

WITH the accent off high speed this much-liked British Motor Corporation's 1100 luxury model now comes fully into its own. It has the thoroughbred lines from Pininfarina of Italy combined with a robust engine that runs at very little cost. It has the now well-proven hydrolastic suspension, a twin-carburetter transverse fitted engine and a most luxurious trim. It has a great future.

CLOSE-UP
Four-cyl.; o.h.v.; 64.58 × 83.72 mm.; 1,098 c.c.; 55 b.h.p. gross; 8.9 to 1 comp.; 2 S.U. carbs.; 4-speed, 14.99, 8.98, 5.83, 4.13 to 1; cen. lvr.; susp. f. and r. ind. rubber-hydraulic; 4-door; 4-seat; hyd. brks., disc front; max. 85 m.p.h.; cruise 75; m.p.g. 35-37; whl. base 7ft. 9½in.; track, f. 4ft. 3½in., r. 4ft. 2⅝in.; lgth. 12ft. 2¾in.; width 5ft. 0⅜in.; ht. 4ft. 4¾in.; g.c. 6in.; turng. cir. 34ft. 9in.; kerb wt. 17¼ cwt.; tank 8 gals.; 12-volt.

£765 + £177 p.t. = £942

VANDEN PLAS PRINCESS R

MUCH-DISCUSSED marriage between Rolls-Royce six-cylinder engine and BMC's big saloon, trimmed by Vanden Plas. Revised body styling, assisted steering, servo brakes, leather upholstery, fold away picnic tables and polished walnut veneer, combine to create luxury at a moderate price. Map reading lamp and twin fog lamps are standard. Recent development has concentrated on improving refinement and road-holding.

CLOSE-UP
Six-cyl.; o.h. inlet, s. exhaust; 95.2 × 91.4 mm.; 3,909 c.c.; 175 b.h.p.; 7.8 to 1 comp.; 2 S.U. carbs.; BW 3-speed auto., 7.56, 4.62, 3.15 to 1; col. lvr.; susp., f. ind. coil, r. half-elliptic; 4-door; 5-seat; hyd. servo brks., disc front; max. 106 m.p.h.; cruise 90; m.p.g. 14-17; whl. base 9ft. 2in.; track, f. 4ft. 7in., r. 4ft. 5½in.; lgth. 15ft. 8in.; width 5ft. 8½in.; ht. 4ft. 11in.; g.c. 6in.; turng. cir. 42ft. 5in.; kerb wt. 31⅞ cwt.; tank 16 gals.; 12-volt.

£1,650 + £480 p.t. = £2,030

VAUXHALL VIVA

308,000 VIVAS have re-established Vauxhall in the small-car market. Now a roomier, rounded, more powerful Viva with bigger engine and new coil spring rear suspension comes in five versions; Viva, Viva de luxe, Viva SL and higher performance "90" versions of the last two with high compression engines giving 59.5 b.h.p. instead of 47. Disc front brakes with servo are standard on "90" models, optional on others.

CLOSE-UP
Four-cyl.; o.h.v.; 77.7 × 61 mm.; 1,159 c.c.; 47 b.h.p.; 8.5 to 1 comp.; Stromberg carb.; 4-speed, 14.68, 8.64, 5.47, 3.9 to 1; cen. lvr.; susp., f. ind. coil, r. coil; 2-door; 4/5-seat; hyd. brks., disc front and servo opt.; max. 80 m.p.h.; cruise 70; m.p.g. 34-39; whl. base 7ft. 11⅞in.; track f. and r. 4ft. 3in.; lgth. 13ft. 5⅝in.; width 5ft. 3in.; ht. 4ft. 5½in.; g.c. 5in.; turng. cir. 31ft. 6in.; kerb wt. 15¼cwt.; tank 8 gals.; 12-volt.

£470 + £109 p.t. = £579

VAUXHALL VICTOR 101

SLIGHT modifications to this very popular car have been made both inside and outside. Engine power is stepped up while greater economy in running the car comes from the new carburation. Add to this smoother performance with the aid of what Vauxhall's call a "flexible wheel". A very sound motor car that is now well established.

CLOSE-UP
Four-cyl.; o.h.v.; 81.63 × 76.2 mm.; 1,595 c.c.; 60 b.h.p.; 9 to 1 comp.; Zenith carb.; 3-speed, 13.2, 6.74, 4.125 to 1; col. lvr. 4-speed or auto. opt.; susp., f. ind. coil, r. half-elliptic; 4-door; 5-seat; hyd. brks., disc front opt.; max. 84 m.p.h.; cruise 75; m.p.g. 29-32; whl. base 8ft. 4in.; track f. 4ft. 3in., r. 4ft. 4½in.; lgth. 14ft. 7in.; width 5ft. 5in.; ht. 4ft. 9in.; g.c. 7in.; turng. cir. 31ft.; kerb wt. 20¼ cwt.; tank 10 gals.; 12-volt.

£570 + £132 p.t. = £702

VAUXHALL CRESTA

SLIGHT changes to this Vauxhall bread-winning car include improvements to the gear change and exhaust system aimed at giving a quieter ride. The anti-burst door locks have been improved for greater safety and the car is now leaping up in the sales brackets. A sound, robust product of a large car empire known for its technical efficiency and modern thinking.

CLOSE-UP
Six-cyl.; o.h.v.; 92×82.6 mm.; 3,294 c.c.; 123 b.h.p.; 8.5 to 1 comp.; Zenith carb.; 3-speed, 8.67, 5.14, 3.45 to 1; col. lvr., 4-speed, auto or overdrive opt.; susp. f. ind. coil, r. half-elliptic; 4-door; 6-seat; hyd. servo brks., disc front; max. 102 m.p.h.; cruise 90; m.p.g. 19-23; whl. base 8ft. 11½in.; track, f. 4ft. 7¼in., r. 4ft. 8¼in.; lgth. 15ft. 7¼in.; width 5ft. 9¾in.; ht. 4ft. 7⅞in.; g.c. 6½in.; turng. cir. 36ft. 6in.; kerb wt. 25 cwt.; tank 15 gals.; 12-volt.

£794+£183 p.t. = £977

VAUXHALL VISCOUNT

MOST luxurious Vauxhall ever marketed. Automatic transmission, disc front brakes with servo, electrically operated side windows, electrically heated rear window and inertia reel harness are included. Distinguish it from the Cresta by Vinyl-covered roof, bigger tyres, square-mesh grille and black surround to the four headlamps. Reversing lamps, map reading lamp, wing mirrors, hide and walnut veneers and extra sound-proofing add to the enjoyment.

CLOSE-UP
Six-cyl.; o.h.v.; 92×82.5 mm.; 3,294 c.c.; 123 b.h.p.; 8.5 to 1 comp.; Zenith carb.; 2-speed auto, 6.27, 3.45 to 1.; col lvr. 4-speed manual opt.; susp., f. ind. coil, r. half-elliptic; 4-door; 5-seat; hyd-servo brks., disc front; max. 100 m.p.h.; cruise, 88; m.p.g. 18-22; whl. base, 8ft. 11½in.; track f. 4ft. 7¼in., r. 4ft. 8¼in.; lgth. 15ft. 7¼in.; width 5ft. 9¾in.; ht. 4ft. 8in.; g.c. 6½in.; turng. cir., 36ft. 6in.; kerb wt., 27⅞ cwt.; tank, 15 gals.; 12-volt.

£1,205+£278 p.t. = £1,483

VOLGA

FROM Gorky comes the GAZ 21C, known in Britain as the Volga. Russia's medium-size family car, it has a 2½-litre four-cylinder engine in a strongly built chassis with conventional four-door five-seater body. Suspension has recently been modified for a better ride, crank-case ventilation has been redesigned and carburation modified for smoother performance. Both saloon and station wagon are assembled in Belgium with alternative of Rover diesel engines.

CLOSE-UP
Four-cyl.; o.h.v.; 92×92 mm.; 2,445 c.c.; 94 b.h.p. gross; 7.5 to 1 comp.; K105 carb.; 3-speed, 14.19, 8.07, 4.56 to 1; cen. lvr.; susp., f. ind. coil, r. half elliptic; 4-door; 5-seat; hyd. brks.; max. 83 m.p.h.; cruise 70; m.p.g. 21; whl. base 8ft. 10¼in.; track, f. 4ft. 7½in., r. 4ft. 7½in.; lgth. 15ft. 9¾in.; width 5ft. 10⅞in.; ht. 5ft. 3½in.; g.c. 7½in.; turng. cir. 38ft. 6in.; kerb wt. 28¼ cwt.; tank 13¼ gals.; 12-volt.

£742+£172 p.t. = £914

VOLKSWAGEN 1500

DESIGNED 28 years ago, before many of today's buyers were born, the "beetle" has been kept competitive by countless improvements. Now comes a 1,500 c.c. 44 h.p. engine to give a 78 m.p.h. cruising speed, with disc front brakes and rear compensating spring to improve stability on corners. New door locks, softer control knobs, new rear panel. The popular drum-braked 1,300 model continues with the suspension and body changes.

CLOSE-UP
Four-cyl.; o.h.v. air-cooled; 83×69 mm.; 1,493 c.c.; 44 b.h.p.; 7.5 to 1 comp.; Solex carb.; 4-speed, 15.67, 8.49, 5.19, 3.67 to 1; cen. lvr.; susp., f. and r. ind. torsion bar; 2-door; 4-seat; hyd brks., disc front; max. 78 m.p.h.; cruise 78; m.p.g. 30-32; whl. base 7ft. 10½in.; track f. 4ft. 3¾in., r. 4ft. 5⅛in.; lgth. 13ft. 4½in.; width 5ft. 0¼in.; ht. 4ft. 11in.; g.c. 6in.; turng. cir. 36ft. 4in.; kerb wt. 46 cwt.; tank 8¾ gals.; 6-volt.

VOLKSWAGEN 1600 TL

TWO saloon styles are now available with the 54 h.p. two-carburetter 1.6-litre engine; fast-back "big beetle" and the notched-back one that began as a 1500. Both have the new torsion bar stabiliser spring at the rear to improve ride and road-holding. Both have 12-volt electrics, higher town charging rate, ten fuses. Both have the new higher third gear ratio.

CLOSE-UP
Four-cyl.; o.h.v.; air-cooled; 85.8×69 mm.; 1,584 c.c.; 54 b.h.p.; 7.7 to 1 comp.; 2 Solex carbs.; 4-speed, 15.7, 8.5, 5.4, 3.7 to 1; cen. lvr.; susp. f. and r. ind. torsion bar; 2-door; 4-seat; hyd. brks., disc front; max. 84 m.p.h.; cruise 84; m.p.g. 32-34; whl. base 7ft. 10½in.; track f. 4ft. 3⅜in., r. 4ft. 5in.; lgth. 13ft. 10⅜in.; width 5ft. 3¼in.; ht. 4ft. 10⅜in.; g.c. 5⅝in.; turng. cir. 36ft. 5in.; kerb wt. 18¼ cwt.; tank 8¾ gals.; 12-volt.

£825+£190 p.t. = £1,015

VOLVO 1800S

MORE power, less maintenance is the word on Volvo's successful sports coupe. 101 h.p. from the rugged 1.8-litre four-cylinder engine, with five bearings and twin SU carburetters. Chassis greasing points eliminated. Transmission is by four-speed all-synchromesh gearbox with Laycock de Normanville overdrive. A limited-slip differential is optional and there's a limited-production 120 h.p. engine available to holders of competition licences only.

CLOSE-UP
Four-cyl.; o.h.v.; 84.14×80 mm.; 1,778 c.c.; 101 b.h.p.; 10 to 1 comp.; 2 S.U. carbs.; 4-speed, 14.27, 9.07, 6.17, 4.56 to 1; cen. lvr., overdrive; susp., f. ind. coil, r. coil; 2-door; 2/4-seat; servo brks., disc front; max. 112 m.p.h.; cruise 95; m.p.g. 26-30; whl. base 8ft. 0½in.; track f. and r. 4ft. 3¾in.; lgth. 14ft. 5in.; width 5ft. 7in.; ht. 4ft. 2½in.; g.c. 6in.; turng. cir. 31ft. 3in.; kerb wt. 23½ cwt.; tank 10 gals.; 12-volt.

£1,500+£345 p.t. = £1,845

VOLVO 122S

FROM their fine new Torslanda factory adjoining Gothenburg harbour, Volvo export increasing numbers of these well-built cars and spend £13 million a year in Britain on materials, components and accessories. 122S is the fast twin-carburetter model with the 85 h.p. engine which also powers the estate car. 121 has the single-carburetter 68 h.p. engine. Choice of two or four doors; automatic transmission is optional.

CLOSE-UP
Four-cyl.; o.h.v.; 84.1×80 mm.; 1,778 c.c.; 85 b.h.p.; 8.7 to 1 comp.; 2 S.U. carbs; 4-speed, 12.83, 8.16, 5.58, 4.1 to 1; cen. lvr. Laycock de Normanville overdrive opt.; susp., f. ind. coil, r. coil; 2/4-door; 5-seat; servo brks., disc front; max. 100 m.p.h.; cruise 85; m.p.g. 25-28; whl. base 8ft. 6⅜in.; track f. and r. 4ft. 3¾in.; lgth. 14ft. 6⅞in.; width 5ft. 3¾in.; ht. 4ft. 11½in.; g.c. 6¼in.; turng. cir. 33ft.; kerb wt. 21 cwt.; tank 10 gals.; 12-volt.

£945+£218 p.t. = £1,163

VOLVO 144

SCANDINAVIA'S icy winters make Swedes safety conscious, so Volvo's latest model has a reinforced passenger compartment between end sections designed for controlled crumpling. Extra-strong laminated windscreen, safety steering column which shears off under impact, servo disc brakes with dual operating system, give added security. Longer, lower, wider than existing models, the 144 has the same 1,778 c.c. engine in two versions; 85 or 102 h.p.

CLOSE-UP
Four-cyl.; o.h.v.; 84.1×80 mm.; 1,778 c.c.; 75 b.h.p.; 8.7 to 1 comp. or 100 b.h.p. 10 to 1 comp.; Stromberg or S.U. carbs.; 4-speed, 12.8, 8.2, 5.6, 4.1 to 1; cen. lvr. auto or Laycock de Normanville overdrive opt.; susp., f. ind. coil, r. coil; 4-door; 5-seat; disc servo brks.; max. 95-102 m.p.h.; cruise, 85-90; m.p.g. 24-28; whl. base, 8ft. 6¼in.; track f. and r. 4ft. 5¼in.; lgth. 15ft. 9⅜in.; width 5ft. 8½in.; ht. 4ft. 8½in.; g.c. 7in.; turng. cir., 30ft. 5in.; kerb wt., 23½ cwt.; tank, 12¾ gals.; 12-volt.

WARTBURG

BARRIERS between East and West Germany are lowered to allow this sturdy family car out. Built in the Eisenach factory, once owned by Auto Union, it has a three-cylinder two-stroke engine driving the front wheels. Latest suspension is by coil springs instead of leaf springs and chassis design is new. A new sleeker body is on the way but may not make the London Show.

CLOSE-UP
Three-cyl.; two-stroke; 73.5×78 mm.; 991 c.c.; 45 b.h.p.; 7.5 to 1 comp.; B.V.F. carb.; 4-speed, 14.5, 9.45, 6.06, 4.12 to 1; col. lvr.; susp., f. and r. ind. coil; 4-door; 4/5-seat; hyd. brks.; max. 77 m.p.h.; cruise 70; m.p.g. 30-32; whl. base 8ft. 0½in.; track f. 4ft. 1⅛in., r. 4ft. 3½in.; lgth. 14ft. 1¼in.; width 5ft. 1¾in.; ht. 4ft. 9in.; g.c. 7½in.; turng. cir. 33ft. 5in.; kerb wt. 18½ cwt.; tank 9½ gals.; 6-volt.

£487+£113 p.t. = £600

WOLSELEY HORNET II

ADDITIONS to this neat little car include a remote control gear box and new fresh-air louvres in the dashboard panels. Outwardly, you will note that the car has a slimmer look and the door hinges are concealed. Windows now wind down and within there are other minor modifications. This is a well-liked British Motor Corporation model, and it deserves its popularity.

CLOSE-UP
Four-cyl.; o.h.v.; 64.58×76.2 mm.; 998 c.c.; 38 b.h.p.; 8.3 to 1 comp.; S.U. carb.; 4-speed, 13.66, 8.18, 5.32, 3.76 to 1; cen. lvr.; susp. f. and r. ind. rubber-hyd.; 2-door; 4-seat; hyd. brks.; max. 75 m.p.h.; cruise 62; m.p.g. 40; whl. base, 6ft. 8½in.; track f. 3ft. 11½in., r. 3ft. 10in.; lgth., 10ft. 10¼in.; width 4ft. 7½in.; ht. 4ft. 5in.; g.c. 6½in.; turng. circ., 31ft. 7in.; kerb wt., 12½ cwt.; tank, 5½ gals.; 12-volt.

£478+£111 p.t. = £589

WOLSELEY 1100

ANOTHER of the BMC's 1100 family which now numbers six, the Wolseley has the successful combination of crosswise engine, front wheel drive and Hydrolastic suspension, producing a compact, comfortable family car with four large doors and a good luggage trunk. All doors have child-proof locks. Facia has a polished wood finish; there are bins in the doors for small packages plus a parcel shelf under the facia.

CLOSE-UP
Four-cyl.; o.h.v.; 64.58×83.72 mm.; 1,098 c.c.; 55 b.h.p. gross; 8.9 to 1 comp.; 2 S.U. carbs.; 4-speed, 14.99, 8.98, 5.83, 4.13 to 1; cen. lvr.; susp., f. and r. ind. rubber-hyd.; 4-door; 4-seat; hyd. brks., disc front; max. 85 m.p.h.; cruise 75; m.p.g. 35-38; whl. base 7ft. 9½in.; track f. 4ft. 3½in.; r. 4ft. 2⅞in.; lgth. 12ft. 2¾in.; width 5ft. 0⅜in.; ht. 4ft. 4¾in.; g.c. 6in.; turng. cir. 34ft. 9in.; kerb wt. 16⅝ cwt.; tank 8 gals.; 12-volt.

£623+£144 p.t. = £767

WOLSELEY 16/60

THIS car has proved its worth for quite a time now. It is a neat four-to-five seater saloon with good looks and an adequate road performance. Powered by the sturdy 1,622 c.c. B.M.C. engine, it is the same basic car as other favourites like the Morris Oxford, Riley 4/72 and M.G. Magnette models. A well-behaved car without in any way being flashy.

CLOSE-UP
Four-cyl.; o.h.v.; 76.2×88.9 mm.; 1,622 c.c.; 61 b.h.p.; 8.3 to 1 comp.; S.U. carb.; 4-speed, 15.64, 9.52, 5.91, 4.3 to 1; cen. lvr.; BW auto. opt.; susp., f. ind. coil, r. half-elliptic; 4-door; 4-seat; hyd. brks.; max. 80 m.p.h.; cruise 70; m.p.g. 26-30; whl. base 8ft. 4¼in.; track, f. 4ft. 2¾in., r. 4ft. 3⅜in.; lgth. 14ft. 6½in.; width 5ft. 3½in.; ht. 4ft. 10⅞in.; g.c. 6½in.; turng. cir 37ft. 1in.; kerb wt. 22½ cwt.; tank 10 gals.; 12-volt.

£705+£163 p.t. = £868

Stay me with flagons, comfort me with apples said the poet. These days the cry from chaps needing stay and comfort on the road is for GADGETS, as long as there's room in the boot for the flagons and the apples. And GADGETS are thick on the ground at Earls Court.

by DENNIS MAY

TROUBLED with *ghost images*? Then Joseph Lucas Ltd., rather than the Society for Psychical Research, are your best bet for an exorcising job.

Motor accessory language—accessorese, you could call it—is as fascinating as the products themselves. Like ghost images. These aren't actually visible in the unflesh on Stand 232 at Earls Court but the means of beating them are.

Lucas's haunting phrase crops up in a leaflet on the new back-fixing versions of the well-known Pathfinder and Projector fog and long-range lamps, specially designed for cars with frontispieces offering little or no bottom-fixing toehold. Use of a gas-filled sealed-beam unit eliminates reflector blemishing and thereby *minimises the ghost images*.

Incidentally, if you feel like giving your Pathfinder or Projector hell, go ahead. A pair have been in use for months on one of the famous Canadian Hell Drivers' cars. Scatheless, believe it or not.

Headlamp dipping is one thing and dimming is another, but the twain meet and combine to make nocturnal motoring safer in Thorn Special Products' new Dip Dim device. It's operated from the sidelight switch position and lights up dipped headlamps to one-tenth of their normal brightness. So . . . townee pedestrians can easily see you coming but you dazzle nobody.

Meanwhile, Philips Electrical score a first with an application of the iodine lamp to paired (as distinct from foursome) headlights. The name is the same as the Thorn job's, but hyphenated—Dip-Dim. Up to now, this extra powerful candlery has been confined to fog and spot lamps on the one hand, four-eyes headlamp systems on the other. It will take a while, say Philips, for headlamp manufacturers (which Philips aren't) to develop new reflectors and diffraction frontglasses to complement the Dip-Dim equipment. A step in the right direction, anyway.

What do you ask from a car seat cover? Snazzy looks? Protection for your upholstery? Anything else? Well, Kumficar throw in a bonus with their new GT covers. These are contoured and padded to give an authentic bucket effect in their own right. The formula evidently works because forefront competition drivers—John Cardwell and Peter Bolton for two—are already sitting pretty on GTs. Tailored to fit Minis, 1100s, Anglias, Imps, Vivas and such.

Another standout for Khyber-region comfort is the replacement sports seat marketed by Motor Books and Accessories. Nothing skimped here: correctly shaped sub-thigh bolster and small-of-the-back convexity, ample bucketing, attractively fluted squab, black upholstery as standard but a choice of colours at £1 extra. Seating which ensures that you and your car take the same course round fast corners, instead of quite different ones sometimes, is seldom cheap, of course, and this M. B. and A. line is tagged £13.10.0. plus carriage.

If you're shopping for lumbar luxury at a lower price and are less concerned with resistance to lateral displacement of your person on corners, the new and unusual Adjust-O-Bak backrest, by Autocovers Ltd., may be just your buy. The squab bulge is pneumatic, inflatable, and you can regulate its size and location to suit your physical characteristics, or your front-seat passenger's, or both. Looks good value at 32/6.

At least three leading accessory houses, rising to the challenge of motoring heads a-wobble on their spinal columns, have recently come up with new headrests. The Conway offering, designated Multiway GT (favourite initials right now) is a most inviting-looking dumpling . . . "adjusts upwards and downwards, forwards and backwards, and to a multitude of angles". Price £4.17.6., fits all car seats, six-way choice of colours.

Next-up headrest is by KL Automotive Products and again has a multitude of adjustments. Playing up the safety angle, KL point out that injury to the user's neck is prevented in the event of an up-my-bustle shunt from a following car. Upholstered in washable polyvinyl, either

continued on page 63

Here's the Desmo Headrest, with a foam interior, "moulded to give all round support for the head and neck." This headrest comes in a variety of colours to suit any car's interior and the vinyl surface cleans with a wipe. The recommended retail price is under £3.

In—and out of— the open air there's a gadget for you

continued from page 61

red, blue, black or tan. Price, £6.2.6, suitable for bench or separate seats of most shapes and sizes.

Headrest number three comes from Desmo and would even look good without the girl who models it in our photograph. Easy on the pocket at its recommended retail price of under £3, this neat cranium coddler is narrower than the other two but its appearance confirms a claim that it has been scientifically contoured for maximum head and neck support.

Windscreen disintegration at speed is a shattering experience, and if you're far from home on a winter's day (or night, worse still) when it happens, well, too bad. Not quite so bad, though, if your boot-borne spares include a Compact Temporary Windscreen, brainwaved by Humphrey Thompson Enterprises. It's made from "optically perfect" sheet plastic material, rolls into a neat sausage less than three inches in diameter for stowing, has secure door-jamb attachments at each end, permits normal wiper and washer operation up to 70 m.p.h., claim the makers. Standard pattern costs 45/-, extra large model for screens over 18 ins. deep, 65/-.

A gimmick with a different primary purpose but a passing similarity is Kumficar's clear-plastic windscreen frost shield. A boon to the all-weather commuter who has to abandon his car to our climate for maybe nine hours a day. Pad fixings slot into the car doors, proof against all but really maniac robbers. As a secondary function in an emergency, say Kumficar, this one will stand in as a temporary replacement for a broken screen. Unpricey at 9/11.

In April showers type weather, do you sometimes tire of jitter bugging your screen wipers on and off by hand? B.R.M. Electronics aim to save you this vhf chore with a transistorised device called the Spasmo, which can be switched in to provide regular wiping stints with ten-second lulls between them. (*Thinks*: How often, by the law of averages, would Spasmo wipe when the screen was

dry, desist when wet?) "Less wear and tear on screen and wiper blades, reduced eye fatigue, highly intrigued passengers!" £5.15.6, all in.

If the leading maker of windscreen glass doesn't know how to combat smear, who does? New anti-smear goo called Decosol was developed in Triplex's own laboratories, though another firm markets it. On sale at most garages—5/6 a time. You add Decosol to your squirter water.

A car cosmetic of a different sort, not long on the market, is Prestone Blemish Remover, by Union Carbide. Ingredients include rubbing compound, so the action is mildly abrasive. Good stuff for getting out the less-than-skindeep scratches that most motorists, including those who don't drink *and* drive, find developing in the course of time around their cars' keyholes. 5/6 per tin.

Draining and replacing gearbox and back axle lubricant is a bore that will shortly exist entirely in the past tense, but the long-suffering *boite* will

An urgent and practical solution to the inconvenience, discomfort and hazard of having to drive a car after the initial shock and emergency of a shattered windscreen is now available in the form of stow-away plastic screens which can be fitted speedily. This one is the Compact Temporary Windscreen, invented by Humphrey Thompson Enterprises, a member of the Rootes of Slough Group. It is designed to fit over windscreen areas of all shapes and sizes.

presumably always need periodic topping-up. This is a less dirty, less difficult operation if you use Castrol's specially designed squeeze pack with a long, flexible feed duct. Gives you the last laugh on tucked-away filler orifices. The price is the same, 3/6, whichever your grade of transmission tipple.

continued on page 64

Karobes of Leamington Spa have introduced a series of wheel trims suitable for most popular British cars. They are made of anodised aluminium, are chemically treated to prevent stain, and are easy to clean with water only—no polish is needed. They are fitted by removing the car hub cap, placing the wheel trim into position and snapping the hub cap back into position over the trim.

SAME GIRL, DIFFERENT GADGET

Also from Karobes Ltd. comes the Straddle Saddle which weighs only 2 lb yet can bear 20 stones! It has a solid hide seat, three leg pockets into which wooden legs slip easily, and is suitable for picnicking, camping, fishing.

Off or on the road

continued from page 63

On my left—a rear-end suspension stabiliser bar for Hydrolastic Minis. On my right—a new, wing-fitting, streamlined, rear-view mirror. So what for heaven's sake do these things have in common? Nothing, except that both are the brainchildren of well-known racing drivers, Graham Hill and Alan Rees respectively. Never underrate a product that a competition driver personally designs or develops or both.

Hill's firm, Speedwell Performance Conversions, have of course specialised for years in anti-roll devices for both front and back ends of volume-produced cars, and this latest one, like its companion pieces, was evolved in veritable circuit tests by Graham himself. Incidentally, Speedwell go one better than merely freezing prices—they recently lopped 15% off the cost of nearly all their a-r bars.

Alan Rees, wholesale winner of Formula 2 events for Roy Winkelmann Racing Ltd., wanted a mirror with an oversize reflection area and without the normal ¼-in. circumferential cut-off—and got it. Actual glass diameter of the Winkrace Mirror is 3¾ ins., rim thickness only 1/16 in. All-adhesive (i.e., springless) lens location is claimed to obviate long-term water infiltration and resulting corrosion. A smashed lens can be replaced in minutes. Two prices, up to 30/6.

Reinsert thumb and pull out another plum: Wingard's new Reflex range of rear-view mirrors, which were the first in their field to receive official approval from the Design Centre's recently established motor accessories section. "Unique feature of the head design is the dish-shaped cavity on the rear face, which provides for a greater angular movement of adjustment, which in turn provides a greater field of vision . . ."

(*By the way, this is a general rundown on interesting accessories and preparations which have hit the market lately—you won't necessarily find them all at Earls Court.*)

Some wheel trims embellish wheels, others just mess them up. Karobes' new trim, we'd say, definitely prettifies—even if it's out-prettied by the girl handling it in the photograph. Material is anodised aluminium, chemically treated to prevent stain and cleanable with straight water—no polishing needed. Sizes to fit most popular makes and models, price 49/6 per set.

Unless your next stop, post-Show, is a sunnier clime than ours, you aren't likely to do much carborne picnicking *this* year; but here are a couple of items to keep in mind for the morrow's meals awheel: one, the Variett Multi-Purpose Table; two, the Straddle Saddle. Former is made by Arnex Products of Daventry, has a height adjustment range from 2 to 3 ft, folds flat for stowing, costs about £9.15.0. Latter, price 49/6, weighs only 2 lb. but will take a 20-stone "rider".

Ever envied those rich folk on the movies who drive nonchalantly into their domestic garages through automatically opening doors? Now it seems you don't have to be all *that* rich to enjoy this relief from legwork and fingering. There isn't room here to describe the Pad-O-Matic door opening tackle, beyond saying that motive power for the up-and-over action is mechanical, not electrical; but the point is that the whole works, packaged and delivered for DIY installation, costs no more than £8.17.6. Makers are Anthony Mendelle Ltd., of S. Woodford, E.18.

For slaves of the small screen who include caravanning, automobilious picnicking and camping among their incidental pastimes, Philips have a sure-fire attraction with their T-Vette portable television. At home, you plug it into the mains like any other domestic set; on the run (in the inculpable sense) you throw a switch and hook up your T-Vette to the car's 12-volt battery. Rest of the story, abridged: Fully transistorised; consumption on 12 V., 1½ amps.; 11 in. screen; weight, 23 lbs.; price, BBC 1 and ITV only, £60.14.3. . . all this and BBC 2, £66.0.10.

Quick looks at a few others:—

The Variett, a versatile cantilever table (picture above), folds flat and can easily be stored in the boot of any car. The height is adjustable from 2ft. to 3ft. and enables you, say the makers, "to picnic in the comfort of your car, without having to perform a juggling feat with plates and glasses".

On the right, the Conway Universal wheel glove in foam-backed nylon comes in red, blue, grey or green at 9s. 6d.

1. Ceag's Lumax RA9 car radio aerial does a cent-percent vanishing act when off duty—retracts totally into the wing, like the Indian rope trick in reverse, thus foiling would-be vandals. £2.17.6.

2. Would-be car thieves get *their* latest pain in the neck from the new Autosafe locking device. "Acts as a non-return valve in the hydraulic braking system", so removal of the key provided automatically applies the brakes. Not only that—opening an Autosafed car door also starts the horn blowing. Prices not quoted.

3. Eye-catcher among the current crop of new or newish safety belts is a Wingard number incorporating an instant-release mechanism—the Push-Button Buckle. So you crash. So your life is saved. So the next step is to get overboard, fast. So you just press the button and you're free.

Happy ending.

CROSSWORD SOLUTION

ACROSS:—1. Humber Hawk. 7. Viva. 9. Lagonda. 10. Lane. 11. Sits. 12. Eye (rev.). 13. Parts. 14. Key. 15. Aston. 17. Herald-ry. 22. Traction. 25. Minor. 26. Gas. 27. Lorry. 28. Duo. 29. Isis. 32. Alf-a (Romeo). 33. Ferrari. 34. Asti. 35. Petrol tank. DOWN:—1. Half-shaft. 2. Might. 3. Ed-na. 4. (Austin) Healey. 5. Wolseley. 6. Over-all. 8. Victor. 14. Knot. 16. Tea. 18. Arms. 19. Din. 20. Yardstick. 21. Road race. 23. Rootes. 24. Corsair. 26. Golfer. 30. Scapa (scarper). 31. (Carl) O-Ral (ly).

CARS
OF THE LATE 60'S
BRITISH AND IMPORTED MODELS 1965-1969

MOTOR SHOW REVIEW GUIDE
1967

A - Z
SECTION

As the problem of the roads gets BIGGER

This Peel single-seater has a single-cylinder two-stroke engine driving a single rear wheel, glass fibre body and transparent plastic canopy. It's almost as easy to pick up as a suitcase.

—is it the right answer for the cars to get SMALLER?

AS we choose our new cars from the glittering array on the stands at Earls Court, we know that they are going to be less and less use to us in towns and cities unless drastic action is taken to solve traffic problems. British Governments always proceed on the principle that you can take thousands of millions of pounds in taxes from motor users and go on cramming the traffic into city streets designed for a population half the size. Professor Buchanan has shown that it isn't going to work even if you abolish the private car altogether, but as it is too late to adapt our cities to the traffic, can we adapt the traffic to the streets? Is the City Car the answer?

If you insist on seats for four adults the Mini is probably the smallest practicable car. Alec Issigonis said "The only way I could make the car shorter would be to make the people stand up". Most major manufacturers agree that for mass sales and low prices, four seats are essential but Fiat have sold over a million of the Fiat 500 with space for two adults and two children and the baby Honda is now challenging for the same market. Does the future lie with seriously engineered sub-Mini cars, designed for space saving in city streets? They must be quite unlike the freaks that have lost money for so many eager inventors in the past;

cars you could fold up and park under the stairs, the egg-shaped cars, in which a single person sat with head and shoulders exposed like a chicken in the act of hatching, the tandem cars steered by handle-bars in which two people sat one behind the other. They usually failed because of freakish appearance, poor performance, lack of weather protection, unreliability and poor secondhand value.

The smallest car I have driven was a Peel single-seater with three wheels, made in the

Isle of Man. It looked like a sedan chair on Kart wheels. Steering was terribly sensitive and the first time I tried to take a corner it fell over. The designer must have expected this because skids were built in underneath the plastic body. Nevertheless it was a sound shape for a single-seater town car and parking could not have been easier. You simply lifted the rear with the aid of a built-in handle and swung it into any available corner. A four-wheel version might have been quite a practical proposition.

Eric J. Roberts, a Somerset designer, has a project for a two seat town car only 89 in. long. It could be parked end-on to the kerb and three of them would fit into a normal parking meter space but this wouldn't help much. First, it's illegal; second, you couldn't open the doors to get out. Dennis Adams, formerly with Marcos Cars, designed a single-seater rear-engined coupe in plywood which was so light that you could stand it on end when you reached your destination and a London design student built a single-seater town car on a Kart chassis, also designed to stand on end, but weather protection was minimal and it must have been daunting to sit in traffic jams looking up at the wheels of trucks and buses. To use such cars

This idea for a two-seater town car is by Italian designers. The complete top swings up and over for easy entry in crowded parking places.

In a motor-car built for two?

The E.J.R. two-seater town car on the left has the engine at the rear driving the front wheels. Its extreme steering lock enables it to turn almost in its own length of 89in. On the right is Ford's electric car, the Commuta.

efficiently we need special parking places and special traffic lanes.

The main source of air pollution in British cities is the fuel used in factories, homes, power stations and gas works but the motor vehicle gets most of the blame. The Ministry of Transport report on Cars for Cities has shown that petrol engined city cars could be produced with exhausts innocuous enough for all British needs but large sums have already been spent on experiments with electric city cars, most of which have now been abandoned. Ford are going ahead with their Commuta but in stop-go city driving with fast acceleration from one traffic light to the next, it would need recharging every 20 miles and no significant improvement can be expected until it receives an experimental sulphur-electrolyte battery in 1968. Mass production is probably ten years away. The nice idea of plugging electric city cars into sockets on parking meters for recharging has aleady run into trouble; a battery charger adds 40 or 50 lb. to the weight of a car and it is not considered safe to have wires carrying mains voltage dangling from cars in public places. An electric city car will therefore have to be recharged where its batteries can be plugged in to existing chargers.

Even Ford's stylists have not been able to make anything elegant out of a car 80 in. long and 56 in. high. Nor does it seem very convenient. Parking end-on to the kerb you couldn't open the doors and the only carrying space for bulky parcels is on the back seats which are not easy to reach. Cars designed for parking end-on to kerbs need doors at front and rear but this is not very safe because they can be jammed shut in a collision. An Italian inventor produced a city car with a cylindrical body which rotates so that you can get out at any point where there is room, but who wants to ride around in a mobile dustbin?

The Electricity Council see electrically driven city cars as a rich new market for electric current and have produced figures showing that an electric car could be operated with due allowance for depreciation, insurance, garage and maintenance for 8½d. a mile, against a shilling for an equivalent petrol car in the same conditions, but in Britain motor traffic has to provide tax revenue equal to more than four times what the government spends on the roads. If electric cars reduced the revenue, they would be loaded with taxes to make them as expensive to run as petrol cars. So why put up with all the weight and high cost of batteries?

So far, we have not even begun to make efficient use of the cars we have in city streets. Propagandists for public transport point to the number of cars that travel with driver only

on board, but the law forbids efficient use of cars in cities by making it illegal for commuting passengers to share the running costs.

The report on Cars for Cities shows that there is very little benefit from reducing the size of cars still further so long as they have to travel in the 12-foot wide lanes used by trucks and buses. If we simply re-planned our road lanes to make maximum use of our present cars we could move five people for every four we move today. If we marked out lanes for Minis, Imps and baby Fiats, we could move six people for every four the streets accommodate today, and lanes designed to fit sub-Mini city cars could double the present capacity of existing streets. City cars would also double the capacity of existing parking places and they could travel on cheap, lightweight fly-overs impractical for heavier traffic.

To increase the capacity of the streets beyond this point calls for automatic guidance systems which will steer cars down lanes too narrow for human drivers to use safely. This can now be done, but the more difficult problem is to produce proximity control which senses obstructions ahead and allows vehicles to travel closer behind each other without risk of multiple shunts.

Mrs. Castle seems to prefer schemes for discouraging the use of private cars by restricting off-street parking and diverting the money from parking meters to other uses. (You didn't really believe all those solemn pledges, did you?) She is looking at schemes for roads reserved for buses running under computerised traffic control, but it is a safe bet that any take-over of city streets by public transport will be financed from one source only; from

The Fiat 500 is the smallest car at present in mass production by a major manufacturer. It is the cheapest car on the British market at £410 tax paid. It has a two-cylinder air-cooled engine at the rear driving rear wheels.

further taxation on the only efficient, flexible and self-supporting system of passenger transport we have, and the one which already helps to support all the others: the private car.

A battery electric passenger car. Chief engineer Dr. W. G. Watson and Chief Designer Mr. J. Chalmers photographed with their 'Scamp' commuter car.

Thank goodness at Rover there are still people who think precision engineering comes before mass production.

People running in every engine for perfect smoothness, before it's even fitted into the car. (And then changing the oil to remove any stray speck of dirt that might damage an engine.)

And people taking every single Rover 2000 that's built for mile after mile of test-driving, to ensure that everything works smoothly, silently, at peak efficiency.

While other car makers churn out their products, we take a bit more time and care. We have to. With every Rover 2000 built, our name is at stake.

For more information see your local dealer. Or write to us: Sales Division, The Rover Company Limited, Solihull, Warwickshire.

Rover 2000 prices (inc. purchase tax): SC Manual £1,357.9.10; SC Automatic £1,452.2.8; TC version £1,415.5.2.

Rover 2000 SC/SC Automatic/TC

In an age of mass production thank goodness a Rover is still a Rover

RXC 425F

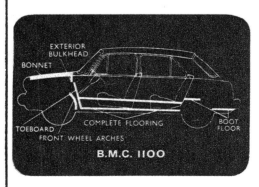

105

1967

drawing by Robb

Now you are on your way . . . with this handy comprehensive A to Z guide

— and an Estate Car BONUS

A.C. 428

THOUGH Cobras continue their striking career, especially in USA, AC are building up production of the 428 for those who want high performance with luxury and style. Choice of convertible or fastback coupe with electrically operated windows styled by Frua on a tubular chassis. Power in plenty comes from a 7-litre Ford V8 engine with choice of four-speed manual or fully automatic transmission.

CLOSE-UP
Eight-cyl.; o.h.v.; 104.9×101.1 mm.; 6,989 c.c.; 345 b.h.p. gross; 10.5 to 1 comp.; Ford 4-choke carb.; 4-speed, 6.68, 4.86, 3.72, 2.88 to 1; cen. lvr. auto. opt.; susp., f. and r. ind coil; 2-door; 2-seat; disc servo brks.; max. 140 m.p.h.; cruise, 115; m.p.g. 13-18; whl. base, 8ft.; track f. 4ft. 7in., r. 4ft. 8in.; lgth., 14ft. 6in.; width 5ft. 7in.; ht. 4ft. 3in.; g.c. 5in.; turng. cir., 35ft.; kerb wt. 28 cwt.; tank 15 gals.; 12-volt.
£3,750 + £861 p.t. = £4,611

ALFA ROMEO GIULIA 1300 TI

SWIMMING against the tide, Alfa Romeo reintroduce the smaller engine of 1,290 c.c. in Giulia saloons and coupes, as an alternative to the 1,570 c.c. unit. They say many lady drivers prefer it. Men too may be glad to save on first cost, and perhaps on insurance, if not on fuel consumption, by taking the smaller unit now that Auntie Castle has destroyed the usefulness of fast cars.

CLOSE-UP
Four-cyl.; o.h.c.; 74×75 mm.; 1,290 c.c.; 82 b.h.p.; 9 to 1 comp.; Solex carb.; 5-speed, 16.93, 10.19, 6.94, 5.13, 4.05 to 1; cen. lvr.; susp., f. ind. coil, r. coil; 4-door; 5-seat; disc brks.; max. 97 m.p.h.; cruise, 88; m.p.g. 21-24; whl. base, 8ft. 2½in.; track f. 4ft. 4in., r. 4ft. 2in.; lgth., 13ft. 7in.; width, 5ft. 2in.; ht. 4ft. 10in.; g.c. 6½in.; turng. cir., 38ft.; kerb wt. 19¼ cwt.; tank, 10 gals.; 12-volt.
£995 + £230 p.t. = £1,225

Abbreviations—g.c.—ground clearance; susp.—suspension; f.—front; r.—rear; comp.—compression; s.v.—side-valves; o.h.v.—overhead valves; o.h.c.—overhead camshaft; hyd.—hydraulic.

ALFA GIULIA GT VELOCE

FASTEST of the regular production Giulia coupes, with the clear-cut Bertone styling. Two twin-choke Weber carburetters boost the power and radial-ply tyres give maximum grip on corners. The same engine goes in the Pininfarina Duetto Spider and for racing there's the aluminium-bodied GTA coupe with twin-ignition and twin fuel pumps which was European touring car champion 1966.

CLOSE-UP

Four-cyl.; o.h.c.; 78×82 mm.; 1,570 c.c.; 107 b.h.p.; 9.1 to 1 comp.; 2 Weber twin-choke carbs.; 5-speed, 15.05, 9.05, 6.17, 5.55, 3.6 to 1; cen. lvr.; susp., f. ind. coil, r. coil; 2-door; 2/4-seat; disc brks.; max. 116 m.p.h.; cruise, 95; m.p.g. 20-25; whl. base, 7ft. 9in.; track f. 4ft. 3½in., r. 4ft. 2in.; lgth., 13ft. 5in.; width 5ft. 2in.; ht. 4ft. 4in.; g.c. 5½in.; turng. cir., 32ft.; kerb wt., 19 cwt.; tank, 10½ gals.; 12-volt.

£1,585+£365 p.t. = £1,950

ASTON MARTIN DB6

THE sudden price cut earlier this year put it into the best seller class of luxury sports cars. One of the first to have the aerodynamic spoiler on the familiar fast-back styling, this Aston Martin holds the road magnificently. Volante is convertible version. And don't miss the sleek new DBS coupe. Same engine, wider, lower body, De Dion rear.

CLOSE-UP

Six-cyl.; o.h.c.; 96×92 mm.; 3,995 c.c.; 282 b.h.p.; 8.75 to 1 comp.; 3 S.U. carbs.; 5-speed, 10.29, 6.64, 4.64, 3.77, 3.14 to 1; cen. lvr., auto. opt.; susp. f. ind. coil, r. coil; 2-door; 4-seat; disc servo brks.; max. 150 m.p.h.; cruise 125; m.p.g. 15-18; whl. base. 8ft. 5½in.; track f. 4ft. 6in., r. 4ft. 5½in.; lgth. 15ft. 2in.; width 5ft. 6in.; ht. 4ft. 5½in.; g.c. 5in.; turng. cir. 34ft.; kerb wt. 29 cwt.; tank 19 gals.; 12-volt.

£3,308+£960 p.t. = £4,068

AUSTIN WESTMINSTER 3-LITRE

INHERITING obvious body features from the roomy 1800, the Westminster is in fact a different, bigger car, with front-mounted six-cylinder engine driving the rear wheels. Like BMC front-drive models it has all-independent Hydrolastic suspension by rubber cones with hydraulic interconnection. Front brakes are discs, power assisted steering is standard. Borg Warner 35 automatic transmission is an optional extra.

CLOSE-UP

Six-cyl.; o.h.v.; 83.3×88.9 mm.; 2,912 c.c.; 118 b.h.p.; 8.2 to 1 comp.; 2 SU carbs.; 4-speed, 13.43, 8.48, 5.4, 3.9 to 1; cen. lvr., auto. opt.; susp. f. and r. ind. rubber-hyd.; 4-door; 5/6-seat; hyd. servo brks., disc front; max. 104 m.p.h.; cruise 85; m.p.g. 18-22; whl. base 9ft. 7½in.; track f. 4ft. 8½in., r. 4ft. 8in.; lgth. 15ft. 5½in.; width 5ft. 6¾in.; ht. 4ft. 8½in.; g.c. 6½in.; turng. cir. 37ft. 6in.; kerb wt. 29½ cwt.; tank 15½ gals.; 12-volt.

AUSTIN MINI COOPER S

THE S could stand for Speed, Safety or Stamina; this legendary little car has them all. Winner of countless races and rallies, it takes rough roads, snow or ice in its stride. Front-wheel drive and Hydrolastic suspension ensure cat-sure road holding and the 1,275 c.c. engine gives performance that leaves many sports cars standing.

CLOSE-UP

Four-cyl.; o.h.v.; 70.64×81.33 mm.; 1,275 c.c.; 75 b.h.p.; 9.75 to 1 comp.; 2 S.U. carbs.; 4-speed, 11.02, 6.6, 4.67, 3.44 to 1; cen. lvr.; susp. f. and r. ind. rubber-hydraulic; 2-door; 4-seat; hyd. servo brks., disc front; max. 95 m.p.h.; cruise 85; m.p.g. 28-32; whl. base 6ft. 8in.; track, f. 4ft. 0⅜in., r. 3ft. 11¼in.; lgth. 10ft. 0⅜in.; width 4ft. 7½in.; ht. 4ft. 5in.; g.c. 6in.; turng. cir. 31½ft.; tank 5½ gals.; 12-volt.

£689+£160 p.t. = £849

AUSTIN 1300

THIS is an interesting addition to the 1300 c.c. range which now has a big following. Latest model has a 1,275 c.c. engine developing 58 b.h.p. With the bigger engine it has a different grille and general good looks. It is a car just as much at home in traffic or out on the road. And it appeals to the owner who wants low cost but robust motoring. A sound B.M.H. product.

CLOSE-UP
Four-cyl.; o.h.v.; 70.6 × 81.3 mm.; 1,275 c.c.; 58 b.h.p.; 8.8 to 1 comp.; SU carb.; 4-speed, 13.23, 7.95, 5.16, 3.65 to 1; cen. lvr., auto opt.; susp. f. and r. ind. rubber-hyd.; 2 or 4-door; 4/5-seat; hyd. brks., disc front; max. 90 m.p.h.; cruise 80; m.p.g. 30-36; whl. base 7ft. 9½in.; track f. 4ft. 3½in.; r. 4ft. 2⅞in.; lgth. 12ft. 2¾in.; width 5ft. 0⅜in.; ht. 4ft. 5in.; g.c. 5¼in.; turng. cir.; 38ft.; kerb wt. 16¾ cwt.; tank 8 gals.; 12-volt.

AUSTIN HEALEY SPRITE MK IV

HERE is a nippy runabout sports car that excels in dodging through traffic as well as swishing through the countryside with a gay, light touch. Minor modifications include changed tail lamps with a rear lamp for going astern. Its winding windows with hinged quarter lights serve both driver and passenger. A sound B.M.H. product that gives its occupants a lot of fun.

CLOSE-UP
Four-cyl.; o.h.v.; 70.6 × 81.3 mm.; 1,275 c.c.; 70 b.h.p.; 9.75 to 1 comp.; 2 S.U. carbs.; 4-speed, 13.5, 8.09, 5.73, 4.22 to 1; cen. lvr.; susp., f. ind. coil, r. half-elliptic; 2-door; 2-seat; hyd. brks., disc front; max. 95 m.p.h.; cruise 80; m.p.g. 26-30; whl base 6ft. 8in.; track, f. 3ft. 10½in., r. 3ft. 8¾in.; lgth. 11ft. 5¼in.; width 4ft. 5in.; ht. 4ft. 0½in.; g.c. 5in.; turng. cir. 32ft.; kerb wt. 13½ cwt.; tank 6 gals.; 12-volt.

£545 + £127 p.t. = £672

AUDI SUPER 90

FRONT-WHEEL-DRIVE star of the Volkswagen group, the Audi has a Mercedes-designed engine with bowl-in-piston combustion chambers and high-swirl inlet ports. New manifolds, twin-choke compound carburetter and capacity hoisted to 1,760 c.c. make the Super 90 a fast, quiet and refined family car with outstanding top-gear flexibility. Lower-priced 70 and 80 are continued.

CLOSE-UP
Four-cyl.; o.h.v.; 81.5 × 84.4 mm.; 1,760 c.c.; 90 b.h.p.; 10.6 to 1 comp.; Solex carb.; 4-speed, 13.22, 7.56, 5.13, 3.63 to 1; col. lvr.; susp., f. ind. torsion bar, r. torsion bar; 2/4-door; 4/5-seat; hyd. brks., disc front; max. 100 m.p.h.; cruise 90; m.p.g. 21-25; whl. base 8ft. 2in.; track, f. 4ft. 4⅞in., r. 4ft. 4⅛in.; lgth. 14ft. 4½in.; width 5ft. 4in.; ht. 4ft. 9⅛in.; g.c. 7½in.; turng. cir. 34ft. 5in.; kerb wt. 19½ cwt., tank 11⅝ gals.; 12-volt.

£970 + £224 p.t. = £1,194

BENTLEY T-TYPE

A true caviar-and-champagne sports car that has just about the lot in sophisticated, sporting motoring. Now that it is being given a drop-head-bodied sister every possible taste is catered for among the privileged and the wealthy. Actually it is a replica of the Rolls-Royce Silver Shadow except for the more sporting Bentley radiator grille. Many of the controls are worked by electrics and it has all-independent, self-levelling suspension.

CLOSE-UP
Eight-cyl.; o.h.v.; 104.1 × 91.4 mm.; 6,230 c.c.; b.h.p. not revealed; 9 to 1 comp.; 2 S.U. carbs.; 4-speed auto., 11.75, 8.1, 4.46, 3.08 to 1; col. lvr.; susp. f. and r. ind. coil, hyd. levelling; 4-door; 5-seat; disc. hyd. servo brks.; max. 120 m.p.h.; cruise 100; m.p.g. 13-16; whl. base 9ft. 11½in.; track f. and r. 4ft. 9½in.; lgth. 16ft. 11½in.; width 5ft. 11in.; ht. 4ft. 11¾in.; g.c. 6½in.; turng. cir. 38ft.; kerb wt. 41½ cwt.; tank 24 gals.; 12-volt.

£5,620 + £1,290 p.t. = £6,910

Abbreviations—g.c.—ground clearance; susp.—suspension; f.—front; r.—rear; comp.—compression; s.v.—side-valves; o.h.v.—overhead valves; o.h.c.—overhead camshaft; hyd.—hydraulic.

BMW 1600

SMALLER car with the high performance and fine handling expected from the famous Bavarian factory, now available with right-hand drive. The compact but roomy two-door body is in typical BMW style. The luggage boot is large and there's a lockable glove box. Headlamp flasher, anti-theft steering lock, two-speed wipers and washer are standard. There's a new high performance T1 version too.

CLOSE-UP
Four-cyl.; o.h.c.; 71 × 84 mm.; 1,573 c.c.; 85 b.h.p.; 8.6 to 1 comp.; Solex carb.; 4-speed, 16.74, 8.95, 5.85, 4.37 to 1; cen. lvr.; susp., f. and r. ind. coil; 2-door; 4-seat; hyd. brks., disc front; max. 100 m.p.h.; cruise, 85; m.p.g. 27-29; whl. base 8ft. 2½in.; track f. and r. 4ft. 4in.; lgth. 14ft. 1½in.; width 5ft. 2⅛in.; ht. 4ft. 7½in.; g.c. 6in.; turng. cir. 31ft. 6in.; kerb wt. 18½ cwt.; tank 10 gals.; 6-volt.
£1,055 + £243 p.t. = £1,298

BMW 2000

BAVARIA, famous for baroque castles and beer, gains extra distinction as the home of the BMW. The 2000, most powerful of the range, comes in various forms; the swift, luxurious, normal saloon, the sporting T1, and the shapely coupes, with two states of engine tune and two kinds of transmission. The Anglicised 2000 T1 carries the Frazer-Nash-BMW name plate and has a vinyl-covered roof.

CLOSE-UP
Four-cyl.; o.h.c.; 89 ∕ 80 mm.; 1,990 c.c.; 100 b.h.p.; 8.5 to 1 comp.; Solex carb.; 4-speed, 15.76, 8.42, 5.51, 4.11 to 1; cen. lvr.; susp., f. and r. ind. coil; 4-door; 5-seat; hyd. servo brks., disc front; max. 104 m.p.h.; cruise, 88; m.p.g. 22-26; whl. base 8ft. 4½in.; track f. 4ft. 4in., r. 4ft. 6in.; lgth., 14ft. 9in.; width 5ft. 5in.; ht. 4ft. 8¾in.; g.c. 6½in.; turng. cir 31ft. 6in.; kerb wt. 21⅞ cwt.; tank, 12 gals.; 12-volt.
£1,445 + £333 p.t. = £1,778

BOND EQUIPE 2-LITRE GT

SUCCESSFULLY launched on quantity production of glass fibre coupes on Herald chassis with Spitfire engines, which are sold by Triumph agents, Bond now present a more ambitious model with Vitesse 2-litre engine. The Vitesse chassis and scuttle are retained with a more sloping windscreen and the car offers inexpensive individuality with full Triumph warranty on mechanical parts. Wire wheels are standard; overdrive is extra.

CLOSE-UP
Six-cyl.; o.h.v.; 74.7 × 76 mm.; 1,998 c.c.; 95 b.h.p.; 9.5 to 1 comp.; 2 Stromberg carbs; 4-speed, 10.31, 6.92, 4.86, 3.89 to 1.; cen. lvr., Laycock de Normanville overdrive opt.; susp., f. ind. coil, r. ind. transv. leaf; 2-door; 2/4-seat; hyd. brks., disc front; max. 100 m.p.h.; cruise, 90; m.p.g. 26-28; whl. base, 7ft. 7½in.; track f. 4ft. 1in., r. 4ft.; lgth., 13ft. 10in.; width, 5ft. 1½in.; ht. 4ft. 4½in.; g.c. 6½in.; turng. cir., 25ft.; kerb wt. 18 cwt.; tank, 9 gals.; 12-volt.
£895 + £201 p.t. = £1,096

BRISTOL 410

A famous aircraft firm which specialises in keen, precision engineering originally produced the car with these attributes. So this new Bristol model is not only a pleasure to own and drive but its workmanship ensures a very long life. Latest improvements aid engine performance, braking and suspension and there are new body and trim refinements. A good-looking car that has a very staunch following.

CLOSE-UP
Eight-cyl.; o.h.v.; 99.3 × 84.07 mm.; 5,211 c.c.; 250 b.h.p. gross; 9 to 1 comp.; Carter 4-choke carb.; 3-speed auto, 7.5, 4.5, 3.07 to 1; push button control; susp., f. ind. coil, r. torsion bar; 2-door; 4-seat; disc servo brks.; max. 125 m.p.h.; cruise 100; m.p.g. 18-20; whl. base 9ft. 6in.; track f. 4ft. 6in., r. 4ft. 6½in.; lgth. 16ft. 1½in.; width 5ft. 8in.; ht. 4ft. 11in.; g.c. 6½in.; turng. cir. 39ft. 6in.; kerb wt. 32 cwt.; tank 18 gals.; 12-volt.
£4,260 + £1,113 p.t. = £5,373

Abbreviations—g.c.—ground clearance; susp.—suspension; f.—front; r.—rear; comp.—compression; s.v.—side-valves; o.h.v.—overhead valves; o.h.c.—overhead camshaft; hyd.—hydraulic.

BUICK RIVIERA

ADMIRED as one of America's best-looking cars, the Riviera has a bolder front end plus cornering lamps; adds four-way hazard warning switch using all four flashers simultaneously and short-duration lane-change indicator. A limited-slip differential curtails wheelspin when the full torque of the 7-litre V8 engine is unleashed, the servo brakes (discs in front) have twin master cylinders and warning lamp to indicate defects.

CLOSE-UP

Eight-cyl.; o.h.v.; 106×99 mm.; 7,047 c.c.; 360 b.h.p. gross; 10.25 to 1 comp.; Rochester 4-choke carb.; 3-speed auto., 8.48, 5.06, 3.42 to 1; col. lvr.; susp. f. ind. coil, r. coil; 2-door; 4-seat; hyd. servo brks., disc front; max. 120 m.p.h.; cruise 100; m.p.g. 13-17; whl. base 9ft. 11in.; track f. 5ft. 3⅜in., r. 5ft. 3in.; lgth. 17ft. 11½in.; width 6ft. 6⅞in.; ht. 4ft. 5⅜in.; g.c. 6in.; turng. cir. 42ft. 4in.; kerb wt. 38¾ cwt.; tank 17½ gals.; 12-volt.

BUICK GRAN SPORT

BOULEVARD Buick with 5.7-litre engine and two-door six-seater body. Power steering, two-speed automatic transmission, limited slip differential, disc front brakes with twin circuits and warning lamp are mechanical features. Four-way electrically operated front seat, remote-control outside mirror, stereo radio and tape player, complete the equipment of a car that is more bird-trap than rally winner.

CLOSE-UP

Eight-cyl.; o.h.v.; 96.5×97.8 mm.; 5,736 c.c.; 285 b.h.p. gross; 10.25 to 1 comp.; Rochester 4-choke carb.; 2-speed auto., 8.48, 5.06, 3.42 to 1; cen. lvr.; susp. f. ind. coil, r. coil; 2-door; 4-seat; hyd. servo brks., disc front; max. 112 m.p.h.; cruise 95; m.p.g. 13-16; whl. base 9ft. 4in.; track f. and r. 4ft. 11in.; lgth. 16ft. 8⅝in.; width 6ft. 3½in.; ht. 4ft. 4⅞in.; g.c. 7in.; turng. cir. 40ft.; kerb wt. 33¾ cwt.; tank 16¾ gals.; 12-volt.

CADILLAC ELDORADO

ULTIMATE in opulence, American style, the front-drive Eldorado has a still bigger engine for 1968. "Tilt and telescope" wheel adjustment on an energy absorbing column, automatic headlamp dipper, light-sensitive switch for parking lamps, electric windows and door locks and a hot seat for cold mornings are extra driving aids. Air conditioning and stereophonic four-speaker radio are additional inducements.

CLOSE-UP

Eight-cyl.; o.h.v.; 109.2×103.1 mm.; 7,736 c.c.; 375 b.h.p. gross; 10.5 to 1 comp.; Rochester 4-choke carb.; 3-speed auto., 7.64, 4.55, 3.08 to 1; cen. lvr.; susp. f. ind. torsion bar, r. half-elliptic; 2-door; 5-seat; hyd. servo brks., disc front; max 128 m.p.h.; cruise 110; m.p.g. 11-15; whl. base, 10ft.; track f. 5ft. 3½in., r. 5ft. 3in.; lgth. 18ft. 5in.; width 6ft. 7in.; ht. 4ft. 5½in.; g.c. 5½in.; turng. cir. 41ft. 4in.; kerb wt. 41⅞ cwt.; tank 20 gals.; 12-volt.

CHEVROLET CAMARO

WORLD'S most popular make in its low-priced sporting form. Now with big 6½-litre V8 engine, three-speed automatic transmission and disc front brakes, power assisted. Concealed headlamps help the uncluttered appearance, but the wire wheels are just clip-on covers. Power-operated windows, limited-slip differential and stereo tape player are among the optional extras. Reversing lamps, electric clock, rear window demister are included.

CLOSE-UP

Eight-cyl.; o.h.v.; 104×95.5 mm.; 6,490 c.c.; 325 b.h.p. gross; 10.25 to 1 comp.; Rochester 4-choke carb.; 3-speed auto., 8.41, 3.08 to 1; cen. lvr.; susp. f. ind. coil, r. half-elliptic; 2-door; 4-seat; hyd. brks., disc front; max. 125 m.p.h.; cruise 100; m.p.g. 15-18; whl. base, 9ft.; track f. 4ft. 11in., r. 4ft. 10⅞in.; lgth. 15ft. 4½in.; width 6ft. 6in.; ht. 4ft. 3½in.; g.c. 5½in.; turng. cir. 37ft. 5in.; kerb wt. 27⅝ cwt.; tank 15 gals.; 12-volt.

CHEVROLET CORVETTE

LONG available only as a sports coupe built with the world's most advanced glass-fibre production equipment, the Corvette now emerges as two-seater convertible, with power steering, all-independent suspension, disc brakes all round and limited-slip differential. New features include light monitor to warn of failures in important lamps, wipers concealed under vacuum-operated panel, AM/FM four-speaker stereo radio.

CLOSE-UP
Eight-cyl.; o.h.v.; 101.6×82.5 mm.; 5,359 c.c.; 350 b.h.p. gross; 11 to 1 comp.; Holley carb.; 4-speed, 8.14, 6.07, 5.70, 3.70 to 1; cen. lvr.; susp. f, ind. coil, r. ind. transv. leaf; 2-door; 2-seat; disc servo brks.; max. 120 m.p.h.; cruise 100; m.p.g. 14-17; whl. base 8ft. 2in.; track f. 4ft. 10¼in., r. 4ft. 11in.; lgth. 15ft. 2⅝in.; width 5ft. 9¼in.; ht. 3ft. 11¾in.; g.c. 5in.; turng. cir. 39ft. 10in.; kerb wt. 28¾ cwt.; tank 16¾ gals.; 12-volt.

CHRYSLER 300

ONE of the prestige cars in an 18-model Chrysler line-up for 1968, the 300 has a new grille and new roof to give a more sporty appearance. Cornering lamps and front-seat headrests are optional and the Town and Country station wagon is available with a wiper and washer system for the tailgate window. Automatic headlamp dipper and constant temperature control for air conditioning are other options.

CLOSE-UP
Eight-cyl.; o.h.v.; 109.7×95.2 mm.; 7,206 c.c.; 350 b.h.p. gross; 10.1 to 1 comp.; Carter 4-choke carb.; 3-speed auto., 6.86, 4.21, 2.76 to 1; col. lvr.; susp., f. ind. torsion bar, r. half-elliptic; 2 or 4-door; 6-seat; hyd. servo brks. disc front; max. 120 m.p.h.; cruise, 95; m.p.g. 11-14; whl. base, 10ft. 4in.; track f. 5ft. 2in., r. 5ft. 0¾in.; lgth., 18ft. 5¾in.; width, 6ft. 6¾in.; ht. 4ft. 7⅞in.; g.c. 5¾in.; turng. cir., 44ft.; kerb wt., 38½ cwt.; tank, 20 gals.; 12-volt.

CHRYSLER VALIANT

COMMONWEALTH Preference makes it cheaper for Britons to ship these big roomy cars halfway round the world from Australia rather than buy the American-built equivalents from Detroit. With long-proved American components in a design adapted for Australia's rough rural roads they are offered by Chrysler as a possible alternative to the big Humbers, now discontinued. Choice of six- or eight-cylinder engines, manual or automatic transmissions.

CLOSE-UP
Six-cyl.; o.h.v.; 86.3×79.4 mm.; 2,789 c.c.; 100 b.h.p. gross; 8.5 to 1 comp.; Ball & Ball carb.; 3-speed, 10.4, 6.87, 3.23 to 1; col. lvr. 4-speed or auto. opt.; susp., f. ind. torsion bar, r. half-elliptic; 2 or 4-door; 6-seat; hyd. servo brks.; max. 94 m.p.h.; cruise, 85; m.p.g. 17-21; whl. base, 8ft. 10in.; track f. 4ft. 7⅞in., r. 4ft. 7½in.; lgth., 15ft. 8in.; width, 5ft. 10½in.; ht. 4ft. 5in.; g.c. 6in.; turng. cir., 37ft.; kerb wt., 24 cwt.; tank, 15 gals.; 12-volt.

CITROEN AMI-6

UNIQUE appearance allied to Citroen's individualistic engineering make this a car to see, and it's now available in England. Front wheel drive by flat-twin engine with alternator; transmission by four-speed all-synchromesh gearbox. The coil-spring suspension interconnected front-to-rear with bob-weight dampers. Front brakes are inboard. There are two body styles, four-door saloon and station wagon.

CLOSE-UP
Two-cyl.; o.h.v. air-cooled; 74×70 mm.; 602 c.c.; 26 b.h.p. gross; 7.7 to 1 comp.; Solex carb.; 4-speed, 20.31, 10.39, 6.95, 4.74 to 1; dash lvr.; susp., f. and r. ind. coil; 4-door; 4-seat; hyd. brks.; max. 70 m.p.h.; cruise, 64; m.p.g. 40-42; whl. base, 7ft. 10½in.; track f. 4ft. 1½in., r. 4ft.; lgth., 13ft.; width 5ft.; ht. 4ft. 10¾in.; g.c. 6¼in.; turng. cir., 37ft. 4in.; kerb wt., 13¼ cwt.; tank, 5½ gals.; 12-volt.

£508+£118 p.t. = £626

CITROEN DS 21

SEEING round corners is made easier by the steering-linked swivel headlamps of the luxury Pallas model. One pair turns, the other stays fixed. New front wings to house them make the first major change in style for these advanced cars. Other models have four fixed lamps. To keep the cars fully competitive Citroen have also improved the engine, modified gear ratios and steering gear and fitted an alternator.

CLOSE-UP

Four-cyl.; o.h.v.; 90×85.5 mm.; 2,175 c.c.; 100 b.h.p.; 8.75 to 1 comp.; Weber twin-choke carb.; 4-speed, 14.22, 8.49, 5.56, 3.72 to 1; dash lvr.; susp. f. and r. ind. hyd.-pneu.; 4-door; 5/6-seat; hyd. servo brks., disc front; max. 109 m.p.h.; cruise 95; m.p.g. 25-30; whl. base 10ft. 3in.; track, f. 4ft. 11in., r. 4ft. 3½in.; lgth. 15ft. 10in.; width 5ft. 10½in.; ht. 4ft. 9½in.; g.c. 5⅜in.; turng. cir. 36ft.; kerb wt. 25 cwt.; tank 14 gals.; 12-volt.

£1,462+£337 p.t. = £1,799

DAF DE-LUXE

DAF cars with ordinary gearboxes are as rare as front-engined VWs. Holland's economical baby has always had the belt-drive transmission with variable-ratio pulleys that now powers racing cars, snow runabouts, postal vans and many other vehicles. The flat-twin engine is air cooled, interior trim includes walnut-veneered facia and fitted carpets. Ventilation is aided by extractor vents in rear quarters.

CLOSE-UP

Two-cyl.; o.h.v. air cooled; 85.5×65 mm.; 746 c.c.; 33 b.h.p.; 7.5 to 1 comp.; Solex carb.; auto. belt drive 16.4 to 3.9 to 1; cen. lvr.; susp., f. ind. trans. leaf, r. ind. coil; 2-door; 4-seat; hyd. brks.; max. 65 m.p.h.; cruise 65; m.p.g. 38-48; whl. base 6ft. 8½in.; track f. and r. 3ft. 10½in.; lgth. 11ft. 10½in.; width 4ft. 9in.; ht. 4ft. 6½in.; g.c. 6½in.; turng. cir. 31ft.; kerb wt. 13¼ cwt.; tank, 7 gals.; 6-volt.

£486+£113 p.t. = £599

DAF 44

EXTENDING their car range while maintaining production of heavy trucks and advanced military vehicles, DAF are now building respectable numbers of the 44 with Michelotti-styled body and belt-drive automatic transmission. Rack and pinion steering, independent rear suspension by semi-trailing arms and coil springs, are among the technical features. No differential is needed as the separate automatic transmission to each rear wheel does the job.

CLOSE-UP

Two-cyl.; o.h.v. air-cooled; 85.5×73.5 mm.; 844 c.c.; 40 b.h.p. gross; 7.5 to 1 comp.; Solex carb.; auto. belt drive 15.44 to 3.87 to 1; cen. lvr.; susp., f. ind. transv. leaf, r. ind. coil; 2-door; 4-seat; hyd. brks.; max. 76 m.p.h.; cruise, 76; m.p.g. 36-43; whl. base, 7ft. 4½in.; track f. 4ft. 2½in., r. 4ft. 1½in.; lgth. 12ft. 7½in.; width, 5ft. 0½in.; ht. 4ft. 6½in.; g.c. 6½in.; turng. cir., 31¼ft.; kerb wt., 14¼ cwt.; tank, 8¾ gals.; 6-volt.

£606+£141 p.t. = £747

DAIHATSU COMPAGNO 1000

JAPAN'S fast-growing car industry still makes more lorries than family cars but is expanding output of economy models like this straight-forward design with four-cylinder water-cooled pushrod engine at the front, rear wheel drive, independent front suspension and half-elliptic rear. Fog lamps, radio, wing mirrors, reclining seats are included. The four-seater spider has a twin-choke carburetter.

CLOSE-UP

Four-cyl.; o.h.v.; 68×66 mm.; 958 c.c.; 55 b.h.p.; 9 to 1 comp.; Mikuni carb.; 4-speed, 16.74, 10.6, 6.73, 4.55 to 1.; col. or cen. lvr.; susp., f. ind. torsion bar, r. half-elliptic; 2-door; 4-seat; hyd. brks.; max. 80 m.p.h.; cruise, 70; m.p.g. 30-33; whl. base, 7ft. 5⅜in.; track f. 3ft. 10½in., r. 3ft. 10in.; lgth. 12ft. 8⅜in.; width 4ft. 8⅜in.; ht. 4ft. 7½in.; g.c. 6in.; turng. cir. 30ft. 3in.; kerb wt. 16 cwt.; tank 9 gals.; 12-volt.

£609+£141 p.t. = £750

DAIMLER SOVEREIGN

HERE is a car with the dignity of a Daimler and the urge of a Jaguar with its twin-cam six-cylinder engines. It is just the thing for the better-off motorist whose business takes him to the city but also wants a smooth, quiet, fast car for trips to his country home. Its luxuriously finished interior matches its good looks and powerful mechanics.

CLOSE-UP
Six-cyl.; o.h.c.; 92 \ 106 mm.; 4,235 c.c.; 255 b.h.p. gross; 8 to 1 comp.; 2 S.U. carbs.; 4-speed, 11.46, 7.44, 5.0, 3.77 to 1 with L de N overdrive; cen. lvr. B.W. auto. opt.; susp., f. and r. ind. coil; 4-door; 5-seat; disc servo brks.; max. 120 m.p.h.; cruise 95; m.p.g. 15-19; whl. base 8ft. 11¾in.; track f. 4ft. 7¼in., r. 4ft. 6½in.; lgth. 15ft. 7¾in.; width 5ft. 6¾in.; ht. 4ft. 6½in.; g.c. 7in.; turng. cir. 33ft. 6in.; kerb wt. 31½ cwt.; tank 14 gals.; 12-volt.

£1,724 + £396 p.t. = £2,120

DAIMLER LIMOUSINE

THIS carries on the tradition of the impressive and powerful cars bearing the name of Daimler. Its sumptuous comfort and sense of dignity combine to provide a limousine well-suited for official use at civic functions or government receptions. One of the first cars to be merged with the British Motor Holdings it is still extremely popular with the owner who wants his motoring on a big scale.

CLOSE-UP
Eight-cyl.; o.h.v.; 95.25 \ 80.01 mm.; 4,561 c.c.; 220 b.h.p. gross; 8 to 1 comp.; 2 S.U. carbs.; 3-speed, auto. 8.7, 5.4, 3.77 to 1; col. lvr.; susp., f. ind. coil, r. half-elliptic; 4-door; 8-seat; disc servo brks.; max. 110 m.p.h.; cruise 90; m.p.g. 17-20; whl. base 11ft. 6in.; track f. and r. 4ft. 9in.; lgth. 18ft. 10in.; width 6ft. 1¾in.; ht. 5ft. 5½in.; g.c. 7in.; turng. cir. 44ft.; kerb wt. 40 cwt.; tank 16 gals.; 12-volt.

£2,893 + £664 p.t. = £3,557

DODGE CHARGER

PACEMAKER in Dodge's 1968 series is the sporting Charger offered with a bewildering variety of four V8 engines from 5.2 to 7.2 litres. Disc front brakes are optional. Choice of three-speed gearbox with column shift, four speeds with floor shift, or Torqueflite automatic and various axle ratios. A time switch illuminates the ignition keyhole for 30 seconds after the driver gets in.

CLOSE-UP
Eight-cyl.; o.h.v.; 107.9 / 85.8 mm.; 6,286 c.c.; 270 b.h.p. gross; 8.8 to 1 comp.; Stromberg carb.; 4-speed. 9.40, 6.78, 4.93, 3.55 to 1; cen. lvr., 3-speed or auto. opt.; susp., f. ind. torsion bar, r. half-elliptic; 2-door; 5-seat; hyd. servo brks.; max. 114 m.p.h.; cruise, 90; m.p.g. 13-16; whl. base, 9ft. 8⅞in.; track f. 4ft. 11½in., r. 4ft. 10½in.; lgth., 16ft. 10⅝in.; wdth., 6ft. 3¾in.; ht. 4ft. 5¾in.; g.c. 6½in.; turng. cir., 44ft.; kerb wt. 32½ cwt.; tank, 15¾ gals.; 12-volt.

FAIRTHORPE TX-GT

THE TX-GT is a high performance two-seater grand touring sports car, powered by a 6-cylinder 2-litre 95 h.p. engine. The particular points of interest are the Torix Bennett transverse rod suspension which gives particularly good handling characteristics; a low drag profile light-weight fibreglass body; a top speed of approximately 112 m.p.h.; a boot capacity of 14.2 cu. ft. Available in kit form.

CLOSE-UP
Six-cyl.; o.h.v.; 74.7 / 76 mm.; 1,998 c.c.; 95 b.h.p.; 9.5 to 1 comp.; 2 Stromberg carbs.; 4-speed, 8.66, 5.82, 4.11, 3.27 to 1; cen. lvr.; susp., f. and r. ind. coil; 2-door; 2/4-seat; hyd. brks. disc front; max. 115 m.p.h.; cruise, 90; m.p.g. 20-26; whl. base, 6ft. 11in.; track f. and r. 4ft. 1½in.; lgth., 12ft.; width, 5ft.; ht. 3ft. 10½in.; g.c. 4in.; turng. cir., 25ft. 3in.; kerb wt., 16 cwt.; tank, 9¾ gals.; 12-volt.

FERRARI 275 GTB-4A

FOUR overhead camshafts instead of two, and six twin-choke carburetters instead of three, boost power and performance still further on Ferrari's Gran Turismo Berlinetta. Seating is strictly for two and luggage space is limited but the aim is pure driving enjoyment. Send the chauffeur on in the station wagon with the bulky items. Suspension is all-independent; five-speed gearbox is at rear in unit with differential.

CLOSE-UP

Twelve-cyl.; o.h.c.; 77 × 58.8 mm.; 3,286 c.c.; 300 b.h.p.; 9.2 to 1 comp.; 6 Weber 2-choke carbs.; 5-speed, 10.15, 6.60, 5.19, 4.13, 3.42 to 1; cen. lvr.; susp. f. and r. ind. coil; 2-door; 2-seat; disc servo brks.; max. 160 m.p.h.; cruise 130; m.p.g. 15-20; whl. base 7ft. 10½in.; track, f. 4ft. 7in., r. 4ft. 7¾in.; lgth. 14ft. 5¾in.; width 5ft. 6½in.; ht. 4ft.; g.c. 4¾in.; turng. cir. 45ft.; kerb wt. 22 cwt.; tank 20 gals.; 12-volt.

£5,300+£1,216 p.t. = £6,516

FERRARI 330 GT

WITH V-12 two-cam engine delivering nearly 300 h.p. installed the 330 comes in three versions clad by Pininfarina. Short wheelbase 330 GTC coupe and 330 GTS convertible are two-seaters with all-independent suspension. The long wheelbase 330 GT 2+2 coupe has a rigid rear axle with half elliptic springs and radius arms. 365 California convertible has a 4.4-litre 314 h.p. engine in the long chassis.

CLOSE-UP

Twelve-cyl.; o.h.c.; 77 × 71 mm.; 3,967 c.c.; 300 b.h.p.; 8.8 to 1 comp.; 3 Weber 2-choke carbs.; 5-speed, 10.78, 7.22, 5.34, 4.25, 3.39 to 1; cen. lvr.; susp., f. ind. coil, r. half-elliptic; 2-door; 2/4-seat; disc servo brks.; max. 152 m.p.h.; cruise 130; m.p.g. 12-16; whl. base 8ft. 8⅜in.; track f. 4ft. 7⅛in., r. 4ft. 7⅛in.; lgth. 15ft. 10½in.; width 5ft. 7½in.; ht. 4ft. 5¾in.; g.c. 4¾in.; turng. cir. 45ft.; kerb wt. 27¼ cwt.; tank 19¾ gals.; 12-volt.

£5,300+£1,216 p.t. = £6,516

FIAT 500

PARKING problems melt away and petrol goes further with Fiat's popular baby car. Nimble in city traffic, immunised by air cooling against winter frosts and equipped with a folding roof for maximum enjoyment of sunny days, it is a versatile little runabout carrying two adults and two children in surprising comfort. The larger 600 with water-cooled four-cylinder engine also sells in large numbers.

CLOSE-UP

Two-cyl.; o.h.v.; air cooled; 67.4 × 70 mm.; 499 c.c.; 18 b.h.p.; 7.1 to 1 comp.; Weber carb.; 4-speed, 18.96, 10.59, 6.66, 4.48 to 1; cen. lvr.; susp., f. ind. transv. leaf, r. ind. coil; 2-door; 2/4-seat; hyd. brks.; max. 60 m.p.h.; cruise 55; m.p.g. 55; whl. base 6ft. 0½in.; track f. 3ft. 8½in., r. 3ft. 8½in.; lgth. 9ft. 9in.; width 4ft. 4in.; ht. 4ft. 4½in.; g.c. 5in.; turng. cir. 28ft. 6in.; kerb wt. 10¼ cwt.; tank 4½ gals.; 12-volt.

£338+£79 p.t. = £417

FIAT 850

TURIN'S prolific designers have expanded this basic 850 into a whole range of cars. The saloon comes with option of Idromatic transmission using fluid converter and four-speed gearbox, the shapely coupe was an instant success, the Bertone-bodied spider with 49 h.p. engine is the hottest version, and there's a forward-control five seat Familiare. All have the rear-mounted four-cylinder water-cooled engine and all-independent suspension.

CLOSE-UP

Four-cyl.; o.h.v.; 65 × 64 mm.; 843 c.c.; 34 b.h.p.; 8.8 to 1 comp.; Solex or Weber carb.; 4-speed, 16.8, 9.5, 6.52, 4.45 to 1; cen. lvr.; susp., f. ind. transv. leaf, r. ind. coil; 2-door; 4-seat; hyd. brks.; max. 75 m.p.h.; cruise, 68; m.p.g. 33-40; whl. base, 6ft. 7¾in.; track f. 3ft. 9¼in., r. 3ft. 11¾in.; lgth. 11ft. 8¾in.; width, 4ft. 8in.; ht. 4ft. 6½in.; g.c. 5¾in.; turng. cir. 29ft. 3in.; kerb wt. 13¼ cwt.; tank, 6⅓ gals.; 12-volt.

£453+£106 p.t. = £559

FIAT 124 COUPE

IRRESISTIBLE combination of lovely lines, sporting performance and family car interior space. A car that seems set for as great a success as the 850 coupe, it is mechanically similar to the 124 Spider, with four-cylinder engine using twin belt-driven camshafts, but the gearbox has four speeds, not five. Brakes are discs. The rear axle is on radius arms and Panhard rod with coil springs.

CLOSE-UP

Four-cyl.; o.h.c.; 80 × 71.5 mm.; 1,438 c.c.; 96 b.h.p.; 8.9 to 1 comp.; twin-choke Weber carb.; 4-speed, 15.35, 9.41, 6.11, 4.1 to 1; cen. lvr.; susp., f. ind. coil, r. coil; 2-door; 4-seat; disc servo brks.; max. 105 m.p.h.; cruise, 90; m.p.g. 25-27; whl. base, 7ft. 11¼in.; track f. 4ft. 5in., r. 4ft. 3¾in.; lgth., 13ft. 6in.; width, 5ft. 5¾in.; ht. 4ft. 3¼in.; g.c. 7in.; turng. cir., 36ft.; kerb wt., 17⅞ cwt.; tank, 9⅞ gals.; 12-volt.

FIAT 125

100 m.p.h. with five-seater comfort. The latest in Fiat's vast range of family cars has a similar engine to that of the 124 sports model, with twin belt-driven overhead camshafts. Body has 124 centre section with larger boot, longer bonnet. Rear suspension is like that on the Dino sports model. Brakes are discs with servo. Features include pedal-operated intermittent screen wiper and washer for drizzly weather.

CLOSE-UP

Four cyl.; o.h.c.; 80 × 80 mm.; 1,608 c.c.; 95 b.h.p.; 8.8 to 1 comp.; Weber or Solex carb.; 4-speed, 14.05, 8.61, 5.57, 4.1 to 1; cen. lvr.; susp., f. ind. coil, r. half-elliptic; 4-door; 5-seat; disc servo brks.; max. 100 m.p.h.; cruise, 85; m.p.g. 24; whl. base, 8ft. 2⅝in.; track f. 4ft. 3¾in., r. 4ft. 2⅞in.; lgth., 13ft. 10¼in.; width., 5ft. 3½in.; ht. 4ft. 6⅞in.; g.c. 6⅞ in.; turng. cir., 35ft. 7in.; kerb wt., 19⅞ cwt.; tank, 9¾ gals.; 12-volt.

FIAT DINO

FERRARI-ENGINED Fiat with bodywork by Pininfarina (Spider) or Bertone (Coupe); a star-spangled formula that brings a splendid new car to the sporting scene. The light-alloy V6 engine with four overhead camshafts was designed so that Ferrari could use a 1600 c.c. version in Formula 2 single-seaters while Fiat expanded it to 2-litres for road use. Rear springs have only one leaf; radius arms take torque and braking forces.

CLOSE-UP

Six-cyl.; o.h.c.; 86 × 57 mm.; 1,987 c.c.; 166 b.h.p.; 9.1 to 1 comp.; 3 twin-choke Weber carbs.; 5-speed, 13.05, 8.9, 6.6, 4.87, 4.25 to 1; cen. lvr.; susp., f. ind. coil, r. half-elliptic; 2-door; 2/4-seat; disc servo brks.; max. 125 m.p.h.; cruise, 110; m.p.g. 18; whl. base, 7ft. 6in.; track f. 4ft. 6½in.; r. 4ft. 5¼in.; lgth., 13ft. 5¾in.; width, 5ft. 7¼in.; ht. 4ft. 1in.; g.c. 4¾in.; turng. cir., 35ft.; kerb wt., 22⅜ cwt.; tank, 14½ gals.; 12-volt.

FORD ANGLIA SUPER

THIS is the posh version of a wonderfully popular car that must now be a veteran. Its low price and cheap running appeals to almost every type of motorist from the pocket-conscious owner to the two-car family who want a runabout easy to park in cities for shopping, also to carry and fetch children at their schools. And there's a good station wagon adaptation.

CLOSE-UP

Four-cyl.; o.h.v.; 80.9 × 58.2 mm.; 1,198 c.c.; 48 b.h.p.; 8.7 to 1 comp.; Solex carb.; 4-speed, 14.6, 9.9, 5.8, 4.12 to 1; cen. lvr.; susp., f. ind. coil, r. half-elliptic; 2-door; 4-seat; hyd. brks.; max. 80 m.p.h.; cruise, 70; m.p.g. 35-40; whl. base 7ft. 6½in.; track f. 3ft. 10in., r. 3ft. 9¾in.; lgth. 12ft. 9½in.; width 4ft. 9¼in.; ht. 4ft. 8¾in.; g.c. 6¼in.; turng. cir. 32ft.; kerb wt. 15¼ cwt.; tank 7 gals.; 12-volt.

£525 + £120 p.t. = £645

Abbreviations—g.c.—ground clearance; susp.—suspension; f.—front; r.—rear; comp.—compression; s.v.—side-valves; o.h.v.—overhead valves; o.h.c.—overhead camshaft; hyd.—hydraulic.

FORD CORSAIR E

THIS is one of the cheapest cars in the 2,000 c.c. class and it has swept into favour in its first year of life. Built in the robust Ford tradition, it offers 100 m.p.h. motoring (abroad, of course) and its improved V4 engine with twin choke carburetter gives first class performance figures of from 0 to 60 m.p.h. in 12½ seconds. A splendid newcomer.

CLOSE-UP
Four-cyl.; o.h.v.; 93.7 × 72.4 mm.; 1,996 c.c., 97 b.h.p.; 8.9 to 1 comp.; Weber carb.; 4-speed, 13.38, 9.05, 5.33, 3.78 to 1; cen. lvr.; susp., f. ind. coil, r. half-elliptic; 4-door; 5-seat; hyd. servo brks., disc front; max. 96 m.p.h.; cruise 85; m.p.g. 21-25; whl. base 8ft. 5in.; track, f. 4ft. 2½in., r. 4ft. 2in.; lgth. 14ft. 11¾in.; width 5ft. 3½in.; ht. 4ft. 9in.; g.c. 6in.; turng. cir. 34ft. 4in.; kerb wt. 21¼ cwt.; tank 10 gals.; 12-volt.
£820 + £188 p.t. = £1,008

FORD CORTINA 1600E

EXTRACTING maximum advantage from the new 1600 GT engine with cross-flow head, Ford produce the most advanced four-door Cortina. Lowered suspension like the Cortina Lotus, plated sports-style wheels with wide rims, reclining front seats, leather-covered aluminium steering wheel, wood facia and reversing lamps, figure in the specification of a car that will set a hot pace for competitors. Two-tone horns, lighter, and matt black grille are included.

CLOSE-UP
Four-cyl.; o.h.v.; 80.9 × 77.6 mm.; 1,599 c.c.; 92 b.h.p. gross; 9 to 1 comp.; Weber 2-choke carb.; 4-speed, 11.59, 7.84, 5.45, 3.9 to 1.; cen. lvr.; susp., f. ind. coil, r. half-elliptic; 4-door; 4-seat; hyd. brks., disc front; max. 95 m.p.h.; cruise, 85; m.p.g. 27-31; whl. base, 8ft. 2in.; track f. 4ft. 4½in., r. 4ft. 3in. lgth. 14ft.; width, 5ft. 4½in.; ht. 4ft. 6½in.; g.c. 6½in.; turng. cir., 30ft.; kerb wt., 18¼ cwt.; tank, 10 gals.; 12-volt.

FORD CORTINA LOTUS

FORD-BUILT, the Cortina Lotus is a quieter, more comfortable car for everyday motoring than the Lotus-built original but retains its superb steering and road holding. Twin-cam Ford-Lotus engine, servo brakes with discs in front, rear axle located by radius arms distinguish it from straight Cortinas. The matt black grille, wide rims with radial ply tyres and small Lotus badges are outward identification.

CLOSE-UP
Four-cyl.; o.h.c.; 82.6 × 72.8 mm.; 1,560 c.c.; 109 b.h.p.; 9.5 to 1 comp.; 2 Weber carbs.; 4-speed, 11.21, 8.86, 5.28, 3.78 to 1; cen. lvr.; susp. f. ind. coil, r. half-elliptic; 2-door; 4-seat; hyd. servo brks., disc front; max. 105 m.p.h.; cruise, 90; m.p.g. 22-26; whl. base, 8ft. 2in.; track f. 4ft. 5½in., r. 4ft. 4in.; lgth., 14ft.; width, 5ft. 5in.; ht. 4ft. 6in.; g.c. 5in.; turng. cir., 33ft.; kerb wt., 17⅞ cwt.; tank, 10 gals.; 12-volt.
£869 + £199 p.t. = £1,068

FORD ZEPHYR

DE LUXE versions of Ford's roomy family models broaden their appeal for 1968. For economy with lively performance, the 2-litre four-cylinder engine is first choice; for fast acceleration and hill climbing the 2½ litre V6 is indicated. Front suspension is by MacPherson spring struts, rear suspension is by trailing arms on swinging links and coil springs. Disc brakes on all wheels are servo assisted.

CLOSE-UP
Four-cyl.; o.h.v.; 93.7 × 72.4 mm.; 1,996 c.c.; 88 b.h.p.; 8.9 to 1 comp. (Six-cyl.; 93.7 × 60.3 mm.; 2.495 c.c.; 112 b.h.p.; 9 to 1 comp.); Zenith carb.; 4-speed, 16.3, 8.7, 5.6, 3.7 to 1 (Six, 12.3, 8.6, 5.5, 3.9 to 1); col. lvr.; susp., f. and r. ind. coil; 4-door; 5/6-seat; disc servo brks.; max. 88/96 m.p.h.; cruise, 78/85; m.p.g. 18/26; whl. base, 9ft. 7in.; track f. 4ft. 9in.; r. 4ft. 10in.; lgth., 15ft. 5in.; width, 5ft. 11¼in.; ht. 4ft. 10½in.; g.c. 6in.; turng. cir., 36/36ft.; kerb wt., 24¼/25¾ cwt.; tank, 15 gals.; 12-volt.
Four £773 + £177 p.t. = £949
Six £832 + £191 p.t. = £1,023

FORD EXECUTIVE

ONE of the most luxurious cars ever built by Ford of Britain, this 100 m.p.h. car appeals to those after whom it is named—business executives. The sumptuous interior has all that a boss would want including fresh air ventilation and extraction, fully reclining individual front seats and the entire floor is covered in deep pile carpet. A pace setter in the prestige class, this model serves its purpose elegantly.

CLOSE-UP
Six-cyl.; o.h.v.; 93.6 / 72.4 mm.; 2,994 c.c.; 128 b.h.p.; 8.9 to 1 comp.; Weber 2-choke carb.; 4-speed, 11.7, 8.19, 5.22, 3.7 to 1; cen. lvr., Laycock de Normanville overdrive or Ford auto. opt.; susp. f. and r. ind. coil; 4-door; 5-6-seat; disc servo brks.; max. 102 m.p.h.; cruise 88; m.p.g. 17-24; whl. base 9ft. 7in.; track f. 4ft. 9in. r. 4ft. 10in.; lgth. 15ft. 6in.; wdth 5ft. 11¼in.; ht. 4ft. 10½in.; g.c. 6in.; turng. circ. 38ft. 8in.; kerb wt. 25⅞ cwt.; tank 15 gals.; 12-volt.

£1,275 + £292 p.t. = £1,567

FORD 17M

GERMANY'S middle-range Fords, now sold in Britain, are redesigned with more angular, roomier bodywork and more powerful engines. Body styles are two-door and four-door saloons and sleek two-door coupes. The 17M has V4 engines of 1500 and 1700 c.c.; the 20M has V6 units of 2000 or 2300 c.c. Power varies from 60 to 108 h.p. Different grilles and a "power bulge" distinguish six-cylinder models.

CLOSE-UP
Four-cyl.; o.h.v.; 90 × 66.8 mm.; 1,699 c.c.; 65 b.h.p.; 8 to 1 comp.; Solex carb.; 4-speed, 12.59, 7.29, 5.07, 3.7 to 1; cen. lvr. auto. opt.; susp., f. ind. coil, r. half-elliptic; 2 or 4-door; 5-seat; hyd. servo brks. disc front; max. 87 m.p.h.; cruise, 75; m.p.g. 25-28; whl. base, 8ft. 10½in.; track f. 4ft. 8½in.; r. 4ft. 7¼in.; lgth., 15ft. 3⅝in.; width, 5ft. 9½in.; ht. 4ft. 10½in.; g.c. 7in.; turng. cir., 33ft. 6in.; kerb wt., 20½ cwt.; tank, 9¾ gals.; 12-volt.

FORD MUSTANG

CAR that changed the pattern of American motoring. Its imitators are legion because it appeals to the young-generation Americans and lots of motorists elsewhere too. Sporting lines with room for children and luggage, and a great range of engine and transmission options, cater for many different tastes and pockets. Bodies are convertible, coupe and fastback coupe. Engines vary from a 3.3-litre six to a 7-litre V8.

CLOSE-UP
Eight-cyl.; o.h.v.; 101.6 × 72.9 mm.; 4,728 c.c.; 200 b.h.p. gross; 9.2 to 1 comp.; Ford 2-choke carb; 3-speed, 7.8, 4.7, 2.8 to 1; cen. lvr., four-speed or auto. opt.; susp., f. ind. coil, r. half-elliptic; 2-door; 4-seat; hyd. brks., servo and disc opt.; max. 118 m.p.h.; cruise 98; m.p.g. 14-17; whl. base 9ft.; track f. and r. 4ft. 8in.; lgth. 15ft. 1⅜in.; width 5ft. 8¼in.; ht. 4ft. 3in.; g.c. 7in.; turng. cir. 38ft.; kerb wt. 23.3 cwt.; tank 13 gals.; 12-volt.

£1,883 + £394 p.t. = £2,277

FORD G.T. 40

BRITISH-BUILT at a Slough factory with an American engine specially produced for competitions, the GT 40 is a race-winning result of Anglo-American co-operation which is produced in limited numbers in road-going form for wealthy enthusiasts who want racing-car acceleration and 100-plus cruising and are not deterred by the acrobatics required to get in, or the lack of luggage space.

CLOSE-UP
Eight-cyl.; o.h.v.; 101.6 × 72.9 mm.; 4,736 c.c.; 380 b.h.p. gross; 10 to 1 comp.; 4 Weber carbs.; 5-speed, 10.21, 6.20, 4.60, 4.05, 3.59 to 1; cen. lvr.; susp. f. and r. ind. coil; 2-door; 2-seat; disc brks.; max. 160 m.p.h.; cruise 130; m.p.g. 11-13; whl. base 7ft. 11in.; track f. and r. 4ft. 7in.; lgth. 13ft. 4in.; width 5ft. 10in.; ht. 3ft. 4½in.; g.c. 4in.; kerb wt. 17⅞ cwt.; tank 30 gals.; 12-volt.

GILBERN GENIE

MOST powerful model yet from the only Welsh car manufacturer. A fast four-seater with Ford Zodiac engine in a tubular chassis with glass fibre body. Reclining front seats with finger-tip adjustment, twin-circuit brakes (discs in front) and a hazard warning switch are standard equipment. Steering is by rack and pinion, the rear axle is located by radius arms and Watt linkage, overdrive is optional.

CLOSE-UP
Six-cyl.; o.h.v.; 93.7 × 72.4 mm.; 2,994 c.c.; 141 b.h.p.; 8.9 to 1 comp.; Weber carb.; 4-speed, 10.56, 7.40, 4.72, 3.35 to 1.; cen. lvr.; susp., f. ind. coil, r. coil; 2-door; 4-seat; hyd. brks. disc front; max. 95-100 m.p.h.; cruise, 80; m.p.g. 18-21; whl. base, 7ft. 8¾in.; track f. 4ft. 4½in., r. 4ft. 4in.; lgth., 13ft. 3in.; width, 5ft. 5in.; ht. 4ft. 4in.; g.c. 6in.; turng. cir., 31ft.; kerb wt. 17¾ cwt.; tank, 14 gals.; 12-volt.
£1,425 + £357 p.t. = £1,782

GINETTA G11

NEWCOMERS to the Motor Show, the Essex-based sports car men produce an ambitious range of fast cars with front and rear engines. G.11 is front-engined (MGB), G.10 is similar but with Ford V8 for export. New for the show is a rear-engined coupe with Sports Imp engine at under £1,000 tax paid with all-independent suspension, disc front brakes, laminated windscreen.

CLOSE-UP
Four-cyl.; o.h.v.; 80.3 × 89 mm.; 1,798 c.c.; 95 b.h.p. gross; 8.9 to 1 comp.; 2 S.U. carbs; 4-speed, 14.2, 8.6, 5.4, 3.9 to 1; cen. lvr.; susp., f. ind. coil, r. coil; 2-door; 2-seat; hyd. brks., disc front; max. 110 m.p.h.; cruise, 88; m.p.g. 24; whl. base, 7ft. 6in.; track f. 4ft. 2in.; r. 4ft. 2in.; lgth., 13ft. 4in.; width, 5ft. 1in.; ht. 3ft. 11½in.; g.c. 6in.; turng. cir., 33ft.; kerb wt., 14¾ cwt.; tank, 12 gals.; 12-volt.
£1,098 + £227 p.t. = £1,325

HILLMAN IMP CALIFORNIAN

FAST-BACK coupe to compete with cute Continentals. Basically Super Imp, but fixed rear window, lowered steering wheel and front suspension, more sloping windscreen, distinguish it from the saloon. The rear backrest folds in separate halves to increase luggage space. Overall height is cut by over an inch, weight by 4lb. See also the Imp Sports saloon with 51 h.p. engine, oil cooler, brake servo.

CLOSE-UP
Four-cyl.; o.h.c.; 68 × 60.4 mm.; 875 c.c.; 39 b.h.p.; 10 to 1 comp.; Solex carb.; 4-speed, 16.59, 8.91, 5.70, 4.14 to 1; cen. lvr.; susp., f. and r. ind. coil; 2-door; 4-seat; hyd. brks.; max. 80 m.p.h.; cruise 75; m.p.g. 40; whl. base 6ft. 10in.; track, f. 4ft. 2⅜in., r. 4ft.; lgth. 11ft. 7in.; width 5ft. 0½in.; ht. 4ft. 4⅛in.; g.c. 5½in.; turng. cir. 30ft. 6in.; kerb wt. 14¼ cwt.; tank, 6 gals.; 12-volt.
£525 + £122 p.t. = £647

HILLMAN MINX

MORE space for passengers and luggage, better ride and road holding are plus points for the new Minx with Hunter-style body and strut-type front suspension. Engine size reverts to 1.5 litres from the recent 1.7, restoring the Minx to a popular category. The larger engine is still used with automatic transmission and in some countries export buyers get a 1.7-litre Sunbeam Minx.

CLOSE-UP
Four cyl.; o.h.v.; 81.5 × 71.6 mm.; 1,496 c.c.; 60 b.h.p.; 8.4 to 1 comp.; Zenith Stromberg carb.; 4-speed, 13.04, 8.32, 5.41, 3.89 to 1; cen. lvr.; susp., f. ind. coil, r. half-elliptic; 4-door; 4/5-seat; disc front brks.; max. 80 m.p.h.; cruise, 70; m.p.g. 30-34; whl. base, 8ft. 2½in.; track f. and r. 4ft. 4in.; lgth., 14ft.; width, 5ft. 3½in.; ht. 4ft. 8in.; g.c. 6¾in.; turng. cir., 33ft. 6in.; kerb wt., 18¼ cwt.; tank, 10 gals.; 12-volt.
£595 + £138 p.t. = £733

Abbreviations—g.c.—ground clearance; susp.—suspension; f.—front; r.—rear; comp.—compression; s.v.—side-valves; o.h.v.—overhead valves; o.h.c.—overhead camshaft; hyd.—hydraulic.

HILLMAN HUNTER

STRONGER identity is assured by the new front styling with rectangular headlamps, matt black panels and polished alloy beading. New "breathable" upholstery, redesigned facia with new switches, improved heater controls, complete the changes. Unchanged are the canted-over engine with alloy head and sump, the high gearing which gives effortless and economical motorway cruising and the disc front brakes.

CLOSE-UP
Four-cyl.; o.h.v.; 81.5 × 82.5 mm.; 1,725 c.c.; 74 b.h.p.; 9.2 to 1 comp.; Stromberg carb.; 4-speed, 12.41, 7.92, 5.15, 3.7 to 1.; cen. lvr.; susp., f. ind coil, r. half-elliptic; 4-door; 4/5-seat; hyd. brks., disc front; max. 88 m.p.h.; cruise 75; m.p.g. 28-34; whl. base 8ft. 2½in.; track, f. and r. 4ft. 4in.; lgth. 14ft. 1⅛in.; width 5ft. 3½in.; ht. 4ft. 6½in.; g.c. 6¾in.; turng. cir. 33ft. 6in. kerb wt. 17½ cwt.; tank 10 gals.; 12-volt.
£680 + £158 p.t. = £838

HONDA N500

MINIMISING the Mini. Japan's aggressively successful motor-bike manufacturer follows up his 800 c.c. sports car with a tiny competitor for BMC's best selling baby. It has transverse engine and front-wheel drive, but the engine is two-cylinders, light alloy, air-cooled with an overhead camshaft. Front suspension by MacPherson struts; rear, surprisingly, by rigid axle with half-elliptic springs.

CLOSE-UP
Two-cyl.; o.h.c. air-cooled; 74 × 54.8 mm.; 497 c.c.; 40 b.h.p.; 8.6 to 1 comp.; 4-speed; cen. lvr.; susp., f. ind. coil, r. half-elliptic; 2-door; 4-seat; hyd. brks.; max. 80 m.p.h.; cruise, 65; m.p.g. 60-65; whl. base, 6ft. 6½in.; lgth., 9ft. 11¾in.; width, 4ft. 3in.; ht. 4ft. 2⅞in.; g.c. 7in.; turng. cir., 28ft. 9in.; kerb wt., 9¾ cwt.; tank, 5¾ gals.; 12-volt.

HUMBER SCEPTRE

LATEST and most luxurious version of the Hunter series, with twin carburetter engine, reclining front seats, separate rear seats, upholstered in Ambla. Wood-veneer facia has complete instrumentation including tachometer, steering column length is adjustable, steering wheel centre is padded. Black leathercloth on the roof, slotted alloy wheel discs, bright beading on wheel arches and a decorative panel for rear light clusters distinguish the exterior.

CLOSE-UP
Four-cyl.; o.h.v.; 81.5 × 82.5 mm.; 1,725 c.c.; 87 b.h.p.; 9.2 to 1 comp.; 2 Stromberg carbs.; 4-speed, plus Laycock de Normanville overdrive, 12.41, 7.92, 5.15, 3.7 to 1.; cen. lvr.; susp., f. ind. coil, r. half-elliptic; 4-door; 4-seat; hyd. servo brks., disc front; max. 97 m.p.h.; cruise, 80; m.p.g. 25-30; whl. base, 8ft. 2½in.; track f. and r, 4ft. 4in.; lgth. 14ft. 2in.; width, 5ft. 3½in.; ht. 4ft. 8in.; g.c. 6½in.; turng. cir., 33ft. 6in.; kerb wt. 18 cwt.; tank, 10 gals.; 12-volt.
£1,183 + £273 p.t. = £1,456

ISO RIVOLTA

DISTRIBUTED in Britain by Lambretta Trojan, these swift cars combine the appeal of Italian styling with the serviceability of American engines. Bertone does the bodies; Chevrolet the V8 engines and gearboxes. The four-seater coupe comes with a 5.4-litre engine; the two-seater Iso Grifo has 345 h.p. and shorter wheelbase. Sensational and new: the Ghia four-door saloon.

CLOSE-UP
Eight-cyl.; o.h.v.; 101.6 × 82.5 mm.; 5,359 c.c.; 295 b.h.p. gross; 10.5 to 1 comp.; Holley 4-choke carb.; 4-speed, 8.53, 6.45, 5.07, 3.36 to 1; cen. lvr., 5-speed opt.; susp., f. ind. coil, r. de Dion coil; 2-door; 4-seat; disc servo brks.; max. 135 m.p.h.; cruise, 110; m.p.g. 13-15; whl. base, 8ft. 10⅛in.; track f. and r. 4ft. 7½in.; lgth., 15ft. 7½in.; width, 5ft. 8⅜in.; ht. 4ft. 7¾in.; g.c. 4½in.; turng. cir., 42ft.; kerb wt., 30½ cwt.; tank, 23 gals.; 12-volt.
£4,095 + £940 p.t. = £5,035

Abbreviations—g.c.—ground clearance; susp.—suspension; f.—front; r.—rear; comp.—compression; s.v.—side-valves; o.h.v.—overhead valves; o.h.c.—overhead camshaft; hyd.—hydraulic.

JAGUAR 240

ENGINE changes to this 2.4 litre saloon include a straight-port type cylinder head, twin S.U. carburetters and a new inlet manifold. These, with a dual exhaust system in place of a single exhaust, raise the power output from 120 b.h.p. to 133 b.h.p. A paper element air cleaner is used instead of the 'oil bath' type but the capacity of the twin overhead camshaft XK engine remains unchanged at 2,483 c.c.

CLOSE-UP
Six-cyl.; o.h.c.; 83×76.5 mm.; 2,483 c.c.; 133 b.h.p. gross; 8 to 1 comp.; 2 Solex carbs.; 4-speed, 14.42, 7.94, 5.48, 4.27 to 1; cent. lvr., de Normanville overdrive or BW auto. opt.; susp., f. ind. coil, r. cantilever leaf; 4-door; 5-seat; servo disc brks.; max. 110 m.p.h.; cruise 75-80; m.p.g. 23; whl. base 8ft. 11⅜in.; track. f. 4ft. 7in., r. 4ft. 5⅜in.; lgth. 15ft. 0¾in.; width 5ft. 6¾in.; ht. 4ft. 9½in.; g.c. 7in.; turng. cir. 33ft. 6in.; kerb wt. 28½ cwt.; tank 12 gals.; 12-volt.

JAGUAR 420

PRICE cuts follow use of Ambla upholstery instead of leather, omission of foglamps and use of tufted carpets on 3.4 and 3.8 S models. This follows up the successful move to simplified equipment and trim on Mark 2 models which made Jaguar ownership possible for more motorists. Optional automatic transmission is now the modern BW Type 35 instead of DG-type on S-type and the otherwise unchanged 420.

CLOSE-UP
Six-cyl.; o.h.c.; 92.1×106 mm.; 4,235 c.c.; 255 b.h.p. gross; 8 to 1 comp.; 2 S.U. carbs.; 4-speed, 10.76, 6.98, 4.7, 3.54 to 1; cen. lvr.; susp. f. and r. ind. coil; 4-door; 5-seat; disc servo brks.; max. 120 m.p.h.; cruise 100; m.p.g. 16-19; whl. base 8ft. 11⅜in.; track f. 4ft. 7⅛in., r. 4ft. 6⅛in.; lgth. 15ft. 7¾in.; width 5ft. 6¾in.; ht. 4ft. 6½in.; g.c. 7in.; turng. cir. 33½ft.; kerb wt. 30.7 cwt.; tank, 14 gals.; 12-volt.

£1,569 + £361 p.t. = £1,930

JAGUAR E-TYPE 2+2

UNIVERSALLY acclaimed as the ideal modern sports car that goes as fast as it looks, the E-type continues for 1968 in its two forms; two-seater (available as coupe or convertible) and the longer-wheelbase 2+2 which provides rear seat space for two children. An all-synchromesh gearbox and limited-slip differential have increased the pleasure of fast driving and headlamps are modified for better illumination.

CLOSE-UP
Six-cyl.; o.h.c.; 92.1×106 mm.; 4,235 c.c.; 265 b.h.p. gross; 9 to 1 comp.; 3 S.U. carbs.; 4-speed, 8.23, 5.34, 3.90, 3.07 to 1; cen. lvr., auto. opt.; susp. f. torsion bar, r. ind. coil; 2-door; 2-4-seat; disc servo brks.; max. 140 m.p.h.; cruise, 115; m.p.g. 18-20; whl. base 8ft. 9in.; track f. and r. 4ft. 2in.; lgth. 15ft. 4⅛in.; width 5ft. 5½in.; ht. 4ft. 2in.; g.c. 5½in.; turng. cir. 41ft.; kerb wt. 24 cwt.; tank 18 gals.; 12-volt.

£1,857 + £427 p.t. = £2,284

JENSEN FF

EAGERLY awaited since press reports acclaimed the unique safety margins conferred by its combination of Ferguson four-wheel drive and Maxaret non-skid braking, the FF has had to wait while production of the lower-priced rear-drive Interceptor got going. However, this is a years-ahead conception that cannot date quickly and buyers who can afford the expenditure will find it well worth waiting for.

CLOSE-UP
Eight-cyl.; o.h.v.; 108×86 mm.; 6,276 c.c.; 330 b.h.p.; 10 to 1 comp.; Carter 4-choke carb.; 3-speed auto., 7.5, 4.44, 3.07 to 1; col. lvr.; susp., f. ind. coil, r. half-elliptic; 2-door; 4-seat; disc servo brks. with Maxaret; max. 130 m.p.h.; cruise 110; m.p.g. 15-17; whl. base 9ft. 1in.; track f. and r. 4ft. 8⅛in.; lgth. 15ft. 11in.; width 5ft. 9in.; ht. 4ft. 7in.; g.c. 5in.; turng. cir. 39ft.; kerb wt. 34 cwt; tank 16 gals.; 12-volt.

£4,343 + £997 p.t. = £5,340

Abbreviations—g.c.—ground clearance; susp.—suspension; f.—front; r.—rear; comp.—compression; s.v.—side-valves; o.h.v.—overhead valves; o.h.c.—overhead camshaft; hyd.—hydraulic.

JENSEN INTERCEPTOR

ITALIAN influences of both Superleggera and Vignale give flair and distinction to this car's styling. With a powerful Chrysler engine developing well over 300 brake horse power, matched to automatic transmission, the Interceptor telescopes miles into minutes with an effortless stride. Lush interior fittings match the high quality engineering and the whole is a beautiful motor-car that gives a glide-ride.

CLOSE-UP
Eight-cyl.; o.h.v.; 108 × 86 mm.; 6,276 c.c.; 325 b.h.p.; 10 to 1 comp.; Carter 4-choke carb.; 3-speed auto., 7.5, 4.44, 3.07 to 1; col. lvr.; susp., f. ind. coil, r. half-elliptic; 2-door; 4-seat; disc servo brks.; max. 132 m.p.h.; cruise 110; m.p.g. 15–18; whl. base 8ft. 9in.; track f. 4ft. 7⅞in., r. 4ft. 8⅜in.; lgth. 15 ft. 8in.; width 5ft. 9in.; ht. 4ft. 5in.; g.c. 5½in.; turng. cir. 38ft.; kerb wt. 31¼ cwt.; tank 16 gals.; 12-volt.
£3,043 + £700 p.t. = £3,743

LAMBORGHINI 400 GT 2+2

NOW officially on sale in England after several enthusiastic owners made the pilgrimage to the factory near Bologna, the Lamborghini is one wealthy manufacturer's idea of the perfect GT car. V-12 engine with four overhead camshafts, a fine 5-speed gearbox and all-independent suspension. And purely for fun, there's the Bertone-bodied Muira with a 345 h.p. engine crosswise at the rear.

CLOSE-UP
Twelve-cyl.; o.h.c.; 82 × 62 mm.; 3,930 c.c.; 325 b.h.p.; 9 to 1 comp.; 6 twin-choke Weber carbs.; 5-speed, 9.5, 6.54, 4.62, 3.77, 3.07 to 1; cen. lvr.; susp., f. and r. ind. coil; 2-door; 2/4-seat; disc servo brks.; max. 160 m.p.h.; cruise, 135; m.p.g. 14–17; whl. base, 8ft. 4¾in.; track f. and r. 4ft. 6¾in.; lgth., 15ft. 2⅝in.; width 5ft. 7⅞in.; ht. 4ft. 2in.; g.c. 5in.; turng. cir. 37ft. 8in.; kerb wt. 25½ cwt.; tank 17 gals.; 12-volt.
£5,124 + £1,320 p.t. = £6,444

LANCIA FLAVIA MILLEOTTO

STUDENTS of styling found the original Fulvia saloon a classic example of how not to do it. The new body retains the character (grille almost unaltered) but has the assured line expected of Italy. Three engines; 1.4-litre, 1.8-litre and a special version of the latter with Kugelfischer injection to give a maximum speed of over 100 m.p.h. More efficient ventilation and an electrically driven engine fan are features.

CLOSE-UP
Four-cyl.; o.h.v.; 88 × 74 mm.; 1,800 c.c.; 92 b.h.p.; 9 to 1 comp.; Solex carb.; 4-speed, 12.24, 7.31, 5.16, 3.71 to 1; col. lvr.; susp., f. ind. transv. leaf, r. half-elliptic; 4-door; 4/5-seat; disc servo brks.; max. 98 m.p.h.; cruise, 85; m.p.g. 26–30; whl. base, 8ft. 8½in.; track f. 4ft. 4in.; r. 4ft. 2in.; lgth., 15ft.; width, 5ft. 3⅜in.; ht. 4ft. 11in.; g.c. 5½in.; turng. cir., 36ft.; kerb wt., 23½ cwt.; tank, 10 gals.; 12-volt.
£1,422 + £328 p.t. = £1,750

LANCIA FULVIA GT

UPWARD trends in engine size find Lancia introducing two new versions of the charming little Fulvia; a 1,216 c.c. saloon with performance which at last matches its road holding and a 1.3-litre coupe which holds an astonishingly easy 100 m.p.h. on Continental motorways. Canted-over twin-cam engine, front-wheel drive, disc brakes all round, are mechanical points and finish is in the discreet Lancia quality style.

CLOSE-UP
Four-cyl.; o.h.c.; 76 × 67 mm.; 1,216 c.c.; 80 b.h.p.; 9 to 1 comp.; 2 Weber 2-choke carbs.; 4-speed, 16.77, 9.37, 6.10, 4.3 to 1; cen. lvr.; susp., f. ind. transv. leaf, r. half-elliptic; 4-door; 4/5-seat; disc brks.; max. 95 m.p.h.; cruise, 84; m.p.g. 28–34; whl. base, 8ft. 1⅜in.; track f. 4ft. 3⅛in.; r. 4ft. 2⅛in.; lgth., 13ft. 7in.; width, 5ft. 1¼in.; ht. 4ft. 7in.; g.c. 5in.; turng. cir., 37ft.; kerb wt., 19½ cwt.; tank, 8½ gals.; 12-volt.
£1,211 + £279 p.t. = £1,490

LOTUS ELAN+2

FIRST four-seater sports car from Lotus, the Elan + 2 provides long distance travel for two adults, two children and luggage at speeds up to 120 m.p.h. Twin-cam Lotus-Ford engine, close-ratio four-speed gearbox, steel backbone chassis with all-independent coil spring suspension, servo-assisted disc brakes and moulded glass fibre body are features. Windows are electrically operated, headlamps retract. Two-seater Elans continue unchanged.

CLOSE-UP

Four-cyl.; o.h.c.; 82.55×72.7 mm.; 1,558 c.c.; 118 b.h.p.; 9.5 to 1 comp.; 2 Weber carbs.; 4-speed, 11.19, 7.58, 5.28, 3.77 to 1; cen. lvr.; susp., f. and r. ind. coil; 2-door; 2/4-seat; disc brks.; max. 125 m.p.h.; cruise, 110; m.p.g. 26; whl. base, 8ft.; track f. 4ft. 6in., r. 4ft. 7in.; lgth., 14ft. 1in.; width, 5ft. 6in.; ht. 3ft. 11in.; g.c. 6in.; turng. cir., 28ft.; kerb wt. 25½ cwt.; tank, 13½ gals.; 12-volt.

£1,554+£369 p.t. = £1,923

MARCOS 1600

LIGHT, rigid and rust proof, the plywood structure of the Marcos is the secret of its performance; it goes so fast the woodworm gets no time to settle in. The Volvo engine is now supplemented by the option of two Fords; a Cortina GT and a hot one developed by Chris Lawrence. Seats are fixed in this ultra-low coupe; column and pedals are adjustable.

CLOSE-UP

Four-cyl.; o.h.v.; 85×73 mm.; 1,650 c.c.; 120 b.h.p.; 10.5 to 1 comp.; Solex carb.; 4-speed, 11.19, 7.58, 5.28, 3.77 to 1; cen. lvr.; susp., f. ind. coil, r. coil; 2-door; 2-seat; hyd. brks. disc front; max. 116 m.p.h.; cruise, 95; m.p.g. 22-26; whl. base, 7ft. 5½in.; track f. 4ft. 0¾in., r. 4ft. 3in.; lgth., 13ft. 4½in.; width, 5ft. 2½in.; ht. 3ft. 6½in.; g.c. 4½in.; turng. cir., 29ft. 6in.; kerb wt. 14⅞ cwt.; tank, 10 gals.; 12-volt.

£1,500+£360 p.t. = £1,860

MASERATI GHIBLI

SPEEDY lines of Ghia styling match the performance of this low-built two-seater coupe on the Maserati V8 chassis. Its 4.7-litre V8 engine, made of light alloy, is the biggest version of the four-cam unit and has dry sump lubrication. A five-speed gearbox makes the most use of its potential and maximum speed in fifth gear is reputed to be over 170 m.p.h.

CLOSE-UP

Eight-cyl.; o.h.c.; 94×85 mm.; 4,719 c.c.; 330 b.h.p.; 8.5 to 1 comp.; 4 twin-choke Weber carbs.; 5-speed, 8.91, 5.61, 3.96, 3.31, 2.80 to 1; cen. lvr.; susp. f. ind coil, r. half-elliptic; 2-door; 2-seat; disc servo brks.; max. 174 m.p.h.; cruise 150; m.p.g. 13-15; whl. base 8ft. 4¼in.; track f. 4ft. 8⅞in., r. 4ft. 7⅜in.; lgth. 15ft. 0⅜in.; width 5ft. 10⅞in.; ht. 3ft. 9⅜in.; g.c. 5½in.; turng. cir. 36ft.; tank 22 gals.; 12-volt.

MASERATI V8 QUATTROPORTE

FOUR-DOOR styling by Frua and a four-camshaft light alloy V8 engine are main elements in the Maserati formula for fast family travel. The de Dion rear axle is replaced by a rigid axle on half-elliptic springs and radius arms, transmission is through five-speed all-synchromesh gearbox. Iodine headlamps, reclining seats, rear window demister are included. There is also the four-seater Mexico coupe by Vignale.

CLOSE-UP

Eight-cyl.; o.h.v.; 88×85 mm.; 4,136 c.c.; 260 b.h.p.; 8.5 to 1 comp.; 4 Weber carbs.; 5-speed, 9.66, 6.22, 4.35, 3.54, 3.0 to 1; cen. lvr.; BW auto. opt.; susp., f. ind. coil, r. half-elliptic; 4-door; 5-seat; disc servo brks.; max. 143 m.p.h.; cruise 110; m.p.g. 17-18; whl. base 8ft. 8in.; track, f. 4ft. 7in., r. 4ft. 8in.; lgth. 16ft. 4in.; width 5ft. 8in.; ht. 4ft. 5in.; g.c. 7in.; turng. cir. 42ft. 9in.; kerb wt. 33½ cwt.; tank 18 gals.; 12-volt.

£5,030+£1,155 p.t. = £6,185

MAZDA 1500

BERTONE styling gives this new Japanese contender the uncluttered international look and an overhead camshaft engine gives it performance to match. Side windows are curved, there's face-level fresh air ventilation; grab handles in the roof, an illuminated glove box, anti-dazzle mirror and laminated windscreen are additional features. Suspension is quite conventional. Borg Warner automatic transmission is an optional extra.

CLOSE-UP
Four-cyl.; o.h.c.; 78×78 mm.; 1,490 c.c.; 78 b.h.p.; 8.2 to 1 comp.; Stromberg. carb.; 4-speed, 15.37, 9.04, 5.87, 4.11 to 1; col. lvr., BW auto. opt.; susp., f. ind. coil, r. half-elliptic; 4-door; 4/5-seat; hyd. brks.; max. 93 m.p.h.; cruise, 80; m.p.g. 27-34; whl. base, 8ft. 3in.; track f. and r. 4ft. 4in.; lgth., 14ft. 4in.; width, 5ft. 4in.; ht. 4ft. 7in.; turng. cir., 32ft.; kerb wt., 21 cwt.; tank, 11 gals.; 12-volt.

MERCEDES-BENZ 250 SE

PIONEER work on dynamic and passive safety equipped Mercedes models with many of today's safety demands in advance, but recent refinements include flexible-topped ignition keys, energy absorbing steering columns and a warning light to show if fluid loss endangers either of the twin brake circuits. A vacuum-operated lock prevents tip-up seats of coupe and convertible models moving after starting.

CLOSE-UP
Six-cyl.; o.h.c.; 82×78.8 mm.; 2,496 c.c.; 150 b.h.p.; 9.3 to 1 comp.; Bosch injection; 4-speed, 15.88, 8.74, 5.49, 3.92 to 1; cen. or col. lvr., auto opt.; susp. f. and r. ind. coil, hyd.-pneu. levelling; 4-door; 5-seat; disc servo brks.; max. 118 m.p.h.; cruise 100; m.p.g. 18-28; whl. base 9ft. 0½in.; track, f. 4ft. 10⅓in., r. 4ft. 10½in.; lgth. 16ft. 1in.; width 5ft. 11¼in.; ht. 4ft. 8½in.; g.c. 6in.; turng. cir. 37ft.; kerb wt. 28.3 cwt.; tank 18 gals.; 12-volt.

£2,434 + £560 p.t. = £2,994

MERCEDES-BENZ 250 SL

INSTALLING a fuel-injection 2.5-litre six-cylinder engine instead of the 2.3-litre unit, Mercedes-Benz gave this coveted sports model the performance boost admirers always felt it needed. It also gets disc brakes all round, with twin master cylinders and servo assistance. Transmission is by manual gearboxes with four or five speeds to choice, or by Daimler Benz four-speed automatic.

CLOSE-UP
Six-cyl.; o.h.c.; 82×78.8 mm.; 2,436 c.c.; 150 b.h.p.; 9.5 to 1 comp.; Bosch injection; 4-speed, 15.87, 8.74, 6.48, 3.92t 0 1; cen. lvr., 5-speed or auto. opt.; susp. f. and r. ind. coil; 2-door; 2-seat; disc servo brks.; max. 125 m.p.h.; cruise 110; m.p.g. 20-23; whl. base 7ft. 10⅓in.; track, f. and r. 4ft. 10½in.; lgth. 14ft. 1½in.; width 5ft. 9½in.; ht. 4ft. 3½in.; g.c. 5in.; turng. cir. 33ft. 4in.; kerb wt. 27 cwt.; tank 14¼ gals.; 12-volt.

£2,936 + £675 p.t. = £3,611

MERCEDES-BENZ 600

IMPOSING prestige car of the German motor industry, available as saloon, or as Pullman limousine with three rows of seats and electrically operated division. Self-levelling hydraulic-pneumatic suspension, disc brakes operated by compressed-air, servo automatic transmission and power steering, ensure comfort and driving ease. Even the door locks are hydraulically operated, so slamming is unnecessary. Rear-window demister, reclining seats and headrests are additional amenities.

CLOSE-UP
Eight-cyl.; o.h.c.; 103.1×95 mm.; 6,329 c.c.; 245 b.h.p; 9.0 to 1 comp.; Bosch injection; 4-speed auto., 12.85, 8.14, 5.10, 3.23 to 1; col. lvr.; susp., f. and r. ind. pneu.; 4-door; 5-seat; disc compressed air servo brks.; max. 125 m.p.h.; cruise 100; m.p.g. 11-17; whl. base 10ft. 6in.; track f. 5ft. 2⅓in., r. 5ft. 2in.; lgth. 18ft. 2in.; width 6ft. 4⅜in.; ht. 4ft. 11½in.; g.c. 8in.; turng. cir. 40ft. 6in.; kerb wt. 48 cwt.; tank 26 gals.; 12-volt.

£7,295 + £1,673 p.t. = £8,968

MERCURY COUGAR

OFFERING a natural step-up to Mustang owners, the Ford group's Cougar has smoothly-sculptured sporting lines with extra performance and more luxurious equipment. 1968 models have many safety features, including energy absorbing steering column to protect the driver, redesigned interior padding and controls, twin-circuit brakes and a four-way hazard switch to set all turn indicator lamps flashing if the car is disabled at the roadside.

CLOSE-UP
Eight-cyl.; o.h.v.; 101.6 × 72.89 mm.; 4,727 c.c.; 220 b.h.p. gross; 9 to 1 comp.; Ford 4-choke carb.; 3-speed, 8.28, 5.07, 3 to 1; cen. lvr.; 4-speed or auto. opt.; susp., f. ind. coil, r. half-elliptic; 2-door; 2/4-seat; hyd. servo brks.; max. 118 m.p.h.; cruise 90; m.p.g. 13-17; whl. base 9ft. 5in.; track f. and r. 4ft. 10in.; lgth. 15ft. 8⅝in.; width 5ft. 10¼in.; ht. 4ft. 4in.; g.c. 6in.; turng. cir. 40ft. 6in.; kerb wt. 25½ cwt.; tank 17 gals.; 12-volt.

M.G. MGB

JUST the car for a fast spin into the country when the weather smiles. It laps up the miles with a fine, well-proven engine, a simple clear-cut chassis and body, and a constant urge to go fast with safety. Inside there are snug-fitting bucket seats and the controls are easy to get at. A winner with M.G. fans and likely to be for some time yet.

CLOSE-UP
Four-cyl.; o.h.v.; 80.26 × 89 mm.; 1,798 c.c.; 95 b.h.p. gross; 8.9 to 1 comp.; 2 S.U. carbs.; 4-speed, 14.21, 8.66, 5.37, 3.91 to 1; cen. lvr., de Normanville overdrive opt.; susp., f. ind. coil, r. half-elliptic; 2-door; 2/3 seat; hyd. brks., disc front; max. 108 m.p.h.; cruise 85; m.p.g. 26-28; whl. base 7ft. 7in.; track, f. 4ft. 1in., r. 4ft. 1¼in.; lgth. 12ft. 9⅛in.; width 4ft. 11⅞in.; ht. 4ft. 1⅜in.; g.c. 5in.; turng. cir. 32ft.; kerb wt. 18¼ cwt.; tank 10 gals.; 12-volt.

£746 + £173 p.t. = £919

M.G. MGC

PUT a 2.9-litre six-cylinder engine in the space that previously housed a 1.8-litre four-cylinder and things begin to happen. The result is the latest production MG, with effortless performance that can be enjoyed with the normal four speeds, with added overdrive, or with automatic transmission. The engine is the redesigned BMC six-cylinder unit with seven main bearings. Choice of coupe or convertible bodies.

CLOSE-UP
Six-cyl.; o.h.v.; 83.3 × 88.9 mm.; 2,912 c.c.; 145 b.h.p.; 9 to 1 comp.; 2 S.U. carbs.; 4-speed, 7.03, 6.81, 4.23, 3.07 to 1; cen. lvr. auto. opt.; susp., f. ind. torsion bar, r. half-elliptic; 2-door; 2-seat; hyd. servo brks., disc front; max. 120 m.p.h.; cruise, 100; m.p.g. 20-23; whl. base, 7ft. 7in.; track f. 4ft. 2in.; r. 4ft. 1⅛in.; lgth. 12ft. 9½in.; width 4ft. 11in.; ht. 4ft. 1¾in.; g.c. 5in.; turng. cir., 33ft.; kerb wt., 19¼ cwt.; tank, 10 gals.; 12-volt.

MORGAN PLUS 4 2-SEATER

WORLDWIDE interest in traditional-style sports cars has led Italians and Americans to start building replicas of pre-war models. Britain didn't need to. The Morgan hasn't changed and there are buyers for all the cars the little Malvern factory can produce. The versatile chassis copes with a variety of engines from Ford Cortina to Triumph TR4 and Ford V8.

CLOSE-UP
Four-cyl.; o.h.v.; 86 × 92 mm.; 2,138 c.c.; 100 b.h.p.; 9 to 1 comp.; 2 Stromberg carbs.; 4-speed, 11.08, 6.5, 4.49, 3.73 to 1; cen. lvr.; susp., f. ind. coil, r. half-elliptic; 2-door; 2-seat; hyd. brks., disc front; max. 110 m.p.h.; cruise 95; m.p.g. 25-28; whl. base 8ft.; track f. 3ft. 11in., r. 4ft. 1in.; lgth. 12ft.; width 4ft. 8in.; ht. 4ft. 4in.; g.c. 6½in.; turng. cir. 33ft. 9in.; kerb wt. 17 cwt.; tank 8½ gals.; 12-volt.

£715 + £165 p.t. = £880

MORRIS MINI DE LUXE

PACEMAKER of the modern mini cult, the world-famous Issigonis creation swings towards new success with a bigger engine for faster getaway and quicker cruising. Visible signs of the transformation include new grille and revised interior trim with remote-control gear lever. For those interested in maximum economy the original version with 848 c.c. engine now enters its ninth year of production.

CLOSE-UP

Four-cyl.; o.h.v.; 64.6 × 76.2 mm.; 998 c.c.; 38 b.h.p.; 8.3 to 1 comp.; S.U. carb.; 4-speed, 13.66, 8.18, 5.32, 3.76 to 1; cen. lvr., auto opt.; susp. f. and r. ind. rubber-hyd.; 2-door; 4-seat; hyd. brks.; max. 78 m.p.h.; cruise 70; m.p.g. 32-40; whl. base 6ft. 8in.; track, f. 3ft. 11⅜in., r. 3ft. 9⅞in.; lgth. 10ft.; width 4ft. 7½in.; ht. 4ft. 5in.; g.c. 6⅛in.; turng. cir. 31ft. 7in.; kerb wt. 11¾ cwt.; tank 5½ gals.; 12-volt.

MORRIS MINOR 1000

LIKE Tennyson's brook, this highly functional car seems to go on for ever. Now in its 15th year, its popularity shows no sign of flagging. And the secret? A well proportioned small car, easy on the pocket, with a robust engine that refuses to lie down. And with the spare wheel stowed at the back, there is still room for seven cubic feet of luggage space.

CLOSE-UP

Four-cyl.; o.h.v.; 64.6 × 83.7 mm.; 1,098 c.c.; 48 b.h.p.; 8.5 to 1 comp.; S.U. carb.; 4-speed, 15.27, 9.16, 5.96, 4.22 to 1; cen. lvr.; susp., f. ind. torsion bar, r. half-elliptic; 2- or 4-door; 4-seat; hyd. brks.; max. 75 m.p.h.; cruise 55; m.p.g. 36-48; whl. base 7ft. 2in.; track f. 4ft. 2⅜in., r. 4ft. 2⅛in.; lgth. 12ft. 4in.; width 5ft.; ht. 5ft.; g.c. 6¾in.; turng. cir. 33ft.; kerb wt. 15¼ cwt.; tank 6½ gals.; 12-volt.

£446 + £104 p.t. = £550

MORRIS 1800

SPACE to spare is no idle phrase here; the biggest of the BMC front-drive models has one of the roomiest interiors obtainable at any price, thanks to the compact transverse engine and front-wheel-drive. Its image is becoming less elderly since BMC's competition department tweaked the engine, put on light alloy wheels and won the Danube rally. Also available as an Austin.

CLOSE-UP

Four-cyl.; o.h.v.; 80.26 × 88.9 mm.; 1,798 c.c.; 80 b.h.p.; 8.2 to 1 comp.; S.U. carb.; 4-speed, 12.77, 8.60, 5.37, 3.88 to 1; cen. lvr.; susp., f. and r. ind. rubber hydraulic; 4-door; 5-seat; hyd. servo brks., disc front; max. 90 m.p.h.; cruise 80; m.p.g. 24-28; whl. base 8ft. 10in.; track f. 4ft. 8in., r. 4ft. 7½in.; lgth. 13ft. 8¼in.; width 5ft. 7in.; ht. 4ft. 8in.; g.c. 6⅛in.; turng. cir. 37ft.; kerb wt. 22¾ cwt.; tank 10½ gals.; 12-volt.

£717 + £166 p.t. = £883

MOSKVITCH

FROM a Russian factory now being re-equipped with Renault aid, this strongly built four-door saloon has modern lines and conventional mechanical design. The three-bearing engine, a gearbox with synchromesh on the top three speeds only, a rear axle mounted on half-elliptic springs and drum brakes all round, mark it as the product of state industry which does not change models very often.

CLOSE-UP

Four-cyl.; o.h.v.; 76 × 75 mm.; 1,357 c.c.; 55 b.h.p.; 7 to 1 comp.; K-59 carb.; 4-speed, 16.1, 10.2, 6.1, 4.2 to 1; col. lvr.; susp., f. ind. coil, r. half-elliptic; 4-door; 4/5-seat; hyd. brks.; max. 75 m.p.h.; cruise 60; m.p.g. 30-35; whl. base 7ft. 10½in.; track f. 4ft. 0¾in., r. 4ft. 0¼in.; lgth. 13ft. 5½in.; width 5ft. 1¼in.; ht. 4ft. 10½in.; g.c. 7in.; turng. cir. 33ft.; kerb wt., 18½ cwt.; tank 10 gals.; 12-volt.

£485 + £113 p.t. = £598

NSU 110

ROOMIEST of the rear-engined NSUs, the 110 with its transverse light alloy overhead camshaft, air-cooled engine is now available in touring and sports versions. The 110 engine of 1,055 c.c. delivers 49 h.p. installed in the car; the 1,177 c.c. engine of the 110 SC gives 60 h.p. to make this a surprisingly fast car through the heavy traffic of British highways. Added for 1968 is the 1200 with still bigger engine.

CLOSE-UP

Four-cyl.; o.h.c. air-cooled; 72×66.6 mm.; 1,085 c.c.; 53 b.h.p.; 8 to 1 comp.; Solex carb.; 4-speed, 16.5, 9.1, 5.8, 4.1 to 1; cen. lvr.; susp. f. and r. ind. coil; 2-door; 4-seat; hyd. brks., disc front; max. 88 m.p.h.; cruise 80; m.p.g. 25-30; whl. base 8ft. 0½in.; track, f. 4ft. 2½in., r. 4ft. 1in.; lgth. 13ft. 1½in.; width 4ft. 11in.; ht. 4ft. 6in.; g.c. 7in.; turng. cir. 31ft.; kerb wt. 14 cwt.; tank 9¾ gals.; 12-volt.

£636+£147 p.t. = £783

NSU RO.80

TRIPLE-TIPPED rotors turning in twin trochoids drive the front wheels of this fast Wankel-engined family car. Ride and road holding are in the top class. The twin-circuit disc brakes (inboard in front) have servo and a load-sensitive anti-locking valve. Transmission is semi-automatic with torque converter, three-speed gearbox and automatic clutch. Electrically heated rear window and stainless steel bumpers are standard.

CLOSE-UP

Twin-rotor Wankel; 995 c.c.; 115 b.h.p.; 9 to 1 comp.; 2 Solex carbs; 3-speed, semi-auto., 9.98, 5.87, 3.83 to 1.; cen. lvr.; susp., f. and r. ind. coil; 4-door; 5-seat; disc servo brks.; max. 112 m.p.h.; cruise, 100; m.p.g. 24; whl. base, 9ft. 4¾in.; track f. 4ft. 10½in., r. 4ft. 8⅜in.; lgth., 15ft. 8in.; width, 5ft. 9½in.; ht. 4ft. 7½in.; g.c. 6½in.; turng. cir., 38ft. 9in.; kerb wt. 23½ cwt.; tank, 18 gals.; 12-volt.

OLDSMOBILE TORONADO

400 horsepower is a nice round figure and even if it doesn't all get through to the front wheels, it means the 1968 Toronado, with 7½-litres against 6.8, will get away faster than ever. Current features include twin-circuit brakes with warning lamp, electrically operated windows, six-way power-operated bench seat, retractable headlamps and reminder buzzer to prevent the driver leaving the ignition key in the lock.

CLOSE-UP

Eight-cyl.; o.h.v.; 104.8×107.9 mm.; 7,497 c.c.; 400 b.h.p. gross; 10.5 to 1 comp.; Rochester four-choke carb.; 3-speed auto., 7.64, 4.55, 3.08 to 1; cen. lvr.; susp., f. ind. torsion bar, r. half-elliptic; 2-door; 6-seat; hyd. servo brks., disc front; max. 130 m.p.h.; cruise 100; m.p.g. 10-15; whl. base 9ft. 11in.; track, f. 5ft. 3½in., r. 5ft. 3in.; lgth. 17ft. 7⅜in.; width 6ft. 6½in.; ht. 4ft. 4¾in.; g.c. 6in.; turng. cir. 42ft. 10in.; kerb wt. 40½ cwt.; tank 20 gals.; 12-volt.

OLDSMOBILE 4-4-2

STILL bigger engines and higher axle ratios for easier motorway cruising are features of 1968 Oldsmobiles. The 4-4-2, performance leader in the F85 range, is offered in USA with nine engine-transmission options. New styling, dual exhaust outlets through the rear bumper, concealed wipers to cut dazzle, hazard warning flashers and larger wheel cylinders in drum brakes distinguish 1968 models.

CLOSE-UP

Eight-cyl.; o.h.v.; 98.3×107.9 mm.; 6,556 c.c.; 350 b.h.p. gross; 10.5 to 1 comp.; Rochester 4-choke carb.; 3-speed auto., converter max. 2.5, axle 3.08 to 1; cen. lvr.; susp., f. ind. coil, r. coil; 2 or 4-door; 6-seat; hyd. servo brks., disc front; max. 110 m.p.h.; cruise, 90; m.p.g. 11-16; whl. base 9ft. 4in.; track f. and r. 4ft. 11in.; lgth. 16ft. 9⅜in.; width, 6ft. 4½in.; ht. 4ft. 4¾in.; g.c. 5½in.; turng. cir. 40ft.; kerb wt., 32⅝ cwt.; tank, 16¾ gals.; 12-volt.

Abbreviations—g.c.—ground clearance; susp.—suspension; f.—front; r.—rear; comp.—compression; s.v.—side-valves; o.h.v.—overhead valves; o.h.c.—overhead camshaft; hyd.—hydraulic.

OPEL COMMODORE

THIRTY years ago GM horrified British car makers by tossing Opels on to the British market at what seemed give-away prices. They return here with a big range of highly developed cars; 2-door and 4-door saloons and coupes at prices inflated by import duty and purchase tax which hide the formidable competition they offer overseas. The fast Commodore has a six-cylinder engine with belt-driven overhead camshaft.

CLOSE-UP

Six-cyl.; o.h.c.; 87×69.8 mm.; 2,490 c.c.; 115 b.h.p.; 9.5 to 1 comp.; Solex carb.; 4-speed, 11.38, 7.17, 4.54, 3.32 to 1; cen. lvr., auto opt.; susp., f. ind. coil, r. coil; 2-door; 5-seat; hyd. servo brks., disc front; max. 108 m.p.h.; cruise, 85; m.p.g. 16-22; whl. base, 8ft. 9in.; track f. and r. 4ft. 7½in.; lgth., 15ft. 1in.; width, 5ft. 9⅛in.; ht. 4ft. 7¾in.; g.c. 5⅛in.; turng. cir., 36ft. 5in.; kerb wt., 23 cwt.; tank, 12 gals.; 12-volt.

OPEL REKORD L

GENERAL MOTORS in Germany build this fast, roomy family car which now comes onto the British market for the first time. Modern overhead camshaft engines and efficient rear suspension with coil springs and radius arms guarantee lively performance and good road holding. Sleek two-door coupes, four-door saloons and roomy station wagons are the body styles and there is a choice of four- or six-cylinder engines.

CLOSE-UP

Four-cyl.; o.h.c.; 93×69.8 mm.; 1,897 c.c.; 90 b.h.p.; 9 to 1 comp.; Solex carb.; 4-speed, 11.21, 5.83, 3.47 to 1; col. lvr., 4-speed or auto. opt.; susp., f. ind. coil, r. coil; 4-door; 5-seat; hyd. servo brks., disc front; max. 95 m.p.h.; cruise, 80; m.p.g. 20-25; whl. base, 8ft. 9in.; track f. and r. 4ft. 7⅛in.; lgth., 15ft. 1⅛in.; width, 5ft. 9¼in.; ht. 4ft. 9¼in.; g.c. 5¼in.; turng. cir., 35ft. 9in.; kerb wt. 21 cwt.; tank, 12 gals.; 12-volt.

PEUGEOT 204

IN a world of giants, the Peugeot family firm have come in out of the cold by establishing a working partnership with Renault, but they retain independence in operation and design policy. Take for example the 204 coupe and Spider; two short-wheelbase models that supplement the saloon and station wagon. All have light alloy transverse engines with overhead camshaft and removable cylinder liners.

CLOSE-UP

Four-cyl.; o.h.c.; 75×64 mm.; 1,130 c.c.; 53 b.h.p.; 8.8 to 1 comp.; Solex carb.; 4-speed, 15.15, 9.25, 6.06, 4.23 to 1; col. lvr.; susp. f. and r. ind. coil; 4-door; 4-seat; hyd. brks., disc front; max. 86 m.p.h.; cruise 78; m.p.g. 26-30; whl. base 8ft. 6in.; track, f. 4ft. 4in., r. 4ft. 1½in.; lgth. 13ft.; width 5ft. 1½in.; ht. 4ft. 7in.; g.c. 5½in.; turng. cir. 31ft. 2in.; kerb wt. 16¾ cwt.; tank 9¼ gals.; 12-volt.

£798+£185 p.t.=£983

PEUGEOT 404

CRUISING at 80 down the Routes Nationales the 404 exemplifies what the average Frenchman expects from a middle-range car; solid construction to stand up to foot-on-the-floor driving and suspension that takes rough roads in its stride. The gear change is improved for 1968. Besides the saloon there are a station wagon, plus coupe and convertibles by Pininfarina with fuel injection.

CLOSE-UP

Four-cyl.; o.h.v.; 84×73 mm.; 1,618 c.c.; 70 b.h.p.; 7.4 to 1 comp.; Solex carb.; 4-speed, 16.80, 9.42, 6.05, 4.2 to 1; col. lvr.; susp., f. ind. coil, r. coil; 4-door; 4/5-seat; hyd. brks.; max. 90 m.p.h.; cruise 75-80; m.p.g. 30; whl. base 8ft. 8¼in.; track f. 4ft. 4¾in., r. 4ft. 2¼in.; lgth. 14ft. 6in.; width 5ft. 5¼in.; ht. 4ft. 9¼in.; g.c. 6in.; turng. cir. 32ft.; kerb wt. 20½ cwt.; tank 11 gals.; 12-volt.

£903+£209 p.t.=£1,112

Abbreviations—g.c.—ground clearance; susp.—suspension; f.—front; r.—rear; comp.—compression; s.v.—side-valves; o.h.v.—overhead valves; o.h.c.—overhead camshaft; hyd.—hydraulic.

PLYMOUTH BARRACUDA

MORE power and performance options, a new grille and three body styles, fastback coupe, hardtop and convertible, give a wide choice to buyers of Chrysler's sporting family car. Front-seat locks, headrests, rear window demister, and low-profile tyres are among the available features and there's a new lightweight V8 engine of 5.6-litres among the options.

CLOSE-UP

Eight-cyl.; o.h.v.; 99.3 × 84.1 mm.; 5,211 c.c.; 240 b.h.p.; 10.5 to 1 comp.; Carter 2-choke carb.; 4-speed, 9.25, 6.14, 4.52, 3.23 to 1; cen. lvr., auto. opt.; susp., f. ind. torsion bar; r. half-elliptic; 2-door; 5/6-seat; hyd. servo brks., disc front; max. 120 m.p.h.; cruise, 100; m.p.g. 14-18; whl. base, 9 ft.; track f. 4ft. 7⅞in.; r. 4ft. 7½in.; lgth., 16ft. 0¾in.; width, 5ft. 11¾in.; ht. 4ft. 4¾in.; g.c. 5¾in.; turng. cir., 40ft. 6in.; kerb wt., 27¼ cwt.; tank, 15 gals.; 12-volt.

PONTIAC PARISIENNE

CANADIAN-BUILT with right-hand drive for British buyers, the Parisienne has a big V8 engine modified to reduce exhaust pollution, automatic transmission by torque converter and two-speed planetary gear, plus power-assisted steering and brakes. The convertible has power operation for windows and folding top. New safety features include twin-circuit brakes, four-way hazard warning flasher and a collapsible neck on the fuel tank.

CLOSE-UP

Eight-cyl.; o.h.v.; 98.4 × 82.6 mm.; 5,032 c.c.; 200 b.h.p. gross; 9 to 1 comp.; Rochester 2-choke carb.; 2-speed auto., 5.6, 3.08 to 1; col. lvr.; susp., f. ind. coil, r. coil; 2 or 4-door; 6-seat; hyd. servo brks.; max. 102 m.p.h.; cruise, 88; m.p.g. 15-17; whl. base, 9ft. 11in.; track f. 5ft. 3⅓in.; r. 5ft. 3⅜in.; lgth., 17ft. 10¾in.; width, 6ft. 7⅜in.; ht. 4ft. 6⅝in.; turng. cir., 10ft. 9in.; kerb wt., 33⅞ cwt.; tank, 20 gals.; 12-volt.

PORSCHE 912

PLEASURE and prestige of Porsche ownership, with more modest performance and operating costs make the four-cylinder 912 a favourite with lady drivers. Now there's a new 911 T (Tourisme) with 912 trim and equipment allied to a de-tuned 110 h.p. version of the six-cylinder engine to produce a fast and untemperamental car at a useful price saving on previous six-cylinder models.

CLOSE-UP

Four-cyl.; o.h.v.; air-cooled; 82.5 × 74 mm.; 1,582 c.c.; 90 b.h.p.; 9.3 to 1 comp.; 2 Solex carbs.; 5-speed, 13.68, 8.37, 5.84, 4.61, 3.51 to 1; cen. lvr.; susp. f. and r. ind. torsion bar; 2-door; 2/4-seat; disc brks.; max. 110 m.p.h.; cruise 100; m.p.g. 30; whl. base 7ft. 3in.; track, f. 4ft. 4⅓in., r. 4ft. 3⅓in.; lgth. 13ft. 8in.; width 5ft. 3⅓in.; ht. 4ft. 4in.; g.c. 6in.; turng. cir. 33ft.; kerb wt. 19 cwt.; tank 13½ gals.; 12-volt.

£1,974 + £454 p.t. = £2,428

PORSCHE 911S

NOTHING confirms the trend to easier driving more clearly than the move to two-pedal control by leading sports car manufacturers. Porsche's solution on the six-cylinder 911 is semi-automatic, using the normal four-speed gearbox with an automatic clutch and fluid torque converter which extends the performance range in each gear. Start smoothly on the converter; stir the gears by hand.

CLOSE-UP

Six-cyl.; o.h.c.; air-cooled; 80 × 66 mm.; 1,991 c.c.; 160 b.h.p.; 9.8 to 1 comp.; 2 triple-choke Weber carbs.; 5-speed, 13.68, 8.37, 5.84, 4.61, 3.51 to 1; cen. lvr.; susp., f. and r. ind. torsion bar; 2-door; 2/4-seat; hyd. disc brks.; max. 140 m.p.h.; cruise 120; m.p.g. 23-25; whl. base 7ft. 3in.; track f. 4ft. 4⅓in., r. 4ft. 3⅓in.; lgth. 13ft. 6⅜in.; width 5ft. 3in.; ht. 4ft. 4in.; g.c. 6in.; turng. cir. 33ft.; kerb wt. 20 cwt.; tank, 13½ gals.; 12-volt.

£2,892 + £664 p.t. = £3,556

RAMBLER REBEL

DRASTIC price cuts produced a dramatic increase in Nash Rambler sales on the American market. They even got their cheapest six-cylinder model down near VW prices. For 1968 an improved range of six-cylinder and V8 cars is produced with the addition of a sporty Javelin coupe to cash in on the boom in family sporting cars that is sweeping the world.

CLOSE-UP

Eight-cyl.; o.h.v.; 95.25/83.3 mm.; 4,749 c.c.; 224 b.h.p. gross; 9 to 1 comp.; Holley 2-choke carb.; 3-speed auto, 7.65, 5.14, 3.15 to 1; col. lvr.; susp., f. ind. coil, r. coil; 2- or 4-door; 5/6-seat; hyd. servo brks., disc front; max. 104 m.p.h.; cruise 85; m.p.g. 14-18; whl. base 9ft. 4in.; track, f. 4ft. 10½in., r. 4ft. 9½in.; lgth. 16ft. 3in.; width 6ft. 2½in.; ht. 4ft. 6⅜in.; g.c. 6in.; turng. cir. 39ft. 11in.; kerb wt. 31¾ cwt.; tank 15¾ gals.; 12-volt.

£1,751 + £402 p.t. = £2,153

RELIANT REBEL

BOLD effort by a small firm to challenge the big groups in the economy car market, Reliant's Rebel now has an engine enlarged from 598 to 700 c.c. to produce an extra three horsepower for better acceleration and easier hill climbing, while retaining fuel economy in the 50 m.p.g. area. Compact dimensions commend it for city driving and a new station wagon offers extra space for family outings.

CLOSE-UP

Four-cyl.; o.h.v.; 700 c.c.; 30 b.h.p.; 8.5 to 1 comp.; Solex carb.; 4-speed, 18.69, 10.76, 6.36, 4.38 to 1; cen. lvr.; susp., f. ind. coil, r. half-elliptic; 2-door; 4-seat; hyd. brks.; max. 68 m.p.h.; cruise 60; m.p.g. 55; whl. base 7ft. 5in.; track f. 3ft. 11⅛in., r. 3ft. 10⅝in.; lgth. 11ft. 6in.; width 4ft. 10in.; ht. 4ft. 7½in.; g.c. 6in.; turng. cir. 29ft.; kerb wt. 11 cwt.; tank 6 gals.; 6-volt.

£433 + £101 p.t. = £534

RELIANT SCIMITAR

INTENSIVE development has turned this Ogle-styled glass-bodied 2+2 coupe into an outstanding high-speed long-distance tourer. Latest rear suspension with rigid axle on Watt linkage and coil springs combines with radial-ply tyres to improve road grip. A V6 Zodiac engine provides the power. Overdrive and an electric sliding roof are among the options. Face-level fresh air ventilation is added. Engine and boot are illuminated.

CLOSE-UP

Six-cyl.; o.h.v.; 93.7×72.4 mm.; 2,994 c.c.; 128 b.h.p.; 8.9 to 1 comp.; Weber carb.; 4-speed, 11.31, 7.92, 5.05, 3.58 to 1, Laycock de Normanville overdrive opt.; cen. lvr.; susp., f. ind. coil, r. coil; 2-door; 2/4-seat; hyd. brks., disc front; max. 120 m.p.h.; cruise, 100; m.p.g. 19-22; whl. base, 7ft. 8½in.; track f. 4ft. 3½in., r. 4ft. 2¾in.; lgth., 13ft. 11in.; width, 5ft. 2in.; ht. 4ft. 3½in.; g.c. 6½in.; turng. cir., 34ft. 3in.; kerb wt. 21⅜ cwt.; tank, 21 gals.; 12-volt.

£1,232 + £284 p.t. = £1,516

RENAULT 8 GORDINI

FAMILIAR sight among the leaders in international rallies, this French sports special uses the light short-nosed body of the R8 with an engine enlarged to 1,255 c.c. and developed by former racing ace Gordini, with high compression head and two twin-choke Weber carburetters. Transmission is by five-speed gearbox, there are disc brakes all round with servo assistance, and twin rear dampers.

CLOSE-UP

Four cyl.; o.h.v.; 74.5×72 mm.; 1,255 c.c.; 110 b.h.p.; 10.5 to 1 comp.; 2 Weber twin-choke carbs.; 5-speed, 14.89, 9.78, 7.01, 5.36, 4.25 to 1; cen. lvr.; susp., f. and r. ind. coil; 4-door; 4-seat; disc servo brks.; max. 108 m.p.h.; cruise, 95; m.p.g. 25; whl. base, 7ft. 5½in.; track f. 4ft. 1⅛in., r. 4ft.; lgth., 13ft. 1in.; width, 4ft. 10½in.; ht. 4ft. 4in.; g.c. 6in.; turng. cir., 30½ft.; kerb wt., 16⅝ cwt.; tank, 14¼ gals.; 12-volt.

£1,000 + £230 p.t. = £1,230

RENAULT 1100

THE 1,108 c.c. engine is now standard in both R8 (previously 956 c.c.) and 1100 but the 1100 has new rectangular headlamps and the tail lamp clusters have three separate lenses instead of one. At £649 the R8 is a low-priced 1100 c.c. car with heater, face-level ventilation, anti-theft steering lock, new, more comfortable seats and under-body corrosion protection as standard.

CLOSE-UP
Four-cyl.; o.h.v.; 70×72 mm.; 1,108 c.c.; 46 b.h.p.; 8.5 to 1 comp.; coil ign.; Solex carb.; 4-speed, 14.93, 9.28, 6.11, 4.23 to 1; cen. lvr., auto. opt.; susp. f. and r. ind. coil; 4-door; 4-seat; hyd. disc brks.; max. 83 m.p.h.; cruise 70; m.p.g. 35-39; whl. base 5½in.; track, f. 4ft. 1½in., r. 4ft.; lgth. 13ft. 9½in.; width 4ft. 10½in.; ht. 4ft. 7½in.; g.c. 6in.; turng. cir. 30ft. 6in.; kerb wt. 15⅝ cwt.; tank 8½ gals.; 12-volt.

£567 + £132 p.t. = £699

RENAULT 16

SPLIT-PERSONALITY family car, Renault front-drive 16 can be anything from fast sedan with lock-away luggage boot, to roomy cargo carrier with fold-away rear seat and lift-up rear door. The gear change is now modified for easier engagement of reverse, the choke reverts to manual from automatic. The light which announces front disc brake pads are worn doubles as handbrake reminder.

CLOSE-UP
Four-cyl.; o.h.v.; 76×81 mm.; 1,470 c.c.; 58 b.h.p.; 8.5 to 1 comp.; Solex carb.; 4-speed, 13.6, 8.48, 5.58, 3.88 to 1; col. lvr.; susp. f. and r. ind. torsion bar; 5-door; 5-seat; hyd. brks., disc front; max. 86 m.p.h.; cruise 78; m.p.g. 26-29; whl. base 8ft. 9½in.; track f. 4ft. 4⅜in., r. 4ft. 2⅜in.; lgth. 13ft. 10½in.; width 5ft. 4⅜in.; ht. 4ft. 9in.; g.c. 6in.; turng. cir. 32ft. 8in.; kerb wt. 19¼ cwt.; tank 12 gals.; 12-volt.

£705 + £163 p.t. = £868

RILEY ELF Mark II

ONE of the classier versions of the ubiquitous Minis, the 1968 Elf has some extra luxury inside but the basic mechanics remain as before. That means this front wheel drive, hydrolastic suspension model with wind up windows will still hold its place in the hearts of Riley enthusiasts. Many believe that with the 70 m.p.h. all-country speed limit, they don't need a faster quality car.

CLOSE-UP
Four-cyl.; o.h.v.; 64.58×76.2 mm.; 998 c.c.; 38 b.h.p.; 8.3 to 1 comp.; S.U. carb.; 4-speed, 13.66, 8.18, 5.32, 3.76 to 1; cen. lvr.; susp., f. and r. ind. rubber-hyd.; 2-door; 4-seat; hyd. brks.; max. 75 m.p.h.; cruise 62; m.p.g. 40; whl. base 6ft. 8in.; track f. 3ft. 11½in., r. 3ft. 10in.; lgth. 10ft. 10½in.; width 4ft. 7½in.; ht. 4ft. 5in.; g.c. 6⅛in.; turng. cir. 31ft. 7in.; kerb wt. 13 cwt.; tank 5½ gals.; 12-volt.

£525 + £122 p.t. = £647

RILEY KESTREL

ENHANCING its popularity in the 1100 market, the new Kestrel has a more sophisticated interior, different wheels, flashing indicator repeaters on the front wings and new switches for the lights. It is one of the most luxurious B.M.H. front-drive cars while retaining the individualistic stamp of a Riley. A compact and busy car that has many followers, it telescopes saloon car comfort into a very small space.

CLOSE-UP
Four-cyl.; o.h.v.; 70.6×81.3 mm.; 1,275 c.c.; 58 b.h.p.; 8.8 to 1 comp.; S.U. carb.; 4-speed, 13.23, 7.95, 5.16, 3.65 to 1; cen. lvr.; susp. f. and r. ind. rubber-hyd.; 4-door; 4/5-seat; hyd. brks., disc front; max. 90 m.p.h.; cruise 80; m.p.g. 30-36; whl. base 7ft. 9½in.; track f. 4ft. 3½in., r. 4ft. 2¾in.; lgth. 12ft. 2¾in.; width 5ft. 0⅜in.; ht. 4ft. 5in.; g.c. 5¼in.; turng. cir. 38ft.; kerb wt. 16¾ cwt.; tank 8 gals.; 12-volt.

£692 + £160 p.t. = £852

Abbreviations—g.c.—ground clearance; susp.—suspension; f.—front; r.—rear; comp.—compression; s.v.—side-valves; o.h.v.—overhead valves; o.h.c.—overhead camshaft; hyd.—hydraulic.

ROLLS-ROYCE SILVER SHADOW

FIRST open body on the Silver Shadow platform chassis, this convertible by the Rolls-Royce subsidiary H. J. Mulliner-Park Ward features a power-operated folding top worked by an electric-hydraulic system. All the usual Rolls-Royce features are naturally included; super-smooth V8 engine and automatic transmission, triple-circuit disc brakes, all-independent suspension with hydraulic levelling, seats electrically adjustable for reach, height and slope.

CLOSE-UP
Eight-cyl.; o.h.v.; 104.1 × 91.4 mm.; 6,230 c.c.; b.h.p., not revealed; 9 to 1 comp.; 2 S.U. carbs.; 4-speed auto., 11.75, 8.1, 4.46, 3.08 to 1; col. lvr.; susp. f and r. ind. coil, hyd. levelling; 2/4-door; 5-seat; disc hyd. servo brks.; max. 120 m.p.h.; cruise 100; m.p.g. 13-16; whl. base 9ft. 11½in.; track f. and r. 4ft. 9½in.; lgth. 16ft. 11½in.; width 5ft. 11in.; ht. 4ft. 11¾in.; g.c. 6½in.; turng. cir. 38ft.; kerb wt. 41 cwt.; tank 24 gals.; 12-volt.
£8,550 + £1,961 p.t. = £10,511

ROLLS-ROYCE PHANTOM V

A car that conjures every superlative in the motoring book. Britain's most munificent offering in any showroom, the car accommodates seven cosseted passengers in addition to the chauffeur. Power steering and automatic transmission make it docile in town yet it carries crowned heads and presidents long distances with speed and super elegance. And inside no possible luxury has been spared. A wonderful advertisement for the home country wherever it goes.

CLOSE-UP
Eight-cyl.; o.h.v.; 104.14 × 91.44 mm.; 6,230 c.c.; b.h.p. not revealed; 9 to 1 comp.; 2 S.U. carbs.; 4-speed auto., 14.86, 10.23, 5.64, 3.89 to 1; col. lvr.; susp., f. ind. coil, r. half-elliptic; 4-door; 7-seat; hyd. servo brks.; max. 100 m.p.h.; cruise 85; m.p.g. 12; whl. base 12ft.; track, f. 5ft. 0⅞in., r. 5ft. 4in.; lgth. 19ft. 10in.; width 6ft. 7in.; ht. 5ft. 9in.; g.c. 7¼in.; turng. cir. 48ft. 9in.; kerb wt. 50 cwt.; tank 23 gals.; 12-volt.
£8,700 + £1,995 p.t. = £10,695

ROVER 2000 TC

SWEEPING along as Britain's leading 2-litre, Rover's advanced 2000 needs no changes either in standard or twin-carburetter form to boost its popularity, but there is continuous refinement of mechanical details and accessories to improve reliability and durability. Though part of the Leyland group, Rover have ambitious plans for new and original designs. There'll be no Triumphs with Rover badges.

CLOSE-UP
Four-cyl.; o.h.c.; 85.7 × 85.7 mm.; 1,987 c.c.; 107 b.h.p.; 9 to 1 comp.; coil ign.; 2 S.U. carbs.; 4-speed, 12.83, 7.55, 4.92, 3.54 to 1; cen. lvr.; susp., f. ind. coil, r. de Dion coil; 4-door; 4-seat; disc servo brks.; max. 110 m.p.h.; cruise 98; m.p.g. 28-32; whl. base 8ft. 7½in.; track, f. 4ft. 5½in., r. 4ft. 4½in.; lgth. 14ft. 10½in.; width 5ft. 6¼in.; ht. 4ft. 6¾in.; g.c. 8¼in.; turng. cir. 31ft. 6in.; kerb wt. 24¾ cwt.; tank 12 gals.; 12-volt.
£1,150 + £265 p.t. = £1,415

ROVER 3.5-LITRE

BOOST the power by 30 per cent; slash the weight on the front wheels by 200 lb. A sure-fire recipe for success in front-engined cars which Rover achieved with a light alloy V8 engine replacing their cast iron six. Based on a General Motors design for the original Buick Compact it is mated to a Borg Warner Type 35 transmission. Power steering is standard.

CLOSE-UP
Eight-cyl.; o.h.v.; 88.9 × 71.1 mm.; 3,528 c.c.; 160 b.h.p.; 10.5 to 1 comp.; 2 S.U. carbs; 3-speed, auto., 8.46, 5.13, 3.54 to 1; cen. lvr.; susp., f. ind. torsion bar, r. half-elliptic; 4-door; 5-seat; hyd. servo brks., disc front; max. 115 m.p.h.; cruise 95; m.p.g. 16-18; whl. base, 9ft. 2½in.; track f. 4ft. 7⅜in.; r. 4ft. 8in.; lgth. 15ft. 6½in.; width, 5ft. 10½in.; ht. 5ft. 1in.; g.c. 6⅝in.; turng. cir., 40ft.; kerb wt. 31¼ cwt.; tank, 14 gals.; 12-volt.
£1,625 + £374 p.t. = £1,999

SAAB V4

FANATICAL two-stroke fans aiming at simplicity and long life can have the three-cylinder 841 c.c. engine with three carburetters which gave the Carlssons so many rally victories, but most buyers now take the more powerful V4 four-stroke built by Ford in Germany. Two-door saloon or a station wagon seating up to seven are the body options. Free-wheel is a rare standard item; brakes have been twin-circuit for years; an automatic clutch is an extra.

CLOSE-UP

Four-cyl.; o.h.v.; 90×58.9 mm.; 1,498 c.c.; 65 b.h.p.; 9 to 1 comp.; Solex carb.; 4-speed, 16.98, 10.19, 6.34, 4.09 to 1; col. lvr.; susp., f. ind. coil, r. coil; 2-door.; 4-seat; hyd brks., disc front; max. 94 m.p.h.; cruise, 85; m.p.g. 30-33; whl. base, 8ft. 2in.; track f. and r. 4ft.; lgth., 13ft. 8in.; width 5ft. 2in.; ht. 4ft. 10in.; g.c. 7½in.; turng. cir. 35ft.; kerb wt., 17.2 cwt.; tank, 8¾ gals.; 12-volt.

£650+£151 p.t.=£801

SIMCA 1100

INFLUENCED in mechanical design if not in styling, by the Italian team that produced the Autobianchi Primula, Simca's first front-drive model has a transverse engine with separate gearbox. Five doors and chunky lines mark it as one of the new-style utility saloons capable of carrying bulky loads for week-day work or week-end fun. Simca, now Chrysler-controlled, have high hopes for it.

CLOSE-UP

Four-cyl.; o.h.v.; 74×65 mm.; 1,118 c.c.; 56 b.h.p.; 9.6 to 1 comp.; Solex carb.; 4-speed, 14.45, 9.06, 5.99, 4.25 to 1; cen. lvr., semi-auto opt.; susp., f. and r. ind. torsion bar; 3/5-door; 4-seat; hyd. brks., disc front; max. 88 m.p.h.; cruise, 78; m.p.g. 30-34; whl. base, 8ft. 3⅛in.; track f. 4ft. 5⅜in., r. 4ft. 3⅜in.; lgth., 12ft. 11¼in.; width 5ft. 2½in.; ht. 4ft. 9⅜in.; g.c. 5½in.; turng. cir., 36ft. 1in.; kerb wt., 17¼ cwt.; tank 9¼ gals.; 12-volt.

SIMCA 1301/1501

CHRYSLER-CONTROLLED, and thus a French partner of Rootes, this vigorous French group offers its biggest car with choice of two engines and two types of trim. There is also a choice of saloon or station wagon bodies and four-speed manual or fully automatic transmissions. Draughtless ventilation is assured by extractor vents in the rear quarter panels. Front engine, rear drive on this one.

CLOSE-UP

Four-cyl.; o.h.v.; 74×75 mm.; 1,290 c.c.; 62 b.h.p. gross; or 75.2×83 mm.; 1,475 c.c.; 81 b.h.p. gross; 8.3/9.3 to 1 comp.; Solex or Weber carb.; 4-speed, 16.22, 9.14, 6.15, 4.45 to 1; cen. lvr.; susp., f. ind. coil, r. coil; 4-door; 4-seat; hyd. brks., disc front on 1501; max. 85/93 m.p.h.; cruise 70-80; m.p.g. 28-32; whl. base 8ft. 3¼in.; track, f. 4ft. 4in., r. 4ft. 3in.; lgth. 14ft. 7¼in.; width 5ft. 2in.; ht. 4ft. 7¼in.; g.c. 6in.; turng. cir. 32ft.; kerb wt. 19¾-20¼ cwt.; tank 12 gals.; 12-volt. **1301LS £698+£162 p.t.=£860**

1501GL £798+£185 p.t.=£983

SINGER CHAMOIS Mk II

THERE are three versions of the Chamois and this earns its full share of success. Essentially a neat and compact car for town or nipping into the country, the Coupe version has a lively with-it engine, lots of comfort for driver and passenger inside, and quality fittings. It is said to be an ideal car for two on honeymoon. But city gents like it too as you will see in any city.

CLOSE-UP

Four-cyl.; o.h.c.; 68×60.37 mm.; 875 c.c.; 39 b.h.p.; 10 to 1 comp.; Solex carb.; 4-speed, 16.595, 8.905, 5.702, 4.132 to 1; cen. lvr.; susp., f. and r. ind. coil; 2-door; 4-seat; drum brks.; max. 77 m.p.h.; cruise, 68; m.p.g. 40; whl. base, 6ft. 10in.; track f. 4ft. 1½in., r. 4ft. 0½in.; lgth., 11ft. 9¼in.; width., 5ft. 0¼in.; ht. 4ft. 6½in.; g.c. 5½in.; turng. cir., 30ft. 6in.; kerb wt., 15¼ cwt.; tank, 10 gals.; 12-volt.

£502+£117 p.t.=£619

Abbreviations—g.c.—ground clearance; susp.—suspension; f.—front; r.—rear; comp.—compression; s.v.—side-valves; o.h.v.—overhead valves; o.h.c.—overhead camshaft; hyd.—hydraulic.

SINGER GAZELLE

ONE of the popular Rootes family saloons, this five-seater continues to be a strong favourite. Interior luxuries include a smart central console, a lockable glove box, twin sun visors with a vanity mirror for the passenger, four individual ashtrays—one in each door—a door-operated courtesy light and twin coat hooks. Details, perhaps, but they give an indication of the quality and thought that have gone into the car.

CLOSE-UP
Four-cyl.; o.h.v.; 81.5×71.6 mm.; 1,496 c.c.; 60 b.h.p.; 8.4 to 1 comp.; Zenith Stromberg carb.; 4-speed, 13.04, 8.32, 5.41, 3.89 to 1; cen. lvr.; susp., f. ind. coil, r. half-elliptic; 4-door; 4/5-seat; disc front brks.; max. 80 m.p.h.; cruise, 70; m.p.g. 30-40; whl. base, 8ft. 2½in.; track f. and r. 4ft. 4in.; lgth., 14ft.; width., 5ft. 3½in.; ht. 4ft. 8in.; g.c. 6¾in.; turng. cir., 33ft. 6in.; kerb wt., 18¼ cwt.; tank, 10 gals.; 12-volt.

£648 + £150 p.t. = £798

SINGER VOGUE

ONE of the new range of light and lively cars that have rejuvenated the Rootes image in the past year. More space for passengers and luggage, combined with a big cut in weight, which gives a real surge of acceleration and effortless fast cruising with moderate fuel consumption. Canted-over four-cylinder engine, strut-type front suspension and disc front brakes are features.

CLOSE-UP
Four-cyl.; o.h.v.; 81.5 ⁄ 82.5 mm.; 1,725 c.c.; 80 b.h.p.; 9.2 to 1 comp.; Stromberg carb.; 4-speed, 12.41, 7.92, 5.15, 3.7 to 1; cen. lvr., L de N. overdrive or BW. auto. opt.; susp., f. ind. coil, r. half-elliptic; 4-door; 4/5-seat; hyd. brks., disc front; max. 88 m.p.h.; cruise 75; m.p.g. 28-34; whl. base 8ft. 2½in.; track, f. and r. 4ft. 4in.; lgth. 14ft. 1½in.; width 5ft. 3½in.; ht. 4ft. 8in.; g.c. 6¾in.; turng. cir. 33ft. 6in.; kerb wt. 18½ cwt.; tank 10 gals.; 12-volt.

£740 + £171 p.t. = £911

SKODA 1000 MB

CZECHOSLOVAKIA'S rear-engined saloon now appears in de luxe form with still more comprehensive equipment. Radial-ply tyres, outside mirror, fully carpeted floor and boot, deeper seats, twin reversing lamps, wheel embellishers and laminated windscreen, enhance a specification that was already exceptional in its price class. Neater intakes supply air to the rear engine. There's a coupe too, with higher compression and twin carburetters.

CLOSE-UP
Four-cyl.; o.h.v.; 68×68 mm.; 988 c.c.; 45 b.h.p. gross; 8.3 to 1 comp.; Jikov c rb.; 4-speed, 16.87, 9.41, 6.26, 4.26 to 1; cen. lvr. susp. f. and r. ind. coil; 4-door; 4-seat; hyd. brks.; max. 75 m.p.h.; cruise 68; m.p.g. 36-38; whl base 7ft. 10½in.; track, f. 4ft. 2½in.; r. 4ft. 1in.; lgth. 13ft. 8¾in.; width 5ft. 4in.; ht. 4ft. 7in.; g.c. 7in.; turng. cir. 35ft.; kerb wt. 14¾ cwt.; tank 7 gals.; 12-volt.

£438 + £102 p.t. = £540

SUNBEAM RAPIER

COMPLETELY new two door fastback styling replaces the old hardtop model and gives sports car performance and getaway. Top speed is above 100 m.p.h. but inside comfort has also been studied. There are twin headlamps, pillarless doors and retractable rear side windows for a good look at the countryside. Interior fittings include fully reclining individual front seats with two bucket seats behind, new upholstery is punched so that it can "breathe".

CLOSE-UP
Four-cyl.; o.h.v.; 81.5×82.5 mm.; 1,725 c.c.; 94 b.h.p. gross; 9.2 to 1 comp.; 2 Stromberg carbs.; 4-speed and de Normanville overdrive, 12.14, 7.75, 5.04, 3.89 to 1; cen. lvr., auto. opt.; susp., f. ind. coil, r. half-elliptic; 2-door; 4-seat; hyd. brks. disc front; max. 102 m.p.h.; cruise, 90; m.p.g. 24-26; whl. base, 8ft. 2½in.; track f. and r. 4ft. 4in.; lgth., 14ft. 1in.; width, 5ft. 3½in.; ht. 4ft. 7in.; g.c. 6½in.; turng. cir., 33ft. 6in.; kerb wt., 17½ cwt.; tank, 10 gals.; 12-volt.

SUNBEAM STILETTO

ULTIMATE in Imps, if you except special racing and rally models. Californian coupe body with twin-carburetter engine, high-lift overhead camshaft, oil cooler and servo brakes. Four headlamps give the front a distinctive appearance and the roof has a black leather-cloth finish. Slotted alloy wheel discs, chromium-ended tail pipe, radial ply tyres, reclining front seats. Circular instruments, including tachometer appear on a new facia.

CLOSE-UP
Four-cyl.; o.h.c.; 68×60.4 mm.; 875 c.c.; 51 b.h.p.; 10 to 1 comp.; 2 Zenith-Stromberg carbs; 4-speed, 16.59, 8.91, 5.70, 4.14 to 1; cen. lvr.; susp., f. and r., ind. coil; 2-door; 4-seat; hyd. servo brks.; max. 88 m.p.h.; cruise, 80; m.p.g. 35-42; whl. base, 6ft. 10in.; track f. 4ft. 2⅜in., r. 4ft.; lgth., 11ft. 7in.; width, 5ft. 0½in.; ht. 4ft. 4½in.; g.c. 5½in.; turng. cir., 30ft. 6in.; kerb wt. 14¾ cwt.; tank, 6 gals.; 12-volt.

SUNBEAM TIGER

THE smile on the face of the Tiger may have something to do with the switch from a 4.2-litre V8 engine to a newer Ford unit of 4.7 litres. Performance, already exciting, is now electrifying, with acceleration that is making this a popular choice with executives in a hurry. And the effortless top gear pull means you don't have to be changing gear incessantly.

CLOSE-UP
Eight cyl.; o.h.v.; 101.66 × 73 mm.; 4,737 c.c.; 200 b.h.p. gross; 9.3 to 1 comp.; Ford 2-choke carb.; 4-speed, 8.0, 5.56, 3.92, 2.88 to 1; cen. lvr.; susp. f. ind. coil, r. half-elliptic; 2-door; 2-seat; hyd. servo brks., disc front; max. 125 m.p.h.; cruise, 115; m.p.g. 14-19; whl. base 7 ft. 2 in.; track f. 4 ft. 3¾ in.; r. 4 ft. 0½ in.; lgth. 13 ft. 2 in.; width 5 ft. 0½ in.; ht. 4 ft. 3½ in.; g.c. 5 in.; turng. cir. 37 ft. 9 in.; kerb wt. 23⅝ cwt.; tank 11¾ gals.; 12-volt.

TOYOTA COROLLA

NEW competition in the 1100 c.c. class arrives with this lively Japanese model, available as two-door saloon or three-door station wagon. Its five-bearing engine has a twin-choke carburetter. Front suspension is unusual; MacPherson coil spring struts plus a transverse leaf spring as stabiliser. Transmission is by four-speed box, fully synchronised, but Toyota's own automatic is an optional alternative.

CLOSE-UP
Four-cyl.; o.h.v.; 75×61 mm.; 1,077 c.c.; 60 b.h.p. gross; 9 to 1 comp.; Aisan twin-choke carb.; 4-speed, 15.53, 8.75, 5.72, 4.22 to 1; cen. lvr.; susp., f. ind. coil and transv. leaf, r. half-elliptic; 2-door; 4-seat; hyd. brks.; max. 86 m.p.h.; cruise, 75; m.p.g. 32-35; whl. base, 7ft. 6in.; track f. 4ft. 0⅜in., r. 4ft. 0½in.; lgth., 12ft. 7⅜in.; width 4ft. 10½in.; ht. 4ft. 6⅝in.; g.c. 6½in.; turng. cir., 29ft. 9in.; kerb wt., 14¼ cwt.; tank, 12 gals.; 12-volt.

TOYOTA 1600S

WELL-ESTABLISHED on the British market with the Corona saloon, Toyota now aim at the sports coupe buyer with this modern two-door model powered by an enlarged engine with twin carburetters. Four headlamps, repeater turn indicators on the sides, wheel trim discs and disc front brakes are standard equipment. A brake servo is available and the front seats have reclining backrests.

CLOSE-UP
Four-cyl.; o.h.v.; 80.5×78 mm.; 1,587 c.c.; 90 b.h.p. gross; 9.2 to 1 comp.; 2 S.U. carbs.; 4-speed, 15.08, 8.67, 5.75, 4.11 to 1; cen. lvr.; susp. f. ind. coil, r. half-elliptic; 2-door; 4-seat; hyd. brks.; disc front; max. 100 m.p.h.; cruise 85; m.p.g. 26-30; whl. base, 7ft. 11in.; track f. and r. 4ft. 2in.; lgth. 13ft. 4in.; width 5ft. 1in.; ht. 4ft. 8in.; g.c. 7in.; turng. cir. 32ft. 6in.; kerb wt. 18¼ cwt.; tank 10 gals.; 12-volt.

£908+£210 p.t. = £1,118

TRIUMPH HERALD 13/60

BIGGER engine, new styling and improved interior details rejuvenate a popular family model. A new grille and Vitesse-style front wings frame headlamps shorn of projecting cowls. Interior safety is improved by recessed switches. Triumph were pioneers of the telescopic safety steering column and their 25-foot turning circle gives unique parkability. The range includes station wagon, saloon with folding roof and four-seater convertible.

CLOSE-UP

Four-cyl.; o.h.v.; 73.7×76 mm.; 1,296 c.c.; 56 b.h.p.; 8.5 to 1 comp.; Solex carb.; 4-speed, 15.4, 8.9, 5.7, 4.1 to 1; cen. lvr.; susp., f. ind. coil, r. ind. transv. leaf; 2-door; 4-seat; hyd. brks., disc front; max. 85 m.p.h.; cruise, 80; m.p.g. 32-36; whl. base, 7ft. 7½in.; track f. 4ft. 1in., r. 4ft.; lgth., 12ft. 9in.; width., 5ft.; ht. 4ft. 4in.; g.c. 6⅜in.; turng. cir., 25ft.; kerb wt., 17 cwt.; tank, 6½ gals.; 12-volt.

TRIUMPH 1300

STYLE and finish like the 2000 in compact form for today's crowded roads. Front-wheel drive, with gears under the engine and all-independent suspension for good ride and road holding. Safety points include fold-away window winders and an eight-light monitor for mechanical functions. New for 1968 is the high-performance TC version with Spitfire-type cylinder head.

CLOSE-UP

Four-cyl.; o.h.v.; 73.7×76 mm.; 1,296 c.c.; 60 b.h.p. gross; 8.5 to 1 comp.; Stromberg carb.; 4-speed, 13.97, 8.87, 5.96, 4.37 to 1; cen. lvr.; susp. f. and r. ind. coil; 4-door; 4/5-seat; hyd. brks., disc front; max. 85 m.p.h.; cruise 75; m.p.g. 30-33; whl. base 8ft. 0⅝in.; track f. 4ft. 5in.; r. 4ft. 4⅝in.; lgth. 12ft. 11in.; width 5ft. 1⅜in.; ht. 4ft. 6in.; g.c. 5⅜in.; turng. cir. 30ft.; kerb wt. 18 cwt.; tank 11¾ gals.; 12-volt.

£678 + £157 p.t. = £835

TRIUMPH SPITFIRE MK 3

HERE is a robust little sports car that leapt into favour from the day it was announced earlier this year. Radical changes included the hood folding away in seconds behind the seats, repositioning of the front bumper and a new one-piece radiator grille. Wrap-round rear bumpers are raised and the overriders are discarded. Engine power also goes up by 8 b.h.p. to 75 b.h.p.

CLOSE-UP

Four-cyl.; o.h.v.; 73.7×76 mm.; 1,296 c.c.; 75 b.h.p.; 9 to 1 comp.; 2 SU carbs.; 4-speed, 15.4, 8.9, 5.7, 4.1 to 1; cen. lvr., Laycock de Normanville overdrive opt.; susp. f. ind. coil, r. ind. transv. leaf; 2-door; 2-seat; hyd. brks., disc front; max. 100 m.p.h.; cruise, 85; m.p.g. 24-28; whl. base 6ft. 11in.; track f. 4ft. 1in., r. 4ft.; lgth. 12ft. 2in.; width 4ft. 9in.; ht. 3ft. 8⅓in.; g.c. 5in.; turng. cir. 24ft.; kerb wt. 14½ cwt.; tank 8¾ gals.; 12-volt.

£582 + £135 p.t. = £717

TRIUMPH TR5

FAMILIAR face but a changed character. The smoothness of a six-cylinder engine replaces the rugged big four; the extra urge of 2½-litres pushes the performance upwards, while fuel injection keeps down fuel consumption and exhaust pollution. Winding windows and a well-tailored folding top guarantee a snug interior in bad weather and the luggage boot is a really useful size.

CLOSE-UP

Six-cyl.; o.h.v.; 2,500 c.c.; Lucas injection; 4-speed; cen. lvr.; susp. f. and r. ind. coil; 2-door; 2/3-seat; servo brks., disc front; max. 120 m.p.h.; cruise, 100; m.p.g. 20-25; whl. base 7ft. 4in.; track f. 4ft. 2in., r. 4ft. 1in.; lgth. 12ft. 7in.; width 4ft. 9½in.; ht. 4ft. 2in.; g.c. 6in.; turng. cir., 33ft. 7in.; tank, 11¾ gals.; 12-volt.

T.V.R. TUSCAN

THE Blackpool sports car makers offer the ultimate in acceleration with a Special Equipment version of their Ford-powered fun car. A V8 engine of 4.7-litres instead of 4.2, four-choke carburetter, limited-slip differential and wide-rim wheels are main features of a tiny coupe which accelerates from standstill to 100 mph in 14 seconds and does about 155 m.p.h. flat out. Tubular chassis, plastic body.

CLOSE-UP
Eight-cyl.; o.h.v.; 101.6×72.9 mm.; 4,727 c.c.; 270 b.h.p. gross; 11 to 1 comp.; Ford 4-choke carb.; 4-speed, 7.24, 5.46, 4.33, 3.07 to 1; cen. lvr.; susp., f. and r. ind. coil; 2-door; 2-seat; hyd. servo brks., disc front; max. 155 m.p.h.; cruise, 130; m.p.g. 16-18; whl. base, 6ft. 11½in.; track f. 4ft. 5½in., r. 4ft. 6⅝in.; lgth., 11ft. 9½in.; width, 5ft. 4in.; ht. 4ft.; g.c. 5in.; turng. cir., 32ft. 3in.; kerb wt., 20¼ cwt.; tank, 15 gals.; 12-volt.

£1,922+£442 p.t. = £2,364

VANDEN PLAS PRINCESS

THERE seems no end to the highly successful versions of B.M.H.'s Hydrolastic, twin-carburetter, transverse-fitted engine cars. This is one the most luxurious on a small but handsome scale. Its shape comes from the famous Pininfarina coachwork stable in Italy, coupled with first class mechanics provided at Longbridge, Birmingham. It is precocious but well proven and with its new power should do even better.

CLOSE-UP
Four-cyl.; o.h.v.; 70.6×81.3 mm.; 1,275 c.c.; 58 b.h.p.; 8.8 to 1 comp.; SU carb.; 4-speed, 13.23, 7.95, 5.16, 3.65 to 1; cen. lvr., auto opt.; susp. f. and r. ind. rubber hyd.; 4-door; 4/5-seat; hyd brks., disc front; max. 90 m.p.h.; cruise 80; m.p.g. 30-36; whl base 7ft. 9½in.; track f. 4ft. 3½in., r. 4ft. 2⅞in.; lgth. 12ft. 2¾in.; width 5ft. 0⅞in.; ht. 4ft. 5in.; g.c. 5½in.; turng. cir. 38ft.; kerb wt. 16¾ cwt.; tank 8 gals.; 12-volt.

VAUXHALL VIVA

SOARING demand for the latest Viva has boosted Vauxhall's share of the British market to over 14 per cent this year. Clean-cut style, lots of space, powerful engines and new rear suspension made a combination that quickly caught on and there is a wide range of trim and performance options, through SL luxury and 90 engines to the Brabham conversions which can be fitted by local dealers.

CLOSE-UP
Four-cyl.; o.h.v.; 77.7×61 mm.; 1,159 c.c.; 47 b.h.p.; 8.5 to 1 comp.; Stromberg carb.; 4-speed, 14.68, 8.64, 5.47, 3.9 to 1; cen. lvr.; susp., f. ind. coil, r. coil; 2-door; 4/5 seat; hyd. brks., disc front and servo opt.; max. 80 m.p.h.; cruise 70; m.p.g. 34-39; whl. base 7ft. 11½in.; track f. and r. 4ft. 3in.; lgth. 13ft. 5½in.; width 5ft. 3in.; ht. 4ft. 5in.; g.c. 5in.; turng. cir. 31ft. 6in.; kerb wt. 15¼ cwt.; tank 8 gals.; 12-volt.

£492+£114 p.t. = £606

VAUXHALL VICTOR/2000

NEW all through; body, engine, suspension, the latest Victor comes with a four-cylinder engine in two sizes, each boasting belt-driven overhead camshaft. Transmission is three-on-the-column or four-on-the-floor with option of Birfield-built de Normanville overdrive. BW automatic is available on 2000 which also has disc front brakes. New heater ventilation system employs rear-quarter extractors.

CLOSE-UP
Four-cyl.; o.h.c.; 85.7×69.2 mm.; 1,599 c.c. (2000, 95.25×69.24 mm.; 1,975 c.c.); 72/88 b.h.p.; 8.5 to 1 comp.; Zenith-Stromberg carb.; 3-speed, 13.14, 6.74, 4.12 to 1 (2000, 11.18, 6.38, 3.9 to 1); col. lvr., 4-speed and Birfield de Normanville overdrive opt.; susp., f. ind. coil, r. coil; 4-door; 5-seat; hyd. brks. (disc front, 2000); max. 87-94 m.p.h.; cruise, 78-85; m.p.g. 28/25; whl. base, 8ft. 6in.; track f. and r. 4ft. 6in.; lgth., 14ft. 8½in.; width, 5ft. 6⅜in.; ht. 4ft. 3⅜in.; g.c. 5⅛in.; turng. cir., 33ft. 5in.; kerb wt. 20¾ cwt. (2000 21 cwt.); tank, 12 gals.; 12-volt.

VAUXHALL CRESTA

PERFORMANCE, comfort and generous space for passengers and luggage make the Cresta a natural choice for business and family motoring where something more than average is required. For those who want maximum luxury at a reasonable price, the Viscount is indicated; included in the price are automatic transmission, power steering, reclining front seats, reversing lights, rear window demister, and innumerable detail refinements.

CLOSE-UP

Six-cyl.; o.h.v.; 92×82.6 mm.; 3,294 c.c.; 123 b.h.p.; 8.5 to 1 comp.; Zenith carb.; 3-speed, 9.00, 5.14, 3.45 to 1; col. lvr., 4-speed, auto or overdrive opt.; susp., f. ind. coil, r. half-elliptic; 4-door; 6-seat; hyd. servo brks., disc front; max. 102 m.p.h.; cruise 90; m.p.g. 19-23; whl. base 8ft. 11½in.; track, f. 4ft. 7¼in., r. 4ft. 8¼in.; lgth. 15ft. 7in.; width 5ft. 9¾in.; ht. 4ft. 8½in.; g.c. 5½in.; turng. cir. 36ft. 6in.; kerb wt. 25 cwt.; tank 15 gals.; 12-volt.

£815+£188 p.t.=£1,003

VOLKSWAGEN 1200

BEAT-THE-SLUMP model successfully re-introduced with modern improvements. The original three-way fuel tap replaces a gauge, rear suspension compensator is omitted, brakes are drums, trim is simplified, bright metal reduced, but it has the latest wide track plus the VW finish and meticulous development of mechanical parts that have sold Beetles by the million.

CLOSE-UP

Four cyl.; o.h.v., air-cooled; 77×64 mm.; 1,192 c.c.; 41 b.h.p.; 7.1 to 1 comp.; Solex carb.; 4-speed; cen. lvr.; susp., f. and, r. ind. torsion bar; 2-door; 4-seat; drum brks.; max. 78 m.p.h.; cruise, 78; m.p.g. 37; whl. base, 7ft. 10½in.; track f. 4ft. 3¼in., r. 4ft. 5⅛in.; lgth., 13ft. 4¼in.; width, 5ft. 0½in.; ht. 4ft. 5¼in.; g.c. 5¾in.; turng. cir., 36ft.; kerb wt., 13¾ cwt.; tank, 8¾ gals.; 6-volt.

£483+£112 p.t.=£595

VOLKSWAGEN 1500

SAFETY dictates the main mods to the Beetle. A collapsible steering column and new instrument control knobs improve crash protection; higher rear bumper reduces risks of casual damage to the engine compartment. External access to the fuel filler saves lifting the bonnet and headlamps with vertical lenses improve vision for night driving. Semi-automatic transmission is optional with new rear suspension.

CLOSE-UP

Four-cyl.; o.h.v.; air-cooled; 83×69 mm.; 1,493 c.c.; 44 b.h.p.; 7.5 to 1 comp.; Solex carb.; 4-speed, 15.67, 8.49, 5.19, 3.67 to 1; cen lvr.; susp., f. and r. ind. torsion bar; 2-door; 4-seat; hyd brks., disc front; max. 78 m.p.h.; cruise 78; m.p.g. 30-32; whl. base 7ft. 10½in.; track f. 4ft. 3⅜in., r. 4ft. 5⅛in.; lgth. 13ft. 4in.; width 5ft. 0½in.; ht. 4ft. 11in.; g.c. 6in.; turng. cir. 36ft.; kerb wt. 14 cwt.; tank 8¾ gals.; 6-volt.

£566+£131 p.t.=£697

VOLKSWAGEN 1600TL

A fully automatic transmission at extra cost is the big news on the 1600 VWs in their various forms; saloon, fastback TL coupe, station wagon and Karmann Ghia coupe. With it comes a new type of rear suspension with trailing wishbones and double-jointed drive shafts in place of swing axles. A safety steering column is fitted and for USA there is a fume-free fuel injection engine.

CLOSE-UP

Four-cyl.; o.h.v. air-cooled; 85.8×69 mm.; 1,584 c.c.; 54 b.h.p.; 7.7 to 1 comp.; 2 Solex carbs.; 4-speed, 15.7, 8.5, 5.4, 3.7 to 1; cen. lvr., auto. opt.; susp., f. and r. ind. torsion bar; 2-door; 4-seat; hyd. brks., disc front; max. 84 m.p.h.; cruise, 84; m.p.g. 32-34; whl. base, 7ft. 10½in.; track f. 4ft. 3⅝in.; r. 4ft. 5in.; lgth., 13ft. 10⅜in.; width, 5ft. 3¼in.; ht. 4ft. 10⅛in.; g.c. 5⅞in.; turng. cir., 36ft. 5in.; kerb wt., 18¼ cwt.; tank, 8¾ gals.; 12-volt.

£785+£182 p.t.=£967

Abbreviations—g.c.—ground clearance; susp.—suspension; f.—front; r.—rear; comp.—compression; s.v.—side-valves; o.h.v.—overhead valves; o.h.c.—overhead camshaft; hyd.—hydraulic.

VOLVO 131

LOWEST-PRICE leader in a range of strongly built Swedish cars that include a lot of British materials and components. Sufferers from backache and slipped discs should try Volvo's splendid seats, with lumbar contour adjustment. Double-circuit brakes, heater, mud flaps, reversing lights, are standard. Same body with the 103 h.p. engine from the sports coupe makes the 105 m.p.h. 123 GT Coupe.

CLOSE-UP
Four-cyl.; o.h.v.; 84.1 × 80 mm.; 1,778 c.c.; 75 b.h.p.; 8.7 to 1 comp.; Zenith carb; 4-speed, 12.83, 8.16, 5.58, 4.1 to 1; cen. lvr.; susp., f. ind. coil, r. coil; 2-door; 5-seat; hyd. brks., disc front; max. 94 m.p.h.; cruise 80; m.p.g. 24-28; whl. base 8ft. 6⅛in.; track f. and r. 4ft. 3¾in.; lgth. 14ft. 7¼in.; width 5ft. 3¼in.; ht. 4ft. 11½in.; g.c. 8in.; turng. cir. 32ft.; kerb wt. 22 cwt.; tank 10 gals.; 12-volt.
£865 + £200 p.t. = £1,065

VOLVO 144

AHEAD of America, the safety-conscious Swedes built currently fashionable features into the 144 from the start; controlled crumpling of front and rear ends, collapsible steering column, twin-circuit brakes, extra-thick laminated windscreen. 144S is the high performance 103 m.p.h. version with twin-carburetter 103 h.p. engine. Front-seat safety harness and two-speed wipers are standard.

CLOSE-UP
Four-cyl.; o.h.v.; 84.1 × 80 mm.; 1,778 c.c.; 75 b.h.p.; 8.7 to 1 comp. or 100 b.h.p. 10 to 1 comp.; Stromberg or 2 S.U. carbs.; 4-speed, 12.8, 8.2, 5.6, 4.1 to 1; cen. lvr. auto or Laycock de Normanville overdrive opt.; susp., f. ind. coil, r. coil; 4-door; 5-seat; disc servo brks.; max. 95-102 m.p.h.; cruise, 85-90; m.p.g. 24-28; whl. base, 8ft. 6⅛in.; track f. and r. 4ft. 5⅛in.; lgth., 15ft. 9⅝in.; width 5ft. 8⅛in.; ht. 4ft. 8⅝in.; g.c. 7in.; turng. cir., 30ft. 5in.; kerb wt., 23½ cwt.; tank, 12¾ gals.; 12-volt.
£1,100 + £254 p.t. = £1,354

WARTBURG KNIGHT

DOING well in the RAC Rally, the Wartburg Knight has demonstrated its practical qualities before a big British audience. Made in East Germany, it has a three-cylinder two-stroke engine driving the front wheels. Many items, normally extras, are included in the price; parking lights, radiator blind, mudflaps, electric screen washer and headlamps with beam which can be adjusted for load.

CLOSE-UP
Three-cyl.; two-stroke; 72.5 × 78 mm.; 991 c.c.; 45 b.h.p.; 7.5 to 1 comp.; BVF carb.; 4-speed, 14.49, 9.45, 6.06, 4.24 to 1; cen. lvr.; susp., f. and r. ind. coil; 4-door; 4/5-seat; hyd. brks.; max. 72 m.p.h.; cruise, 62; m.p.g. 23-29; whl. base, 8ft.; track f. 4ft. 2in., r. 4ft. 3in.; lgth., 14ft.; width, 5ft. 3in.; ht. 4ft. 8in.; g.c. 6in.; turng. cir., 33ft.; kerb wt., 17¾ cwt.; tank, 9½ gals.; 12-volt.
£503 + £117 p.t. = £620

WOLSELEY 18/85

THIS is a well-balanced, four-door saloon with good lines and a thrustful engine. Its 1,798 c.c. engine provides good take-off speeds, fast but easy cruising, and can exceed 90 m.p.h. when needed. It is the latest version of the east-to-west engine developed by Alec Issigonis and his men, with of course front wheel drive and hydrolastic suspension. There is power steering and automatic transmission is optional.

CLOSE-UP
Four-cyl.; o.h.v.; 80.26 × 88.9 mm.; 1,798 c.c.; 85 b.h.p.; 8.2 to 1 comp.; S.U. carb.; Borg Warner, 3-speed, 9.417, 5.714, 3.94 to 1; cen. lvr.; susp., f. and r. ind. rubber hydraulic; 4-door; 5-seat; servo brks., disc front; max. 90 m.p.h.; cruise, 80; m.p.g. 24-28; whl. base, 8ft. 10in.; track f. 4ft. 8½in., r. 4ft. 7½in.; lgth. 13ft. 8½in.; width, 5ft. 7in.; ht. 4ft. 7½in.; g.c. 6½in.; turng. cir., 38ft. 6in.; kerb wt., 22¾ cwt.; tank, 10¾ gals.; 12-volt.
£705 + £163 p.t. = £868

Estate Car Section

Once it was called a game brake, in a hangover from Edwardian days. Then the Americans called it the station wagon — why is not clear, since what they meant was a depot automobile. A nice compromise has emerged — and the handy vehicle with a door (or lid) at the back is becoming universally known as the Estate car. And here is the latest report from the E.C. front in words and pictures.

ASTON MARTIN DB6 STATION WAGON

THIS is one of the best-looking and fastest station wagons anywhere in the world. The swift, effortless sports car characteristics of the two-door model are to a great extent inherited by the load-carrying estate car. It is ideal for the monied motorist who wants to tour his estates in a car made for the purpose. An outstanding model from the David Brown stable.

CLOSE-UP

Six-cyl.; o.h.c.; 96×92 mm.; 3,995 c.c.; 282 b.h.p.; 8.9 to 1 comp.; 3 S.U. carbs.; 5-speed, 10.18, 6.64, 4.64, 3.77, 3.14 to 1; cen. lvr., auto opt.; susp., f. ind. coil, r. coil; 2-door; 4-seat; disc servo brks.; max. 148 m.p.h.; cruise 120; m.p.g. 15-18; whl. base 8ft. 2in.; track f. 4ft. 6in., r. 4ft. 5½in.; lgth. 15ft.; width 5ft. 6in.; ht. 4ft. 5in.; g.c. 6¼in.; turng. cir. 34ft.; kerb wt. 29 cwt.; tank 16 gals.; 12-volt.

AUSTIN MINI COUNTRYMAN

MINI with the most room for children, luggage, camping gear or business cargo, the Countryman now has the extra power of a larger engine to keep it lively when fully loaded. Tree lovers can have the applied wood framing. Those who fear weight and woodworm can opt for the lighter all-metal body. Minis can also be had with one of the world's best automatic transmissions.

CLOSE-UP

Four-cyl.; o.h.v.; 64.6×76.2 mm.; 998 c.c.; 38 b.h.p.; 8.3 to 1 comp.; S.U. carb.; 4-speed, 13.66, 8.18, 5.32, 3.76 to 1; cen. lvr., auto opt.; susp. f. and r. ind. rubber-hyd.; 3-door; 4-seat; hyd. brks.; max. 78 m.p.h.; cruise 70; m.p.g. 32-40; whl. base 6ft. 8in.; track, f. 3ft. 11⅜in., r. 3ft. 9⅞in.; lgth. 10ft.; width 4ft. 7½in.; ht. 4ft. 5in.; g.c. 6¼in.; turng. cir. 31ft. 7in.; kerb wt. 12 cwt.; tank 5½ gals.; 12-volt.

CHRYSLER VALIANT REGAL

AUSTRALIA'S outback has proved the possibilities of the vast carrying capacity in this Australian-built station wagon which comes with a choice of engines; straight six or V8, allowing the buyer to adjust power and fuel consumption to his own needs. Besides engine variations there is a choice of transmissions and the flexible seating arrangements make this a versatile family-business load carrier.

CLOSE-UP

Six-cyl.; o.h.v.; 86×105 mm.; 3,687 c.c.; 145 b.h.p. gross; 8.4 to 1 comp.; Carter carb.; 3-speed, 9.53, 5.91, 3.23 to 1; col. lvr.; susp., f. ind. torsion bar, r. half-elliptic; 5-door; 6-seat; hyd. brks., disc front opt.; max. 94 m.p.h.; cruise, 80; m.p.g. 17-19; whl. base, 8ft. 10in.; track f. 4ft. 7⅞in., r. 4ft. 7½in.; lgth., 15ft. 9in.; width, 5ft. 9½in.; ht. 4ft. 8½in.; g.c. 5¼in.; turng. cir., 35ft.; kerb wt., 27¼ cwt.; tank, 14½ gals.; 12-volt.
£1,663+£382 p.t. = £2,045

Abbreviations—g.c.—ground clearance; susp.—suspension; f.—front; r.—rear; comp.—compression; s.v.—side-valves; o.h.v.—overhead valves; o.h.c.—overhead camshaft; hyd.—hydraulic.

CITROEN SAFARI 21

ONE of Europe's biggest station wagons with the unobstructed interior space that front-wheel drive ensures, plus the special benefits of Citroen's advanced design; self-levelling suspension that keeps ride height and headlamp beams constant no matter how much cargo you carry and servo brakes that proportion the braking effort according to load distribution. New front wings now enclose four headlamps.

CLOSE-UP
Four-cyl.; o.h.v.; 90×85.5 mm.; 2,175 c.c.; 100 b.h.p.; 8.75 to 1 comp.; Weber twin-choke carb.; 4-speed, 14.22, 8.49, 5.56, 3.72 to 1; dash lvr.; susp., f. and r. ind. hyd. pneu.; 5-door; 7-seat; hyd. servo brks., disc front; max. 102 m.p.h.; cruise 90; m.p.g. 24-28; whl. base, 10ft. 3in.; track f. 4ft. 11in., r. 4ft. 3½in.; lgth., 16ft. 4½in.; width 5ft. 10½in.; ht. 5ft. 0½in.; g.c. 5⅜in.; turng. cir., 36ft.; kerb wt. 27¼ cwt.; tank 14 gals.; 12-volt.

£1,543+£355 p.t. = £1,898

CITROEN DYANE

LEAVE a 2CV and an Ami-6 together in a garage all night, and this might be the result. Dyane is a modern-style utility saloon with five doors on a 2CV chassis. With higher compression ratio, power of the flat-twin air cooled 425 c.c. engine rises to 18.5 h.p. and the carburetter has an acceleration pump. Independent suspension is interconnected front-to-rear.

CLOSE-UP
Two-cyl.; o.h.v. air cooled; 66×62 mm.; 425 c.c.; 18.5 b.h.p.; 7.9 to 1 comp.; Solex carb.; 4-speed, 28.5, 13.0, 7.7, 5.6 to 1; dash lvr.; susp. f. and r. ind. coil; 5-door; 4-seat; hyd. brks.; max. 62 m.p.h.; cruise 60; m.p.g. 46-54; whl. base 7ft. 10½in.; track f. and r. 4ft. 1⅜in.; lgth. 12ft. 9½in.; width 4ft. 11in.; ht. 5ft. 0⅜in.; g.c. 6in.; turng. cir. 35ft. 1in.; kerb wt. 11¾ cwt.; tank 4¼ gals.; 12-volt.

FORD CORTINA ESTATE

CROSS-FLOW cylinder heads and bowl-in-piston combustion chambers boost performance of what was already Britain's most popular station wagon, with a claimed 25 per cent of the total market. Power of the 1300 c.c. engine is boosted by 10 per cent to 63 h.p. on the test bed; the new 1600 unit puts out 75 h.p. Simpler controls for the Aeroflow draughtless ventilation are another 1968 feature.

CLOSE-UP
Four-cyl.; o.h.v.; 80.9×77.6 mm.; 1,599 c.c.; 75 b.h.p. gross; 9 to 1 comp.; Ford carb.; 4-speed, 13.82, 9.34, 5.51, 3.9 to 1; cen. lvr.; susp., f. ind. coil, r. half-elliptic; 5-door; 4/5-seat; hyd. brks. disc front; max. 87 m.p.h.; cruise, 80; m.p.g. 29-33; whl. base, 8ft. 2in.; track f. 4ft. 4½in., r. 4ft. 3in.; lgth., 14ft. 1½in.; width, 5ft. 4⅝in.; ht. 4ft. 6¾in.; g.c. 6¼in.; turng. cir., 30ft.; kerb wt., 18¾ cwt.; tank, 10 gals.; 12-volt.

FORD FAIRMONT

IMMENSE outputs from American factories make it economic to offer a big choice of engines, transmissions and equipment on popular models like Ford's latest family station wagon, only one of several in the 1968 range. All the latest safety provisions are included as required by American regulations; shock absorbing steering column, padded panel and recessed controls, twin-circuit brakes and hazard-warning flasher.

CLOSE-UP
Eight-cyl.; o.h.v.; 101.6×72.9 mm.; 4,728 c.c.; 200 b.h.p.; 9.3 to 1 comp.; 2 carbs.; 3-speed auto., 7.72, 4.68, 3.23 to 1; col. lvr.; susp., f. ind. coil, r. half-elliptic; 5-door; 6-seat; hyd. servo brks., disc front; max. 100 m.p.h.; cruise, 90; m.p.g. 15; whl. base, 9ft. 3in.; track f. and r. 4ft. 10in.; lgth., 15ft. 10in.; width, 6ft. 1¾in.; ht. 4ft. 7in.; g.c. 7in.; turng. cir., 36ft. 6in.; kerb wt., 28½ cwt.; tank, 13 gals.; 12-volt.

£1,940+£446 p.t. = £2,386

FIAT 500 GIARDINERA

SMALLEST of the station wagons, the little Fiat can carry surprisingly bulky objects, thanks it its fold-back roof. The two-cylinder air-cooled engine lies on its side under the flat rear floor. Cooling air is taken in through grilles in the rear quarter panels. Rear seat and backrest fold flat and there is extra cargo space under the bonnet.

CLOSE-UP

Two-cyl.; o.h.v., air-cooled; 67.4 × 70 mm.; 499 c.c.; 18 b.h.p.; 7.1 to 1 comp.; Weber carb.; 4-speed, 16.75, 10.55, 6.76, 4.46 to 1; cen. lvr.; susp., f. ind. trans. leaf, r. ind. coil; 3-door; 4-seat; hyd. brks.; max. 60 m.p.h.; cruise, 55; m.p.g. 51; whl. base, 6ft. 4½in.; track f. 3ft. 8in., r. 3ft. 8½in.; lgth., 10ft. 5in.; width, 4ft. 4in.; ht. 4ft. 5½in.; g.c. 5¼in.; turng. cir., 28ft.; kerb wt., 10 cwt.; tank, 4½ gals.; 12-volt.

£411 + £96 p.t. = £507

FIAT 124

VOTED Car of the Year in 1965 in saloon form, Fiat's popular family model now appears with this neat and roomy station wagon body. Its pushrod four-cylinder engine has a light alloy head and twin-choke carburetter which uses only one choke for low-speed running. Front suspension is conventional. At the rear, coil springs are helped by radius arms and Panhard rod.

CLOSE-UP

Four-cyl.; o.h.v.; 73 × 71.5 mm.; 1,197 c.c.; 60 b.h.p.; 8.8 to 1 comp.; Solex 2-choke carb.; 4-speed, 16.7, 10.25, 6.65, 4.44 to 1; cen. lvr.; susp., f. ind. coil, r. coil; 5-door; 4/5-seat; disc brks.; max. 86 m.p.h.; cruise, 80; m.p.g. 30; whl. base, 7ft. 11¼in.; track f. 4ft. 4⅜in., r. 4ft. 3¼in.; lgth., 13ft. 2⅞in.; width, 5ft. 4in.; ht. 4ft. 7⅞in.; g.c. 8in.; turng. cir., 35ft.; kerb wt., 16.9 cwt.; tank, 8½ gals.; 12-volt.

£710 + £164 p.t. = £874

OLDSMOBILE VISTA CRUISER

FAMILY observation car for vacation trips, with passenger and luggage capacity that makes it an all-year-round asset. A big car with everything to make driving easy; automatic transmission, power-assisted steering and brakes (discs in front) and electric operation for side windows, tail gate and seat adjustment. Four-link rear suspension and limited slip differential make effective use of the V8 engine's power.

CLOSE-UP

Eight-cyl.; o.h.v.; 103 × 85.9 mm.; 5,736 c.c.; 310 b.h.p. gross; 10.25 to 1 comp.; Rochester 4-choke carb.; 3-speed auto, Converter max 2.2; Axle 3.08 to 1; col. lvr.; susp., f. ind. coil, r. coil; 5-door; 6-seat; hyd. servo brks., disc front; max. 112 m.p.h.; cruise, 95; m.p.g. 13-17; whl. base, 10ft. 1in.; track f. and r. 4ft. 11in.; lgth., 18ft. 1½in.; width, 6ft. 3⅞in.; ht. 4ft. 8½in.; turng. cir., 41ft. 8in.; kerb wt., 37¾ cwt.; tank, 16¾ gals.; 12-volt.

HILLMAN HUSKY

SUCCESSOR to a popular little front-engined station wagon, the latest Husky uses the Imp's light alloy overhead camshaft engine canted over to lie flat under the rear floor. There's space for luggage under the bonnet too, so this handy family transporter has carrying space from bumper to bumper. Other features like the all-independent suspension and all-synchro gearbox come from the Imp.

CLOSE-UP

Four-cyl.; o.h.c.; 68 × 60.3 mm.; 875 c.c.; 39 b.h.p.; 10 to 1 comp.; Solex carb.; 4-speed, 16.595, 8.905, 5.702, 4.138 to 1; cen. lvr.; susp., f. and r. ind. coil; 3-door; 4-seat; hyd. brks.; max. 75 m.p.h.; cruise, 60; m.p.g. 35-40; whl. base, 6ft. 10in.; track f. 4ft. 2⅓in., r. 3ft. 11½in.; lgth., 11ft. 8½in.; width., 5ft. 0¼in.; ht. 4ft. 10½in.; g.c. 5½in.; turng. cir., 30ft. 6in.; kerb wt., 14⅞ cwt.; tank, 6 gals.; 12-volt.

£505 + £117 p.t. = £622

MERCEDES BENZ 230S UNIVERSAL

COMMON market collaboration produces the only Mercedes-Benz station wagon, the 230S with body conversion done in Belgium. Its 2.3-litre overhead camshaft six-cylinder engine gives it a good margin of power to handle a full load. All-independent suspension with self-pumping hydro-pneumatic compensator at the rear ensures a good ride full or empty. Twin-circuit brakes, with discs in front.

CLOSE-UP

Six-cyl.; o.h.c.; 82×72.8 mm.; 2,306 c.c.; 120 b.h.p.; 9 to 1 comp.; 2 Zenith carbs.; 4-speed, 16.52, 9.09, 5.71, 4.08 to 1; cen. lvr., auto. opt.; susp., f. and r. ind. coil with level control, 5-door; 5-seat; hyd. servo brks., disc front; max. 108 m.p.h.; cruise, 90; m.p.g. 23-26; whl. base, 9ft. 0½in.; track f. 4ft. 10½in.; r. 4ft. 10⅜in.; lgth., 16ft. 0⅜in.; width, 5ft. 7⅜in.; ht. 5ft. 0⅜in.; g.c. 5⅜in.; kerb wt., 29 cwt.; tank, 14¼ gals.; 12-volt.

MORRIS 1300 TRAVELLER

HIGHER speed, better acceleration and quieter motorway cruising, plus the ability to handle heavy loads with less effort come from the new 1,275 c.c. engine. And thanks to higher gearing, fuel consumption is little if any higher. This BMC utility model appeals to those who want the versatility of a station wagon within compact overall dimensions. Suspension is rubber-hydraulic Hydrolastic; front brakes are discs.

CLOSE-UP

Four-cyl.; o.h.v.; 70.6×81.3 mm.; 1,275 c.c.; 58 b.h.p. 8.8 to 1 comp.; SU carb.; 4-speed, 13.23, 7.95, 5.16, 3.65 to 1; cen. lvr., auto opt.; susp. f. and r. ind. rubber hyd.; 3-door; 4/5 seat; hyd. brks., disc front; max. 90 m.p.h.; cruise 80; m.p.g. 30-36; whl base 7ft. 9½in.; track f. 4ft. 3½in., r. 4ft. 2⅞in.; lgth. 12ft. 2¾in.; width 5ft. 0⅜in.; ht. 4ft. 5in.; g.c. 5½in.; turng. cir. 38ft.; kerb wt. 16¾ cwt.; tank 8 gals.; 12-volt.

PEUGEOT 204

TRANSVERSE engine, front-wheel drive but with a difference. The engine is in light alloy and has an overhead camshaft. Front drive gives the flat floor for maximum cargo space in this compact utility model with the big lift-up rear door. Suspension is all-independent, front brakes are discs. The range also includes saloon, a sporting coupe and a convertible.

CLOSE-UP

Four-cyl.; o.h.c.; 75×64 mm.; 1,130 c.c.; 53 b.h.p.; 8.8 to 1 comp.; Solex carb.; 4-speed, 15.15, 9.25, 6.06, 4.23 to 1; col. lvr.; susp., f. and r. ind. coil; 5-door; 4/5-seat; hyd. servo brks., disc front; max. 86 m.p.h.; cruise, 78; m.p.g. 26-30; whl. base, 8ft. 6in.; track f. 4ft. 4in.; r. 4ft. 1in.; lgth., 13ft. 0½in.; width, 5ft. 1in.; ht. 4ft. 7in.; g.c. 5½in.; turng. cir., 31ft. 2in.; tank, 9½ gals.; 12-volt.

£825+£191 p.t.=£1,016

RAMBLER REBEL STATION WAGON

WITH a choice of engines; straight six or V8, this big, powerful family and freight carrier copes easily with six people and a large amount of luggage. Automatic transmission and servo brakes with discs in front are standard items and suspension by coil springs all round gives a comfortable ride. The rear window winds down into the tailgate and there is a built-in roof rack.

CLOSE-UP

Six-cyl.; o.h.v.; 95.25×88.9 mm.; 3,802 c.c.; 155 b.h.p. gross; 9 to 1 comp.; 4-choke Holley carb.; 3-speed auto; col. lvr.; susp. f. ind. coil, r. coil; 5-door; 6-seat; hyd. servo brks., disc front; max. 98 m.p.h.; cruise, 85; m.p.g. 20-25; whl. base 9 ft. 6 in.; track f. 4 ft. 10¼ in., r. 4 ft. 10½ in.; lgth. 16 ft. 6 in.; width, 6 ft. 5¼ in.; ht. 4 ft. 7 in.; g.c. 6½ in.; turng. cir. 37 ft. 6 in.; kerb wt. 31 cwt.; tank 17½ gals.; 12-volt.

£1,732+£399 p.t.=£2,131

Abbreviations—g.c.—ground clearance; susp.—suspension; f.—front; r.—rear; comp.—compression; s.v.—side-valves; o.h.v.—overhead valves; o.h.c.—overhead camshaft; hyd.—hydraulic

RENAULT 4

FOREMOST among France's utility saloons, the R4 is a versatile passenger and cargo carrier with big lift-up rear door and optional opening roof. For 1968 a full-width grille and sturdier bumpers with rubber overriders improve the appearance. A four-speed all-synchromesh gearbox is now standard and there is a plated gear lever with better-shaped knob. No increase in price.

CLOSE-UP

Four-cyl.; o.h.v.; 58×80 mm.; 845 c.c.; 30 b.h.p.; 8 to 1 comp.; Solex carb.; 4-speed, 15.68, 8.50, 5.61, 4.28 to 1; col. lvr.; susp., f. and. r. ind. torsion bar; 5-door; 4-seat; drum brks.; max. 70 m.p.h.; cruise, 60; m.p.g. 37-48; whl. base, 7ft. 11½in.; track f. 4ft. 1½in.; r. 4ft. 0¾in.; lgth., 12ft.; width, 4ft. 10¼in.; ht. 4ft. 9½in.; g.c. 8in.; turng. cir., 28½ft.; kerb wt., 12¾ cwt.; tank, 5 gals.; 6-volt.

£441 + £102 p.t. = £543

SKODA OCTAVIA COMBI

ROUGH roads behind the Iron Curtain demand rugged construction and the Skoda is built to stand them. It's unusual among small station wagons in having a lift-up rear window and drop-down tailgate. Front engine, rear drive and all-independent suspension on backbone chassis. Heater, screen washer, reclining seats and under-body anti-rust coating are included in the low price.

CLOSE-UP

Four-cyl.; o.h.v.; 72×75 mm.; 1,221 c.c.; 44 b.h.p.; 7.5 to 1 comp.; Jikov carb.; 4-speed, 20.4, 11.8, 7.2, 4.78 to 1; col. lvr.; susp., f. ind. coil, r. ind. transv. leaf; 3-door; 4-seat; hyd. brks.; max. 77 m.p.h.; cruise 65; m.p.g. 35-40; whl. base 7ft. 10½in.; track, f. 3ft. 11⅜in., r. 4ft. 1in.; lgth. 13ft. 4in.; width 5ft. 3in.; ht. 4ft. 8½in.; g.c. 6¾in.; turng. cir. 38ft.; kerb wt. 18¼ cwt.; tank 6½ gals.; 12-volt.

£495 + £115 p.t. = £610

SINGER VOGUE ESTATE CAR

THIS is a frisky car of its class being powered by a 73 b.h.p. version of the Rootes 1,725 c.c. five-bearing engine giving a top speed of more than 85 m.p.h. This adds up to brisk getaway and a low fuel thirst. With the back seat flat load space is 62 cubic feet and when the seat is in position there is still 34 cubic feet for baggage.

CLOSE-UP

Four-cyl.; o.h.v.; 81.5×82.5 mm.; 1,725 c.c.; 80 b.h.p.; 9.2 to 1 comp.; Stromberg carb.; 4-speed, 12,41, 7.92, 5.15, 3.7 to 1; cen. lvr., L de N. overdrive or BW. auto. opt.; susp., f. ind. coil, r. half-elliptic; 5-door; 4/5-seat; hyd. brks., disc front; max. 88 m.p.h.; cruise 75; m.p.g. 28-34; whl. base 8ft. 2½in.; track, f. and r. 4ft. 4in.; lgth. 14ft. 1½in.; width 5ft. 3½in.; ht. 4ft. 8in.; g.c. 6¾in.; turng. cir. 33ft. 6in.; kerb wt. 19 cwt.; tank 10 gals.; 12-volt.

£798 + £185 p.t. = £983

TRIUMPH 2000 STATION WAGON

A worthy sister of the well-proven 2000 Saloon, this station wagon is easy on the eye, functional and capacious. Its six-cylinder, twin carburetter engine with all-independent suspension carries five people and a reasonable load smartly, smoothly and without fuss. There is a four-speed all-synchromesh gearbox with options of overdrive or automatic. It is one of the best 2-litre cars in this class of vehicle.

CLOSE-UP

Six-cyl.; o.h.v.; 74.7 × 76 mm.; 1,998 c.c.; 90 b.h.p.; 9 to 1 comp.; 2 Stromberg carbs.; 4-speed, 13.45, 8.61, 5.68, 4.1 to 1.; cen. lvr., Laycock de Normanville overdrive or BW auto opt.; susp., f. and r. ind. coil; 5-door; 5/6-seat; servo brks., disc front; max. 95 m.p.h.; cruise, 80; m.p.g. 22-27; whl. base, 8ft. 10in.; track f. 4ft. 4in., r. 4ft. 2½in.; lgth. 14ft. 5½in.; width 5ft. 5in.; ht. 4ft. 8in.; g.c. 6in.; turng. cir., 32ft.; kerb wt., 24 cwt.; tank, 11½ gals.; 12-volt.

£1,183 + £273 p.t. = £1,456

VAUXHALL VIVA STATION WAGON

THE word has got around about the qualities of the latest Viva. This practical, good looking station wagon is the latest addition to a range that includes normal saloons, de luxe saloons and the performance SL 90. And of course there are the Brabham modifications available through Vauxhall dealers.

CLOSE-UP
Four cyl.; o.h.v.; 77.7 × 61 mm.; 1,159 c.c.; 47 b.h.p.; 8.5 to 1 comp.; Solex carb.; 4-speed, 15.531, 9.129, 5.792, 4.125 to 1; cen. lvr.; susp., f. ind. coil, r. coil; 3-door; 4-seat; hyd. brks., disc. front, optional power assisted; max. 83 m.p.h.; cruise, 73; m.p.g. 28; whl. base, 7ft. 11¾in.; track f. and r. 4ft. 3in.; lgth., 13ft. 5in.; width, 5ft. 3in.; ht. 4ft. 5½in.; g.c. 4¾in.; turng. cir., 31ft. 9in.; kerb wt., 16⅝ cwt.; tank, 8 gals.; 12-volt.

£592 + £137 p.t. = £729

VOLKSWAGEN CLIPPER

RE-STYLED and roomier, this famous cargo and passenger carrier also has a larger engine and new rear suspension with triangular links for 1968. Big sliding side doors are standard, front seats are separate with a gangway between. The 1600 engine replaces the 1500, the fuel tank is larger and intakes in the rear quarters feed the new fresh-air ventilation system.

CLOSE-UP
Four-cyl.; o.h.v., air-cooled; 85.5 × 69 mm.; 1,584 c.c.; 47 b.h.p.; 7.7 to 1 comp.; Solex carb.; 4-speed; cen. lvr.; susp., f. and r. torsion bar; 3-door; 8-seat; drum brks.; max. 65 m.p.h.; cruise, 65; m.p.g. 27; whl. base, 7ft. 10½in.; track f. 4ft. 6½in., r. 4ft. 8in.; lgth., 14ft. 7in.; width, 5ft. 11½in.; ht. 6ft. 4½in.; g.c. 7¼in.; kerb wt., 24¼ cwt.; tank, 13 gals.; 12-volt.

£865 + £200 p.t. = £1,065

Abbreviations—g.c.—ground clearance; susp.—suspension; f.—front; r.—rear; comp.—compression; s.v.—side-valves; o.h.v.—overhead valves; o.h.c.—overhead camshaft; hyd.—hydraulic.

144

DENNIS MAY

is on the
accessories
kick . . .

So let's talk about FOG f'rinstance and FITTINGS . . . .

The girl's name is Anita Taylor and she was photographed at a Brands Hatch practice. But what you're supposed to be looking at are Lucas's new fog and long-range lamps. Their names are the Silver Sabre and the Silver Lance.

Nobody told us what this girl's name is, but what she is demonstrating are new lap and diagonal seat belts marketed by Headquarters & General Supplies Ltd at 25s 9d a harness.

COUPLE of things you might never know if we didn't tell you— A: In Britain, which American films depict as perpetually enveloped in pea-soup from sea level to stratosphere, only 30 per cent of cars built since 1959 are fitted with fog-lamps. B: Nineteen out of twenty cars on our roads have something wrong with their brakes, and 30 per cent of them are in a potentially dangerous condition.

So if *you* are numbered among the imperilled majorities, take time during your Earls Court visit to consult the promulgators of these disquieting stats, Joseph Lucas and Automotive Products.

Lucas's latest soup-penetration campaign centres on the Silver Sabre foglamp, which scores a first in its field by incorporating a quartz-Halogen (alias quartz-iodine) bulb in a sealed-beam unit. So you win both ways— quartz-Halogen's proved superiority in candle-power plus the lifelong brightness consistency of s-b technique.

The 55 watt Silver Sabre, 5¾ins. in diameter by only 3¾ins. front/back depth, has an outwardly identical twin, the Silver Lance long-range lamp.

Colonising no fewer than three Show stands, Automotive Products find room not only for the group's diverse wardware—Lockheed brakes, Borg and Beck clutches, Purolator filters, AP steering components and small-car automatic transmissions—but also a Technical Information Centre. Here, the writing on the wall says 'Any Questions?' with special reference to braking problems and other matters bearing on road safety. So if it's a good pull-up for car men you're after, get your word in fast.

Talking of words and their communication, the Smiths Industries display—vast and varied as usual—includes a new-at-the-Show tape player unit for use in conjunction with car radio; it's also detachable for operation in any environment you choose. World Radio, a sister division to Radiomobile in the Smiths consortium, offer bait for D.I.Y. people in the form of a car radio, including speaker, which is supplied as a kit of parts for owner assembly.

When is a twin set not a suit of female woollies? When it's a Twinset, Ekco's recently introduced dual-role receiver. As light as a loofah (well, almost, at 2lb.), this compact unit has its own battery and either locks into its appointed fascia niche or stands in its own grounds; invaluable at sports meetings, on picnics, etc.

continued on page 63

145

. . . or about FASCIAS

continued from page 61

A Hove, Sussex, firm, Siran Ltd., brings new blood to the car radio business, challenging the established leaders with the R96 model (among others) at 14gns. Briefly — 12 v. only, 3-watt audio output, rotary control for tuning and volume, pushbutton tone and on/off switches, measurements 6½ins. wide, 3½ins. deep, 1⅞ins. high.

Earls Court '67 brings the usual crop of speciality accessories tailored to particular makes and models; like KL Automotive's rain excluders, designed to clip to the top of Vauxhall Cresta and Victor front doors. Positively no wetting for fug-allergic travellers who like to keep their windows open even in stormy weather. Vauxhall-approved, price £3.2.6d. per pair.

Not quite so instant fitting but well within the pierce-and-cut scope of the average handyman is a new supplementary instrument panel for Hillman Imps. This occupies the left-hand side of the dash but is so formed that the three instruments provided for (two 2ins. diameter, one 3ins.) look sidelong at the driver. Material is Royalite plastic, makers are Mada Accessories, Ingatestone, Essex.

Gadgets exclusively for Minis are still proliferating. Here are some examples from the autumn collections:
1. Italian-made, ultra-compact Mini Demon air horns, specially designed to squeeze into these cars' limited engine-bay space. 8gns. per pair. Marketed here by Autocar Marine and Diesel Co. Ltd., Stonehouse St., SW4.

continued on page 64

TURN ON with a Radiomobile for the news. Who knows there might be a jolly bulletin about road jams ahead? The Worth-Looking-At girl below is inexplicably in someone's boot, but her mind (THINKS) is clearly on a Smith's instrument panel

. . . or about *FANCY BITS*

continued from page 63

2. Set of three fitted suitcases, with companion shoe tray, shaped and dimensioned for the Mini's not too capacious boot. Strong and light, made in special laminated fibreboard. £7.8s. per set, by Nomad Box Co. Ltd., Rockingham Rd., Mkt. Harborough, Leics.

3. Wood-grained facia-*cum*-glovebox, designed to take over the Mini's passenger-side area of dash shelf. Mating sections of panelling frame the big central instrument dial and house a radio speaker grille. Makers are T. G. Supplies (Autofactors) Ltd., Luton, Beds. Various styles, prices start at £4.2.6d.

Gotta screw loose, mate? If, worst of all, it shakes loose at night, and it's one of those recluse type screws skulking in some dark cranny, a self-illuminating screwdriver may be just your salvation. The Pool Clock Co. of 47 Newman St., WC2, make such a tool, reasonably priced at 6/11. Source of current is a torch battery, holstered in the handle.

Then if your problem is nocturnal note jotting rather than screwdriving, Vilem B. Haan (London) Ltd., 91 Pimlico Rd., SW1, have the answer with their light-up pen. Brass body is satin finished, holds two batteries. Price, £1.13s., includes one initial ink charge and three reloads. (*Incidentally, makers of products reviewed here aren't all Show exhibitors, and you won't necessarily find their wares among factors' displays. Purpose of this feature is to take a by-and-large look at interesting accessories and preparations that have reached the market-place recently, or will be launched at the Show.*)

Prominent in this Show-launched category are the new alternators which Joseph Lucas (Electrical) are making the focal point of their stand. Lucas, of course, pioneered the trend from dynamos to alternators, and tell a convincing story of (a) the latter's high output in relation to engine speed, and (b) reduced weight. An integrated unit with its regulator in-built, on exhibition for the first time anywhere in the world, is the big draw on Stand 224.

If you see visitors rubbing their eyes in disbelief along the Stand 217 frontage, it will be because the prices of many Dagenite and Exide batteries have gone DOWN recently, by 10 per cent. Not only that but the guarantee period has been extended. New from Dagenite and Exide respectively are the low priced but fully guaranteed Dart and Excel batteries, costing from £5.12.6d. upwards.

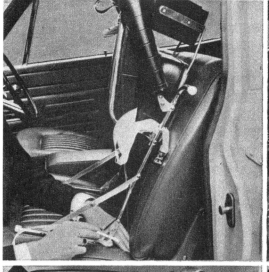

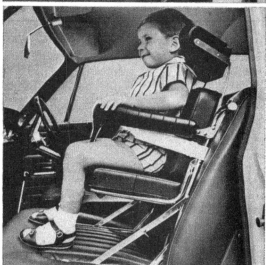

Nothing really fancy about this set-up, really. The four pictures show, top, the two stages of installing the elaborate American safety seat for tots called the Strolee, and then the harness as it looks with and without its passenger. The makers claim it gives protection against frontal, side and rear shunts.

This twin exhaust comes in five sizes from $1\frac{1}{8}$ to $1\frac{5}{8}''$ and screws on to the existing system. It is marketed by Headquarters & General Supplies at 29s 6d.

For the first time—real wire wheel trims for any Mini. They cost £14 a set of four, are made by Dunlop and distributed by G.T. Wheels Ltd, and will, so 'tis said, give a standard Mini a touch of Gran' Turismo.

hey Fog! meet your Waterloo

For generations, motorists have fought a losing battle against fog. Some drivers favour sidelamps or low powered foglamps. But these scarcely penetrate thick fog.

Others favour bright lamps. But they light up the fog instead of the road.

The remainder favour the train.

What you really need in fog is a powerful, piercing beam, carefully controlled to prevent stray shafts of light from bouncing back into your eyes. With a lamp like that, you could really cut fog down to size. Well, now there is a lamp like that.

Lucas' top lighting boffins have been working on it for years. Now they've perfected it; the world's first sealed-beam quartz-halogen foglamp.

They call it the Silver Sabre.

This is a totally new kind of foglamp. It's broad, flat-topped beam is so powerful it can slash a path through the worst pea-souper. That's the quartz-halogen bit.

And the beam is controlled so critically, back-glare due to stray light rays is cut to an absolute minimum.

That's because the beam is sealed, for life.

The Silver Sabre is not cheap. It's built to win battles, not just admiring glances (though it does that, too).

At £6.10s, it ought to be the most effective fog beater in the world. It is.

Your local garage man will tell you lots more about the Silver Sabre. And about the matching Silver Lance driving lamp. You may find him a shade smug. People who hold the ultimate weapon often are.

Cut fog down to size with a Lucas Silver Sabre – world's first sealed-beam quartz-halogen foglamp

MOTOR SHOW · EARLS COURT · STAND NO. 290

AUTOLITE SPARKED ALL THESE 1967 WINNERS

1st	Swedish Rally	Feb. 8/13	B. Soderstrom/ G. Palm	Ford Cortina Lotus
1st	Sebring (12 Hour Sports)	April 1	B. McLaren/ M. Andretti	Ford Mk. 4
1st	Shell 4000 Rally	May 2/10	R. Clark/ J. Peters	Ford Cortina Lotus
1st	Indianapolis '500'	May 31	A. J. Foyt	Coyote Ford
1st	Dutch Grand Prix (F.1)	June 4	J. Clark	Lotus Ford
1st	Scottish Rally	June 5/9	R. Clark/ J. Porter	Ford Cortina Lotus
1st	Le Mans 24 Hours	June 10/11	D. Gurney/ A. J. Foyt	Ford Mk. 4
1st	British Grand Prix (F.1.)	July 15	J. Clark	Lotus Ford
1st	Guards Int. European Championship (F.2)	Aug. 28	J. Rindt	Brabham Cosworth

Le Mans. Indianapolis. British Grand Prix. Rallies like the gruelling Canadian Shell 4000 and the demanding Swedish Rally. And many, many more this year. Winners of events like these need performance and dependability. They find it in their choice of spark plugs. AUTOLITE. Take the lead of the winners. Fit long-nosed AUTOLITE POWERTIP spark plugs in your car. In 1946, the average compression ratio of the family car was 6.5 : 1. Nowadays, it is 8 or even 9 : 1. Greater fuel economy on small throttle openings is the direct benefit you get from a higher compression ratio. Modern cars cruise faster, with higher engine speeds. This, in its turn, means that the spark plug has to spark up to 15% more often in conditions of greater pressure and heat. So spark plugs have had to be improved.

Hence the AUTOLITE POWERTIP spark plug. The main feature of this modern plug is that the long nose extends further into the flame, which scours it clean every time the plug sparks. The 15% more sparks per mile and hotter flame are dealt with by heavier nickel-chromium alloy electrodes, which have great ability to cope with high temperatures. Ford specify Autolite exclusively.

Where performance is wanted, the spark plug to choose is AUTOLITE POWERTIP

Hi-density insulators. Finest ceramic materials are carefully formulated and combined with Autolite's exclusive high density extrusion process.

Hot-pressed shell construction. This special process of insulator-to-shell construction provides 'minimum leakage' under the most severe conditions of operation.

Copper-glass seal. Permanently seals the centre electrode and provides long dependable service under the most adverse conditions.

Accurate rolled threads. This type of thread is stronger, prevents stripping, and reduces friction during installation and removal.

Special alloy electrodes. The two special alloys used in Autolite spark plug electrodes provide maximum efficiency, long life and dependable service.

FIT THE MODERN SPARK PLUG IN YOUR CAR...

LONG-NOSED

AUTOLITE POWERTIP

For leaflet and free car sticker, write to : Autolite Motor Products, Ltd., Dept. D.E.R. Enfield, Middx.

The dashing new Herald 13/60.
Get the new look, get the new feel of 27% more power.

The latest Triumph Herald has put on some extra muscle.
When you drive it you can feel it.
You change gear less.
Overtake more easily.
Accelerate faster.
Because the spanking new engine is capable of an honest 85 mph.
And of reaching 50 mph from scratch in just 12 seconds.
What else is new?
A bold new look up front.

Front disc brakes and heater as standard.
A new dash with very comprehensive instruments.
More leg room behind.
And super new seats all round.
Naturally you'll find all the famous Herald safety features in the new 13/60.
The sturdy steel girder chassis.
The fantastic 25′ turning circle.
All independent suspension.
Adjustable steering column that telescopes on impact. Wrap-around

rubber bumpers. They're all here.
Because when it comes to building a car, Leyland engineers reckon you can't have too much of a good thing.
Come and talk shop at your Triumph dealer. And while you're there keep an eye out for the new Triumph 1300 TC and the new Triumph TR5 PI.
Triumph Herald 13/60 £699·17·8, (sunshine roof extra); 13/60 Convertible £755·3·11; 13/60 Estate £773·12·8.
Prices ex-works inc. purchase tax.

Triumph puts you safely ahead

CARS
OF THE LATE 60'S
BRITISH AND IMPORTED MODELS 1965-1969

MOTOR SHOW REVIEW GUIDE
1968

A - Z
SECTION

Meeting the challenge

by Sir George Harriman

President of the Society of Motor Manufacturers and Traders.

EARLS Court in October is the shop window for the world of motoring—the Mecca of car buyers, motor traders and enthusiasts of all ages. This Review has a special place among the mass of material published about the Motor Show. Its outstanding coverage of the newest and most interesting show features and the wealth of detailed information have established it as a wonderful pre-show-guide and reference work.

This has been a year of redoubled export effort for the British motor industry—a mighty challenge which the manufacturers have pulled out all stops to meet. Hard effort, helped by devaluation, has resulted in a pleasing rise in the overseas sales curve, and production to date is well ahead of the comparable 1967 period.

The pages of this Review are crammed with data on the latest products of the motor industries of the world, which are on display at what has long been regarded as the top motor exhibition.

In the car section, some 66 companies are showing the products of Britain, the United States, Canada, Australia, Czechoslovakia, East Germany, France, Holland, Israel, Italy, Japan, Russia, Sweden, Turkey, and West Germany.

In addition the "couturiers" of the car industry—the specialist bodybuilders—have taken ten stands to show their tempting wares.

No show visit is complete without a look at the vast array of accessories, components and garage equipment on the ground and first floors and this Review gives a glimpse of the attractions in this field.

Every manufacturer in our biggest single manufacturing industry has extended his resources to the full to ensure the finest motoring display of all time. This excellent Review will help to guide you through the wonders of Earls Court and will afterwards prove to be a valuable reference book and reminder of the 1968 Motor Show.

Competition warms up

by Basil Cardew

I doubt whether a Motor Show has ever opened on a note of higher optimism among British car manufacturers. Optimism because of the effects of devaluation which, by slashing prices in foreign markets, has given new life to sales of British cars abroad.

Optimism, too, comes from the new and vital changes in the motor industry in the past year which can only lead to streamlining of effort, smoother organisation and cheaper production.

As a result of the giant £500 million merger between the British Motor Corporation and Leyland, Sir Donald Stokes is now in command of a vast number of makes—including Morris, Austin, Triumph, Rover, Riley, Wolseley, MG, Jaguar, Daimler—together with many kinds of commercial vehicles.

In another high competitive camp the huge Chrysler company, No 3 among American carmakers, is now responsible for all products of the Rootes Group as well as the French Simca firm.

This means that there are now only four big car empires left in Britain—British Leyland, Ford, Rootes and Vauxhall, the offshoot of General Motors. Although of course one or two individual carmakers like Rolls Royce and Aston Martin continue to flourish.

I should not be surprised to see this kind of rationalisation spreading to other car-producing countries in Europe, with the State-owned Renault perhaps taking over Citroen and Peugeot; Mercedes and Volkswagen jointly merging with smaller German companies like N.S.U.; and Italy's giant Fiat company absorbing Lancia, Ferrari and Lamborghini.

Some of the effects of this streamlining in Britain can already be seen by observant visitors as they wander through the plush corridors of Earls Court. Duplication of stands and models have been kept to a minimum. Reductions in overheads have helped to stabilise prices.

I have little doubt that the record numbers of visitors to Motor Shows in recent years will be maintained.

A report just issued shows that the total number of vehicles in Britain rose last year by 811,601 to 14,097,000. This means that the potential interest in cars and motoring is zooming sky-high.

Unfortunately, it also means that on the major trunk and secondary roads of the country there are fewer than 12 yards of space for every vehicle. Our roads are now the most congested in the world, carrying 55.3 vehicles a mile—double the density of traffic both in the United States and France.

Last year road-users paid a record £1,269 million in tax, including £820 million in fuel tax, with mighty little of it returned in the form of road building.

Inside Earls Court, you will see two definite new trends. The first is that more and more British cars are being fitted with optional automatic transmission.

I welcome this because it is about to sweep the world in popularity. More than 90 per cent of cars built in the United States are equipped with automatic transmission. British cars must fall into line, if only for the sake of exports.

The second trend is the effort of British designers to build more safety factors into their cars.

America started the trend and now a great number of our cars have features like collapsible steering columns, recessed door handles, super-efficient seat belts, and fewer protuberances which could injure an occupant in a crash.

Again I am including in this Review a special section devoted to estate cars, as they are steadily gaining in popularity. Many motorists now demand that extra door at the back so that they can convert their car into a utility vehicle to cope with special cargoes or for ferrying bundles of children to and fro from school.

Cleverly, most car makers have given their estate cars a graceful line and an elegance that compares favourably with the standard saloons.

In broadening the scope of the Review, I have sought to make it worth keeping as a quick reference guide. I also hope it will prove of interest to less fortunate car enthusiasts who cannot get to Earls Court and sample for themselves the bustling atmosphere and the gleaming new exhibits, and the absorbing diversities of this ever-popular show.

The cover of the Daily Express Motor Show Guide is the work of photographer David Steen.
The car is one built by Alan Mann Racing, who prepare competition cars for Fords, as a 'dream car' star for a film.
It was photographed with a special lens which multiplies the image.
Design by Don Roberts

The kind of traffic drivers will meet on the winding roads of the Khyber Pass . . . a local bus full up on top

Tough going—for 10,000 miles

by David Benson

A hundred cars leave London soon on the greatest motor rally ever held. It will take ten days, cover 10,000 miles, and will be worth £1 a mile to the winner.

It is the Daily Express sponsored London-Sydney Marathon—a prestige event which has attracted entries from all the big carmakers in Britain, Sweden, Germany, France, Australia and Russia. For the winner, victory will mean a big boost in sales of his cars throughout the world, particularly in underdeveloped countries.

The 100-car cavalcade leaves London in the early afternoon of November 24, crosses the Channel at Dover, and heads for the first checkpoint in Paris.

From there contestants swoop down the famous French *routes nationales*, through the Mont Blanc tunnel to Turin. From Italy the cars, running at 60-second intervals, cross into Yugoslavia with its traffic-free roads, then onto Istanbul, to take the ferry across the Bosphorus.

All the way through Turkey, Persia and Afghanistan the cars will be travelling at

altitudes up to 13,000 feet as they cross some of the highest mountain passes in the world. Most of the roads are normally used only by specially built buses and trucks and the odd camel train.

In Afghanistan especially, with its primitive tracks and mud-hut villages, drivers may well imagine they have stepped 1,000 years back in history. During this section they will be lucky if they face less than 500 miles of ice and snow-swept roads. But once they have taken the

romantic Khyber Pass down to the plains of India and Pakistan, the competing crews will be sweating it out in their shirtsleeves as they pick their way along roads crowded with pedestrians and ox-drawn carts, not to mention the occasional elephant going about its master's business.

After seven days of almost non-stop day and night driving, the mud-spattered survivors reach Bombay. There they embark on the P and O liner *Chusan* for a well-earned rest on the way to Fremantle in Australia.

Then the flat-out grind starts all over again, with deserts, mountains, good and bad roads to be negotiated. And so, after three more days, to Sydney where the Daily Express Trophy and the big £10,000 prize will be waiting for the winner.

Why did the Daily Express decide to sponsor an event like this? Because it believes that the spirit of adventure is very much alive.

And because no other competition offers so many chances to test and prove new ideas in motoring.

Desert Buggy from America. It uses the chassis from a crashed Volkswagen, with plastic body, wide-rim wheels and cast-off racing tyres.

The revolt against comfort

by Gordon Wilkins

EARLS Court is packed with cars geared to the demand for comfort. Heaters and through ventilation are taken for granted; full air-conditioning is catching on.

There are reclining seats and headrests, seats that rise and fall, slope forward and back, even heated seats on Cadillacs. There are electrically operated side windows and electrically heated rear windows. Automatic transmissions, power steering and power assisted brakes take the effort out of driving, and on some models one flick of a key will lock doors, bonnet, boot lid and fuel filler simultaneously.

But outside Earls Court the revolt is on. The revolt of the young and those who still feel

Dune Buggy for dude ranchers. Ford's Bronco has padded roll-over bar, racing-style fuel filler and hub caps, suede leather interior.

young against being cocooned in comfort. Remember how Lotus stole the show last year with a car that never got into Earls Court at all? It was a single seater racer, prettied up with wings and lamps and psychedelic colours as the ultimate in outdoor motoring.

It's part of the open-air kick started by the telly ads to stir dreams among City-bound commuters and it is creating a wave of new cars as basic as a bicycle with no more weather protection than a rowing boat.

The Italians showed the way with exotic creations by Pininfarina, Ghia, Bertone and others, who made fine playcars to carry on millionaires' yachts. But now we have the Mini Moke, the Renault 4 Plein Air, Citroen's

Lightweight Land Rover for airborne forces. A good candidate for France's classic Rallye des Cimes across mountain tops in the Pyrenees.

Mehari . . . in fact, anything from a Fiat 500 to a Lancia Beachbus.

You don't have to go to the seaside for sand. America's deserts have spawned a new animal—the Desert Buggy. The recipe: Take a crashed VW Beetle which has been written off, throw away the body, cut a chunk out of the chassis to shorten the wheelbase. Add a rollover bar and get the wheel rims widened to take second-hand racing tyres.

Garnish with a one-piece moulded plastic body shell and add bonnet, instrument panel, seats, lights, screen wipers and a more compact exhaust system. You now have an astonishingly quick fun car that corners like a racing car and goes across country like a rocket-

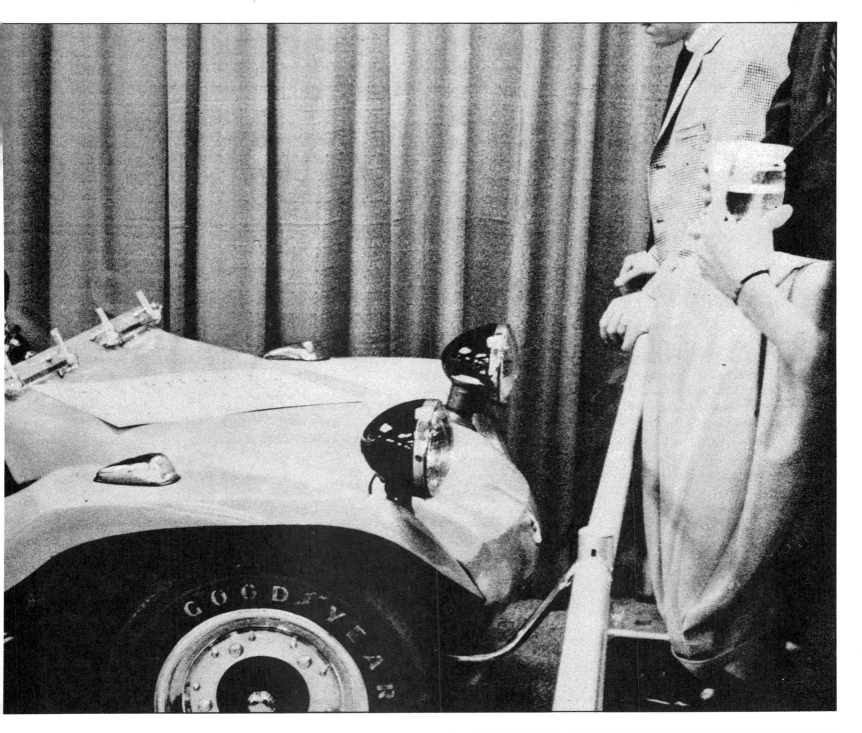

With the Renault 4 Plein Air, the French too join the search for fresh-air motoring that brings back some of the fun.

International Harvester's Scout is aimed at the fun car market. But most enthusiasts prefer something that can easily be lifted out of trouble.

The Mini Moke has started a cult of its own. With way-out decoration it becomes a beach car or general "funabout".

propelled Land Rover for something under £350.

In the USA the craze has already sent the price of crashed VWs rocketing five fold in twelve months. Now it's starting over here, but as we don't have deserts it is being called the Beach Buggy.

Down at the ranch they used to be satisfied with a Jeep or a Land Rover, with perhaps something like the International Harvester's Scout for formal occasions. But the real motorised dude now uses something like Ford's Bronco for off-the-road motoring, with plated handrail everywhere and a padded rollover bar in case of accidents.

America's dragsters erupting in spurts of flame and blazing rubber have also made their mark on the fun car business. The road-going dragster with two-seater body usually based on a Model T Ford is an established favourite.

Now the Opus HRF offers a British equivalent with a body and chassis for around £100. On this you can hang your own chassis components from a crashed Ford—or new parts and a new Cortina engine according to the funds available and you're ready to take to the autocross circuits or just go shopping in the Kings Road.

Perhaps the ultimate in off-the-road action is cross-country racing with four-wheel-drive cars. In America this has quite a strong following, and in the Pyrenees the Rallye des Cimes—a high-speed, high-altitude thrash over mountains where there are no roads or even mule tracks—has become an annual classic.

It has produced a steady crop of exotic four-wheel-drive devices, some of them twin-engined. Land Rovers have done well at it and the new lightweight version for airborne troops should make a very good mountain racer.

Finally, for those who want something small and light, including crossing rivers and lakes, America has just introduced the Terra Tiger with a plastic body like a hip bath carried on six balloon tyres inflated to only 2 lb. per sq. in. The drive is by chain from a small single-cylinder, two-stroke engine and it is steered by handle bars.

graphics by John Hill

MOTOR SHOW

1968
YOUR A-Z GUIDE

A.C. 428

AFTER the Cobras, into which the Americans crammed more power than was really good for them, comes the 428, with chassis designed from the start to use Ford's beefy 7-litre V8 engine. Coupe and convertible bodies are made in Italy by Frua. The disc brakes have dual circuits and dual servos and suspension is coil spring independent all-round. Windows are electrically operated.

CLOSE-UP
Eight-cyl.; o.h.v.; 104.9×101.1 mm.; 6,989 c.c.; 345 b.h.p. gross; 10.5 to 1 comp.; Ford 4-choke carb.; 4-speed, 6.68, 4.86, 3.72, 2.88 to 1; cen. lvr. auto. opt.; susp. f. and r. ind coil; 2-door; 2-seat; disc servo brks.; max. 145 m.p.h.; cruise, 115; m.p.g. 13-18; whl. base 8ft.; track f. 4ft. 7in., r. 4ft. 8in.; lgth 14ft. 6in.; width 5ft. 7in.; ht. 4ft. 3in.; g.c. 5in.; turng. cir. 35 ft.; kerb wt. 28 cwt.; tank 15 gals.; 12-volt.

£4,050＋£1,127 p.t. = £5,177

ALFA ROMEO GIULIA 1300 GT

BY opting for the smallest engine in the Giulia's racy Bertone body, the buyer saves nearly £150 and comes into a convenient class for competition driving, but he may not save much petrol if he drives hard, as the engine has to rev harder, needs more gear changes than the 1750 in the same body shell. This is the successor to the much-coveted Giulietta.

CLOSE-UP
Four-cyl.; o.h.c.; 74×75 mm.; 1,290 c.c.; 92 b.h.p.; 9 to 1 comp.; 2 Weber 2-choke carbs.; 5-speed, 15.03, 9.05, 6.17, 4.55, 3.91 to 1; cen. lvr.; susp. f. ind. coil, r. coil; 2-door; 2/4-seat; disc servo brks.; max. 107 m.p.h.; cruise 95; m.p.g. 24-27; whl. base, 7ft. 9in.; track f. 4ft. 3½in., r. 4ft. 2in.; lgth. 13ft. 5in.; width 5ft. 2in.; ht. 4ft. 4in.; g.c. 5½in.; turng. cir. 34ft.; kerb wt. 19 cwt.; tank 10½ gals.; 12-volt.

£1,367＋£382 p.t. = £1,749

Abbreviations—g.c.—ground clearance; susp.—suspension; f.—front; r.—rear; comp.—compression; s.v.—side-valves; o.h.v.—overhead valves; o.h.c.—overhead camshaft; hyd.—hydraulic.

ALFA ROMEO 1750

NAMED after Alfa's famous sports model of the 1930s the new 1750 is developed from the Giulia with larger engine, re-styled body, improved suspension, new interior and new heater-ventilation system. High-mounted speedometer and tachometer for maximum vision, horn buttons in steering wheel spokes, grab handles in doors and roof, foot-operated wipers and washers, stamp it as the product of men who understand fast motoring.

CLOSE-UP

Four-cyl.; o.h.c.; 80×88.5 mm.; 1,779 c.c.; 122 b.h.p.; 9.5 to 1 comp.; 2 twin-choke Weber carbs.; 5-speed, 14.2, 8.55, 5.82, 4.3, 3.4 to 1; cen. lvr.; susp., f. ind. coil, r. coil; 4-door; 4/5-seat; disc servo brks.; max. 115 m.p.h.; cruise, 95; m.p.g. 20-26; whl. base, 8ft. $5\frac{1}{2}$in.; track f. 4ft. 4in., r. 4ft. 2in.; lgth., 14ft. 5in.; width, 5ft. $1\frac{3}{4}$in.; ht. 4ft. $8\frac{1}{2}$in.; g.c. 6in.; turng. cir. 39ft.; kerb wt., $21\frac{3}{4}$ cwt.; tank, 10 gals.; 12-volt.

£1,484 + £414 p.t. = £1,898

ANADOL

TURKISH delight at having a motor industry of their own springs from collaboration with Reliant in England who ship essential mechanical items for local assembly with Turkish-built chassis and glass fibre body. Engine and gearbox are Ford. Production target is 60 a week. Ogle did the body design. Equipment includes disc front brakes, screen washer, reclining seats, recirculating ball steering.

CLOSE-UP

Four-cyl.; o.h.v.; 80.98×63 mm.; 1,298 c.c.; 54 b.h.p.; 9 to 1 comp.; Solex carb.; 4-speed, 14.61, 9.88, 5.82, 4.12 to 1; cen. lvr.; susp., f. ind. coil, r. half-elliptic; 2-door; 4-seat; hyd. brks. disc front; max. 78 m.p.h.; cruise, 73; m.p.g. 28-35; whl. base, 8ft. 5in.; track f. 4ft. 4in., r. 4ft. $1\frac{1}{2}$in.; lgth., 14ft. $4\frac{1}{2}$in.; width 5ft. $4\frac{3}{4}$in.; ht. 4ft. 8in.; g.c. $6\frac{1}{2}$in.; turng. cir., 34ft. 7in.; kerb wt., $16\frac{3}{4}$ cwt.; tank, 8 gals.; 12-volt.

ASTON MARTIN DBS

LEAN, low lines with international appeal enclose practical space for four people and luggage to travel at speeds up to twice Britain's legal limit. The 280 h.p. twin-cam six-cylinder engine is basically that of the DB6, but rear axle is De Dion against live axle with radius arms. Iodine vapour headlamps to go; twin-circuit disc brakes with twin servos to stop.

CLOSE-UP

Six-cyl.; o.h.c.; 96×92 mm.; 3,995 c.c.; 282 b.h.p.; 8.9 to 1 comp.; 3 SU carbs.; 5-speed, 11.38, 6.64, 4.64, 3.77, 3.14 to 1; cen. lvr. BW auto opt.; susp. f. ind. coil, r. de Dion coil; 2-door; 2/4-seat; disc servo brks.; max. 145 m.p.h.; cruise 120; m.p.g. 13-17; whl. base 8ft. $6\frac{3}{4}$in.; track f. and r. 4ft. 11in.; lgth. 15ft. $0\frac{1}{2}$in.; width 6ft.; ht. 4ft. $4\frac{1}{2}$in.; g.c. $5\frac{1}{2}$in.; turng. cir. 36ft.; kerb wt. $31\frac{1}{4}$ cwt.; tank 21 gals.; 12-volt.

£4,473 + £1,245 p.t. = £5,718

AUSTIN 3-LITRE

TWIN headlamps instead of two rectangular ones are the main external change, but a lot has gone on unseen since last year's Show. More luxurious interior trim, modified power steering, and suspension and extra equipment figure on the latest version, introduced for the first time at Earls Court. Front engine, rear drive, and Hydrolastic suspension, for a soft pitch-free ride are the main mechanical features.

CLOSE-UP

Six-cyl.; o.h.v.; 83.3×88.9 mm.; 2,912 c.c.; 118 b.h.p.; 8.2 to 1 comp.; 2 S.U. carbs.; 4-speed, 13.43, 8.48, 5.4, 3.9 to 1; cen. lvr., BW auto. opt.; susp. f. and r. ind. rubber-hyd.; 4-door; 5/6-seat; servo brks., disc front; max. 104 m.p.h.; cruise 85; m.p.g. 18-22; whl. base 9ft. $7\frac{1}{2}$in.; track f. 4ft. $8\frac{1}{2}$in., r. 4ft. 8in.; lgth. 15ft. $5\frac{1}{2}$in.; width 5ft. $6\frac{1}{2}$in.; ht. 4ft. $8\frac{1}{2}$in.; g.c. $6\frac{1}{2}$in.; turng. cir. 37ft. 6in.; kerb wt. $29\frac{3}{4}$ cwt.; tank $15\frac{1}{2}$ gals.; 12-volt.

£1,153 + £322 p.t. = £1,475

Abbreviations—g.c.—ground clearance; susp.—suspension; f.—front; r.—rear; comp.—compression; s.v.—side-valves; o.h.v.—overhead valves; o.h.c.—overhead camshaft; hyd.—hydraulic.

157

AUSTIN MINI 1000 DE LUXE MK. 2

GROWING up in power and performance, but not in size, the Mini holds its own against increasing competition and the automatic transmission with instant over-ride offers a new sensation in Mini-motoring. Accent is now on the 998 c.c. engine but the original economy 848 is still available. Hydrolastic suspension, padded visors, better heater, safer outside door handles are recent improvements.

CLOSE-UP

Four-cyl.; o.h.v.; 64.6×76.2 mm.; 998 c.c.; 38 b.h.p.; 8.3 to 1 comp.; S.U. carb.; 4-speed, 12.49, 7.46, 4.85, 3.44 to 1; cen. lvr., auto opt.; susp. f. and r. ind. rubber-hyd.; 2-door; 4-seat; drum brks.; max. 78 m.p.h.; cruise 70; m.p.g. 32-40; whl. base 6ft. 8¼in.; track f. 3ft. 11⅜in., r. 3ft. 9⅞in.; lgth. 10ft.; width 4ft. 7½in.; ht. 4ft. 4in.; g.c. 6⅛in.; turng. cir. 31ft. 7in.; kerb wt. 12¼ cwt.; tank 5½ gals.; 12-volt.

£495 + £140 p.t. = £635

AUSTIN 1300 SUPER DE LUXE

FIERCE competition demanded the step-up from 1100 to 1300 c.c. and now the roomy BMC family saloon with the billiards-table ride is not likely to be trampled in the rush when the lights turn to green. Body styles include two- and four-door saloons and station wagon. New wheels, grilles, tail lamp groupings, recently rejuvenated the appearance.

CLOSE-UP

Four-cyl.; o.h.v.; 70.6×81.3 mm.; 1,275 c.c.; 58 b.h.p.; 8.8 to 1 comp.; SU carb.; 4-speed, 13.23, 7.95, 5.16, 3.65 to 1; cen. lvr., auto opt.; susp. f. and r. ind. rubber-hyd.; 2 or 4-door; 4/5-seat; hyd. brks., disc front; max. 90 m.p.h.; cruise 80; m.p.g. 30-33; whl. base 7ft. 9½in.; track f. 4ft. 3½in., r. 4ft. 2⅞in.; lgth. 12ft. 2¾in.; width 5ft. 0⅜in.; ht. 4ft. 5in.; g.c. 5¼in.; turng. cir. 38ft.; kerb wt. 16¾ cwt.; tank 8 gals.; 12-volt.

£585 + £165 p.t. = £750

AUSTIN HEALEY SPRITE MK. IV

SPRIDGET is the name in sporting circles, as one basic car, with minor differences, doubles as Sprite and Midget. Originally a fairly spartan two-seater, it is now a snug convertible with winding side windows and hinged quarter lights. Bigger engine and semi-elliptic instead of quarter-elliptic suspension have kept it competitive over the years and it still has a big export sale.

CLOSE-UP

Four-cyl.; o.h.v.; 70.6×81.3 mm.; 1,275 c.c.; 64 b.h.p.; 8.8 to 1 comp.; 2 S.U. carbs.; 4-speed, 13.5, 8.09, 5.73, 4.22 to 1; cen. lvr.; susp. f. ind. coil, r. half-elliptic; 2-door; 2-seat; hyd. brks., disc front; max. 95 m.p.h.; cruise 80; m.p.g. 30-34; whl. base 6ft. 8in.; track f. 3ft. 10¼in., r. 3ft. 8¾in.; lgth. 11ft. 5¼in.; width 4ft. 7in.; ht. 4ft. 0½in.; g.c. 5½in.; turng. cir. 32ft.; kerb wt. 13¾ cwt.; tank 6 gals.; 12-volt.

£564 + £160 p.t. = £724

AUDI SUPER 90

TOP car in a range that extends from the 1,696 c.c. Audi 70 economy model via Audi 80 saloon and station wagon to the bigger-engined Super 90. All have canted high-compression engines with bowl-in-piston combustion chambers and high-swirl inlet ports. All have front wheel drive. Twin-choke carburetter on Super 90 opens one side only at low speeds for economy and flexibility.

CLOSE-UP

Four-cyl.; o.h.v.; 81.5×84.4 mm.; 1,760 c.c.; 90 b.h.p.; 10.6 to 1 comp.; Solex carb.; 4-speed, 13.22, 7.56, 5.13, 3.63 to 1; col. lvr.; susp., f. ind. torsion bar, r. torsion bar; 2/4-door; 4/5 seat; hyd. brks., disc front; max. 100 m.p.h.; cruise 90; m.p.g. 21-25; whl. base 8ft. 2in.; track, f. 4ft. 4⅞in., r. 4ft. 4¼in.; lgth. 14ft. 4½in.; width 5ft. 4in.; ht. 4ft. 9⅛in.; g.c. 7½in.; turng. cir. 34ft. 5in.; kerb wt. 20 cwt.; tank 11⅜ gals.; 12-volt.

£981 + £275 p.t. = £1,256

Abbreviations—g.c.—ground clearance; susp.—suspension; f.—front; r.—rear; comp.—compression; s.v.—side-valves; o.h.v.—overhead valves; o.h.c.—overhead camshaft; hyd.—hydraulic.

BENTLEY T TYPE

THE proportion of Bentleys to Rolls-Royces coming out of Crewe has dwindled, but some still prefer the once-great racing name, the more rounded grille (and the slightly lower price) allied to all the Silver Shadow amenities like all-independent suspension with hydraulic levelling, triple-circuit disc servo brakes, electric windows and seats adjusted electrically for reach, slope and height.

CLOSE-UP

Eight-cyl.; o.h.v.; 104.1×91.4 mm.; 6,230 c.c.; b.h.p. not revealed; 9 to 1 comp.; 2 S.U. carbs.; 4-speed auto., 11.75, 8.1, 4.46, 3.08 to 1; col. lvr.; susp. f. and r. ind. coil, hyd. levelling; 2 or 4-door; 5-seat; disc. hyd. servo brks.; max. 120 m.p.h.; cruise 100; m.p.g. 13-16; whl. base 9ft. 11½in.; track f. and r. 4ft. 9½in.; lgth. 16ft. 11½in.; width 5ft. 11in.; ht. 4ft. 11¾in.; g.c. 6½in.; turng. cir. 38ft.; kerb wt. 41½ cwt.; tank 24 gals.; 12-volt.

Mulliner £8,100+£2,252 p.t. = £10,352

BMW 2002

SAY goodbye to the sports cars. A smooth flexible single-carburettor 2-litre engine wafts this neat little saloon from 0 to 50 mph in 7 seconds, gives a relaxed 100 mph cruising speed and uses less petrol than the sporty 1600 TI. There's simpler trim and less family space than in the bigger BMWs but it's a natural for the busy man who has to travel fast on crowded roads.

CLOSE-UP

Four-cyl.; o.h.c.; 89×80 mm.; 1,990 c.c.; 100 b.h.p.; 8.5 to 1 comp.; Solex carb.; 4-speed, 13.98, 9.46, 4.91, 3.64 to 1; cen. lvr.; susp., f. and r. ind. coil; 2-door; 4-seat; hyd. servo brks. disc front; max. 106 m.p.h.; cruise 95; m.p.g. 24-26; whl. base 8ft. 4in.; track f. and r. 4ft. 4in.; lgth. 14ft. 1½in.; wdth. 5ft. 2½in.; ht. 4ft. 7½in.; g.c. 6½in.; turng. cir. 31ft. 6in.; kerb wt. 19 cwt.; tank 10 gals.; 12-volt.

£1,249+£348 p.t. = £1,597

BMW 2000 CS

BESIDE the fast and well-built saloons from 1.6 to 2 litres, BMW offer this low-built comfortable coupe in three forms. The single-carburetter 100 h.p. model is now made with four-speed box or three-speed ZF automatic. The 2000 CS with two twin-choke carburetters and 120 h.p. comes with manual gearbox only and the more powerful engine pulls a higher axle ratio.

CLOSE-UP

Four-cyl.; o.h.c.; 89×80 mm.; 1,990 c.c.; 120 b.h.p.; 9.3 to 1 comp.; 2 Solex 2-choke carbs.; 4-speed, 15.76, 8.44, 5.33, 4.11 to 1; cen. lvr. ZF auto opt.; susp. f. and r. ind. coil; 2-door; 4-seat; disc/drum servo brks.; max. 115 m.p.h.; cruise 100; m.p.g. 21-24; whl. base 8ft. 4½in.; track f. 4ft. 4in., r. 4ft. 6in.; lgth. 14ft. 10in.; width 5ft. 6½in.; ht. 4ft. 6½in.; g.c. 6½in.; turng. cir. 31ft. 6in.; kerb wt. 22½ cwt.; tank 12 gals.; 12-volt.

£2,708+£657 p.t. = £3,365

BOND EQUIPE 2-LITRE GT

THE new Vitesse rear suspension is the key to improved road holding on this redesigned version of Bond's GT coupe, moulded in glass fibre round the Triumph chassis and scuttle. Like their 1300 coupe with Herald chassis and Spitfire engine, it is available through Triumph dealers with Triumph warranty on mechanical parts. Bond also do three-wheelers with Hillman Imp engines.

CLOSE-UP

Six-cyl.; o.h.v.; 74.7×76 mm.; 1,998 c.c.; 104 b.h.p.; 9.25 to 1 comp.; 2 Stromberg carbs; 4-speed, 10.31, 6.92, 4.86, 3.89 to 1; cen. lvr., L de N overdrive opt.; susp., f. ind. coil, r. ind. transv. leaf; 2-door; 2/4-seat; hyd. brks., disc front; max. 105 m.p.h.; cruise 90; m.p.g. 26-28; whl. base 7ft. 7½in.; track f. 4ft. 1in., r. 4ft.; lgth. 13ft. 10in.; width 5ft. 1½in.; ht. 4ft. 4½in.; g.c. 6½in.; turng. cir. 25ft.; kerb wt. 18 cwt.; tank 9 gals.; 12-volt.

Abbreviations—g.c.—ground clearance; susp.—suspension; f.—front; r.—rear; comp.—compression; s.v.—side-valves; o.h.v.—overhead valves; o.h.c.—overhead camshaft; hyd.—hydraulic.

BRISTOL 410

STARTING 20-odd years ago making a basically BMW design with precision born of their aircraft background, Bristol have graduated to this fast, quiet four-seater with Chrysler V8 engine and automatic transmission. Never in the forefront of fashion, they appeal to the connoisseur who prefers the hand-built car produced by craftsmen to the machine-made products of the fast-flowing assembly lines.

CLOSE-UP
Eight-cyl.; o.h.v.; 99.3×84.07 mm.; 5,211 c.c.; 250 b.h.p. gross; 9 to 1 comp.; Carter 4-choke carb.; 3-speed auto, 7.5, 4.5, 3.07 to 1; push button control; susp., f. ind. coil, r. torsion bar; 2-door; 4-seat; disc servo brks.; max. 125 m.p.h.; cruise 100; m.p.g. 18-20; whl. base 9ft. 6in.; track f. 4ft. 6in., r. 4ft. 6½in.; lgth. 16ft. 1½in.; width 5ft. 8in.; ht. 4ft. 11in.; g.c. 6½in.; turng. cir. 39ft. 6in.; kerb wt. 32 cwt.; tank 18 gals.; 12-volt.

£4,692 + £1,305 p.t. = £5,997

BUICK RIVIERA

THROWING away accepted ideas on suspension design, Buick's new front end makes the outer wheel lean outwards on corners, not inwards. It's said to promote straight-line stability on motorways but what it does to cornering remains to be seen. A buzzer sounds if you leave the ignition key in the lock; removing it you can lock rear wheels on both manual and automatic models to foil car thieves.

CLOSE-UP
Eight-cyl.; o.h.v.; 106×99 mm.; 7,047 c.c.; 360 b.h.p. gross; 10.25 to 1 comp.; Rochester 4-choke carb.; 3-speed auto, 8.48, 5.06, 3.42 to 1; col. lvr.; susp. f. ind. coil, r. coil; 2-door; 6-seat; drum servo brks., disc opt.; max 125 m.p.h.; cruise 100; m.p.g. 12-16; wh. base 9ft. 11in.; track f. 5ft. 3½in.; r. 5ft. 3in.; lgth. 17ft. 11½in.; width 6ft. 6¾in.; ht. 4ft. 5½in.; g.c. 5in.; turng. cir. 42ft. 4in.; kerb wt. 38¾ cwt.; tank 17½ gals.; 12-volt.

BUICK SKYLARK CUSTOM

YOU choose from 4-litre six or 5.7-litre V8 as power units and can have an entirely new Turbo-Hydramatic 350 transmission with three speeds and torque converter. Features are a smooth-acting part-throttle downshift for easy overtaking and a compensator to maintain smooth shifts on high mountain roads. The telescopic steering column has ball bearings for easy action and variable-ratio power steering is a new option.

CLOSE-UP
Eight-cyl.; o.h.v.; 96.5×97.8 mm.; 5,736 c.c.; 285 b.h.p. gross; 10.25 to 1 comp.; Rochester 4-choke carb.; 3-speed, 7.82, 4.62, 3.08 to 1; col. lvr., 4-speed or auto. opt.; susp. f. ind. coil, r. coil; 2/4-door; 6-seat; drum servo brks., disc opt.; max. 100 m.p.h.; cruise 90; m.p.g. 15-19; whl. base 9ft. 4in.; track f. and r. 4ft. 11in.; lgth. 16ft. 8½in.; width 6ft. 3½in.; ht. 4ft. 4¾in.; g.c. 5in.; turng. cir. 40ft.; kerb wt. 33¾ cwt.; tank 16¾ gals.; 12-volt.

CADILLAC FLEETWOOD BROUGHAM

19 feet of opulence, American style, with still stronger body, improved ventilation (no ventipanes) and new front-mounted air conditioning. A single key locks ignition, steering and transmission. New tandem-articulated windscreen wipers, and European-style closed circuit cooling are features. The 7.7-litre 375 bhp. V8 engine and three-speed Turbo-Hydramatic transmission are standard on all models and there are ten body styles.

CLOSE-UP
Eight-cyl.; o.h.v.; 109×103 mm.; 7,736 c.c.; 375 b.h.p. gross; 10.5 to 1 comp.; Rochester 4-choke carb.; 3-speed Hydra-Matic, 7.28, 4.35, 2.94 to 1; col. lvr.; susp. f. ind coil, r. coil; 4-door; 6-seat; drum servo brks., disc opt.; max. 118 m.p.h.; cruise 100; m.p.g. 12-15; wh. base 11ft. 1in.; track f. and r. 5ft. 2½in.; lgth. 19ft. 2in.; width 6ft. 7½in.; ht. 4ft. 8½in.; g.c. 5¾in.; turng. cir. 45ft.; kerb wt. 44¼ cwt.; tank 21¾ gals.; 12-volt.

£4,760 + £1,324 p.t. = £6,084

Abbreviations—g.c.—ground clearance; susp.—suspension; f.—front; r.—rear; comp.—compression; s.v.—side-valves; o.h.v.—overhead valves; o.h.c.—overhead camshaft; hyd.—hydraulic.

CHEVROLET CAMARO

SPORTY coupe and convertible bodies are longer and wider for 1969 with concealed headlamps in the optional Rally kit. Six-cylinder models can have a low-cost semi-automatic transmission. SS models have 300 bhp. 5.8-litre V8 or 325 bhp. 6.5-litre (American bench h.p. of course—a lot less at the road wheels). Front brake drums are finned; power discs are optional. Resilient front bumper in body colour is another option.

CLOSE-UP

Eight-cyl.; o.h.v.; 102×83 mm.; 5,359 c.c.; 210 b.h.p. gross; 8.75 to 1 comp.; Rochester 2-choke carb.; 3-speed, 7.82, 4.62, 3.08 to 1; col. lvr. 4-speed or auto. opt.; susp. f. ind. coil, r. half-elliptic; 2-door; 2/4-seat; drum brks. disc opt.; max. 112 m.p.h.; cruise 90; m.p.g. 14-19; whl. base 9ft.; track f. and r. 4ft. 11in.; lgth. 15ft. 4½in.; width 6ft. 6in.; ht. 4ft. 3½in.; g.c. 5½in.; turng. cir. 37ft. 6in.; kerb wt. 27½ cwt.; tank 16½ gals.; 12-volt.

£2,712 + £755 p.t. = £3,467

CHEVROLET CHEVELLE MALIBU

MALIBU saloon, a sample from the middle of a 35-model range designed to consolidate Chevrolet's position as world's top-selling car. Safety features include dual circuit brakes, front seat headrests, self-returning lane-change signal for motorway driving, improved fuel tank anchorage, reinforced side-guard doors, hazard warning flasher. Anti-theft precautions include single lock for ignition, transmission and steering. Styling is revised inside and out.

CLOSE-UP

Eight-cyl.; o.h.v.; 98×82 mm.; 5,032 c.c.; 200 b.h.p. gross; 9 to 1 comp.; Rochester 2-choke carb.; 3-speed, 7.82, 4.62, 3.08 to 1; col. lvr. Hydra-Matic auto. opt.; susp. f. ind. coil, r. coil; 2/4-door; 6-seat; drum servo brks., disc opt.; max. 105 m.p.h.; cruise 90; m.p.g. 14-18; whl. base 9ft. 7⅛in.; track f. and r. 4ft. 11in.; lgth. 16ft. 8¾in.; width 6ft. 4in.; ht. 4ft. 5⅝in.; g.c. 5½ in.; turng. cir. 43 ft.; kerb wt. 31 cwt.; tank 16¾ gals.; 12-volt.

CHRYSLER IMPERIAL

PRESTIGE car of the Chrysler group, available with 4-door saloon or 2-door and 4-door coupe bodies. Headlamps are concealed behind shutters with electric or manual control and there are enormous sequential turn indicators, illegal in Britain, but highly effective on motorways. Available equipment includes 3-speed wipers, limited-slip differential and tyres with glass fibre reinforcements. Door latches are stressed for 30 G emergencies.

CLOSE-UP

Eight-cyl.; o.h.v.; 109.7×95.2 mm.; 7,210 c.c.; 350 b.h.p. gross; 10 to 1 comp.; Holley 4-choke carb.; 3-speed, auto, 7.2, 4.2, 2.94 to 1; col. lvr.; susp. f. ind. torsion bar, r. half-elliptic; 2-door; 4/5-seat; disc/drum servo brks.; max. 120 m.p.h.; cruise 90; m.p.g. 11-16; whl. base 10ft. 7in.; track f. 5ft. 2⅛in., r. 5ft. 1⅛in.; lgth. 19ft. 1⅜in.; width 6ft. 7⅛in.; ht. 4ft. 7⅛in.; g.c. 5⅛in.; turng. cir. 44ft. 10in.; kerb wt. 38½ cwt.; tank 19 gals.; 12-volt.

CITROEN DYANE 6

CITROEN'S reputation for eccentricity in body design, strongly founded on the 2CV and Ami-6, was reinforced by the Dyane, but its five-door layout is highly practical, the swinging-arm suspension interconnected between front and rear gives an undulating but comfortable ride and the larger engine from the Ami-6 now gives it competitive performance. The flat-twin air-cooled engine drives the front wheels.

CLOSE-UP

Two-cyl. air-cooled; o.h.v.; 74×70 mm.; 602 c.c.; 25.5 b.h.p.; 7.75 to 1 comp.; Solex carb.; 4-speed, 20.31, 10.27, 6.95, 4.74 to 1; facia lvr.; susp. f. and r. ind. coil; 5-door; 4-seat; drum brks.; max. 69 m.p.h.; cruise 60; m.p.g. 46-52; whl. base 7ft. 10½in.; track f. and r. 4ft. 1⅜in.; lgth. 12ft. 9½in.; width 4ft. 11in.; ht. 5ft. 0½in.; g.c. 6in.; turng. cir. 36ft. 8in.; kerb wt. 11¾ cwt.; tank 4½ gals.; 12-volt.

CITROEN DS 21

NOTHING else at under three times the price offers a design as advanced as the revolutionary DS, the first saloon car with disc brakes, first with hydraulic-pneumatic self-levelling suspension, plus automatic clutch, hydraulic servo gearshift, automatic adjustment to share braking effort between front and rear according to load. Now headlamps swivelling with the steering to show the way round corner keep Citroen ahead.

CLOSE-UP

Four-cyl.; o.h.v.; 90×85.5 mm.; 2,175 c.c.; 100 b.h.p.; 8.75 to 1 comp.; Weber twin-choke carb.; 4-speed, 14.22, 8.49, 5.56, 3.72 to 1; dash lvr.; susp. f. and r. ind. hyd.-pneu.; 4-door; 5/6-seat; hyd. servo brks., disc front; max. 109 m.p.h.; cruise 95; m.p.g. 23-28; whl. base 10ft. 3in.; track f. 4ft. 11in., r. 4ft. $3\frac{1}{4}$in.; lgth. 15ft. 10in.; width 5ft. $10\frac{1}{2}$in.; ht. 4ft. $9\frac{5}{8}$in.; g.c. $5\frac{3}{8}$in.; turng. cir. 36ft.; kerb wt. 25 cwt.; tank 14 gals.; 12-volt. **£1,461 + £408 p.t. = £1,869**

DAF 33

BELTING along, with his belt-drive automatic transmission providing exactly the right gear ratio for every situation, the DAF driver enjoys a unique motoring sensation. The belt drive is smooth and quiet, grips well on ice or snow and eliminates the universal joints which give a fair amount of trouble on other cars. The 33, smallest model in the range, has an air-cooled flat twin engine.

CLOSE-UP

Two-cyl.; o.h.v. air cooled; 85.5×65 mm.; 746 c.c.; 33 b.h.p.; 7.5 to 1 comp.; Solex carb.; auto. belt drive 16.4 to 3.9 to 1; cen. lvr.; susp., f. ind. trans. leaf, r. ind. coil; 2-door; 4-seat; drum brks.; max. 65 m.p.h.; cruise 65; m.p.g. 38-48; whl. base 6ft. $8\frac{3}{4}$in.; track f. and r. 3ft. $10\frac{1}{2}$in.; lgth. 11ft. $10\frac{1}{2}$in.; width 4ft. 9in.; ht. 4ft. $6\frac{1}{4}$in.; g.c. $6\frac{3}{4}$in.; turng. cir. 31ft.; kerb wt. $13\frac{1}{4}$ cwt.; tank 7 gals.; 6-volt.

£468 + £131 p.t. = £559

DAF 55 COUPE

CONFIDENTLY moving up the performance scale, DAF put a Renault four-cylinder engine in the Michelotti-styled body of the 44, to give 70 m.p.h. cruising and acceleration which, thanks to their fully automatic belt drive leaves most other cars behind away from the traffic lights. The spare wheel is over the engine, leaving maximum boot space for luggage.

CLOSE-UP

Four-cyl.; o.h.v.; 70×72 mm.; 1,108 c.c.; 45 b.h.p. 8.5 to 1 comp.; Solex carb.; variable-ratio belt auto 14.87 to 3.73 to 1; cen. lvr.; susp. f. ind. transv. leaf r. ind. coil; 2-door; 2/4-seat; drum/disc brks.; max. 87 m.p.h.; cruise 87; m.p.g. 30-35; whl. base 7ft. $4\frac{5}{8}$in.; track f. 4ft. $2\frac{1}{2}$in., r. 4ft. $1\frac{1}{4}$in.; lgth. 12ft. $8\frac{3}{4}$in.; width 5ft. $0\frac{5}{8}$in. ht. 4ft. $3\frac{1}{8}$in.; g.c. 6in.; turng. cir. 31ft.; kerb wt. $15\frac{1}{2}$ cwt.; tank $8\frac{3}{8}$ gals.; 12-volt.

£732 + £205 p.t. = £937

DATSUN 1000

SMALL economical family car from Japan with transverse leaf spring front suspension and orthodox rear axle. The de luxe saloon is well equipped with lighter, fuel filler lock, tinted glass, reclining seats, white wall tyres. Optional items include heater, clock and anti-lift windscreen wipers. The gearbox can be three- or four-speed. There is also a small station wagon with good carrying capacity for its size.

CLOSE-UP

Four-cyl.; o.h.v.; 73×59 mm.; 988 c.c.; 62 b.h.p. gross; 8.5 to 1 comp.; Hitachi carb.; 3-speed, 13.89, 7.11, 4.11 to 1; col. lvr., 4-speed opt.; susp. f. ind. transv. leaf, r. half-elliptic; 2/4-door; 4-seat; drum brks.; max. 84 m.p.h.; cruise 74; m.p.g. 33-35; whl. base 7ft. $5\frac{3}{4}$in.; track f. 3ft. $10\frac{7}{8}$in., r. 3ft. $10\frac{5}{8}$in.; lgth. 12ft. $6\frac{3}{8}$in.; width 4ft. $8\frac{7}{8}$in.; ht. 4ft. 5in.; g.c. $6\frac{1}{4}$in.; turng. cir. 27ft.; kerb wt. 13 cwt.; tank $7\frac{1}{2}$ gals.; 12-volt.

£585 + £164 p.t. = £749

Abbreviations—g.c.—ground clearance; susp.—suspension; f.—front; r.—rear; comp.—compression; s.v.—side-valves; o.h.v.—overhead valves; o.h.c.—overhead camshaft; hyd.—hydrauli

DATSUN 1600

AN up-to-date design with overhead camshaft engine, strut-type front suspension and independent rear suspension by semi-trailing wishbones marks this 1600 c.c. family saloon out from its Japanese contemporaries but it still relies on drum brakes all round. Equipment includes reclining seats, extractor ventilation, four headlamps and curved glass in the side windows. It is built with choice of 3- or 4-speed transmission and is said to do up to 100 m.p.h.

CLOSE-UP
Four-cyl.; o.h.c.; 83×73 mm.; 1,595 c.c.; 96 b.h.p. gross; 8.5 to 1 comp.; Hitachi 2-choke carb.; 4-speed, 12.50, 7.45, 4.85, 3.70 to 1; cen. lvr. BW auto. opt.; susp. f. ind. coil, r. half-elliptic; 4-door; 4/5-seat; drum servo brks.; max. 96 m.p.h.; cruise 85; m.p.g. 28-31; whl. base 7ft. 11½in.; track f. 4ft. 2¼in., r. 4ft. 1⅜in.; lgth. 13ft. 6in.; width 5ft. 1½in.; ht. 4ft. 7½in.; g.c. 6¼in.; turng. cir. 31ft.; kerb wt. 18½ cwt.; tank 9¾ gals.; 12-volt.

£740+£207 p.t. = £947

DAIHATSU 1000 SPIDER

A SNUG sports convertible with winding windows on a short wheelbase, with the same mechanical features as the popular small Japanese saloon but with a twin-choke carburetter giving higher power. Disc front brakes are optional and the all synchromesh gearboxes can have three or four speeds but the automatic transmission option is confined to saloon models. There's also a 360 c.c. saloon.

CLOSE-UP
Four-cyl.; o.h.v.; 68×66 mm.; 958 c.c.; 65 b.h.p.; 9.5 to 1 comp.; Mikuni carb.; 4-speed, 16.74, 10.6, 6.73, 4.55 to 1; col. or cen. lvr.; susp. f. ind. torsion bar, r. half-elliptic; 2-door; 2/4-seat; drum brks.; max. 90 m.p.h.; cruise 80; m.p.g. 29-33; whl. base 7ft. 3⅜in.; track f. 3ft. 10¾in., r. 3ft. 10in.; lgth. 12ft. 5in.; width 4ft. 8¾in.; ht. 4ft. 5½in.; g.c. 6in.; turng. cir. 29ft.; kerb wt. 15½ cwt.; tank 9 gals.; 12-volt.

£690+£192 p.t. = £882

DAIMLER V8 250

A true Daimler engine—a light-alloy pushrod V8 from days before the Jaguar link-up—goes in the Jaguar 240 body shell to make a popular executive car with individual character and smoothly impressive performance. High-grade interior finish, comprehensive equipment and the option of automatic transmission plus servo-assisted disc brakes make a conservative car with a modern specification.

CLOSE-UP
Eight-cyl.; o.h.v.; 76.2×69.8 mm.; 2,548 c.c.; 40 b.h.p. gross; 8.2 to 1 comp.; SU carb.; 4-speed, 13.85, 8.98, 6.04, 4.55 to 1; col. lvr., L de N overdrive or BW auto opt.; susp. f. ind. coil, r. half-elliptic; 4-door; 4-seat; disc servo brks.; max. 111 m.p.h.; cruise 95; m.p.g. 19-22; whl. base 8ft. 11⅜in.; track f. 4ft. 7in., r. 4ft. 5⅜in.; lgth. 15ft. 0¾in.; width 5ft. 6¾in.; ht. 4ft. 8½in.; g.c. 7in.; turng. cir. 33ft. 6in.; kerb wt. 28¼ cwt.; tank 12 gals.; 12-volt.

£1,359+£380 p.t. = £1,739

DAIMLER LIMOUSINE

REGAL magnificence at a price that will appeal to many uncrowned heads. A lengthened version of the Jaguar 420 G floor, plus Jaguar's 4.2-litre engine and race-bred rear suspension combine with a new Vanden Plas body to produce a luxurious limousine with high performance, smooth ride and remarkable road holding. Electrically operated windows and division glass are among the optional extras.

CLOSE-UP
Six-cyl.; o.h.c.; 92×106 mm.; 4,235 c.c.; 245 b.h.p. gross; 8 to 1 comp.; 2 SU carbs.; 3-speed BW auto, 3.5, 5.1, 3.4 to 1; col. lvr.; susp. f. and r. ind. coil; 4-door; 7-seat; disc servo brks.; max. 110 m.p.h.; cruise 95; m.p.g. 12-16; whl. base 11ft. 9in.; track f. and r. 4ft. 10in.; lgth. 18ft. 10in.; width 6ft. 7in.; ht. 5ft. 3½in.; g.c. 7in.; turng. cir. 46ft.; kerb wt. 42¾ cwt.; tank 12 gals.; 12-volt.

£3,461+£963 p.t. = £4,424

DODGE DART

DODGE, a popular-priced car from the Chrysler group, offers over 30 models with engines of six and eight cylinders designed to reduce air pollution. They meet all the current Federal American safety requirements, with collapsible steering columns, reinforced structures, dual-circuit brakes and four-way hazard warning flashers. Brakes are drums or discs, transmissions are three- or four-speed manual or automatic. Limited-slip differential, heavy-duty springs and dampers are available.

CLOSE-UP
Eight-cyl.; o.h.v.; 99 / 84 mm.; 4,473 c.c.; 190 b.h.p. gross; 9 to 1 comp.; Ball carb.; 3-speed, 8.85, 5.16, 2.93 to 1, 4-speed or auto opt.; cen. lvr.; susp. f. ind. torsion bar, r. half-elliptic; 2/4-door; 5-seat; drum brks.; max. 95 m.p.h.; cruise 80; m.p.g. 15-20; whl. base 9ft. 3in.; track f. 4ft. 9¾in., r. 4ft. 7⅝in.; lgth. 16ft. 3½in.; width 5ft. 9¾in.; ht. 4ft. 5⅜in.; g.c. 5¾in.; turng. cir. 38ft. 8in.; kerb wt. 28¼ cwt.; tank 15 gals.; 12-volt.

FERRARI 365 GT

THE magnificent 4.4-litre V12 engine perfectly mated to a five-speed all-synchromesh gearbox, gives this luxurious 2+2 coupe an electrifying performance. Body by Pininfarina with reclining front seats, electrically operated windows and individual shaped armchairs in the rear. Steering is power-assisted, a limited-slip differential discourages wheelspin and the disc servo brakes have twin fluid circuits.

CLOSE-UP
Twelve-cyl.; o.h.c.; 81 \ 71 mm.; 4,390 c.c.; 320 b.h.p.; 8.8 to 1 comp.; 3 Weber 2-choke carbs.; 5-speed, 13.09, 9.01, 6.67, 5.31, 4.08 to 1; cen. lvr.; susp. f. and r. ind. coil with hyd.-pneu. levelling; 2-door; 2/4-seat; disc servo brks.; max. 152 m.p.h.; cruise 130; m.p.g. 12-15; whl. base 8ft. 8½in.; track f. 4ft. 8⅝in., r. 4ft. 9⅞in.; lgth. 16ft. 3⅞in.; width 5ft. 10⅜in.; ht. 4ft. 4⅛in.; g.c. 5in.; turng. cir. 43ft.; kerb wt. 31½ cwt.; tank 19¾ gals.; 12-volt.

£6,100 + £1,697 p.t. = £7,797

FERRARI DINO

PININFARINA designed the tiny coupe body and Scaglietti builds it on Ferrari's way-ahead chassis with transverse rear-mounted V6 twin-cam engine. Based on a sports racing car, this is a road-going coupe for people who put style and speed before space, but it does offer luxurious comfort for two with a reasonable amount of luggage.

CLOSE-UP
Six-cyl.; o.h.c.; 86 < 57 mm.; 1,987 c.c.; 180 b.h.p.; 9 to 1 comp.; 3 Weber 2-choke carbs.; 5-speed, 15.01, 8.86, 6.46, 5.10, 3.86 to 1; cen. lvr.; susp. f. and r. ind. coil; 2-door; 2-seat; disc servo brks.; max. 145 m.p.h.; cruise 120; m.p.g. 18-21; whl. base 7ft. 1¾in.; track f. 4ft. 7⅞in., r. 4ft. 7⅛in.; lgth. 13ft. 9¾in.; width 5ft. 6⅞in.; ht. 3ft. 7⅞in.; g.c. 4⅞in.; turng. cir. 43ft.; kerb wt. 18¼ cwt.; tank 13½ gals.; 12-volt.

FIAT 500L

LONG popular as the lowest-priced car on the British market and an ideal city car, Fiat's baby gets a new interior with new facia and a fuel gauge, new steering wheel, parcel shelf, door pockets, new door handles and lower seats with adjustable backrests. Externally it has stronger bumpers, new hub caps and a bright metal line at roof level.

CLOSE-UP
Two-cyl.; o.h.v.; air cooled; 67.4 / 70 mm.; 499 c.c.; 18 b.h.p.; 7.1 to 1 comp.; Weber carb.; 4-speed, 18.96, 10.61, 6.62, 4.46 to 1; cen. lvr.; susp. f. ind. transv. leaf, r. ind. coil; 2-door; 2/4-seat; drum brks.; max. 60 m.p.h.; cruise 55; m.p.g. 47-52; whl. base 6ft. 0½in.; track f. 3ft. 8in., r. 3ft. 8½in.; lgth. 9ft. 9in.; width 4ft. 4⅛in.; ht. 4ft. 4⅛in.; g.c. 5in.; turng. cir. 25ft. 6in.; kerb wt. 9¾ cwt.; tank 4½ gals.; 12-volt.

500F £348 + £99 p.t. = £447

Abbreviations—g.c.—ground clearance; susp.—suspension; f.—front; r.—rear; comp.—compression; s.v.—side-valves; o.h.v.—overhead valves; o.h.c.—overhead camshaft; hyd.—hydraulic

FIAT 850 COUPE

PROLIFIC as ever, Fiat have extended the 850 range with a new Super saloon (8.8 compression, 37 h.p., nearly 80 m.p.h.) and an improved 850 coupe which has a longer tail, four front lamps, and a larger, more powerful engine. Longer stroke, higher compression, bigger oil pump, new valve materials are engine changes. 850 output is 250,000 a year, of which over 32,000 are coupes.

CLOSE-UP
Four-cyl.; o.h.v.; 65×68 mm.; 903 c.c.; 52 b.h.p.; 9.5 to 1 comp.; Weber carb.; 4-speed, 17.7, 10.01, 6.87, 4.7 to 1; cen. lvr.; susp. f. ind. transv. leaf, r. ind. coil; 2-door; 2/4-seat; disc/drum brks.; max. 90 m.p.h.; cruise 78; m.p.g. 38-40; whl. base 6ft. 7¾in.; track f. 3ft. 9½in., r. 3ft. 11¾in.; lgth. 12ft.; width 4ft. 11in.; ht. 4ft. 3in.; g.c. 5¼in.; turng. cir. 29ft. 3in.; kerb wt. 14½ cwt.; tank 6½ gals.; 12-volt.

FIAT 124 COUPE

PLAYING tunes on the fabulous new five-speed gearbox, the driver gets the most out of the smooth rev range of the eager engine with its two belt-driven overhead camshafts. Within the sleek GT coupe outline there is a full four-seater interior and a lot of luggage space. Equipment includes variable-speed wipers, variable-intensity instrument lights and warning lamps.

CLOSE-UP
Four-cyl.; o.h.c.; 80×71.5 mm.; 1,438 c.c.; 96 b.h.p.; 8.9 to 1 comp.; twin-choke Weber carb.; 5-speed, 15.19, 8.92, 5.78, 4.10, 3.74 to 1; cen. lvr.; susp. f. ind. coil, r. coil; 2-door; 4-seat; disc servo brks.; max. 105 m.p.h.; cruise 90; m.p.g. 24-26; whl. base 7ft. 11½in.; track f. 4ft. 5in., r. 4ft. 4in.; lgth. 13ft. 6in.; width 5ft. 6½in.; ht. 4ft. 4½in.; g.c. 5½in.; turng. cir. 33ft.; kerb wt. 18¼ cwt.; tank 10 gals.; 12-volt.
£1,120 + £309 p.t. = £1,429

FIAT 125

SALOON car with sporty sparkle. Belt-driven overhead camshafts and twin-choke compound carburetter are features of the fast-revving but flexible engine that takes this modestly priced family saloon along at speeds up to 100 m.p.h. Equipment includes reclining seats and heater, an intermittent wiper switch for mist and drizzle and warning lights for choke, handbrake, low fuel level.

CLOSE-UP
Four-cyl.; o.h.c.; 80×80 mm.; 1,608 c.c.; 90 b.h.p.; 8.8 to 1 comp.; Weber or Solex carb.; 4-speed, 14.05, 8.61, 5.57, 4.1 to 1; cen. lvr.; susp. f. ind. coil, r. half-elliptic; 4-door; 5-seat; disc servo brks.; max. 100 m.p.h.; cruise 85; m.p.g. 24; whl. base 8ft. 2⅜in.; track f. 4ft. 3¾in., r. 4ft. 2⅞in.; lgth. 13ft. 10¼in.; width 5ft. 3½in.; ht. 4ft. 6⅞in.; g.c. 6⅞in.; turng. cir. 35ft. 7in.; kerb wt. 19⅞ cwt.; tank 9¾ gals.; 12-volt.
£845 + £237 p.t. = £1,082

FORD ESCORT

OUT went the Anglia with 1967: in came the Escort with 1968. Models to suit all pockets, from 1100 de luxe through 1100 and 1300 supers to 1300 GT and on to the Twin Cam with 109 bhp, radius arms on rear suspension and plated wheels. Disc front brakes with servo and wide-rim wheels with radial tyres are standard on GT and Twin Cam, optional on others.

CLOSE-UP
Four-cyl.; o.h.v.; 81×53.3 mm.; 1,098 c.c.; 49 b.h.p., or 81×63 mm.; 1,298 c.c.; 58 b.h.p.; 9 to 1 comp.; Ford carb.; 4-speed, 15.08, 9.01, 5.88, 4.125 to 1; cen. lvr.; susp. f. ind. coil, r. half-elliptic; 2-door; 4-seat; hyd. brks. disc front and servo opt.; max. 79/83 m.p.h.; cruise, 72-78; m.p.g. 29; whl. base, 7ft. 10½in.; track f. 4ft. 0½in., r. 4ft. 1½in.; lgth. 13ft. 4in.; wdth. 5ft. 1¾in.; ht. 4ft. 7in.; g.c. 6½in.; turng. cir. 30ft.; kerb wt. 15¼ cwt.; tank 9 gals.; 12-volt.
1100 £510 + £141 p.t. = £651
1300 £587 + £163 p.t. = £750

FORD CORSAIR 2000 E

BEGINNING with an engine borrowed from the Cortina, the Corsair later acquired a 1·7-litre V4 of its own and now, with 2000 V4 engine it is one of the lowest priced cars in the 2-litre Executive class. The Executive saloon with vinyl covered top and black interior is popular with business men who want style and performance; the roomy station wagon has a strong following as a family and freight carrier.

CLOSE-UP
Four-cyl.; o.h.v.; 93.7 × 72.4 mm.; 1,996 c.c., 97 b.h.p.; 8.9 to comp.; Weber carb.; 4-speed, 13.38, 9.05, 5.33, 3.78 to 1; cen. lvr.; susp. f. ind. coil, r. half-elliptic; 4-door; 5-seat; hyd. servo brks., disc front; max. 96 m.p.h.; cruise 85; m.p.g. 21-25; whl. base 8ft. 5in.; track f. 4ft. 2½in., r. 4ft. 1½in.; lgth. 14ft. 8½in.; width 5ft. 3½in.; ht. 4ft. 9in.; g.c. 6in.; turng. cir. 36ft. 6in.; kerb wt. 20 cwt.; tank 10 gals.; 12-volt.

£868 + £241 p.t. = £1,109

FORD CORTINA SUPER

AN instant success, which set new standards in space and performance among economical family cars. The new five-bearing engines with cross-flow cylinder heads have given a boost to performance and the 1600 E, with its special trim, plated wheels, two-tone horns, matt black grille and broad based tyres has made a hit as a roomy saloon with sporting performance.

CLOSE-UP
Four-cyl.; o.h.v.; 81 × 78 mm.; 1,599 c.c.; 71 b.h.p.; 9 to 1 comp.; Ford carb.; 4-speed, 13.82, 9.34, 5.50, 3.9 to 1; cen. lvr. BW auto. opt.; susp. f. ind. coil, r. half-elliptic; 2/4-door; 4/5-seat; disc/drum brks.; max. 87 m.p.h.; cruise 78; m.p.g. 27-30; whl. base 8ft. 2in.; track f. 4ft. 5½in., r. 4ft. 3in.; lgth. 14ft.; width 5ft. 5in.; ht. 4ft. 7¾in.; g.c. 6¼in.; turng. cir. 30ft.; kerb wt. 17½ cwt.; tank 10 gals.; 12-volt.

£690 + £192 p.t. = £882

FORD ZEPHYR

POPULAR with business users and hire car fleet operators these Fords with all-independent suspension are among Britain's biggest popular saloons. The 2-litre V4 engine is indicated for economy, where fast acceleration and high maximum speed are not the primary needs; the V6 2½-litre unit gives quicker acceleration and higher cruising speed. A 3-litre version is also available and disc brakes are standard.

CLOSE-UP
Four-cyl.; o.h.v.; 93.7 × 72.4 mm.; 1,996 c.c.; 88 b.h.p.; 8.9 to 1 comp. (Six-cyl.; 93.7 × 60.3 mm.; 2,495 c.c.; 112 b.h.p.; 9 to 1 comp.); Zenith carb.; 4-speed, 16.3, 8.7, 5.6, 3.7 to 1 (Six, 12.3, 8.6, 5.5, 3.9 to 1); col. lvr.; susp. f. and r. ind. coil; 4-door; 5/6-seat; disc servo brks.; max. 88/96 m.p.h.; cruise 78/85; m.p.g. 18/26; whl. base 9ft. 7in.; track f. 4ft. 9in., r. 4ft. 10in.; lgth. 15ft. 5in.; width, 5ft. 11¼in.; ht. 4ft. 10½in.; g.c. 6in.; turng. cir. 36ft.; kerb wt. 24¼/25¾ cwt.; tank 15 gals.; 12-volt. **Four £737 + £205 p.t. = £942**
Six £797 + £221 p.t. = £1,018

FORD EXECUTIVE

FOUR headlamps, spot lamps, sun roof and wing mirrors are external items that distinguish this luxury model from the Zephyr. Under the bonnet is a 3-litre V6 engine driving through a BW automatic transmission. Power-assisted steering and servo-assisted disc brakes are standard equipment; so are reclining seats, reversing lamps and many other accessories to add to the enjoyment of quiet cruising at speeds up to 100 m.p.h.

CLOSE-UP
Six-cyl.; o.h.v.; 93.7 × 72.4 mm.; 2,994 c.c.; 128 b.h.p.; 8.9 to 1 comp.; Weber 2-choke carb.; 4-speed, 11.7, 8.19, 5.22, 3.7 to 1; cen. lvr., L de N overdrive or Ford auto. opt.; susp. f. and r. ind. coil; 4-door; 5-6-seat; disc servo brks.; max. 102 m.p.h.; cruise 88; m.p.g. 17-24; whl. base 9ft. 7in.; track f. 4ft. 9in., r. 4ft. 10in.; lgth. 15ft. 6in.; width 5ft. 11¼in.; ht. 4ft. 10½in.; g.c. 6in.; turng. circ. 38 ft.; kerb wt. 26 cwt.; tank 15 gals.; 12-volt.

£1,303 + £362 p.t. = £1,665

Abbreviations—g.c.—ground clearance; susp.—suspension; f.—front; r.—rear; comp.—compression; s.v.—side-valves; o.h.v.—overhead valves; o.h.c.—overhead camshaft; hyd.—hydraulic.

FORD 17 M

IRONING out the kink in the waistline and adding two inches to the length has given a sleeker line to the middle range German Fords which are now offered with a 1.8-litre V6 engine—smallest six in current production—as alternative to the established 1.5- and 1.7-litre V4s. Also new is the 20 M XL which has a new 2.3-litre high performance V6 developing 148 b.h.p.

CLOSE-UP
Four-cyl.; o.h.v.; 90×67 mm.; 1,699 c.c.; 65 b.h.p.; 9 to 1 comp.; Solex carb.; 4-speed, 12.6, 7.3, 5.1, 3.7 to 1; cen. lvr.; susp. f. ind. coil, r. half-elliptic; 2/4-door; 4/5-seat; disc/drum brks.; max. 87 m.p.h.; cruise 75; m.p.g. 25-28; whl. base 8ft 10½in.; track f. 4ft. 8½in., r. 4ft. 7¼in.; lgth. 15ft. 4in.; width 5ft. 11in.; ht. 4ft. 11in.; g.c. 7in.; turng. cir. 35ft.; kerb wt. 23¼ cwt.; tank 12 gals.; 12-volt.

£935+£262 p.t. = £1,197

FORD MUSTANG

MACH 1, shown here, is a dream car but made the production lines in the 1969 range of America's trend setting sports cars. Stiffer springs, dampers and roll bars contribute to better road holding and if anyone fears it might be underpowered with the new 230 b.h.p. 5.7-litre V8 engine, there is always the COBRA JET RAM AIR 7-litre! Usual choice of smaller sixes and V8 engines.

CLOSE-UP
Eight-cyl.; o.h.v.; 102×76 mm.; 4,940 c.c.; 230 b.h.p. gross; 10 to 1 comp.; Autolite 4-choke carb.; 3-speed, 8.98, 5.25, 3.0 to 1; cen. lvr. 4-speed or Ford auto. opt.; susp. f. ind. coil, r. half-elliptic; 2-door; 2/4-seat; disc/drum servo brks.; max. 118 m.p.h.; cruise 95; m.p.g. 15-20; whl. base 9ft.; track f. and r. 4ft. 10in.; lgth. 15ft. 3½in.; width 5ft. 11in.; ht 4ft. 3½in.; g.c. 7in.; turng. cir. 37ft. 6in.; kerb wt. 24 cwt.; tank 13½ gals.; 12-volt.

£2,200+£613 p.t. = £2,813

FORD MARQUIS

THE Mercury Division of Ford launched this distinctive new model in the upper end of the market. Lines of the saloon and hard top coupes recall the prestige Lincoln Continental in some respects. The V8 engine develops 320 or 360 according to carburetters. Options include disc front brakes, power operation for steering, door locks, windows, and a transistor speed control for motorway driving.

CLOSE-UP
Eight-cyl.; o.h.v.; 104.9×101.9 mm.; 7,031 c.c.; 320 b.h.p. gross; 10.5 to 1 comp.; Autolite 4-choke carb.; 3-speed auto, 6.89, 4.09, 2.8 to 1; col. lvr.; susp. f. ind. coil, r. coil; 2/4-door; 6-seat; drum servo brks., disc opt.; max. 120 m.p.h.; cruise 90; m.p.g. 12-17; whl. base 10ft. 4in.; track f. and r. 5ft. 2in.; lgth. 18ft. 8½in.; width 6ft. 6in.; ht. 4ft. 7⅞in.; g.c. 5½in.; turng. cir. 49ft.; kerb wt. 37½ cwt.; tank 20 gals.; 12-volt.

GILBERN GENIE

LOW built coupe from the Land of Song. Built in South Wales, the Grand Touring Genie has a glass fibre body on a steel chassis with 3-litre Ford V6 engine. New for 1969 is a high performance version with Tecalemit Jackson fuel injection to boost power to 165 b.h.p. It also has a limited-slip differential to control wheelspin when the driver is pouring on the power.

CLOSE-UP
Six-cyl.; o.h.v.; 93.7×72.4 mm.; 2,994 c.c.; 141 b.h.p.; 8.9 to 1 comp.; Weber carb.; 4-speed, 11.18, 7.82, 4.99, 3.54 to 1; cen. lvr.; susp. f. ind. coil, r. coil; 2-door; 4-seat; hyd. brks. disc front; max. 95-100 m.p.h.; cruise 80; m.p.g. 18-21; whl. base 7ft. 8¾in.; track f. 4ft. 6in., r. 4ft. 4½in.; lgth. 13ft. 3in.; width 5ft. 5in.; ht. 4ft. 4in.; g.c. 6in.; turng. cir. 31ft.; kerb wt. 19 cwt.; tank 14 gals.; 12-volt.

£1,500+£417 p.t. = £1,917

Abbreviations—g.c.—ground clearance; susp.—suspension; f.—front; r.—rear; comp.—compression; s.v.—side-valves; o.h.v.—overhead valves; o.h.c.—overhead camshaft; hyd.—hydraulic.

167

GINETTA G 15

ESSEX-BUILT small sports coupe with the Rootes Imp engine mounted in the tail of the curvaceous glass fibre body. The tubular chassis has wishbone front suspension and independent rear suspension by semi-trailing arms and coil springs. Front brakes and twin carburetters boost the engine output. Ginetta also build the G.4 with Ford Cortina engine and the G.10 with 4.7-litre V8.

CLOSE-UP
Four-cyl.; o.h.c.; 68×60 mm.; 875 c.c.; 51 b.h.p.; 10 to 1 comp.; 2 Stromberg carbs.; 4-speed, 16,59, 8.90, 5.70, 4.14 to 1; cen. lvr.; susp. f. and r. ind. coil; 2-door; 2-seat; disc/drum brks.; max. 97-100 m.p.h.; cruise 88; m.p.g. 36-40; whl. base 6ft. 10in.; track f. 4ft. 1in., r. 4ft. 0¾in.; lgth. 12ft. 0½in.; width 4ft. 9in.; ht. 3ft. 8½in.; g.c. 6in.; turng. cir. 29ft. 6in.; kerb wt. 10¼ cwt.; tank 7 gals.; 12-volt.

£799 + £224 p.t. = £1,023

HILLMAN IMP

THE revised front end with decorative aluminium trim panel announces a much improved car with printed circuit instrument panel, antiburst door locks, a new facia panel with circular instruments and new steering wheel with padded spokes. Front seats are redesigned with a new slide mechanism giving 5in. of movement and anti-tilt lock prevents them tipping forward in an emergency.

CLOSE-UP
Four-cyl.; o.h.c.; 68×60.4 mm.; 875 c.c.; 39 b.h.p.; 10 to 1 comp.; Solex carb.; 4-speed, 16.59, 8.91, 5.70, 4.14 to 1; cen. lvr.; susp. f. and r. ind. coil; 2-door; 4-seat; drum brks.; max. 80 m.p.h.; cruise 75; m.p.g. 40; whl. base 6ft. 10in.; track f. 4ft. 2⅜in., r. 4ft.; lgth. 11ft. 7in.; width 5ft. 0⅛in.; ht. 4ft. 4⅛in.; g.c. 5⅛in.; turng. cir. 30ft. 6in.; kerb wt. 14⅛ cwt.; tank 6 gals.; 12-volt.

£488 + £138 p.t. = £626

HILLMAN MINX

A de luxe version of this 1,500 c.c. saloon, based on the successful Hunter body shell, is announced for 1969 and all models now have disc front brakes. The de luxe has centre console and fitted carpets. The Minx Estate has the centre console, new lifting handle for rear door and extra bright work. Automatic Minxes have a 73 h.p. version of the 1,725 c.c. engine.

CLOSE-UP
Four-cyl.; o.h.v.; 81.5×71.6 mm.; 1,496 c.c.; 60 b.h.p.; 8.4 to 1 comp.; Zenith Stromberg carb.; 4-speed, 13.04, 8.32, 5.41, 3.89 to 1; cen. lvr.; susp. f. ind. coil, r. half-elliptic; 4-door; 4/5-seat; disc/drum brks.; max. 80 m.p.h.; cruise 70; m.p.g. 30-34; whl. base 8ft. 2½in.; track f. and r. 4ft. 4in.; lgth. 14ft.; width 5ft. 3⅜in.; ht. 4ft. 8in.; g.c. 6⅜in.; turng. cir. 33ft. 6in.; kerb wt. 18¼ cwt.; tank 10 gals.; 12-volt.

£647 + £182 p.t. = £829

HILLMAN HUNTER

THE car that helped to put Rootes finances back in the black. Clean-cut, modern and much lighter than previous Rootes family saloons, it forms the basis of a whole range of cars in varying stages of power and luxury from Hillman Minx to Humber Sceptre. Hunter acquires servo-assisted brakes for 1969. The canted-over engine has an alloy head, front brakes are discs.

CLOSE-UP
Four-cyl.; o.h.v.; 81.5×82.5 mm.; 1,725 c.c.; 74 b.h.p.; 9.2 to 1 comp.; Stromberg carb.; 4-speed, 12.41, 7.92, 5.15, 3.7 to 1; cen. lvr.; susp. f. ind. coil, r. half-elliptic; 4-door; 4/5-seat; servo brks., disc front; max. 88 m.p.h.; cruise 75; m.p.g. 28-34; whl. base 8ft. 2½in.; track f. and r. 4ft. 4in.; lgth. 14ft. 1½in.; width 5ft. 3½in.; ht. 4ft. 6½in.; g.c. 6⅜in.; turng. cir. 33ft. 6in.; kerb wt. 17½ cwt.; tank 10 gals.; 12-volt.

£757 + £212 p.t. = £969

HONDA N 600

DEVELOPED from the N 360, which gives Mini performance plus 50-60 m.p.g. economy on an engine of only 354 c.c., the N 600 gives Mini-Cooper performance from an engine of only 599 c.c. The transverse overhead cam light alloy twin is air-cooled and drives the front wheels. Automatic transmission is available. Lots of noise if you rasp the engine round to 8,000 r.p.m., but lots of fun too.

CLOSE-UP

Two-cyl. air-cooled; o.h.c.; 74×70 mm.; 599 c.c.; 42 b.h.p.; 8.5 to 1 comp.; Keihin carb.; 4-speed, 17.06, 10.56, 6.75, 4.82 to 1; facia lvr., Honda auto. opt.; susp. f. ind. coil, r. half-elliptic; 2-door; 4-seat; drum brks.; max. 82 m.p.h.; cruise 75; m.p.g. 45-50; whl. base 6ft. 6½in.; track f. 3ft. 8½in., r. 3ft. 7½in.; lgth. 10ft. 2in.; width 4ft. 3in.; ht. 4ft. 4½in.; g.c. 6½in.; turng. cir. 29ft.; kerb wt. 10⅝ cwt.; tank 6 gals.; 12-volt.

£459+£130 p.t. = £589

HUMBER SCEPTRE

MOST luxurious of the Rootes 1,775 c.c. saloons and the only car now to bear the respected Humber name, the Sceptre features vinyl covered top, special wheel discs, four headlamps and a luxurious interior with wood veneer facia, reclining seats, adjustable steering column and padded wheels. Overdrive working on third and top is standard, automatic transmission is optional. Equipment includes heated rear window.

CLOSE-UP

Four-cyl.; o.h.v.; 81.5×82.5 mm.; 1,725 c.c.; 88 b.h.p.; 9.2 to 1 comp.; 2 Stromberg carbs.; 4-speed, plus L de N overdrive, 13.04, 8.32, 5.41, 3.89 to 1; cen. lvr.; susp. f. ind. coil, r. half-elliptic; 4-door; 4-seat; hyd. servo brks., disc front; max. 97 m.p.h.; cruise 80; m.p.g. 25-30; whl. base 8ft. 2½in.; track f. and r. 4ft. 4in.; lgth. 14ft. 1½in.; width 5ft. 4in.; ht. 4ft. 8in.; g.c. 6½in.; turng. cir. 33ft. 6in.; kerb wt. 19½ cwt.; tank 10 gals.; 12-volt.

£984+£275 p.t. = £1,259

ISO GRIFO

PROBABLY the fastest production car in the show, the Bertone-bodied Grifo has a 7-litre Chevrolet engine and Warner four-speed gearbox. Compared with the very fast previous Grifo it has bigger clutch and improved brakes to cope with the colossal power and torque and larger headlamps. Wheel rims are wider for still better stability. See also the Ghia-bodied 150 m.p.h. 4-door saloon.

CLOSE-UP

Eight-cyl.; o.h.v.; 95.5×107.9 mm.; 6.998 c.c.; 400 b.h.p. gross; 10.25 to 1 comp.; Rochester 4-choke carb.; 4-speed, 6.34, 3.34, 3.22, 2.88 to 1; cen. lvr.; susp. f. ind. coil, r. de Dion coil; 2-door; 2-seat; disc servo brks.; max. 185 m.p.h.; cruise 160; m.p.g. 11-14; whl. base 8ft. 2⅜in.; track f. and r. 4ft. 7½in.; lgth. 14ft. 6⅜in.; width 5ft. 9⅜in.; ht. 3ft. 11⅜in.; g.c. 4⅜in.; turng. cir. 39ft. 4in.; kerb wt. 27½ cwt.; tank 23 gals.; 12-volt.

£6,807+£1,893 p.t. = £8,700

JAGUAR XJ6

A new saloon that takes corners like a racing car, thanks to its all-independent suspension, low centre of gravity and wide base radial tyres. Replacing 3.4 and 3.8 it comes with choice of 2.8-litre or 4.2-litre six-cylinder engines. Interior features include more padding, less walnut, more powerful heater with separate controls for rear seats, recessed door handles, extractor ventilation.

CLOSE-UP

Six-cyl.; o.h.c.; 83×86 mm.; 2,792 c.c.; 180 b.h.p. gross; 9 to 1 comp.; 2 S.U. carbs.; 4-speed, 12.5, 8.14, 5.93, 4.27 to 1; or 92.7×106 mm.; 4,235 c.c.; 245 b.h.p. 8 to 1 comp.; 4-speed, 10.38, 6.74, 4.92, 3.54 to 1; cen. lvr. L de N overdrive or BW auto. opt.; susp. f. and r. ind. coil; 4-door; 4-seat; disc servo brks.; max. 115-120 m.p.h.; cruise 100; m.p.g. 15-19; whl. base 9ft. 0⅞in.; track f. 4ft. 10in., r. 4ft. 10½in.; lgth. 15ft. 9¾in.; width 5ft. 9¾in.; ht. 4ft. 4½in.; g.c. 6in.; turng. cir. 36ft.; kerb wt. 30¾/31¼ cwt.; tank 23 gals.; 12-volt.

JAGUAR 240

AMBITIONS of many fast car fanciers are centred round this popular model, lowest-priced introduction to Jaguar performance and luxury. The traditional finely furnished English interior with high grade walnut cabinet work offers outstanding value. The four-speed transmission gives ample performance for British speed limits; the optional de Normanville overdrive gives easy cruising up to 100 m.p.h. on Continental motorways.

CLOSE-UP
Six-cyl.; o.h.c.; 83×76.5 mm.; 2,483 c.c.; 133 b.h.p. gross; 8 to 1 comp.; 2 Solex carbs.; 4-speed, 14.42, 7.94, 5.48, 4.27 to 1; cen. lvr., L de N overdrive or BW auto. opt.; susp. f. ind. coil, r. cantilever leaf; 4-door; 5-seat; servo disc brks.; max. 105 m.p.h.; cruise 85; m.p.g. 18-22; whl. base 8ft. 11¾in.; track f. 4ft. 6in., r. 4ft. 7⅜in.; lgth. 15ft.; width 5ft. 6¾in.; ht. 4ft. 9½in.; g.c. 5½in.; turng. cir. 34ft. 6in.; kerb wt. 29 cwt.; tank 12 gals.; 12-volt.

£1,148 + £321 p.t. = £1,469

JAGUAR E TYPE 2+2

SYMBOL of youth, speed and the good life for many who can never hope to own one, the E-Type is available with a choice of three bodies, 2-seater coupe and convertible or the 2+2 coupe on the longer wheelbase which meets the needs of the fast moving young family man. Interior improvements meet new safety requirements and there is even the option of an automatic transmission.

CLOSE-UP
Six-cyl.; o.h.c.; 92.1×106 mm.; 4,235 c.c.; 265 b.h.p. gross; 9 to 1 comp.; 3 S.U. carbs.; 4-speed, 8.23, 5.34, 3.90, 3.07 to 1; cen. lvr., auto. opt.; susp. f. torsion bar, r. ind. coil; 2-door; 2/4-seat; disc servo brks.; max. 140 m.p.h.; cruise 115; m.p.g. 18-20; whl. base 8ft. 9in.; track f. and r. 4ft. 2in.; lgth. 15ft. 4½in.; width 5ft. 5¼in.; ht. 4ft. 2in.; g.c. 5½in.; turng. cir. 41ft.; kerb wt. 26½ cwt.; tank 18 gals.; 12-volt.

£1,922 + £536 p.t. = £2,458

JENSEN FF

STILL the only production car available with the unique combination of Ferguson four-wheel drive and Maxaret braking which gives skid-free cornering even in the worst conditions and safe braking without risk of locking wheels even on ice. If it is true as some predict that four-wheel-drive will one day be as common as four-wheel braking, here is tomorrow's car today.

CLOSE-UP
Eight-cyl.; o.h.v.; 108×86 mm.; 6,276 c.c.; 325 b.h.p. gross; 10 to 1 comp.; Carter 4-choke carb.; 3-speed auto., 7.5, 4.44, 3.07 to 1; col. lvr.; susp. f. ind. coil, r. half-elliptic; 2-door; 4-seat; disc servo brks. with Maxaret; max. 130 m.p.h.; cruise 110; m.p.g. 12-15; whl. base 9ft. 1in.; track f. and r. 4ft. 8⅜in.; lgth. 15ft. 11in.; width 5ft. 10in.; ht. 4ft. 5in.; g.c. 5½in.; turng. cir. 38ft.; kerb wt. 36 cwt.; tank 16 gals.; 12-volt.

£4,708 + £1,310 p.t. = £6,018

JENSEN INTERCEPTOR

A potent brew compounded of Italian styling by Vignale, a light and powerful V8 engine and smooth acting automatic transmission by Chrysler and a robust chassis built for high speed by Jensen. An alternator supplies the current, thermostatically controlled fans cut down noise and loss of power at high speeds and the disc brakes with servo and twin circuits give stopping power to match the performance.

CLOSE-UP
Eight-cyl.; o.h.v.; 108×86 mm.; 6,276 c.c.; 325 b.h.p.; 10 to 1 comp.; Carter 4-choke carb.; 3-speed auto., 7.5, 4.44, 3.07 to 1; col. lvr.; susp. f. ind. coil, r. half-elliptic; 2-door; 4-seat; disc servo brks.; max. 132 m.p.h.; cruise 110; m.p.g. 15-18; whl. base 8ft. 9in.; track f. 4ft. 7⅜in., r. 4ft. 8⅞in.; lgth. 15 ft. 8in.; width 5ft. 9in.; ht. 4ft. 5in.; g.c. 5½in.; turng. cir. 38ft.; kerb wt. 31¼ cwt.; tank 16 gals.; 12-volt.

£3,488 + £972 p.t. = £4,460

Abbreviations—g.c.—ground clearance; susp.—suspension; f.—front; r.—rear; comp.—compression; s.v.—side-valves; o.h.v.—overhead valves; o.h.c.—overhead camshaft; hyd.—hydraulic.

LAMBORGHINI ISLERO

FACED with the sad disappearance of Carrozzeria Touring who did the original bodies for his first front engined coupes Lamborghini evolved this chunkier more aggressive body for the same chassis. The light alloy V12 engine with four overhead camshafts has six twin-choke Weber carburetters and transmission is by Lamborghini's own five-speed gearbox. The tubular chassis has independent coil spring suspension all round.

CLOSE-UP
Twelve-cyl.; o.h.c.; 82 × 62 mm.; 3,929 c.c.; 330 b.h.p.; 9 to 1 comp.; 6 Weber 2-choke carbs.; 5-speed, 9.5, 6.5, 4.6, 3.8, 3.06 to 1; cen. lvr.; susp. f. and r. ind. coil; 2-door; 2/4-seat; disc servo brks.; max. 160 m.p.h.; cruise 135; m.p.g. 14-17; whl. base 8ft. 4½in.; track f. and r. 4ft. 6½in.; lgth. 14ft. 6½in.; width 5ft. 8in.; ht. 4ft. 2in.; g.c. 5in.; turng. cir. 37ft. 9in.; kerb wt. 25½ cwt.; tank 22 gals.; 12-volt.
£5,790 + £1,610 p.t. = £7,400

LAMBORGHINI MIURA

THE car you just have to have. Kings, princes, pop stars and potentates find its appeal irresistible. Only two seats, negligible luggage space and lots of noise but what does it matter with that sexy Bertone styling and the transverse V12 four-cam engine to rocket you from 0 to 100 m.p.h. in a few seconds? Retractable headlamps and slatted rear window give light and shade.

CLOSE-UP
Twelve-cyl.; o.h.c.; 82 × 62 mm.; 3,929 c.c.; 350 b.h.p.; 9.5 to 1 comp.; 4 Weber 3-choke carbs.; 5-speed, 11.7, 8.07, 5.70, 4.65, 3.78 to 1; cen. lvr.; susp. f. and r. ind. coil; 2-door; 2-seat; disc servo brks.; max. 176 m.p.h.; cruise 150; m.p.g. 13-15; whl. base 8ft. 2½in.; track f. and r. 4ft. 7¼in.; lgth. 14ft. 4in.; width 5ft. 9¼in.; ht. 3ft. 5½in.; g.c. 5in.; turng. cir. 35ft. 9in.; kerb wt. 21½ cwt.; tank 23 gals.; 12-volt.
£7,516 + £2,009 p.t. = £9,525

LANCIA FLAVIA

WHILE Lamborghini names his cars after famous breeds of fighting bull, Lancia name theirs after the great highways of ancient Rome. A smooth new styling job has given the Flavia a much wider appeal and there is a choice of three engines 1.5-litres, 80 b.h.p.; 1.8-litres 92 b.h.p., or 1.8 injection 102 b.h.p. Coupe and convertible bodies are made by Pininfarina, Zagato and Vignale.

CLOSE-UP
Four-cyl.; o.h.v.; 88 × 74 mm.; 1,800 c.c.; 92 b.h.p.; 9 to 1 comp.; Solex carb.; 4-speed, 12.24, 7.31, 5.16, 3.71 to 1; col. lvr.; susp. f. ind. transv. leaf, r. half-elliptic; 4-door; 4/5-seat; disc servo brks.; max. 98 m.p.h.; cruise 85; m.p.g. 26-29; whl. base 8ft. 8½in.; track f. 4ft. 4in.; r. 4ft. 2in.; lgth. 15ft.; width 5ft. 3⅜in.; ht. 4ft. 11in.; g.c. 5½in.; turng. cir. 36ft.; kerb wt. 23½ cwt.; tank 10 gals.; 12-volt.
£1,463 + £408 p.t. = £1,871

LANCIA FULVIA RALLYE

ONE of the last creations of the late Ing. Fessia this little Fulvia, like the Flavia, has front wheel drive. Good road holding and the high performance of its compact V4 engine have given it some notable successes in international rallies. For competition enthusiasts there is the HF coupe with weight cut to 16½ cwt and engine tweaked to give 101 b.h.p.

CLOSE-UP
Four-cyl.; o.h.c.; 77 × 70 mm.; 1,298 c.c.; 87 b.h.p.; 9 to 1 comp.; 2 Weber 2-choke carbs.; 4-speed, 13.65, 8.06, 5.25, 3.7 to 1; cen. lvr.; susp. f. ind. transv. leaf, r. half-elliptic; 2-door; 2/4-seat; disc brks.; max. 104 m.p.h.; cruise 95; m.p.g. 27-33; whl. base 7ft. 8in.; track f. 4ft. 3¼in.; r. 4ft. 2¾in.; lgth. 13ft. 1¼in.; width 5ft. 1½in.; ht. 4ft. 3½in.; g.c. 5¼in.; turng. cir. 34ft.; kerb wt. 17⅞ cwt.; tank 8½ gals.; 12-volt.
£1,299 + £363 p.t. = £1,662

LINCOLN CONTINENTAL MK III

SOLD only as a two-door coupe, this is the latest in the line of top prestige cars from Ford. Equipped with power-assisted disc brakes at front, power-assisted steering and automatic transmission, it is offered in a choice of twenty-one colours and nine varieties of leather upholstery, with the option of English oak or East India rosewood for interior cabinet work.

CLOSE-UP
Eight-cyl.; o.h.v.; 110.5 × 97.7 mm.; 7,538 c.c.; 365 b.h.p. gross; 10.5 to 1 comp.; Autolite 4-choke carb.; 3-speed Turbo Drive auto, 6.89, 4.09, 2.8 to 1; col. lvr.; susp. f. ind. coil, r. coil; 2-door; 4-seat; disc/drum servo brks.; max. 120 m.p.h.; cruise 90; m.p.g. 10-15; whl. base 9ft. 9½in.; track f. and r. 5ft. 2in.; lgth. 18ft.; wdth. 6ft. 7⅜in.; ht. 4ft. 4⅞in.; g.c. 5½in.; turng. cir. 42ft.; kerb wt. 42½ cwt.; tank 19 gals.; 12-volt.

£4,400 + £1,224 p.t. = £5,624

LOTUS ELAN S.4

FIRST British car to comply with the American safety rules, the Elan is now available to British buyers with many of the export improvements including collapsible steering column, stronger door hinges, anti-lift wipers and electric washer, new exhaust system, flush fitting door handles. New rear lamp clusters incorporate reversing lamps and the wings are modified to cover wider low profile radial tyres.

CLOSE-UP
Four-cyl.; o.h.c.; 83 × 73 mm.; 1,558 c.c.; 105 b.h.p.; 9.5 to 1 comp.; 2 Weber, 2 choke carbs.; 4-speed, 11.0, 7.42, 5.18, 3.7 to 1; cen. lvr.; susp. f. and r. ind. coil; 2-door; 2-seat; disc brakes; max. 115 m.p.h.; cruise 100; m.p.g. 23-26; whl. base 7ft.; track f. 3ft. 11in., r. 4ft. 0½in.; lgth. 12ft. 1½in.; width 4ft. 8in.; ht. 3ft. 10in.; g.c. 6in.; turng. cir. 31ft.; kerb wt. 13¼ cwt.; tank 10 gals.; 12-volts.

£1,353 + £379 p.t. = £1,732

LOTUS ELAN +2

GRAND Prix experience applied to everyday motoring. Probably no other four-seater coupe in the world will go round corners as fast or as safely. It has a glass fibre body on steel backbone chassis. Retractable headlamps, servo disc brakes are standard. Twin-cam Lotus Cortina engine, suspension by coil spring struts. Good-looking streamlined shape gives remarkable middle-speed fuel consumption.

CLOSE-UP
Four-cyl.; o.h.c.; 82.6 × 72.8 mm.; 1,558 c.c.; 118 b.h.p.; 9.5 to 1 comp.; 2 Weber 2-choke carbs.; 4-speed, 11.19, 7.57, 5.28, 3.17 to 1; cen. lvr.; susp. f. and r. ind. coil; 2-door; 2/4-seat; disc servo brks.; max. 118 m.p.h.; cruise 100; m.p.g. 26-30; whl. base 8ft.; track f. 4ft. 6in., r. 4ft. 7in.; lgth. 14ft.; width 5ft. 3½in.; ht. 3ft. 11in.; g.c. 6in.; turng. cir. 36ft.; kerb wt. 17¾ cwt.; tank 13 gals.; 12-volt.

£1,718 + £481 p.t. = £2,199

MARCOS 1600

UNIQUE wooden chassis and knee-high plastic bodywork give the Marcos style and a low structure weight to hold its own with expensive foreign sports models, yet the power unit is a straightforward Ford Cortina GT which guarantees easy servicing and low cost spare parts. The semi-reclining driving position reflects the current Grand Prix fashion. Radius arms keep the back axle in line during acceleration and braking.

CLOSE-UP
Four-cyl.; o.h.v.; 81 × 77.6 mm.; 1,599 c.c.; 95 b.h.p.; 9.6 to 1 comp.; Weber 2-choke carb.; 4-speed, 11.0, 7.44, 5.17, 3.7 to 1; cen. lvr.; susp. f. ind. coil, r. coil; 2-door; 2-seat; disc/drum brks.; max. 120 m.p.h.; cruise 100; m.p.g. 23-29; wh. base 7ft. 5in.; track f. 4ft. 2½in.; r. 4ft. 4in.; lgth. 13ft. 4½in.; width 5ft. 3½in.; ht. 3ft. 9½in.; g.c. 5in.; turng. cir. 30ft.; kerb wt. 14⅞ cwt.; tank 10 gals.; 12-volt.

£1,500 + £417 p.t. = £1,917

Abbreviations—g.c.—ground clearance; susp.—suspension; f.—front; r.—rear; comp.—compression; s.v.—side-valves; o.h.v.—overhead valves; o.h.c.—overhead camshaft; hyd.—hydraulic.

MASERATI GHIBLI

THE mighty wind from Modena. One of the fast Maseratis named after famous winds, the Ghibli is wafted along at cruising speeds up to 150 m.p.h. by a four-cam V8 engine in light alloy with removable cylinder liners and dry sump lubrication. Its Ghia two-seater body reflects the current Continental style, with waistline sweeping up towards the long flat curve of the roof.

CLOSE-UP

Eight-cyl.; o.h.c.; 94 × 85 mm.; 4,719 c.c.; 330 b.h.p.; 8.5 to 1 comp.; 4 twin-choke Weber carbs.; 5-speed, 9.02, 5.81, 4.06, 3.30, 2.81 to 1; cen. lvr.; susp. f. ind. coil, r. half-elliptic; 2-door; 2-seat; disc servo brks.; max. 174 m.p.h.; cruise 150; m.p.g. 13-15; whl. base 8ft. 4¼in.; track f. 4ft. 8⅝in., r. 4ft. 7⅜in.; lgth. 15ft. 0¾in.; width 5ft. 10⅞in.; ht. 3ft. 9⅝in.; g.c. 5½in.; turng. cir. 36ft.; kerb wt. 28 cwt.; tank 22 gals.; 12-volt.

£7,795 + £2,167 p.t. = £9,962

MASERATI V8 QUATTROPORTE

MASERATI with the most in seating space. One of the world's fastest sports saloons; a genuine four-seater with bodywork by Frua luxuriously equipped with air conditioning, rear window de-mister, halogen headlamps and everything required for fast motoring in comfort. The light alloy V8 engine has four overhead camshafts and transmission is by five-speed ZF gearbox or three-speed BW automatic.

CLOSE-UP

Eight-cyl.; o.h.v.; 88 × 85 mm.; 4,136 c.c.; 260 b.h.p.; 8.5 to 1 comp.; 4 Weber carbs.; 5-speed, 9.66, 6.22, 4.35, 3.54, 3.0 to 1; cen. lvr.; BW auto. opt.; susp. f. ind. coil, r. half-elliptic; 4-door; 5-seat; disc servo brks.; max. 143 m.p.h.; cruise 110; m.p.g. 17-18; whl. base 9ft. 0¼in.; track f. 4ft. 6¾in., r. 4ft. 7½in.; lgth. 16ft. 4in.; width 5ft. 8in.; ht. 4ft. 5in.; g.c. 7in.; turng. cir. 36ft.; kerb wt. 33½ cwt.; tank 18 gals.; 12-volt.

£6,454 + £1,795 p.t. = £8,249

MERCEDES BENZ 220

SOBER exterior and traditional grille conceal major breaks with Mercedes convention: rear suspension by semi-trailing wishbones instead of swing axles, their biggest-yet four-cylinder engine with countless refinements to damp vibration and the option of new four-speed automatic transmission with special ratios and first-gear start. New too are the pedal-operated parking brake, telescopic steering column, twin-circuit brakes, no-grease chassis.

CLOSE-UP

Four-cyl.; o.h.c.; 87 × 92.4 mm.; 2,197 c.c.; 105 b.h.p.; 9 to 1 comp.; Stromberg carb.; 4-speed, 17.7, 12.6, 7.7, 4.5 to 1; cen. lvr., MB auto opt.; susp. f. and r. ind. coil; 4-door; 4/5-seat; disc servo brks.; max. 104 m.p.h.; cruise 95; m.p.g. 24-27; whl. base 9ft. 0¼in.; track f. 4ft. 8¾in., r. 4ft. 8⅝in.; lgth. 15ft. 4½in.; width 5ft. 9⅝in.; ht. 4ft. 8⅝in.; g.c. 5in.; turng. cir. 35ft.; kerb wt. 25¾ cwt.; tank 14¼ gals.; 12-volt.

£1,796 + £501 p.t. = £2,297

MERCEDES BENZ 300 SEL 6.3

STARTLING acceleration, which has set new standards for big, luxurious new five-seater saloons, results from the combination of the 600 fuel injection V8 engine and the long chassis 300 SEL saloon. It rides on air with automatic level control and stops with power-assisted slotted discs using automatic pressure control for the rear brakes. The MB four-speed automatic transmission is standard because no one could get away as fast with a manual box.

CLOSE-UP

Eight-cyl.; o.h.c.; 103 × 95 mm.; 6,329 c.c.; 250 b.h.p.; 9 to 1 comp.; Bosch injection; 4-speed MB auto., 11.34, 7.01, 4.50, 2.85 to 1; cen. lvr.; susp. f. and r. ind. pneu., self levelling; 4-door; 5-seat; disc servo brks.; max. 137 m.p.h.; cruise 120; m.p.g. 12-18; whl. base 9ft. 4¼in.; track f. 4ft. 10¼in., r. 4ft. 10⅝in.; lgth. 16ft. 4⅞in.; width 5ft. 11¼in.; ht. 4ft. 7½in.; g.c. 6¼in.; turng. cir. 40ft.; kerb wt. 34¼ cwt.; tank 23 gals.; 12-volt.

£5,691 + £1,583 p.t. = £7,274

Abbreviations—g.c.—ground clearance; susp.—suspension; f.—front; r.—rear; comp.—compression; s.v.—side-valves; o.h.v.—overhead valves; o.h.c.—overhead camshaft; hyd.—hydraulic.

MERCEDES BENZ 280 SE

WITH the 2½ litre class well catered for by a six-cylinder engine in the 200 series bodyshell, the impressive medium range Mercedes receives an engine of 2.8 litres with carburetters or fuel injection. While the smaller cars switch to trailing wishbone suspension, the larger ones with wider track retain low pivot swing axles with compensator springs and Hydropneumatic level regulator.

CLOSE-UP

Six-cyl.; o.h.c.; 86.5×78.8 mm.; 2,778 c.c.; 160 b.h.p.; 9.5 to 1 comp.; Bosch injection; 4-speed, 18.9, 13.5, 8.5, 4.7 to 1; cen. lvr. MB auto. opt.; susp. f. and r. ind. coil; 4-door; 5-seat; disc servo brks.; max. 118 m.p.h.; cruise 100; m.p.g. 19-23; whl. base 9ft. 0¼in.; track f. 4ft. 10¼in., r. 4ft. 10½in.; lgth. 16ft. 0⅞in.; width 5ft. 11¼in.; ht. 4ft. 8⅝in.; g.c. 6¼in.; turng. cir. 35ft. 6in.; kerb wt. 29¼ cwt.; tank 18 gals.; 12-volt.

£2,600 + £724 p.t. = £3,324

MERCURY COUGAR

FOLLOWING up the runaway success of the Mustang, Ford developed the Cougar in a higher price range. 1969 models are longer and wider and have more power. Convertibles have a new folding top, with hinged rear window in tempered safety glass. Options include a big choice of six- and eight-cylinder engines, 3- or 4-speed gearboxes and automatic transmissions, power steering and disc brakes.

CLOSE-UP

Eight-cyl.; o.h.v.; 5,752 c.c.; 290 b.h.p. gross; 10 to 1 comp.; Autolite 4-choke carb.; 3-speed, 8.34, 4.92, 2.79 to 1; cen. lvr., 4-speed or auto. opt.; susp. f. ind. coil, r. half-elliptic; 2-door; 4-seat; drum servo brks. disc opt.; max 118 m.p.h.; cruise 90; m.p.g. 15-18; whl. base 9ft. 5in.; track f. and r. 4ft. 10⅜in.; lgth. 16ft. 1¾in.; width 6ft. 2¼in.; ht. 4ft. 4in.; g.c. 5in.; turng. cir. 40ft.; kerb wt. 29 cwt.; tank 13 gals.; 12-volt.

MG 1300

UNDER the octagonal badge a much modified engine helps to maintain the MG reputation for Safety Fast. High compression head with larger inlet ports, bigger carburetters, stiffer crankcase and hardened crankshaft raise the performance possibilities and a new close-ratio gearbox with synchromesh on all speeds adds to the pleasure of driving. Interior equipment is redesigned on the pattern of the famous Austin America.

CLOSE-UP

Four-cyl.; o.h.v.; 70.6×81.3 mm.; 1,275 c.c.; 70 b.h.p. gross; 9 to 1 comp.; 2 S.U. carbs.; 4-speed, 12.04, 7.57, 4.93, 3.65 to 1; cen. lvr.; susp. f. and r. ind. rubber-hyd.; 2-door; 4-seat; disc/drum brks.; max. 92 m.p.h.; cruise 83; m.p.g. 30-34; whl. base 7ft. 9½in.; track f. 4ft. 3½in., r. 4ft. 2⅞in.; lgth. 12ft. 2¾in.; width 5ft. 0⅜in.; ht. 4ft. 5in.; g.c. 6in.; turng. cir. 34ft. 9in.; kerb wt. 16¾ cwt.; tank 8 gals.; 12-volt.

£660 + £185 p.t. = £845

MG MGC

A bonnet bulging with horsepower gives the most powerful of the MG line the acceleration demanded by American buyers. Based on the MGB, it has a seven-bearing six-cylinder engine and front suspension is switched from coil springs to torsion bars to make room for the longer cylinder block. Overdrive or automatic transmission are available and there is a choice of convertible or coupe bodies.

CLOSE-UP

Six-cyl.; o.h.v.; 83.3×88.9 mm.; 2,912 c.c.; 145 b.h.p.; 9 to 1 comp.; 2 S.U. carbs.; 4-speed, 7.03, 6.81, 4.23, 3.07 to 1; cen. lvr. auto. opt.; susp. f. ind. torsion bar, r. half-elliptic; 2-door; 2-seat; servo brks., disc front; max. 120 m.p.h.; cruise 100; m.p.g. 20-23; whl. base 7ft. 7in.; track f. 4ft. 2in., r. 4ft. 1½in.; lgth. 12ft. 9½in.; width 4ft. 11in.; ht. 4ft. 1¾in.; g.c. 5in.; turng. cir. 33ft.; kerb wt. 19¼ cwt.; tank 10 gals.; 12-volt.

£925 + £259 p.t. = £1,184

Abbreviations—g.c.—ground clearance; susp.—suspension; f.—front; r.—rear; comp.—compression; s.v.—side-valves; o.h.v.—overhead valves; o.h.c.—overhead camshaft; hyd.—hydraulic.

MORGAN PLUS 8

TYRE burning acceleration takes this new Morgan from a standstill to 100 m.p.h. in under 20 secs. The secret is the Rover light alloy V8 engine in a chassis only two inches longer than before. Light alloy wheels supply an external clue but otherwise it is a traditional Morgan with sliding pillar front suspension and a chassis frame that passes under the rear axle.

CLOSE-UP

Eight-cyl.; o.h.v.; 89×71 mm.; 3,530 c.c.; 168 b.h.p.; 10.5 to 1 comp.; 2 S.U. carbs.; 4-speed, 10.48, 6.16, 4.25, 3.53 to 1; cen. lvr.; susp. f. ind. coil, r. half-elliptic; 2-door; 2-seat; disc/drum servo brks.; max. 124 m.p.h.; cruise 105; m.p.g. 18-22; whl. base 8ft. 2½in.; track f. 4ft., r. 4ft. 3in.; lgth. 12ft. 9in.; width 4ft. 9¾in.; ht. 4ft. 1in.; g.c. 6in.; turng. cir. 38ft.; kerb wt. 17¼ cwt.; tank 13½ gals.; 12-volt.

£1,155+£323 p.t. = £1,478

MORRIS MINI COOPER S Mk. II

NOTHING has been the same since the Mini Cooper made much bigger cars look foolish in production car races and went on to sweep the board in big International rallies. Still a great road car, equally at home in town traffic or on the fast lanes of the motorways it gains extra riding comfort from the pitch-free Hydrolastic suspension.

CLOSE-UP

Four-cyl.; o.h.v.; 70.64×81.33 mm.; 1,275 c.c.; 75 b.h.p.; 9.75 to 1 comp.; 2 S.U. carbs.; 4-speed, 11.02, 6.6, 4.67, 3.44 to 1; susp. f. and r. ind. rubber-hydraulic; 2-door; 4-seat; hyd. servo brks., disc front; max. 95 m.p.h.; cruise 85; m.p.g. 28-32; whl. base 6ft. 8in.; track, f. 4ft. 0⅜in., r. 3ft. 11½in.; lgth. 10ft. 0½in.; width 4ft. 7⅜in.; ht. 4ft. 5in.; g.c. 6in.; turng. cir. 31½ft.; kerb wt. 13 cwt.; tank 5½ gals.; 12-volt.

£710+£211 p.t. = £921

MORRIS MINOR 1000

DEMAND from business users who regard it as one of Britain's most reliable small cars keeps this original Issigonis design going in competition with much later models. Body styles include two-door saloon, four-door saloon, two-door convertible and a roomy station wagon. After several engine changes over the years, the current 1100 unit provides today's blend of performance and economy.

CLOSE-UP

Four-cyl.; o.h.v.; 64.6×83.7 mm.; 1,098 c.c.; 48 b.h.p.; 8.5 to 1 comp.; S.U. carb.; 4-speed, 15.27, 9.16, 5.96, 4.22 to 1; cen. lvr.; susp. f. ind. torsion bar, r. half-elliptic; 2/4-door; 4-seat; drum brks.; max. 78 m.p.h.; cruise 68; m.p.g. 28-34; whl. base 7ft. 2in.; track f. 4ft. 2⅝in., r. 4ft. 2⅝in.; lgth. 12ft. 4in.; width 5ft. 1in.; ht. 5ft.; g.c. 6¾in.; turng. cir. 33ft.; kerb wt. 15½ cwt.; tank 6½ gals.; 12-volt.

£501+£141 p.t. = £642

MORRIS 1800S

THOSE who liked the enormous body space but wanted higher performance are offered this extra model with high compression twin carburetter engine equipped with new induction manifold and tuned exhaust to give an extra 10 h.p. Bigger front disc brakes with four-piston calipers provide extra stopping power. Basic layout, with transverse engine, front-wheel-drive, Hydrolastic suspension, remains unchanged.

CLOSE-UP

Four-cyl.; o.h.v.; 80.26×88.9 mm.; 1,798 c.c.; 100 b.h.p. gross; 9.5 to 1 comp.; 2 S.U. carbs.; 4-speed, 12.77, 7.98, 5.35, 3.88 to 1; cen. lvr.; susp. f. and r. ind. rubber hydraulic; 4-door; 5-seat; hyd. servo brks., disc front; max. 93 m.p.h.; cruise 82; m.p.g. 23-27; whl. base 8ft. 10in.; track f. 4ft. 8in., r. 4ft. 7½in.; lgth. 13ft. 8¼in.; width 5ft. 7in.; ht. 4ft. 8in.; g.c. 6½in.; turng. cir. 37ft.; kerb wt. 22¾ cwt.; tank 10½ gals.; 12-volt.

Abbreviations—g.c.—ground clearance; susp.—suspension; f.—front; r.—rear; comp.—compression; s.v.—side-valves; o.h.v.—overhead valves; o.h.c.—overhead camshaft; hyd.—hydraulic.

175

MOSKVITCH 412

COMMUNIST university dons and trades union bosses, hoping for a place in some future Russian puppet Government of Britain, may make ritual obeisance here but even they are unlikely to buy until the creaking Russian car industry is brought up to date with factories built by Western capitalism to make vehicles designed by Fiat, and other Western consultants.

CLOSE-UP

Four-cyl.; o.h.v.; 82 ⁄ 70 mm.; 1,479 c.c.; 80 b.h.p. gross; 8.8 to 1 comp.; K-59 carb.; 4-speed, 16.1, 10.2, 6.1, 4.2 to 1; col. lvr.; susp. f. ind. coil, r. half-elliptic; 4-door; 4/5-seat; hyd. brks.; max. 83 m.p.h.; cruise 70; m.p.g. 28-32; whl. base 7ft. 10½in.; track f. 4ft. 0¾in., r. 4ft. 0¼in.; lgth. 13ft. 5½in.; width 5ft. 1⅛in; ht. 4ft. 10½in.; g.c. 7in.; turng. cir. 35ft.; kerb wt. 18½ cwt.; tank 10 gals.; 12-volt.

£525 + £148 p.t. = £673

NSU SUPER PRINZ

THOUGH the engine is at the back, a grille on the front is one of the additions for the English market. Other items on this specially equipped version of NSU's nimble economy model: carpets instead of rubber on the floor, clock, folding rear seats for extra luggage space, adjustable front backrests, headlamp flasher, special instrument panel and parking lights.

CLOSE-UP

Two-cyl.; o.h.c. air-cooled; 76 × 66 mm.; 598 c.c.; 27 b.h.p.; 7.5 to 1 comp.; Solex carb.; 4-speed, 18.74, 10.0, 6.39, 4.52 to 1; cen. lvr.; susp. f. and r. ind. coil; 2-door; 4-seat; drum brks.; max. 75 m.p.h.; cruise 65; m.p.g. 45-48; whl. base 6ft. 8½in.; track f. 4ft. 0½in., r. 3ft. 11⅜in.; lgth. 11ft. 3½in.; width 4ft. 10¾in.; ht. 4ft. 5½in.; g.c. 7in.; turng. cir. 28ft. 11in.; kerb wt. 11 cwt.; tank 8 gals.; 12-volt.

£444 + £125 p.t. = £569

NSU Ro 80

SMALL size and light weight of the twin-rotor Wankel engine have helped NSU to build what many connoisseurs claim is the best handling saloon car on the market today. The engine drives the front wheels through a semi-automatic transmission with torque converter, three-speed gear box and an automatic clutch freed by finger pressure on the gear lever.

CLOSE-UP

Twin-rotor Wankel; 995 c.c.; 115 b.h.p.; 9 to 1 comp.; 2 Solex carbs; 3-speed, semi-auto., 9.98, 5.87, 3.83 to 1; cen. lvr.; susp. f. and r. ind. coil; 4-door; 5-seat; disc servo brks.; max. 112 m.p.h.; cruise 100; m.p.g. 24; whl. base 9ft. 4¾in.; track f. 4ft. 10¼in., r. 4ft. 8¾in.; lgth. 15ft. 8in.; width 5ft. 9¼in.; ht. 4ft. 7½in.; g.c. 6½in.; turng. cir. 38ft. 9in.; kerb wt. 23½ cwt.; tank 18 gals.; 12-volt.

£1,745 + £487 p.t. = £2,232

OLDSMOBILE TORONADO

REVISED rear-end styling increases the length of Oldsmobile's racy front-drive model. Variable ratio power steering makes parking easier. New single-piston disc brakes and tyres with glass-fibre reinforcement are optional extras. A single key locks ignition, steering and automatic transmission on all Oldsmobiles for 1969, so car thieves will have to learn new techniques. Suspension is improved, and an electrically heated rear window is an optional extra.

CLOSE-UP

Eight-cyl.; o.h.v.; 105 × 108 mm.; 7,457 c.c.; 375 b.h.p. gross; 10.25 to 1 comp.; Rochester 4-choke carb.; 3-speed Hydra-Matic, 7.64, 4.56, 3.08 to 1; col. lvr.; susp. f. ind. torsion bar, r. half-elliptic; 2-door; 4-seat; drum servo brks., disc opt.; max. 130 m.p.h.; cruise 100; m.p.g. 10-15; whl. base 9ft. 11in.; track f. 5ft. 3½in., r. 5ft. 3in.; lgth. 17ft. 11in.; width 6ft. 6½in.; ht. 4ft. 4½in.; g.c. 5in.; turng. cir. 42ft. 9in.; kerb wt. 40 cwt.; tank 20 gals.; 12-volt.

Abbreviations—g.c.—ground clearance; susp.—suspension; f.—front; r.—rear; comp.—compression; s.v.—side-valves; o.h.v.—overhead valves; o.h.c.—overhead camshaft; hyd.—hydraulic.

OLDSMOBILE F85 CUTLASS

ONE of the smallest in a range of ten series and thirty body styles, the Cutlass is a mere 17ft. 2in. long and comes with a choice of two engines; 4-litre six or 5.7-litre V8 giving up to 310 b.h.p. Four transmissions to choose from; three- or four-speed manual and two automatics. Reinforced doors and screen pillars are new safety features on the big Oldsmobiles.

CLOSE-UP

Eight-cyl.; o.h.v.; 103×85 mm.; 5,727 c.c.; 250 b.h.p. gross; 9 to 1 comp.; Rochester 2-choke carb.; 3-speed, 7.82, 4.62, 3.08 to 1; col. lvr. 4-speed or auto opt.; susp. f. ind. coil, r. coil; 2/4-door; 6-seat; drum servo brks.; max. 100 m.p.h.; cruise 90; m.p.g. 13-16; whl. base 9ft. 4in.; track f. and r. 4ft. 11in.; lgth. 16ft. 9¾in.; width 6ft. 4¼in.; ht. 4ft. 4¾in.; g.c. 6in.; turng. cir. 41ft. 3in.; kerb wt. 29 cwt.; tank 16 gals.; 12-volt.

OPEL OLYMPIA

THE de luxe four-seater coupe is a well finished car equivalent in size to the Vauxhall Viva. It has a high performance for its size and is equipped with practical items like two-speed wipers and washer, headlamp flasher, and an anti-theft lock on the steering, plus a clock and lamps in glove box, luggage boot and engine compartment.

CLOSE-UP

Four-cyl.; o.h.v.; 75×61 mm.; 1,078 c.c.; 60 b.h.p.; 9.2 to 1 comp.; 2 Solex carbs.; 4-speed, 15.01, 8.59, 6.88, 3.89 to 1.; cen. lvr.; susp. f. ind. transverse leaf, r. coil; 2/4-door; 4-seat; disc/drum servo brks.; max. 90 m.p.h.; cruise 80; m.p.g. 30-34; whl. base 7ft. 11½in.; track f. 4ft. 1½in., r. 4ft. 2½in.; lgth. 13ft. 8¾in.; width 5ft. 1¾in.; ht. 4ft. 7¼in.; g.c. 6in.; turng. cir., 32ft. 5in.; kerb wt. 15 cwt.; tank 8¾ gals.; 12-volt.

£812+£228 p.t. = £1,040

OPEL REKORD

THE hardtop coupe with four-cylinder overhead camshaft engine is an attractive model from the range of the General Motors German factory. Inbuilt safety features include dual circuit braking system, with discs in front, energy absorbing steering column, padded wheel and panel and soft control knobs and coat hooks. Electric clock and heated rear window are additional items.

CLOSE-UP

Four-cyl.; o.h.c.; 93×69.8 mm.; 1,897 c.c.; 90 b.h.p.; 9.5 to 1 comp.; Solex 2-choke carb.; 4-speed, 13.3, 8.4, 5.3, 3.9 to 1.; cen. lvr.; susp., f. ind. coil, r. coil; 2/4-door; 5-seat; disc/drum servo brks.; max. 98 m.p.h.; cruise 80; m.p.g. 23-26; whl. base 8ft. 9in.; track f. and r. 4ft. 7½in.; lgth. 15ft. 1in.; width 5ft. 9½in.; ht. 4ft. 9½in.; g.c. 6in.; turng. cir. 35ft. 7in.; kerb wt. 21 cwt.; tank 12 gals.; 12-volt.

£1,072+£300 p.t. = £1,372

PEUGEOT 204

IN the pursuit of safety and security the smallest model from Sochaux gets improved front brakes, anti-roll bars front and rear, and improved interior trim with padded centre to the steering wheel. New engine mountings and exhaust system cut noise and vibration. There are new rubber inserts in bumpers. Coupe and convertible now have iodine-vapour lamps for better night vision.

CLOSE-UP

Four-cyl.; o.h.c.; 75×64 mm.; 1,130 c.c.; 53 b.h.p.; 8 to 1 comp.; Solex carb.; 4-speed, 15.15, 9.25, 6.06, 4.23 to 1; col. lvr.; susp. f. and r. ind. coil; 4-door; 4-seat; hyd. brks., disc front; max. 86 m.p.h.; cruise 78; m.p.g. 27-30; whl. base 8ft. 6in.; track f. 4ft. 4in., r. 4ft. 1½in.; lgth. 13ft.; width 5ft. 1½in.; ht. 4ft. 7in.; g.c. 5½in.; turng. cir. 31ft. 2in.; kerb wt. 16¾ cwt.; tank 9¼ gals.; 12-volt.

£812+£228 p.t. = £1,040

PEUGEOT 504

POP-UP headrests on full reclining seats are an unusual feature of a safety-conscious interior on Peugeot's new big car. Burst-proof locks, double-jointed steering column and heavily padded steering wheel give added protection. The canted-over engine is developed from the 404 unit. Optional final injection gives 97 h.p. Front suspension is by MacPherson struts, rear by trailing wishbones.

CLOSE-UP

Four-cyl.; o.h.v.; 84×81 mm.; 1,796 c.c.; 82 b.h.p.; 8.3 to 1 comp.; Solex carb.; 4-speed, 14.27, 8.44, 5.48, 3.89 to 1; cen. lvr.; susp. f. and r. ind. coil; 4-door; 5-seat; disc servo brks.; max. 97 m.p.h.; cruise 88; m.p.g. 25; whl. base 8ft. 11⅞in.; track f. 4ft. 7⅞in., r. 4ft. 5⅜in.; lgth. 14ft. 8⅝in.; width 5ft. 6½in.; ht. 4ft. 9½in.; g.c. 6in.; turng. cir. 35ft. 9in.; kerb wt. 23½ cwt.; tank 12¼ gals.; 12-volt.

PLYMOUTH FURY

1969 models are longer, wider and heavier, reflecting the inflationary process which afflicts all American cars until a new range of compacts starts it all over again. Features include better automatic brake adjustment, new disc brakes and a seven-position tilting steering wheel. A slotted air deflector in the roof of the station wagon is designed to keep mud and spray off the rear window.

CLOSE-UP

Eight-cyl.; o.h.v.; 99×84 mm.; 5,210 c.c.; 230 b.h.p. gross; 9.2 to 1 comp.; Ball carb.; 3-speed, 9.75, 5.68, 3.23 to 1; col. lvr.; susp. f. ind. torsion bar, r. half-elliptic; 2/4-door; 5/6-seat; drum brks., disc opt.; max. 110 m.p.h.; cruise 90; m.p.g. 14-18; whl. base 10ft.; track f. 5ft. 2½in., r. 5ft. 0¾in.; lgth. 17ft. 10½in.; width 6ft. 7⅞in.; ht. 4ft. 7¾in.; g.c. 5¾in.; turng. cir. 42ft. 9in.; kerb wt. 34 cwt.; tank 19 gals.; 12-volt.

£2,294+£639 p.t. = £2,933

PONTIAC GRAND PRIX

CLAIMED to have the longest bonnet in American production, the GP is distinctively styled. Driver and front passenger are surrounded by padding on curved facia and console. The radio aerial is built into the windscreen glass. Options include 7-litre 370 b.h.p. engine, ride control, power assisted disc brakes in front and glass-reinforced tyres. Following the GM trend for 1969, wheels are bigger (15in. against 14in.) and tyres are wider.

CLOSE-UP

Eight-cyl.; o.h.v.; 104.7×95.2 mm.; 6,556 c.c.; 265 b.h.p. gross; 10.5 to 1 comp.; Rochester 4-choke carb.; 3-speed, 8.59, 5.70, 3.55 to 1; cen. lvr., 4-speed or auto opt.; susp. f. ind. coil, r. coil; 2-door; 4-seat; drum servo brks., disc opt.; max. 120 m.p.h.; cruise 90; m.p.g. 13-18; whl. base 9ft. 10in.; track f. 5ft. 2in., r. 5ft.; lgth. 17ft. 6½in.; width 6ft. 3¾in.; ht. 4ft. 4in.; g.c. 5¾in.; turng. cir. 40ft. 9in.; kerb wt. 32½ cwt.; tank 21 gals.; 12-volt.

PONTIAC FIREBIRD

BOLD and unusual front end styling marks this big convertible out from the crowd. Stability is increased by wheels with seven-inch rims and a five-foot track. On all Firebirds the driver can lock ignition, steering and gear lever with a single turn of a master key. Options include disc front brakes, an electrically erected radio aerial and full air conditioning.

CLOSE-UP

Six-cyl.; o.h.c.; 98×90 mm.; 4,098 c.c.; 175 b.h.p. gross; 9 to 1 comp.; Rochester carb.; 3-speed, 10.12, 5.96, 3.55 to 1; cen. lvr., 4-speed or auto opt.; susp. f. ind. coil, r. half-elliptic; 2-door; 4-seat; drum servo brks., disc opt.; max. 105 m.p.h.; cruise 90; m.p.g. 17-22; whl. base 9ft.; track f. and r. 5ft.; lgth. 15ft. 11in.; width 6ft. 0¼in.; ht. 4ft. 0½in.; g.c. 5⅛in.; turng. cir. 38ft. 6in.; kerb wt. 27⅞ cwt.; tank 15½ gals.; 12-volt.

£2,825+£787 p.t. = £3,612

PORSCHE 912

SUCCESSOR to the original four cylinder models, the Porsche 912 has improved ventilation eliminating swivelling quarter windows. A longer wheelbase obtained by moving the rear wheels rearwards improves weight distribution and road holding. Heated rear window, three speed wipers, twin circuit brakes are current equipment.

CLOSE-UP
Four-cyl.; o.h.v.; air-cooled; 82.5 × 74 mm.; 1,582 c.c.; 90 b.h.p.; 9.3 to 1 comp.; 2 Solex carbs.; 4-speed, 13.68, 7.22, 4.61, 3.50 to 1; cen. lvr.; susp. f. and r. ind. torsion bar; 2-door; 2/4-seat; disc brks.; max. 115 m.p.h.; cruise 100; m.p.g. 30; whl. base 7ft. 5½in.; track, f. 4ft. 4⅓in., r. 4ft. 3⅓in.; lgth. 13ft. 8in.; width 5ft. 3½in.; ht. 4ft. 4in.; g.c. 6in.; turng. cir. 33ft.; kerb wt. 19½ cwt.; tank 13½ gals.; 12-volt.

£2,176 + £607 p.t. = £2,783

PORSCHE 911S

WIDER wings shelter broad-based tyres which combine with an extension of over two inches in the wheelbase to improve ride and road holding on Porsche's fastest production model. Fuel injection increases engine power and flexibility, new disc brakes with aluminium calipers and quartz iodine headlamps promote peace of mind for 100 m.p.h. motoring. A high voltage capacitor ignition system supplies the sparks.

CLOSE-UP
Six-cyl.; o.h.c.; 80 × 66 mm.; 1,991 c.c.; 170 b.h.p.; 9.9 to 1 comp.; Bosch injection; 5-speed, 13.66, 8.33, 5.84, 4.61, 3.50 to 1; cen. lvr.; susp. f. and r. ind. torsion bar; 2-door; 2/4-seat; disc brks.; max. 140 m.p.h.; cruise 120; m.p.g. 23-26; whl. base 7ft. 9¼in.; track f. 4ft. 6in., r. 4ft. 5⅜in.; lgth. 13ft. 7⅞in.; width 5ft. 3⅜in.; ht. 4ft. 4in.; g.c. 6in.; turng. cir. 35ft.; kerb wt. 20 cwt.; tank 13¼ gals.; 12-volt.

RELIANT SCIMITAR GT/E

STATION wagon with a spoiler on top. An original body design by Tom Karen of Ogle produces a Reliant GT coupe which has sports car speed and station wagon versatility. It can carry four adults or with rear seats folded away presents a flat platform to carry 40 cu. ft. of baggage. The Scimitar Coupe continues with a choice of two Ford V6 engines of 2.5 or 3 litres.

CLOSE-UP
Six-cyl.; o.h.v.; 93.7 × 72.4 mm.; 2,994 c.c.; 128 b.h.p.; 8.9 to 1 comp.; Weber carb.; 4-speed, 11,31, 7.92, 5.05, 3.58 to 1, Laycock de Normanville overdrive opt.; cen. lvr.; susp., f. ind. coil, r. coil; 3-door; 2/4-seat; hyd. brks., disc front; max. 120 m.p.h.; cruise, 100; m.p.g. 22; whl. base, 8ft. 3½in.; track f. 4ft. 7in., r. 4ft. 5in.; lgth. 14ft. 3in.; width 5ft. 4½in.; ht. 4ft. 4in.; g.c. 5½in.; turng. cir. 36ft.; kerb wt. 21⅜ cwt.; tank 17 gals.; 12-volt.

RELIANT REBEL

SINGLE minded devotion to the production of individualistic cars ranging from three wheelers to fast GT coupes has made Reliant Europe's biggest producers of glass fibre bodywork. The Rebel is a light, compact and economical family car powered by Reliant's own 700 c.c. engine. Styling is by Ogle; the steel box section chassis has independent front suspension and a conventional rear end.

CLOSE-UP
Four-cyl.; o.h.v.; 60.5 × 60.9 mm.; 700 c.c.; 31 b.h.p.; 8.8 to 1 comp.; Zenith carb.; 4-speed, 18.69, 10.76, 6.36, 4.38 to 1; cen. lvr.; susp. f. ind. coil, r. half elliptic; 2-door; 4-seat; drum brks.; max. 70 m.p.h.; cruise 60; m.p.g. 43-47; whl. base 7ft. 5in.; track f. 4ft., r. 3ft. 10⅝in.; lgth. 11ft. 6in.; width 4ft. 10in.; ht. 4ft. 7in.; g.c. 5in.; turng. cir. 29ft.; kerb wt. 10¾ cwt.; tank 6 gals.; 12-volt.

£462 + £130 p.t. = £592

Abbreviations—g.c.—ground clearance; susp.—suspension; f.—front; r.—rear; comp.—compression; s.v.—side-valves; o.h.v.—overhead valves; o.h.c.—overhead camshaft; hyd.—hydraulic.

179

RENAULT 16 TS

FRANCE'S leading factory used no half measures when producing this high-performance version on the versatile five-door saloon. A bigger engine with new cylinder head and twin-choke Weber carburetter supplies the power, bigger section tyres and bigger front disc brakes handle the extra urge and a more luxurious interior includes cigarette lighter and a reading lamp for the front passenger.

CLOSE-UP

Four-cyl.; o.h.v.; 77 × 84 mm.; 1,565 c.c.; 87.5 b.h.p.; 8.6 to 1 comp.; Solex carb.; 4-speed, 13.6, 8.48, 5.58, 3.88 to 1; col. lvr.; susp. f. and r. ind. torsion bar; 5-door; 5-seat; hyd. brks., disc front; max. 101 m.p.h.; cruise 88; m.p.g. 25-28; whl. base 8ft. 9½in.; track f. 4ft. 4⅜in., r. 4ft. 2⅜in.; lgth. 13ft. 10½in.; width 5ft. 4⅝in.; ht. 4ft. 9in.; g.c. 6in.; turng. cir. 32ft 8in.; kerb wt. 19¼ cwt.; tank 12 gals.; 12-volt.

£890 + £249 p.t. = £1,139

RENAULT 6

SLOTTED between the 4 and 16, Renault's roomy new family model develops the same design theme in a clean cut five-door car, combining saloon comfort with station wagon carrying capacity. Points of interest; load-sensitive valve to prevent rear brakes locking, staggered switches on a functional facia, full-width radiator behind the dash for the new heater system. Due in Britain in 1969.

CLOSE-UP

Four-cyl.; o.h.v.; 58 × 80 mm.; 845 c.c.; 34 b.h.p.; 8 to 1 comp.; Solex carb.; 4-speed, 15.67, 10.72, 5.61, 4.25 to 1; facia lvr.; susp. f. and r. ind. torsion bar; 5-door; 4/5-seat; drum brks.; max. 73 m.p.h.; cruise 65; m.p.g. 34-37; whl. base 7ft. 10½in.; track f. 4ft. 2½in., r. 4ft. 1in.; lgth. 12ft. 7⅞in.; width 5ft. 0½in.; ht. 4ft. 11in.; g.c. 7in.; turng. cir. 34ft.; kerb wt. 14¾ cwt.; tank 7 gals.; 12-volt.

ROVER 2000 TC

ALTHOUGH the V8 engine has made this year's headlines many keen drivers still prefer the combination of twin-carburetter four-cylinder engine and manual gearbox which gives them equivalent acceleration at less cost. The interior has pioneer safety features including crushable containers in front of the knees and fully framed instrument panel, and the protective structure does not rely on the outside panels for strength.

CLOSE-UP

Four-cyl.; o.h.c.; 85.7 × 85.7 mm.; 1,978 c.c.; 107 b.h.p.; 10 to 1 comp.; coil ign.; 2 S.U. carbs.; 4-speed, 12.83, 7.55, 4.92, 3.54 to 1; cen. lvr.; susp. f. ind. coil, r. de Dion coil; 4-door; 4-seat; disc servo brks.; max. 110 m.p.h.; cruise 98; m.p.g. 23-27; whl. base 8ft. 7½in.; track f. 4ft. 5½in., r. 4ft 4½in.; lgth. 14ft. 10½in.; width 5ft. 6½in.; ht. 4ft. 6¾in.; g.c. 8½in.; turng. cir. 31ft. 6in.; kerb wt. 24¾ cwt.; tank 12 gals.; 12-volt.

£1,200 + £335 p.t. = £1,535

ROVER 3500

REPLACE the four-cylinder engine with a V8 of nearly twice the size and you have the recipe for a car of breath-taking performance. Add the fact that the V8, in light alloy weighs little more than the four and you guarantee good handling too. The transmission is automatic and the interior has all the usual Rover refinements.

CLOSE-UP

Eight-cyl.; o.h.v.; 88.9 × 71 mm.; 3,532 c.c.; 160 b.h.p.; 10.5 to 1 comp.; 2 S.U. carbs.; 3-speed BW auto, 7.36, 4.47, 3.08 to 1; cen. lvr.; susp. f. ind coil, r. de Dion coil; 4-door; 4-seat; disc servo brks.; max. 117 m.p.h.; cruise 98; m.p.g. 18-20; whl. base 8ft. 7½in.; track f. 4ft. 5½in., r. 4ft. 3¾in.; lgth. 14ft. 11¾in.; width 5ft. 6in.; ht. 4ft. 8in.; g.c. 7½in.; turng. cir. 33ft. 6in.; kerb wt. 26¼ cwt.; tank 15 gals.; 12-volt.

£1,400 + £391 p.t. = £1,791

Abbreviations—g.c.—ground clearance; susp.—suspension; f.—front; r.—rear; comp.—compression; s.v.—side-valves; o.h.v.—overhead valves; o.h.c.—overhead camshaft; hyd.—hydraulic

RILEY KESTREL

THIS front-drive 1300 takes on a new lease of life with redesigned high compression engine and completely new interior. Tuned inlet and exhaust pipes, larger carburetters, stiffer cylinder block and a hardened crankshaft suggest an engine which will give more power and stand up to harder work. New close ratio gears help the driver to get the best out of it.

CLOSE-UP

Four-cyl.; o.h.v.; 70.6 × 81.3 mm.; 1,275 c.c.; 70 b.h.p. gross; 9.5 to 1 comp.; S.U. carb.; 4-speed, 12.04, 7.57, 4.93, 3.65 to 1; cen. lvr.; susp. f. and r. ind. rubber-hyd.; 4-door; 4/5-seat; hyd. brks., disc front; max. 90 m.p.h.; cruise 80; m.p.g. 30-36; whl. base 7ft. 9½in.; track f. 4ft. 3⅛in., r. 4ft. 2⅞in.; lgth. 12ft. 2¾in.; width 5ft. 0⅜in.; ht. 4ft. 5in.; g.c. 5¼in.; turng. cir. 38ft.; kerb wt. 16¾ cwt.; tank 8 gals.; 12-volt.

£712 + £200 p.t. = £912

RILEY ELF Mark II

MANOEUVRABLE as a Mini but ten inches longer, the Elf has an extended tail to give a larger luggage boot, and a more luxurious interior with winding side windows and a special instrument panel. A 998 c.c. engine with single carburetter gives good top gear flexibility and the Hydrolastic suspension gives an unbeatable smooth ride over rough roads and mountain tracks.

CLOSE-UP

Four-cyl.; o.h.v.; 64.58 × 76.2 mm.; 998 c.c.; 38 b.h.p.; 8.3 to 1 comp.; S.U. carb.; 4-speed, 13.66, 8.18, 5.32, 3.76 to 1; cen. lvr.; susp., f. and r. ind. rubber-hyd.; 2-door; 4-seat; drum brks.; max. 75 m.p.h.; cruise 62; m.p.g. 40; whl. base 6ft. 8½in.; track f. 3ft. 11½in., r. 3ft. 10in.; lgth. 10ft. 10¼in.; width 4ft. 7½in.; ht. 4ft. 5in.; g.c. 6⅛in.; turng. cir. 31ft. 7in.; kerb wt. 13 cwt.; tank 5½ gals.; 12-volt.

£550 + £155 p.t. = £705

ROLLS-ROYCE SILVER SHADOW

BRITAIN'S most advanced car, built with the incomparable Rolls-Royce attention to detail. Ten years from now you will be able to get a replacement door fillet from the same walnut log as the original. Meanwhile you enjoy the power of the V8 engine, the triple circuit disc brakes, the independent suspension with hydraulic levelling and the seats electrically adjustable for reach, height and slope.

CLOSE-UP

Eight-cyl.; o.h.v. 104.1 × 91.4 mm.; 6,230 c.c.; b.h.p. not revealed; 9 to 1 comp.; 2 S.U. carbs.; 4-speed auto., 11.75, 8.1, 4.46, 3.08 to 1; col. lvr.; susp. f. and r. ind. coil, hyd. levelling; 2/4-door; 5-seat; disc servo brks.; max. 116 m.p.h.; cruise 100; m.p.g. 11-14; whl. base 9ft. 11½in.; track f. and r. 4ft. 9½in.; lgth. 16ft. 11½in.; width 5ft. 11in.; ht. 4ft. 11¾in.; g.c. 6½in.; turng. cir. 38ft.; kerb wt. 41½ cwt.; tank 24 gals.; 12-volt.

£6,095 + £1,685 p.t. = £7,790

ROLLS-ROYCE PHANTOM V

THE natural choice of the Queen and anyone else who aspires to own the best that Britain builds. The V8 engine is the same as that in the Silver Shadow but the steel springs and drum brakes with gearbox-driven mechanical servo continue the tradition of the famous Silver Cloud. Mulliner-Park Ward build the bodywork with standards of craftsmanship that become rarer every year.

CLOSE-UP

Eight-cyl.; o.h.v.; 104.14 × 91.44 mm.; 6,230 c.c.; b.h.p. not revealed; 9 to 1 comp.; 2 S.U. carbs.; 4-speed auto., 14.64, 10.23, 5.64, 3.89 to 1; col. lvr.; susp. f. ind. coil, r. half-elliptic; 4-door; 7-seat; drum servo brks.; max. 100 m.p.h.; cruise 85; m.p.g. 12; whl. base 12ft. 1in.; track f. 5ft. 0⅞in., r. 5ft. 4in.; lgth. 19ft. 10in.; width 6ft. 7in.; ht. 5ft. 9in.; g.c. 6½in.; turng. cir. 48ft. 9in.; kerb wt. 50½ cwt.; tank 23 gals.; 12-volt.

£8,700 + £2,419 p.t. = £11,119

Abbreviations—g.c.—ground clearance; susp.—suspension; f.—front; r.—rear; comp.—compression; s.v.—side-valves; o.h.v.—overhead valves; o.h.c.—overhead camshaft; hyd.—hydraulic.

RAMBLER JAVELIN

CASHING in late on the boom in family sports cars, American Motors produced one of the best looking, with a choice of three engines; one six-cylinder and two V8s. Optional equipment includes automatic transmission and a limited slip differential and cars with V8 engines have disc brakes in front. Still faster is the short wheelbase AMX fastback coupe.

CLOSE-UP

Eight-cyl.; o.h.v.; 95.25 × 83.3 mm.; 4,749 c.c.; 224 b.h.p. gross; 10 to 1 comp.; Holley 4-choke carb.; 3-speed auto, 7.65, 5.14, 3.15 to 1; col. lvr., 3 or 4-speed manual opt.; susp. f. ind. coil, r. coil; 2-door; 5-seat; hyd. servo brks., disc front; max. 104 m.p.h.; cruise 85; m.p.g. 14-18; whl. base 9ft. 1in.; track f. 4ft. 9⅞in., r. 4ft. 9in.; lgth. 15ft. 9in.; width 6ft.; ht. 4ft. 4in.; g.c. 5⅛in.; turng. cir. 37ft.; kerb wt. 26½ cwt.; tank 15¾ gals.; 12-volt.

£2,215 + £617 p.t. = £2,832

SAAB V4

THE new Saab 99 with overhead camshaft engine built by Standard Triumph is not due in England until 1969. Even then it will not replace the smaller streamlined coupe with the V4 engine built by the group that makes Sweden's superb Draken and Viggen jet fighters. Saab's twin circuit brakes safeguard at least one front brake and the opposite rear brake in emergencies.

CLOSE-UP

Four-cyl.; o.h.v.; 90 × 58.9 mm.; 1,498 c.c.; 65 b.h.p.; 9 to 1 comp.; Solex carb.; 4-speed, 16.98, 10.19, 6.34, 4.09 to 1; col. lvr.; susp. f. ind. coil, r. coil; 2-door; 4-seat; disc/drum brks.; max. 90 m.p.h.; cruise 82; m.p.g. 28-33; whl. base 8ft. 2½in.; track f. and r. 4ft.; lgth. 13ft. 8in.; width 5ft. 2in.; ht. 4ft. 10in.; g.c. 7in.; turng. cir. 35ft.; kerb wt. 17 cwt.; tank 8¾ gals.; 12-volt.

£664 + £187 p.t. = £851

SIMCA 1100 GLS

COMBINING a compact transverse engine and front wheel drive with a modern five-door utility saloon body, Simca have produced a car which has exceptional carrying capacity allied to lively performance and good road holding. There is also a three-door version and various stages of trim and equipment are available to suit a variety of family budgets. A semi-automatic transmission is an optional extra.

CLOSE-UP

Four-cyl.; o.h.v.; 74 × 65 mm.; 1,118 c.c.; 56 b.h.p.; 9.6 to 1 comp.; Solex carb.; 4-speed, 14.45, 9.06, 5.99, 4.25 to 1; cen. lvr., semi-auto opt.; susp. f. and r. ind. torsion bar; 3/5-door; 4-seat; hyd. brks., disc front; max. 88 m.p.h.; cruise 78; m.p.g. 30-34; whl. base 8ft. 3⅛in.; track f. 4ft. 5¼in., r. 4ft. 3⅜in.; lgth. 12ft. 11½in.; width 5ft. 2½in.; ht. 4ft. 9⅜in.; g.c. 5⅛in.; turng. cir. 36ft.; kerb wt. 17½ cwt.; tank 9¼ gals.; 12-volt.

£576 + £162 p.t. = £738

SIMCA 1301/1501

BUILT by the Chrysler-controlled Simca group in France, this five-seater saloon in contemporary style is offered with a choice of two engines and transmissions, with variations in grille and interior trim to match. Front suspension is by conventional wishbones and coil springs. The rear axle is located for acceleration and braking by radius arms and a transverse stabiliser bar.

CLOSE-UP

Four-cyl.; o.h.v.; 74 × 75 mm.; 1,290 c.c.; 54 b.h.p.; or 75.2 × 83 mm.; 1,475 c.c.; 68 b.h.p.; 8.6/9.3 to 1 comp.; Solex or Weber carb.; 4-speed, 16.22, 9.14, 6.15, 4.45 to 1; cen. lvr.; susp. f. ind. coil, r. coil; 4-door; 4-seat; hyd. brks., disc front on 1501; max. 83/92 m.p.h.; cruise 70-80; m.p.g. 25-28; whl. base 8ft. 3½in.; track f. 4ft. 4in., r. 4ft. 3in.; lgth. 14ft. 7½in.; width 5ft. 2in.; ht. 4ft. 6in.; g.c. 5¼in.; turng. cir. 32ft. 3in.; kerb wt. 19½-20 cwt.; tank 12 gals.; 12-volt.

1301GL £763 + £214 p.t. = £977
1501GL £812 + £228 p.t. = £1,040

Abbreviations—g.c.—ground clearance; susp.—suspension; f.—front; r.—rear; comp.—compression; s.v.—side-valves; o.h.v.—overhead valves; o.h.c.—overhead camshaft; hyd.—hydraulic.

SINGER CHAMOIS Mk II

FOUR headlamps feature in the re-styled front end and the grille incorporates a concealed push-button lock for the luggage compartment. Side mouldings with coloured inserts are also new; white on saloon, red on Chamois Sport. Interior changes are full width facia with circular instruments including volt meter and oil pressure gauge, new front seats, anti-burst door locks, improved heater controls.

CLOSE-UP
Four-cyl.; o.h.c.; 68×60.4 mm.; 875 c.c.; 39 b.h.p.; 10 to 1 comp.; Solex carb.; 4-speed, 16.59, 8.90, 5.70, 4.13 to 1; cen. lvr.; susp. f. and r. ind. coil; 2-door; 4-seat; drum brks.; max. 77 m.p.h.; cruise 68; m.p.g. 40; whl. base 6ft. 10in.; track f. 4ft. 2½in., r. 4ft. 0½in.; lgth. 11ft. 9½in.; width 5ft. 0½in.; ht. 4ft. 6½in.; g.c. 6¼in.; turng. cir. 30ft. 6in.; kerb wt. 14½ cwt.; tank 10 gals.; 12-volt.

£550 + £155 p.t. = £705

SINGER VOGUE

POWER-ASSISTED brakes are a new driving aid for 1969 on both the Vogue and the Gazelle, which has a 1,500 c.c. engine with the same body shell. Both models have reclining front seats, disc front brakes, centre console, anti-burst door locks and child-proof safety locks. Automatic transmission is available on Vogue and Gazelle (coupled with 1,725 c.c. engine on Gazelle).

CLOSE-UP
Four-cyl.; o.h.v.; 81.5×82.5 mm.; 1,725 c.c.; 74 b.h.p.; 9.2 to 1 comp.; Stromberg carb.; 4-speed, 12.41, 7.92, 5.15, 3.7 to 1; cen. lvr., L de N. overdrive or BW. auto. opt.; susp. f. ind. coil, r. half-elliptic; 4-door; 4/5-seat; hyd. brks., disc front; max. 87 m.p.h.; cruise 75; m.p.g. 27-30; whl. base 8ft. 2½in.; track f. and r. 4ft. 4in.; lgth. 14ft. 1½in.; width 5ft. 3½in.; ht. 4ft. 8in.; g.c. 6¾in.; turng. cir. 33ft. 6in.; kerb wt. 18½ cwt.; tank 10 gals.; 12-volt.

£818 + £229 p.t. = £1,047

SKODA 1100MB

WITH hopes of a better life once again shattered by the invading Red Army, the stoic Czechs and Slovaks continue production of their individualistic and well-equipped rear-engined saloons. Boot, engine compartment and fuel filler are all locked when the car doors are locked. Headlamp flasher, toolkit, windscreen washer, coat hooks and twin roof lights are standard equipment. Front seats have reclining backrests and rear seats are removable.

CLOSE-UP
Four-cyl.; o.h.v.; 72×68 mm.; 1,107 c.c.; 46 b.h.p.; 8.5 to 1 comp.; Jikov carb.; 4-speed, 16.87, 9.41, 6.26, 4.26 to 1; cen. lvr.; susp. f. and r. ind. coil; 4-door; 4-seat; hyd. brks.; max. 82 m.p.h.; cruise 72; m.p.g. 32-35; whl. base 7ft. 10½in.; track f. 4ft. 2½in., r. 4ft. 1½in.; lgth. 13ft. 8in.; width 5ft. 4in.; ht. 4ft. 7in.; g.c. 7in.; turng. cir. 35ft. 4in.; kerb wt. 15½ cwt.; tank 7 gals.; 12-volt.

£533 + £150 p.t. = £683

SUNBEAM RAPIER

WHILE the standard Rapier continues as a quick, good looking coupe with the family car interior space, the new H120 is added to the range with engine modified by Holbay Racing to produce 110 b.h.p. gross. Gas-flow head 9.6 to 1 compression and two Weber twin-choke carburetters contribute to the extra output. H120 external features include tail spoiler, side stripes, new wheels.

CLOSE-UP
Four-cyl.; o.h.v.; 81.5×82.5 mm.; 1,725 c.c.; 88 b.h.p.; 9.2 to 1 comp.; 2 Stromberg carbs.; 4-speed and L de N overdrive, 13.16, 8.40, 5.46, 4.22 to 1; cen. lvr., auto. opt.; susp. f. ind. coil, r. half-elliptic; 2-door; 4-seat; hyd. servo brks., disc front; max. 100 m.p.h.; cruise 90; m.p.g. 24-28; whl. base 8ft. 2½in.; track f. and r. 4ft. 4in.; lgth. 14ft. 6¾in.; width 5ft. 4½in.; ht. 4ft. 7in.; g.c. 5in.; turng. cir. 33ft.; kerb wt. 20 cwt.; tank 16 gals.; 12-volt.

£1,034 + £289 p.t. = £1,323

SUNBEAM STILETTO

LIKE other sport versions of the Imp, this has 51 h.p. twin-carburetter engine with high-lift camshaft and oil cooler, plus servo-assisted brakes and radial ply tyres. The new Stiletto front seats have reclining backrests and breathable trim, and it has rear seats folding down for additional luggage space. Instruments include a tachometer and the panel employs printed-circuit wiring.

CLOSE-UP

Four-cyl.; o.h.c.; 68 × 60.4 mm.; 875 c.c.; 51 b.h.p.; 10 to 1 comp.; 2 Zenith-Stromberg carbs.; 4-speed, 16.59, 8.91, 5.70, 4.14 to 1; cen. lvr.; susp., f. and r. ind. coil; 2-door; 4-seat; hyd. servo brks.; max. 88 m.p.h.; cruise, 80; m.p.g. 35-42; whl. base, 6ft. 10in.; track f. 4ft. 2$\frac{5}{8}$in., r. 4ft.; lgth., 11ft. 7in.; width, 5ft. 0$\frac{1}{4}$in.; ht. 4ft. 4$\frac{1}{8}$in.; g.c. 5$\frac{1}{2}$in.; turng. cir., 30ft. 6in.; kerb wt., 14$\frac{3}{8}$ cwt.; tank, 6 gals.; 12-volt.

£635 + £178 p.t. = £813

TOYOTA COROLLA

THERE'S no mechanical mystery about the growing Japanese invasion of world markets. Toyota's small saloon is typical of their straightforward design with pushrod engine at the front driving through four speed gearbox to an ordinary rear axle on half elliptic springs. And the brakes are drums. Their main sales pitch is based on good detail finish, reliability and strong spares backing.

CLOSE-UP

Four-cyl.; o.h.v.; 75 × 61 mm.; 1,077 c.c.; 60 b.h.p. gross; 9 to 1 comp.; Aisan twin-choke carb.; 4-speed, 15.53, 8.65, 5.84, 4.22 to 1; cen. lvr., auto. opt.; susp., f. ind. coil and transv. leaf, r. half-elliptic; 2-door; 4-seat; hyd. brks.; max. 85 m.p.h.; cruise, 75; m.p.g. 32-34; whl. base, 7ft. 6in.; track f. 4ft. 0$\frac{3}{8}$in., r. 4ft. 0$\frac{1}{8}$in.; lgth., 12ft. 7$\frac{3}{8}$in.; width, 4ft. 10$\frac{1}{2}$in.; ht. 4ft. 6$\frac{3}{8}$in.; g.c. 6$\frac{1}{2}$in.; turng. cir., 29ft. 9in.; kerb wt., 14$\frac{1}{4}$ cwt.; tank, 8 gals.; 12-volt.

£604 + £170 p.t. = £774

TOYOTA CORONA

ALREADY a familiar sight on British roads with its backwards sloping front intake enclosing four headlamps, the Corona is available as four-door saloon or three-door station wagon or five-door saloon. There is also a 1600 S version with high compression engine boosting output to 90 b.h.p. and a 1600 GT coupe which does well over 100 m.p.h.

CLOSE-UP

Four-cyl.; o.h.v.; 78 × 78 mm.; 1,490 c.c.; 70 b.h.p. 8 to 1 comp.; Aisan 2-choke carb.; 4-speed, 13.59, 7.81, 5.18, 3.7 to 1; cen. lvr.; susp. f. ind. coil, r. half-elliptic; 4-door; 4/5 seat; drum brks.; max. 86 m.p.h.; cruise 74; m.p.g. 28-33; whl. base 7ft. 11$\frac{1}{4}$in.; track f. and r. 4ft. 2in.; lgth. 13ft. 5$\frac{3}{4}$in.; width 5ft. 1in.; ht. 4ft. 8in.; g.c. 6$\frac{3}{4}$in.; turng. cir. 32ft. 6in.; kerb wt. 18$\frac{3}{4}$ cwt.; tank 9$\frac{7}{8}$ gals.; 12-volt.

£695 + £195 p.t. = £890

TOYOTA CROWN DE LUXE

NEW to the British market is this spacious six-cylinder saloon which is sold with remarkably complete equipment. It has a station seeking radio with electrically erected aerial, map reading lamp, inspection lamp, tinted windscreen, heater demister, white wall tyres, electric clock, cigar lighter and reclining seats. The engine has a seven bearing crankshaft to ensure smooth running and a fluid coupling for the fan limits noise and power losses at high engine revs.

CLOSE-UP

Six-cyl.; o.h.c.; 75 × 85 mm.; 2,253 c.c.; 115 b.h.p. gross; 8.8. to 1 comp.; Aisan 2-choke carb.; 3-speed, 13.37, 7.17, 4.37 to 1; cen. lvr., 4-speed or Toyoglide auto opt.; susp. f. ind. coil, r. coil; 4-door; 5/6-seat; disc/drum servo brks.; max. 98 m.p.h.; cruise 85; m.p.g. 19-24; whl. base 8ft. 9$\frac{7}{8}$in.; track f. 4ft. 5$\frac{1}{2}$in., r. 4ft. 6$\frac{1}{4}$in.; lgth. 15ft. 3$\frac{5}{8}$in.; width 5ft. 6$\frac{1}{2}$in.; ht. 4ft. 8$\frac{7}{8}$in.; g.c. 6$\frac{3}{4}$in.; turng. cir. 36ft.; kerb wt. 24$\frac{1}{2}$ cwt.; tank 14$\frac{1}{4}$ gals.; 12-volt.

Abbreviations—g.c.—ground clearance; susp.—suspension; f.—front; r.—rear; comp.—compression; s.v.—side-valves; o.h.v.—overhead valves; o.h.c.—overhead camshaft; hyd.—hydraulic.

TRIUMPH HERALD 13/60

CHOICE is limited for the motorist who wants fresh air and four seats but the Herald with its latest 1300 c.c. engine, new grille and Vitesse-style front wings is one of Britain's most successful convertibles. It had a telescopic steering column long before the safety experts took them up and its 25ft. turning circle makes it incredibly easy to park.

CLOSE-UP

Four-cyl.; o.h.v.; 73.7×76 mm.; 1,296 c.c.; 61 b.h.p.; 8.5 to 1 comp.; Solex carb.; 4-speed, 15.4, 8.9, 5.7, 4.1 to 1; cen. lvr.; susp., f. ind. coil, r. ind. transv. leaf; 2-door; 4-seat; hyd. brks., disc front; max. 85 m.p.h.; cruise 80; m.p.g. 32-36; whl. base 7ft. 7½in.; track f. 4ft. 1in., r. 4ft.; lgth. 12ft. 9in.; width 5ft.; ht. 4ft. 4in.; g.c. 6¾in.; turng. cir. 25ft.; kerb wt. 17 cwt.; tank 6½ gals.; 12-volt.

£583 + £164 p.t. = £747

TRIUMPH 2500

SUBSTITUTING a 2.5-litre fuel injection engine for the previous 2-litre carburettor six has rejuvenated the Michelotti-styled Triumph saloon with important gains in speed, acceleration and flexibility, plus the hope of no great increase in fuel costs, thanks to the superior economy of fuel injection over carburettors. The 2000 with carburettors continues unchanged.

CLOSE-UP

Six-cyl.; o.h.v.; 74.7×95 mm.; 2,498 c.c.; 132 b.h.p.; 9.5 to 1 comp.; Lucas injection; 4-speed, 11.31, 7.24, 4.78, 3.45 to 1; cen. lvr., L de N overdrive or BW auto opt.; susp. f. and r. ind. coil; 4-door; 5-seat; disc/drum servo brks.; max. 100 m.p.h.; cruise 90; m.p.g. 23-27; whl. base 8ft. 10in.; track f. 4ft. 4in., r. 4ft. 2½in.; lgth. 14ft. 5¾in.; width 5ft. 5in.; ht. 4ft. 8in.; g.c. 6in.; turng. cir. 32ft.; kerb wt. 23½ cwt.; tank 11½ gals.; 12-volt.

£1,133 + £316 p.t. = £1,449

TRIUMPH GT 6

BASED on the Spitfire, but with a six-cylinder 2-litre engine to give a high power to weight ratio, the GT 6 advances into a much higher performance range. Now the new rear suspension gives better control of wheel angles, cuts down oversteer and makes it easier for drivers to exploit the full performance without too much opposite-lock work on corners.

CLOSE-UP

Six-cyl.; o.h.v.; 74.7×76 mm.; 1,998 c.c.; 104 b.h.p.; 9.25 to 1 comp.; 2 Stromberg carbs.; 4-speed, 8.66, 5.82, 4.11, 3.27 to 1; cen. lvr. Laycock de Normanville overdrive opt.; susp. f. ind. coil, r. ind. transv. leaf; 2-door; 2-seat; hyd. brks. disc front; max. 110 m.p.h.; cruise 90; m.p.g. 26; whl. base 6ft. 11in.; track f. and r. 4 ft. 1in., lgth. 12ft. 1in.; width 4ft. 9in.; ht. 3ft. 11in.; g.c. 4in.; turng. cir. 25ft. 3in.; kerb wt. 17¼ cwt.; tank 9¾ gals.; 12-volt.

£879 + £246 p.t. = £1,125

TRIUMPH TR5 PI

WITH a year's experience behind it, the latest version of Triumph's sports convertible gains big dividends in speed and smoothness from the use of a powerful six-cylinder engine with petrol injection to replace the former four. Specially popular in the United States, this is an important element in Britain's sports car exports. Independent rear suspension improves the ride and the brakes have twin circuits.

CLOSE-UP

Six-cyl.; o.h.v.; 74.7×95 mm.; 2,498 c.c.; 150 b.h.p.; 9.5 to 1 comp.; Lucas injection; 4-speed, 10.83, 6.93, 4.58, 3.45 to 1; cen. lvr.; susp. f. and r. ind. coil; 2-door; 2/3-seat; servo brks., disc front; max. 120 m.p.h.; cruise 100; m.p.g. 20-24; whl. base 7ft. 4in.; track f. 4ft. 2in., r. 4ft. 1in.; lgth. 12ft. 9in.; width 4ft. 9½in.; ht. 4ft. 2in.; g.c. 5in.; turng. cir. 33ft.; tank 11¼ gals.; 12-volt.

£985 + £276 p.t. = £1,261

Abbreviations—g.c.—ground clearance; susp.—suspension; f.—front; r.—rear; comp.—compression; s.v.—side-valves; o.h.v.—overhead valves; o.h.c.—overhead camshaft; hyd.—hydraulic.

TRIUMPH VITESSE MK II

THE sensation of riding a tiger is diminished with introduction of new rear suspension by wishbones and radius arms which gives smaller variations in wheel camber than the old swing axles and much safer handling, especially in the wet. The interesting combination of powerful six-cylinder 2-litre engine in a light Herald-sized car should now receive wider recognition.

CLOSE-UP

Six-cyl.; o.h.v.; 74.7×76 mm.; 1,998 c.c.; 104 b.h.p.; 9.25 to 1 comp.; 2 Stromberg carbs.; 4-speed, 10.31, 6.92, 4.86, 3.89 to 1; cen. lvr., L de N overdrive opt.; susp. f. ind. coil, r. ind. transv. leaf; 2-door; 4-seat; disc-drum brks.; max. 105 m.p.h.; cruise 90; m.p.g. 25-28; whl. base, 7ft. 7½in.; track f. 4ft. 1in., r. 4ft. 4in.; lgth. 12ft. 9in.; width 5ft. 1in.; g.c. 5½in.; turng. cir. 25ft.; kerb wt. 18½ cwt.; tank 8¾ gals.; 12-volt.

£743+£208 p.t. = £951

TVR VIXEN

LONGER wheelbase and longer body lines give more room for passengers and luggage in the fast sports coupe powered by the Ford Cortina GT 1600 engine. The multi-tube chassis has independent suspension all round. A dual-circuit braking system, burst-proof door locks and brake fluid warning light are among the safety ideas. Wire wheels and leather-covered steering wheel are standard.

CLOSE-UP

Four-cyl.; o.h.v.; 80.9×77.5 mm.; 1,598 c.c.; 90 b.h.p.; 9.1 to 1 comp,; Weber carb.; 4-speed, 11.62, 7.86, 5.52, 3.91 to 1; cen. lvr.; susp. f. and r. ind. coil; 2-door; 2-seat; disc/drum servo brks.; max. 105 m.p.h.; cruise 90; m.p.g. 24-28; whl. base 7ft. 2in.; track f. 4ft. 3in., r. 4ft. 4½in.; lgth. 11ft. 9½in.; width 5ft. 4in.; ht. 3ft. 11in.; g.c. 5in.; turng. cir. 26ft.; kerb wt. 16 cwt.; tank 15 gals.; 12-volt.

£1,095+£292 p.t. = £1,387

VAUXHALL VIVA DE LUXE

A new four-door saloon, available in de luxe, SL, 90 de luxe, 90 SL, 1600 de luxe, 1600 SL, Brabham 90 de luxe and Brabham 90 SL versions, brings the total models in the fast-selling range to a bewildering 26. And they can be varied with automatic transmission, alternator, heated rear window, heavy duty suspension and tyres and other extras.

CLOSE-UP

Four-cyl.; o.h.v.; 77.8×61 mm.; 1,159 c.c.; 47 b.h.p.; 8.5 to 1 comp.; Solex carb.; 4-speed, 14.64, 8.61, 5.46, 3.9 to 1; cen. lvr. BW. auto opt.; susp. f. ind. coil, r. coil; 2/4-door; 4-seat; drum brks. disc front opt.; max. 78 m.p.h.; cruise 70; m.p.g. 29-34; whl. base 7ft. 11¾in.; track f. and r. 4ft. 3in.; lgth. 13ft. 5in.; width 5ft. 3in.; ht. 4ft. 5in.; g.c. 5in.; turng. cir. 31ft. 9in.; kerb wt. 15¾ cwt.; tank 8 gals.; 12-volt.

2-door £551+£155 p.t. = £706

VAUXHALL VICTOR 2000

ORIGINALLY introduced with a 1.6 litre engine, Vauxhall's roomy family car is promoted to a higher performance class with the optional 2-litre engine. Both versions have the quiet running durable belt-drive for the overhead camshafts. Gearboxes are three or four speed with options of overdrive or automatic. Four headlamps for fast cruising, an efficient heater ventilation system with rear extractors and a big boot, are added attractions.

CLOSE-UP

Four-cyl.; o.h.c.; 95.25×69.24 mm.; 1,975 c.c.; 88 b.h.p.; 8.5 to 1 comp.; Zenith carb.; 3-speed, 11.18, 6.38, 3.9 to 1; col. lvr. 4-speed or BW opt.; susp. f. ind. coil, r. coil; 4-door; 5-seat; disc/drum brks.; max. 95 m.p.h.; cruise 85; m.p.g. 23-26; whl. base 8ft. 6in.; track f. and r. 4ft. 6½in.; lgth. 14ft. 8½in.; width 5ft. 7in.; ht. 4ft. 3¾in.; g.c. 5½in.; turng. cir. 33ft.; kerb wt. 21 cwt.; tank 12 gals.; 12-volt.

£760+£213 p.t. = £973

Abbreviations—g.c.—ground clearance; susp.—suspension; f.—front; r.—rear; comp.—compression; s.v.—side-valves; o.h.v.—overhead valves; o.h.c.—overhead camshaft; hyd.—hydraulic.

VAUXHALL VENTORA

INTRODUCED early this year, the Ventora extends the Victor development still further, with a 3.3 six-cylinder engine, more than twice the size of the original four. This is a compact quick car for the busy man who needs to exploit every gap in the traffic without fuss or effort. Reclining front seats, rear window demister, and disc front brakes with servo assistance are included in the equipment.

CLOSE-UP

Six-cyl.; o.h.v.; 92×82.6 mm.; 3,294 c.c.; 124 b.h.p.; 8.5 to 1 comp.; Zenith carb.; 4-speed, 8.69, 6.17, 4.66, 3.45 to 1; cen. lvr. Powerglide auto opt.; susp. f. ind. coil, r. coil; 4-door; 5-seat; disc/drum servo brks.; max. 103 m.p.h.; cruise 88; m.p.g. 20-23; whl. base 8ft. 6in.; track f. 4ft. 6¾in., r. 4ft. 6¼in.; lgth. 14ft. 8½in.; width 5ft. 7in.; ht. 4ft. 4in.; g.c. 5¼in.; turng. cir. 34ft.; kerb wt. 23¼ cwt.; tank 12 gals.; 12-volt.

£895+£251 p.t.=£1,146

VOLKSWAGEN 1200

BACK to basics, the lowest priced VW has drum brakes, limited bright metal, simple trim, a fuel reserve tap instead of a fuel gauge and swing axle suspension without the compensator spring but it has the current wide track and hundreds of other improvements which have kept millions of buyers loyal to the Beetle for 20 years.

CLOSE-UP

Four-cyl.; o.h.v.; air-cooled; 77×64 mm.; 1,192 c.c.; 34 b.h.p.; 7.1 to 1 comp.; Solex carb.; 4-speed, 16.6, 9.0, 5.5, 3.9 to 1; cen. lvr.; susp., f. and r. ind. torsion bar; 2-door; 4-seat; drum brks.; max. 74 m.p.h.; cruise, 74; m.p.g. 32-36; whl. base, 7ft. 10½in.; track f. 4ft. 3¼in., r. 4ft. 5⅛in.; lgth., 13ft. 4¼in.; width, 5ft. 0½in.; ht. 4ft. 5¼in.; g.c. 5¾in.; turng. cir., 36ft.; kerb wt., 14¾ cwt.; tank, 8¾ gals.; 6-volt.

£515+£145 p.t.=£660

VW 411

BIGGEST, plushiest VW yet. First with no chassis; first with four doors, coil spring suspension and big luggage boot. Fastest revving engine ever from VW, but it's still air cooled, still runs on cheap regular fuel. New silent four-speed gearbox or fully automatic transmission and a super petrol burning heater. Seats for five; on those in front you can even change the shape of the backrest (on de luxe).

CLOSE-UP

Four-cyl.; o.h.v. air cooled; 90×66 mm.; 1,679 c.c.; 76 b.h.p. gross; 7.8 to 1 comp.; 2 Solex carbs.; 4-speed, 14.21, 7.87, 5.22, 3.73 to 1; cen. lvr. auto opt.; susp., f. and r. ind. coil; 2 or 4-door; 5-seat; hyd. brks., disc front; max. 90 m.p.h.; cruise, 90; m.p.g. 25; whl. base, 8ft. 2⅜in.; track f. 4ft. 6¼in.; r. 4ft. 4¾in.; lgth., 14ft. 10in.; width, 5ft. 4⅜in.; ht. 4ft. 10½in.; g.c. 5⅜in.; turng. cir., 37ft. 5in.; kerb wt., 20¼ cwt.; tank, 11 gals.; 12-volt.

£980+£275 p.t.=£1,255

VOLKSWAGEN 1600 TL

FASTBACK styling with saloon car seating space make this a family car with a sporting spirit and there is now a lower priced version, available in Britain, the 1600T at £998 including tax. Fully automatic transmission is available and rear suspension on all models is now the modified type with trailing wishbones instead of swing axles. Collapsible steering column and hazard warning flasher are standard.

CLOSE-UP

Four-cyl.; o.h.v. air-cooled; 85.5×69 mm.; 1,584 c.c.; 54 b.h.p.; 7.7 to 1 comp.; 2. Solex carbs.; 4-speed, 15.7, 8.5, 5.4, 3.7 to 1; cen. lvr., auto. opt.; susp., f. and r. ind. torsion bar; 2-door; 4-seat; hyd. brks., disc front; max. 84 m.p.h.; cruise, 84; m.p.g. 28-32; whl. base, 7ft. 10½in.; track f. 4ft. 3⅝in., r. 4ft. 5in.; lgth., 13ft. 10⅜in.; width, 5ft. 3¼in.; ht. 4ft. 10⅛in.; g.c. 5⅞in.; turng. cir., 36ft. 5in.; kerb wt., 18¾ cwt.; tank, 8¾ gals.; 12-volt.

£863+£242 p.t.=£1,105

Abbreviations—g.c.—ground clearance; susp.—suspension; f.—front; r.—rear; comp.—compression; s.v.—side-valves; o.h.v.—overhead valves; o.h.c.—overhead camshaft; hyd.—hydraulic.

VOLVO 144S

TOP of the Volvo saloon range with the new twin-carburetter 2-litre engine. To cut exhaust fumes a thermostatic valve directs inlet air through an exhaust heat exchanger at low temperatures. On single-carburetter models the heater is in the carburetter. Silicone rubber protects plugs from damp. A hydraulic coupling limits power loss through the fan at high speeds. Cloth upholstery is in new anti-static material.

CLOSE-UP

Four-cyl.; o.h.v.; 88.9×80 mm.; 1,985 c.c.; 118 b.h.p. gross; 9.5 to 1 comp.; 2 Stromberg carbs.; 4-speed, 13.46, 8.56, 5.85, 4.30 to 1; cen. lvr. L de N overdrive opt.; susp. f. ind. coil, r. coil; 4-door; 5-seat; disc servo brks.; max. 98-100 m.p.h.; cruise 90; m.p.g. 24-27; whl. base 8ft. 6½in.; track f. and r. 4ft. 5in.; lgth. 15ft. 2½in.; width 5ft. 8in.; ht. 4ft. 8½in.; g.c. 7in.; turng. cir. 30ft. 5in.; kerb wt. 26 cwt.; tank 12¾ gals.; 12-volt.

£1,150+£322 p.t. = £1,472

VOLVO 165

FOR their fast new six, Volvo use the 140 series body with longer wheelbase and new grille, recalling the 1929 original. Twin-carburettor engine with controlled intake heating for cleaner exhaust, twin-circuit servo brakes safeguarding both front and one rear if something breaks. 164 has four-speed box, 165 adds overdrive and sun roof; 166 has BW automatic and power steering.

CLOSE-UP

Six-cyl.; o.h.v.; 88.9×80 mm.; 2,979 c.c.; 145 b.h.p. gross; 9 to 1 comp.; 2 Zenith-Stromberg carbs.; 4-speed and L de N overdrive, 11.67, 7.42, 5.07, 3.73 to 1; cen. lvr.; susp., f. ind. coil, r. coil; 4-door; 5-seat; disc servo brks.; max. 110 m.p.h.; cruise 100; m.p.g. 19-23; whl. base 8ft. 10in.; track f. and r. 4ft. 5in.; lgth. 15ft. 5½in.; width 5ft. 8in.; ht. 4ft. 8½in.; g.c. 7in.; turng. cir. 32ft.; kerb wt. 25¼ cwt.; tank 12.7 gals.; 12-volt.

WARTBURG KNIGHT

THOUGH clamped in the Stalinist straight jacket, the former Auto Union factories in East Germany have managed to follow most Western advances except for the switch to four-stroke engines. By ruthless deprivation of the home market, cars are exported to win foreign currency at very low prices, fully equipped with adjustable headlamps to compensate for load variations, electric screen washer, radiator blind and anti-theft steering lock.

CLOSE-UP

Three-cyl.; two-stroke; 73.5×78 mm.; 991 c.c.; 45 b.h.p.; 7.5 to 1 comp.; BVF carb.; 4-speed, 14.49, 9.45, 6.06, 4.24 to 1; cen. lvr.; susp., f. and r. ind. coil; 4-door; 4/5-seat; hyd. brks.; max. 75 m.p.h.; cruise, 65; m.p.g. 26-30; whl. base 8ft. 0½in.; track f. 4ft. 1½in., r. 4ft. 1¾in.; lgth. 13ft. 10in.; width 5ft. 5in.; ht. 4ft. 9¾in.; g.c. 5½in.; turng. cir. 29ft.; kerb wt. 17¾ cwt.; tank 9½ gals.; 12-volt.

£519+£146 p.t. = £665

WOLSELEY 18/85

FIRST of the big front-wheel-drive saloons from the BMC to have the option of power assistance for the rack and pinion steering and first to have the BW automatic transmission ingeniously fitted into the transverse engine casing, the Wolseley continues with improved power output and enhanced interior comfort for 1969. Hydrolastic suspension with fluid connection between front and rear is the secret of its smooth pitch-free ride.

CLOSE-UP

Four-cyl.; o.h.v.; 80.26×88.9 mm.; 1,798 c.c.; 85 b.h.p. gross; 8.4 to 1 comp.; S.U. carb.; 4-speed, 12.77, 8.60, 5.37, 3.88 to 1; cen. lvr., BW auto opt.; susp. f. and r. ind. rubber hydraulic; 4-door; 5-seat; servo brks., disc front; max. 90 m.p.h.; cruise 80; m.p.g. 22-27; whl. base 8ft. 10in.; track f. 4ft. 8in., r. 4ft. 7½in.; lgth. 13ft. 10in.; width 5ft. 7in.; ht. 4ft. 7½in.; g.c. 6½in.; turng. cir. 37ft.; kerb wt. 23¼ cwt.; tank 10¾ gals.; 12-volt.

£845+£237 p.t. = £1,082

Abbreviations—g.c.—ground clearance; susp.—suspension; f.—front; r.—rear; comp.—compression; s.v.—side-valves; o.h.v.—overhead valves; o.h.c.—overhead camshaft; hyd.—hydraulic.

Estate Car Bonus

graphics by John Hill

AUSTIN MINI COUNTRYMAN

AVAILABLE as an Austin or Morris, with traditional wood framing or with a lighter, sleeker all metal body, this popular little car has all the nimble character and sure footed handling that made the Mini famous, plus carrying capacity that makes it a versatile family transport. Station wagons, on a longer wheelbase than the saloon, have Moulton rubber suspension instead of Hydrolastic.

CLOSE-UP
Four-cyl.; o.h.v.; 64.6 × 76.2 mm.; 998 c.c.; 38 b.h.p.; 8.3 to 1 comp.; SU carb.; 4-speed, 12.5, 7.5, 4.9, 3.4 to 1; cen. lvr. AP auto. opt.; susp. f. and r. ind. rubber; 3-door; 4-seat; drum brks.; max. 75 m.p.h.; cruise 68; m.p.g. 38–40; whl. base 7ft.; track f. 3ft. 11½in., r. 3ft. 9⅞in.; lgth. 10ft. 9¾in.; width 4ft. 7½in.; ht. 4ft. 5in.; g.c. 6⅛in.; turng. cir. 30ft.; kerb wt. 13 cwt.; tank 5½ gals.; 12-volt.

£525 + £147 p.t. = £672

CITROEN SAFARI

A station wagon with a ride so smooth that it is widely used as an ambulance on the Continent. Citroen's hydraulic-pneumatic suspension soaks up the bumps and the self-levelling feature keeps the headlamp beam correctly aimed no matter how much the load may vary. Braking effort is proportioned automatically to suit the load distribution. Choice of two engines; 1,985 or 2,175 c.c.

CLOSE-UP
Four-cyl.; o.h.v.; 86 × 85.5 mm.; 1,985 c.c.; 78 b.h.p.; 8 to 1 comp.; Solex carb.; 4-speed, 14.21, 8.49, 5.58, 3.73 to 1; col. lvr.; susp. and r. ind. hyd.-pneu.; 5-door; 5-seat; disc/drum servo brks.; max. 106 m.p.h.; cruise 90; m.p.g. 21–23; whl. base 10ft. 3in.; track f. 4ft. 11in., r. 4ft. 3in.; lgth. 16ft. 4½in.; width 5ft. 10½in.; ht. 5ft. 0½in.; g.c. 5¾in.; turng. cir. 36ft.; kerb wt. 26½ cwt.; tank 14 gals.; 12-volt.

£1,543 + £431 p.t. = £1,974

DAF 55 ESTATE

NEW for the London Motor Show is this estate car version of the most powerful DAF with the Renault 1100 water cooled engine; whether running light or fully laden its automatic transmission with reinforced rubber belts continuously adjusts itself to provide the ideal ratio for every condition. Push the lever forward to go forward, pull it back to go back; there's nothing else to learn.

CLOSE-UP
Four-cyl.; o.h.v.; 70 × 72 mm.; 1,108 c.c.; 45 b.h.p.; 8.5 to 1 comp.; Solex carb.; variable-ratio belt auto., 14.87 to 3.73 to 1; cen. lvr.; susp. f. ind. transv. leaf, r. ind. coil; 3-door; 4-seat; drum/disc brks.; max. 84 m.p.h.; cruise 84; m.p.g. 30–36; whl. base 7ft. 4⅜in.; track f. 4ft. 2⅜in.; r. 4ft. 1⅛in.; lgth. 12ft. 8¾in.; width 5ft. 0⅛in.; ht. 4ft. 6¾in.; g.c. 6¾in.; turng. cir. 31ft.; kerb wt. 15¾ cwt.; tank 8⅜ gals.; 12-volt.

£702 + £197 p.t. = £899

Abbreviations—g.c.—ground clearance; susp.—suspension; f.—front; r.—rear; comp.—compression; s.v.—side-valves; o.h.v.—overhead valves; o.h.c.—overhead camshaft; hyd.—hydraulic.

DATSUN 2000 ESTATE

EIGHT people can be carried on three rows of seats in this roomy Japanese car. With two rows folded away there is a cargo floor 6.3ft. long to carry loads up to 1,100 lb. Its six-cylinder engine has been proved in notable performances in the East African Safari. Heater, demister, radio with automatically erected aerial and electrically operated rear window are included in the price.

CLOSE-UP
Six-cyl.; o.h.v.; 73×78.6 mm.; 1,973 c.c.; 109 b.h.p. gross; 8.2 to 1 comp.; Hitachi carb.; 4-speed, 14.59, 9.03, 5.83, 4.11 to 1; col. lvr. BW auto. opt.; susp. f. ind. coil, r. half-elliptic; 5-door; 8-seat; drum brks.; max. 90 m.p.h.; cruise 84; m.p.g. 23-26; whl. base 8ft. 9⅞in.; track f. and r. 4ft. 6½in.; lgth. 15ft. 4¾in.; width 5ft. 6½in.; ht. 4ft. 9⅞in.; g.c. 7¼in.; turng. cir. 37ft.; kerb wt. 26¾ cwt.; tank 12¼ gals.; 12-volt.
£1,093+£305 p.t. = £1,398

FORD CORTINA SUPER ESTATE

WITH sales exceeding 1½ million, Ford's best-seller gets a new, easier gear change, new window regulators and a fully fused electrical system for 1969. Interior trim and fittings are now colour matched more closely and the radiator grille finish is revised. Light switches and wiper control are redesigned for greater safety and the bonnet release is now operated from inside the car.

CLOSE-UP
Four-cyl.; o.h.v.; 81×78 mm.; 1,599 c.c.; 71 b.h.p.; 9 to 1 comp.; Ford carb.; 4-speed, 13.82, 9.34, 5.50, 3.9 to 1; cen. lvr.; susp. f. ind. coil, r. half-elliptic; 5-door; 4/5-seat; disc/drum brks.; max. 86 m.p.h.; cruise 75; m.p.g. 23-26; whl. base 8ft. 2in.; track f. 4ft. 5½in., r. 4ft. 3in.; lgth. 14ft. 2in.; width 5ft. 5in.; ht. 4ft. 9in.; g.c. 6½in.; turng. cir. 30ft. 3in.; kerb wt. 19¾ cwt.; tank 8 gals.; 12-volt.
£765+£213 p.t. = £978

FORD ESCORT ESTATE

RACING on towards a quarter-million sales within its first year of production, the Escort range has been improved in detail for 1969. The pedals have new style pads and there are new colour schemes for steering wheel, steering column shroud and heater panel. The Estate car version caught on immediately as a good looker with remarkable carrying capacity and there is a new range of body colours to be seen at the Show.

CLOSE-UP
Four-cyl.; o.h.v.; 80.9×53.3 mm.; 1,098 c.c.; 49.5 b.h.p.; 9 to 1 comp.; Ford carb.; 4-speed, 15.05, 9.02, 5.88, 4.12 to 1; cen. lvr.; susp. f. ind. coil, r. half-elliptic; 3-door; 4-seat; drum brks.; max. 80 m.p.h.; cruise 70; m.p.g. 28-30; whl. base 7ft. 10in.; track f. 4ft. 1in., r. 4ft. 2in.; lgth. 13ft. 5in.; width 5ft. 1⅜in.; ht. 4ft. 5in.; g.c. 6½in.; turng. cir. 29ft.; kerb wt. 14¾ cwt.; tank 9 gals.; 12-volt.
£605+£168 p.t. = £773

FIAT 124 ESTATE

FAMILIARE is Fiat's name for this capacious station wagon version of their lively award winning 124 family car. Its high efficiency five-bearing engine with twin-choke carburetter handles full loads with alacrity and sure, fade-free braking on long descents is guaranteed by disc brakes on all four wheels. Coil spring rear suspension, with the axle located by radius arms and a Panhard rod, ensures stability when fully laden.

CLOSE-UP
Four-cyl.; o.h.v.; 73×71.5 mm.; 1,197 c.c.; 60 b.h.p.; 8.8 to 1 comp.; Solex 2-choke carb.; 4-speed, 16.7, 10.2, 6.6, 4.4 to 1; cen. lvr.; susp. f. ind. coil, r. coil; 5-door; 4/5-seat; disc brks.; max. 85 m.p.h.; cruise 78; m.p.g. 32; whl. base 7ft. 11½in.; track f. 4ft. 4⅛in., r. 4ft. 3½in.; lgth. 13ft. 2⅞in.; width 5ft. 4in.; ht. 4ft. 7⅞in.; turng. cir. 35ft.; kerb wt. 18½ cwt.; tank 10¼ gals.; 12-volt.
£730+£205 p.t. = £935

Abbreviations—g.c.—ground clearance; susp.—suspension; f.—front; r.—rear; comp.—compression; s.v.—side-valves; o.h.v.—overhead valves; o.h.c.—overhead camshaft; hyd.—hydraulic.

HILLMAN HUSKY

WITH a canted over Imp engine concealed under the rear floor, the Husky offers full-length carrying capacity. Rear seats fold away to give 50 cu. ft. of load space. Front seats are re-designed; and the new full width facia has circular instruments. The front end is re-designed with satin aluminium name panel. A one-piece lift-up rear door makes it easy to load freight or luggage.

CLOSE-UP
Four-cyl.; o.h.c.; 68×60.4 mm.; 875 c.c.; 39 b.h.p.; 10 to 1 comp.; Solex carb.; 4-speed, 16.59, 8.91, 5.70, 4.14 to 1; cen. lvr.; susp. f. and r. ind. coil; 3-door; 4-seat; drum brks.; max. 78 m.p.h.; cruise 70; m.p.g. 33-36; whl. base 6ft. 10in.; track f. 4ft. 1½in., r. 4ft.; lgth. 11ft. 9in.; width 5ft. 0½in.; ht. 4ft. 10in.; g.c. 6½in.; turng. cir. 31ft.; kerb wt. 14¾ cwt.; tank 6 gals.; 12-volt.

£545+£153 p.t. = £698

MORRIS 1300 TRAVELLER

AVAILABLE in both Morris and Austin versions, this three-door station wagon version of the popular BMC family car with transverse engine and front drive crams a lot of useful space into compact overall dimensions. More popular than ever since the engine size was increased from 1,100 to 1,275 c.c., it has ex-cellent ride and road holding qualities.

CLOSE-UP
Four-cyl.; o.h.v.; 70.6×81.3 mm.; 1,275 c.c.; 58 b.h.p.; 8.8 to 1 comp.; SU carb.; 4-speed, 12.85, 8.09, 5.23, 3.65 to 1; cen. lvr.; susp. f. and r. ind. rubber-hyd.; 3-door; 4-seat; disc/drum brks.; max. 88 m.p.h.; cruise 78; m.p.g. 31-34; whl. base 7ft. 9½in.; track f. 4ft. 3½in., r. 4ft. 2¾in.; lgth. 12ft. 2¾in.; width 5ft. 0½in.; ht. 4ft. 5in.; g.c. 6in.; turng. cir. 34ft. 9in.; kerb wt. 16½ cwt.; tank 8 gals.; 12-volt.

£645+£181 p.t. = £826

PEUGEOT 204 ESTATE

A front wheel drive estate car from one of France's most respected manufacturers. Its transverse engine is remarkably light, thanks to the use of aluminium alloys. An overhead camshaft helps efficiency and the five-bearing crankshaft ensures smooth running. A 1,255 c.c. lightweight diesel engine is produced as an alternative. All-independent suspension gives it a good ride over the worst roads and disc front brakes have reserve capacity to handle heavy loads.

CLOSE-UP
Four-cyl.; o.h.c.; 75×64 mm.; 1,130 c.c.; 53 b.h.p.; 8.8 to 1 comp.; Solex carb.; 4-speed, 15.1, 9.25, 6.06, 4.23 to 1; col. lvr.; susp. f. and r. ind. coil; 5-door; 4-seat; drum/disc servo brks.; max. 86 m.p.h.; cruise 77; m.p.g. 29-34; whl. base 8ft. 6in.; track f. 4ft. 4in., r. 4ft. 1½in.; lgth. 13ft.; width 5ft. 1½in.; ht. 4ft. 7in.; g.c. 5½in.; turng. cir. 31ft.; kerb wt. 17¾ cwt.; tank 9¼ gals.; 12-volt.

£864+£152 p.t. = £1,016

RAMBLER REBEL SIX ESTATE

FEW vehicles can match the style and carrying capacity of the typical American station wagon, designed to carry large families with luggage and sports kit on long vacation trips. It is practical-ly part of the American way of life and the Rambler is one of the few available to British buyers. A roof rack is built in for items too bulky to go inside, and the rear window winds down into the tailgate.

CLOSE-UP
Six-cyl.; o.h.v.; 95.3×88.9 mm.; 3,802 c.c.; 155 b.h.p. gross; 8.5 to 1 comp.; Carter 2-choke carb.; 3-speed BW auto., 8.09, 4.88, 3.15 to 1; col. lvr.; susp. f. ind. coil, r. coil; 5-door; 6-seat; disc/drum servo brks.; max. 98 m.p.h.; cruise 85; m.p.g. 18-20; whl. base 9ft. 6in.; track f. and r. 4ft. 10in.; lgth. 16ft. 6in.; width 6ft. 6in.; ht. 5ft.; g.c. 6½in.; turng. cir. 37ft. 9in.; kerb wt. 30¾ cwt.; tank 17⅞ gals.; 12-volt.

£2,085+£581 p.t. = £2,666

Abbreviations—g.c.—ground clearance; susp.—suspension; f.—front; r.—rear; comp.—compression; s.v.—side-valves; o.h.v.—overhead valves; o.h.c.—overhead camshaft; hyd.—hydraulic.

RELIANT REBEL ESTATE

A compact but roomy little station wagon, it has glass fibre body styled by Ogle on the sturdy Reliant chassis, powered by their economical little 700 c.c. engine. The engine, with light alloy block and head is popular with amateur builders of racing sports cars, and replaces the now almost unobtainable Austin Seven unit in cars of the 750 Formula.

CLOSE-UP

Four-cyl.; o.h.v.; 60.5×60.9 mm.; 700 c.c.; 31 b.h.p.; 8.4 to 1 comp.; Zenith carb.; 4-speed, 18.67, 10.76, 6.37, 4.38 to 1; cen. lvr.; susp. f. ind. coil, r. half-elliptic; 3-door; 4-seat; drum brks.; max. 70 m.p.h.; cruise 60; m.p.g. 38-40; whl. base 7ft. 5in.; track f. 4ft., r. 3ft. 10⅝in.; lgth. 12ft. 2in.; width 4ft. 10in.; ht. 4ft. 7in.; g.c. 5½in.; turng. cir. 32ft.; kerb wt. 12 cwt.; tank 6 gals.; 6-volt.

£507 + £143 p.t. = £650

RENAULT 4

A more artistic radiator grille and improved interior trim have strengthened the appeal of Renault's pioneer five-door utility saloon without diminishing its ability to stand up to hard work and neglect. It is the only car with different lengths of wheelbase on right and left sides because that happens to be the simplest way to accommodate the transverse torsion bars of the rear suspension.

CLOSE-UP

Four-cyl.; o.h.v.; 58×80 mm.; 845 c.c.; 27 b.h.p.; 8.1 to 1 comp.; Solex carb.; 4-speed, 15.68, 8.50, 5.61, 4.28 to 1; facia lvr.; susp. f. and r. ind. torsion bar; 5-door; 4/5-seat; drum brks.; max. 68 m.p.h.; cruise 60; m.p.g. 37-45; whl. base 8ft. 0½in.; track f. 4ft. 1½in., r. 4ft. 0¾in.; lgth. 12ft.; width 4ft. 10½in.; ht. 5ft.; g.c. 7¾in.; turng. cir. 30ft.; kerb wt. 12⅝ cwt.; tank 5¼ gals.; 6-volt.

£458 + £129 p.t. = £587

SIMCA 1500 GLS

THE French, who like comfort on their motoring picnics, devised a lift-out rear floor which doubles as a picnic table for this family station wagon. Clean cut lines help to avoid a heavy appearance, although there is lots of room inside and the slim pillars give excellent all-round vision. The same car is also available with the smaller engine of 1,290 c.c.

CLOSE-UP

Four-cyl.; o.h.v.; 75.2×83 mm.; 1,475 c.c.; 69 b.h.p.; 9.3 to 1 comp.; Solex carb.; 4-speed, 16.22, 9.14, 6.15, 4.45 to 1; cen. lvr.; susp. f. ind. coil, r. coil; 5-door; 4/5-seat; disc/drum brks.; max. 93 m.p.h.; cruise 80; m.p.g. 26-30; whl. base 8ft. 4in.; track f. 4ft. 1½in., r. 4ft. 0½in.; lgth. 14ft. 1½in.; width 5ft. 2in.; ht. 4ft. 7in.; g.c. 5½in.; turng. cir. 34ft.; kerb wt. 21½ cwt.; tank 12 gals.; 12-volt.

£967 + £270 p.t. = £1,237

SINGER VOGUE

LONG crisp lines make this one of the best looking station wagons in the medium sized range and the 1,725 c.c. engine gives it plenty of power to cope with loads of five people and a lot of luggage. There are three transmissions to choose from; the brakes are servo assisted. Two-speed wipers and reclining front seats are standard.

CLOSE-UP

Four-cyl.; o.h.v.; 81.5×82.5 mm.; 1,725 c.c.; 74 b.h.p.; 9.2 to 1 comp.; Stromberg carb.; 4-speed, 12.41, 7.92, 5.15, 3.7 to 1; cen. lvr., L de N overdrive or BW auto opt.; susp. f. ind. coil, r. half-elliptic; 5-door; 4/5-seat; disc/drum servo brks.; max. 88 m.p.h.; cruise 78; m.p.g. 27-30; whl. base 8ft. 2½in.; track f. and r. 4ft. 4in.; lgth. 14ft. 4½in.; width 5ft. 3¼in.; ht. 4ft. 8in.; g.c. 6¾in.; turng. cir. 33ft. 6in.; kerb wt. 19½ cwt.; tank 10 gals.; 12-volt.

£919 + £257 p.t. = £1,176

Abbreviations—g.c.—ground clearance; susp.—suspension; f.—front; r.—rear; comp.—compression; s.v.—side-valves; o.h.v.—overhead valves; o.h.c.—overhead camshaft; hyd.—hydraulic.

TRIUMPH HERALD 13/60 ESTATE

THE recently re-styled front end made a big improvement in the appearance of this lively but economical wagon with the separate chassis and all-independent suspension. Front wings and bonnet rise forward in one piece to give instant access to engine, steering, front suspension and brakes. Interior finish is much improved and switches and controls are now more logically grouped on the redesigned facia panel.

CLOSE-UP

Four-cyl.; o.h.v.; 73.7 × 76 mm.; 1,296 c.c.; 61 b.h.p.; 8.5 to 1 comp.; Stromberg carb.; 4-speed, 15.42, 8.88, 5.73, 4.11 to 1; cen. lvr.; susp. f. ind. coil, r. ind. transv. leaf; 3-door; 4-seat; disc/drum brks.; max. 80 m.p.h.; cruise 70; m.p.g. 30-32; whl. base 7ft. 7½in.; track f. 4ft. 1in., r. 4ft.; lgth. 12ft. 9in.; width 5ft.; ht. 4ft. 4in.; g.c. 6¾in.; turng. cir. 25ft.; kerb wt. 17¾ cwt.; tank 7 gals.; 12-volt.

£643 + £181 p.t. = £824

VAUXHALL VICTOR 2000 ESTATE

WITH a choice of 1,600 c.c. or 2,000 c.c. engines, each with belt-driven overhead camshafts, the buyer of this roomy estate car can place the accent on economy or performance according to requirements. With the big engine an automatic transmission is available as an alternative to the three-speed or four-speed manual gearboxes and front brakes are discs with the large engine.

CLOSE-UP

Four-cyl.; o.h.c.; 95.3 × 69.2 mm.; 1,975 c.c.; 88 b.h.p.; 8.5 to 1 comp.; Zenith carb.; 3-speed, 11.18, 6.38, 3.9 to 1; col. lvr. 4-speed or BW auto. opt.; susp. f. ind. coil, r. coil; 5-door; 4/5-seat; disc/drum brks.; max. 95 m.p.h.; cruise 84; m.p.g. 24-26; whl. base 8ft. 6in.; track f. 4ft. 6⅜in., r. 4ft. 6in.; lgth. 14ft. 8½in.; width 5ft. 6⅛in.; ht. 4ft. 7in.; g.c. 5½in.; turng. cir. 32ft. 6in.; kerb wt. 21 cwt.; tank 12 gals.; 12-volt.

£835 + £234 p.t. = £1,069

VW 1600 VARIANT

CARRYING capacity extends from front bumper to rear bumper on this well finished wagon. The flat four engine lies under the rear floor. Recent improvements include a collapsible steering column and twin circuit brakes (discs in front). Rear suspension is the new type with trailing wishbones instead of swing axles, giving improved road holding and greater riding comfort. A hazard warning switch is a new feature.

CLOSE-UP

Four-cyl. air-cooled; o.h.v.; 85.5 × 69 mm.; 1,584 c.c.; 54 b.h.p.; 7.7 to 1 comp.; 2 Solex carbs.; 4-speed, 15.67, 8.49, 5.44, 3.67 to 1; cen. lvr.; susp. f. and r. ind. torsion bar; 3-door; 4/5-seat; disc/drum brks.; max. 85 m.p.h.; cruise 85; m.p.g. 25-27; whl. base 7ft. 10⅜in.; track f. 4ft. 3⅜in., r. 4ft. 5in.; lgth. 13ft. 10⅜in.; width 5ft. 3¼in.; ht. 4ft. 10½in.; g.c. 6in.; turng. cir. 36ft.; kerb wt. 20½ cwt.; tank 8½ gals.; 12-volt.

£920 + £258 p.t. = £1,178

VOLVO 145

EXTRA urge to handle heavy loads in this handsome, well built Swedish station wagon comes from the new 2-litre engine available with single or twin carburettors. Closed-circuit cooling, strengthened gearbox, electric supply by alternator, are other 1969 features. Latest safety measures include twin-circuit brakes with twin servo (always at least three brakes in action), two anti-skid valves at rear.

CLOSE-UP

Four-cyl.; o.h.v.; 88.9 × 80 mm.; 1,986 c.c.; 90 b.h.p. gross; 8.7 to 1 comp.; Stromberg carb.; 4-speed, 13.46, 8.56, 5.85, 4.3 to 1; cen. lvr.; susp. f. ind. coil, r. coil; 5-door; 5-seat; disc servo brks.; max. 100 m.p.h.; cruise 88; m.p.g. 20-23; whl. base 8ft. 6½in.; track f. and r. 4ft. 5½in.; lgth. 15ft. 3in.; width 5ft. 8in.; ht. 4ft. 9in.; g.c. 7½in.; turng. cir. 30ft. 10in.; kerb wt. 23⅞ cwt.; tank 13½ gals.; 12-volt.

£1,235 + £345 p.t. = £1,580

Abbreviations—g.c.—ground clearance; susp.—suspension; f.—front; r.—rear; comp.—compression; s.v.—side-valves; o.h.v.—overhead valves; o.h.c.—overhead camshaft; hyd.—hydraulic.

Accessories

by David Benson

5" X 10"   MINI WHEEL

HALF-A-MILLION people will visit this year's motor show at Earls Court. They will gaze and envy the highly polished top-priced machinery on view. Few of them will take the opportunity of going upstairs to the galleries and examining the accessory market.

Here at least the Walter Mittys can satisfy their craving for more advanced cars with real accessories that will materially advance their own cars.

My favourite is at the "Slot Stereo" stand. Here you will get an up to date version of the old penny-in-the-slot music player. A compact unit, no bigger than the normal car radio and playing through existing speakers, provides the best of stereo music in the car. Cartridges

of ready made stereo tapes are simply slotted into the unit as easily as you programme your home washing machine.

The result: perfect stereo reproduction and balanced output at even the highest motorway speeds. So much better than Radio One—with this at least you can select your own programme.

I have tested the car stereo unit in my home through an existing expensive Quad set and loudspeaker combine. My verdict? Fabulous. Who needs records?

At stand 332 a new type of streamlined weather-shield is on view. It gives good venti-

Pity to spoil such a beautiful shape —that steering wheel (above) could be lethal. For safety's sake she's had Britax automatic belts fitted in her car. The two beauties in our picture (left) are seen with a giant-sized version of K.L.G.'s G.T. Super Spark Plug.

ation and prevents irritating draughts whilst being shaped to prevent extra drag on the shape of the car. At £4. 10s. it is an interesting buy.

The big 'in' thing on Minis this year is aluminium or duralium wheel hubs. Most are very expensive and far too pricey for the average motorist. Cosmic Car Accessories are showing a new range of aluminium alloy wheels at the show which start in price at 59s. 6d. a pair.

Stand No. 90 owned by Philips shows a variety of electrical accessories ranging from car radios, spare bulb kits, car radios to battery operated electric shavers.

Having used a Philips battery shaver for the last four years I can only say that it gives me a cool, clean shave and I have never been accused of being a "bluebeard" Nixon type. For a dark-haired man that is praise indeed.

With winter not far away the time has come to consider aids to easy morning starting for cars garaged outdoors. I have tried a new product—the Freezmaster Shield recently put on the market in this country at 21s. It is a plastic sheet with suction cups that fits over the windscreen preventing icing and frosting overnight.

In the USA a speed control is almost an

195

Women drivers— no longer a joke

by *Alix Palmer*

THE age-old argument about whether women drivers are as good as men has suddenly become muted and still. Any man who even mentions it is hastily shushed and everyone starts talking in loud voices.

This transformation has been brought about by that most dreaded of contraptions—the breathalyser. Rather than cut down on their drinking, men prefer to take the wife along to drive them home after the last pint. Once having admitted the need for the wife, or girlfriend, to take the wheel, what man dare criticise her driving?

In the last year, there has been a tremendous upsurge in the number of women learning to drive. Most driving schools report that at least half their pupils are women.

An instructor friend told me: "Many of them have been press-ganged into learning by their husbands who are fed-up with counting the number of Scotches.

"But I think some of the husbands are in for a shock. Most of the wives I have taught to drive have been planning to make certain demands of their own.

"If they're going to have to lay off the drink every time their husbands want to go it, then they want to be rewarded for the sacrifice. And that means either full use of the car at any time, or a car of their own. So I fear that husbands are going to have to pay dearly for that extra drink."

All this goes to prove that women are going to have an even bigger say in choosing a car in the future. What do they look for?

For the woman with children, especially small ones, there are a number of basic rules to observe. A single door car is essential, so that when she chucks the kids in the back she knows they can't get out without climbing over her first.

Non-burstable locks are another must. Even travel-trained children tend to lunge around and act like a battering ram on a fragile lock. They also like to press and pull any available button or switch, especially if they have recently seen a James Bond film. So the ideal mother-and-family car should have as few gadgets as possible.

An ordinary Mini is not really convenient, because it isn't big enough to take children *and* all the paraphernalia they like to cart around with them. Accidents are easily caused by a small child fighting to get out from under a crush of baskets, blankets and all the etceteras, and cuffing the driver across the head at crucial moment. But a Mini Traveller is perfect, large enough to take children, neighbour' children and even the pet dog.

The woman with no family has a much wide choice, but doesn't always exercise it. In he youth, she had dreams of nippy white sport cars, but they were usually accompanied by handsome Romeo.

Now that she is respectably married an isn't supposed to think about young Romeo she goes for something safer and more solid the car line. But it must be easy to drive— which is why women like automatics. The purr nicely along with the minimum of effor and make her look efficient.

The woman who uses her car for work want one that is reliable, easy to park and can be re paired in the shortest possible time. This rule out foreign cars because she hasn't got time search round for the special garage that wi service them.

The wife who is choosing for her husband less finicky. She will probably treat the car a status symbol, to impress the neighbours an persuade her parents that she chose the righ man after all. This is the kind of woman wh delights the salesman. She will drink in his tal eagerly, be persuaded that it's worth spendin the extra £200 on this model because it has couple of unnecessary extras, and even give u her new cooker this year just for the pleasu of having a car which she knows no one else her district has got.

But most women are more sensible. The really do think about cars. Not so mechani ally as men do, perhaps, but they know wha they like and what they wouldn't have for a the Romeos in the world.

Make for the cars that make sense.

Why has one car more excitement for you than another? When price for price, there's nothing in it? At BMC, we believe it takes more than a flick of chrome or an extra dial on the dash. We believe it starts with common sense. With design that recognises and answers your real needs.

A new power in the space age: the luxurious 3-litre.

Like BMC's transverse engine. By laying the unit crossways in the car, we cut inches off the outside without pinching anything inside. Easier for parking, garaging, and coping with today's crowded roads.

Comfort?

New 1800: we've redecorated the room for you.

BMC's Hydrolastic® suspension enables small cars to ride as smoothly as big cars. Safety? Common sense again. Millions are now enjoying the added sureness of BMC frontwheel drive. This is creative engineering. Less outside bulk, more inside space — new standards of comfort —

If you don't own at least one Mini, you'll never forgive yourself.

Once you've driven this 1300, you're cornered.

strict fuel economy — just some of the ways we make cars that make sense.

So when you start looking at cars, look at Austin, Austin Healey, MG, Morris, Riley and Wolseley—always.

BRITISH LEYLAND

BMC

197

See the new Fiats
Stand 125

PUL 947G

FIAT
FIAT 850
850 SPECIAL
COUPÉ

Creating an exciting new world of luxury motoring
The new Jaguar XJ6

FOUR years ago, Jaguar gave their designers a brief: "Design a saloon car that sets new standards of comfort and luxury, road-holding and ride, steering and braking, performance and safety—all in one car—with a level of outstanding value that Jaguar have traditionally made their own."

Now, Jaguar announce the 2.8 and 4.2 litre XJ6 models.

Come and see how completely the XJ6 fulfils its brief. Look down at the long, low roof. The steel body was rustproofed, painted 7 times, baked 3 times: now a pool of colour holds your reflection. Step inside. Beneath your feet, deep pile carpet. Beneath that, thick felt. Road noise, already minimised by fine engineering, will be lost in its soft meshes. Your seat holds you in a sustaining but never restricting embrace. Adjust the seat. Adjust the fully reclining backrest. Adjust the steering column. Adjust the temperature control of the new ventilation system. Comfort is total. Pause to admire the view. Visibility all round is virtually unrestricted. Switch on—and watch the rev. counter! It's the surest way to know that the engine is running. With the body insulated from front to rear, and double silencers on both exhausts, you can hardly expect to *hear* it. And with the engine doubly-insulated—its front rubber mountings rest on a separate suspension beam itself rubber mounted to the body—you'll have a job to *feel* it.

Two pedals or three? The XJ6 offers a choice: 4-speed synchromesh gearbox (with overdrive if you wish) or full automatic transmission. Disc brakes on all four wheels are servo-assisted.

As you move forward, feel how responsive and light the steering is. There's a hazard on the road. You brake hard and discover one of the most reassuring things about the XJ6. The stop is rapid, yet the nose dips only slightly. This is 'anti-dive geometry' at work to give extreme stability. This Jaguar *lopes:* it does not bound.

Unleash the XJ6 along a familiar road. The hills seem smaller. The bends less sharp. The road smoother—shorter. The XJ6 has cut it down to size. There are several reasons for this. The power of a twin-overhead-camshaft, six cylinder engine, race-bred for reliability as well as performance. The road-holding of wheels set wide apart and independently suspended. And the tyres, specially made by Dunlop to meet Jaguar's demand for an unprecedented reserve of cornering power, are wider than anything you will see off a race track. The precision of rack-and-pinion steering straightens the road. The fully independent suspension smooths it. Road-holding, braking, acceleration, steering, tyres, and fatigue-banishing comfort all add up to a new standard of safety.

One question remains. What happens if the XJ6 is involved in an accident? It has to be faced, and Jaguar have faced it. In the interior: recessed knobs, handles and switches, soft sunvisors, padded dash surround, burst-proof doorlocks, collapsible steering column. In the layout: fuel tanks are in separate compartments. And if the engine was forced back it would be deflected away from the passenger compartment, not into it. The front and rear sections are strong indeed, but they cannot match the passenger compartment. In a collision, the ends will absorb impact as they crumple, before the centre section is affected.

But mere words cannot do full justice to the work of four years. Only a detailed inspection can. So see and try the XJ6 soon. You will be glad that you did.

NEW JAGUAR XJ6

The Jaguar range also includes the 240 Saloon the 420 'G' Saloon and the 'E' Type G.T. models
London Showrooms, 88 Piccadilly, W.1.

JOIN THE GT/E SET!

—with the new Scimitar GT/E

Grand touring elegance *plus* estate versatility

The GT/E set is the most exclusive in the country. *Only* Reliant offer the benefits of a grand tourer *and* a capacious estate in one luxurious car. The three litre version tops 120 miles an hour, yet returns an easy 25 miles to the gallon. And, there's seating for four adults with all their luggage.

Why didn't anyone think of a GT/E before?

SCIMITAR GT/E

3 and 2.5 Litre
Reliant Motor Company Limited
Tamworth, Staffordshire
Telephone: 0827 4151

Four seats in the Reliant stable - at Earls Court!

Your new car is about to become obsolete.

They're making the facelift that makes most models new and yours out of date.

At Rover we have a different philosophy. Instead of built-in obsolescence, we build in safety and performance features which do not date. And only make changes that actually improve the car. So your Rover 2000 will be the current model for years to come.

And, instead of just padding, a safety cage that surrounds and protects you and your passengers. Instead of brief checks, giving every engine a full bench test. And we drive every car round and round our test track until we're satisfied.

It's these standards, these features and the thinking behind them that make a Rover new. Year after year after year.

BRITISH LEYLAND ROVER

In this age of mass production, a Rover is still a Rover.

J.D. BARCLAY
OF OXFORD

242-254 BANBURY ROAD, OXFORD
Telephone: OXFORD 59944

ROLLS-ROYCE SILVER SHADOW
Drop-head Coupé by H. J. Mulliner

Officially appointed ROLLS-ROYCE distributor

We are now accepting orders for all models of the best car in the world, the Rolls-Royce Silver Shadow:— the 4-Door Saloon with optional air conditioning and both the 2-Door Saloon and

Drop-head Coupé by H. J. Mulliner. In addition we can offer an unusually fine selection of low mileage models and are always pleased to buy good quality used Rolls-Royce cars.

FIAT 125

FIAT distributor for Oxfordshire

See Europe's widest range of cars, including the highly successful Fiat 125 and Fiat 124 Coupé as well as the newly launched Fiat 850 Special and

high powered Fiat 850 Coupé at our showrooms. As main dealers, we are able to offer very early, if not immediate, delivery of all Fiat models.

CARS

OF THE LATE 60'S

BRITISH AND IMPORTED MODELS 1965-1969

MOTOR SHOW REVIEW GUIDE

1969

A - Z

SECTION

A hundred reasons that will keep Britain ahead

by BASIL CARDEW

IN a tough world, the British motor industry comes out on top as you will see at the highly successful and imaginative Earls Court Motor Show.

Tough world? Curbs on the home front with higher hire purchase tax, mounting Government charges and higher licence duties are so bad that it often seems to me that motoring in Britain is now almost an offence. But in the plush corridors and on the floodlit stands at Earls Court is the manufacturers' reply to what could so easily be a depressing picture.

More than 100 brand-new models, designed from scratch three years ago, will fascinate buyers at home and from more than a score of overseas countries.

The men who built these cars in Britain's widespread plants and factories have good reason to be optimistic. For, according to latest figures, the total value of British motoring exports in a year has reached an all-time record of £896,500,000 compared with £735,800,000 the year before.

So the car men have established without doubt that their industry is the country's biggest foreign currency earner—more than £500m a year ahead of their nearest export competitor.

So they can have no fear of the overseas challenge when it is known that the total import of cars from foreign countries numbered 102,767 cars against Britain's total car production for the last available year of 1,815,936.

Of the foreign effort German Volkswagen, Mercedes and NSU car companies imported into Britain some 26,000 cars, against Italy's Fiats, Lancias and Ferraris 24,238.

British optimism stems from many new and vital changes in her factories in the past 12 months which have led to economies in production, streamlining of effort, smoother organisation and cheaper products.

Much of the success of British cars comes from the fact that only four big car empires remain in Britain—British Leyland, Ford, Rootes and Vauxhall. Rootes is now an offshoot of American Chrysler and Vauxhall a splinter of General Motors. So these huge car makers can cut down production costs and sell more cheaply.

But remember that there are still outstanding individual car makers like Rolls-Royce, Aston Martin, Jensen and Morgan (rapidly becoming a favourite in Chelsea's Kings Road).

Safety is the biggest single issue in the motor industry throughout the world. Many of the cars in the show incorporate collapsible steering, dual braking systems, clear dashboard layouts (no projections), and child-proof door locks recommended by safety expert Ralph Nader for the U.S. market.

But an even bigger problem arises in some parts of the world, notably Los Angeles (and don't forget that the west coast of California is the largest buyer of British sports cars). Los Angeles has a huge smog problem caused by surrounding mountains and exhaust fumes from cars that lie low on the roads.

British car manufacturers have gone further than anybody else in combating this problem and can probably claim the clearest exhaust systems fitted on modern production cars. Other engineers notably Lear in California and Donald Healey in Britain offer an answer to the pollution with steam cars.

These advances are discussed in the Daily Express Motor Show Review, which also includes a section on estate cars as they continue to grow in popularity.

Family motorists demand that extra door at the back to convert their car into a utility vehicle to carry extra luggage and children. So one of Britain's leading manufacturers has recently launched a family saloon with a fifth door. Another trend is to give a fifth top gear in place of overdrive to simplify handling.

In presenting this latest Review, my aim has been to provide not only a guide to those who can attend Earls Court, but a guide and reference to those car enthusiasts who cannot get to the show and enjoy the glamour and bustling tempo around the highly polished exhibits at a show that should attract more than half a million people.

A MESSAGE from Mr. Douglas Richards, President of the Society of Motor Manufacturers and Traders and Chairman of the Zenith Carburettor Company.

This show will attract buyer —and browser

THE Daily Express Motor Show Review has gained an enviable reputation for the way that each year it presents its lucid 'run-down' on the Earls Court exhibition. For the visitor it is an attractive and useful illustrated adjunct to the technically detailed official catalogue.

The Motor Show is both a buyer's and browser's exhibition, just as the review is a buyer's and browser's publication. There is sufficient information in it to delight the motoring man, woman, and, perhaps just as important, child.

It is suitably simple for the non-technical reader while containing a concise mechanical specification guide for those with a little more knowledge of the motoring facts of life.

The tightly written and detailed explanatory paragraphs and outline specifications show British and foreign cars alongside each other, emphasising the truly international nature of the world's motor industry.

One of the values of the international show is that all these products, the majority British, are displayed to potential customers from throughout the motoring world.

Each exhibitor has a stand calculated to attract; each has a display of products eminently suited to some aspect of motoring; and many of the companies showing their products have already contributed to your own particular brand of driving.

The review also previews some of the accessories which will be on display on the first floor and around the perimeter of the ground floor at Earls Court.

The Daily Express has prepared this review for all who find motoring interesting; to whom motoring is more than a mere means of transport. I am sure that it is a valuable addition to the vast accumulation of booklets, leaflets and catalogues which so many of us collect at exhibitions.

Douglas Richards

The rising costs that stop us all going automatic

THERE are more cars than ever with automatic transmissions for simpler driving and more than ever with five-speed gearboxes which seem to make driving more complicated. It is not really a contradiction.

Each is a way of getting the best out of the engine; automatic transmission for the driver who doesn't want to be bothered with gear changing and is prepared to spend a fraction more on petrol; five-speeds for the man who likes to do it himself for efficiency and economy.

Automatic transmissions go back a long way. A lot of work was done in the 1920s and in the early thirties, Austin had a go with the Hayes friction drive. It failed then but the same idea is now being developed again under the name of a "Toroidal" transmission.

By 1939 America had some good transmissions in production and they have progressed steadily so that today 80 per cent of United States cars are automatic and a manual box is really only for the sports car driver.

Automatic transmission becomes more attractive as traffic jams increase and driving becomes more of a stop-go drudgery. We long ago reached that position in Britain but automatic transmissions haven't yet caught on for several reasons.

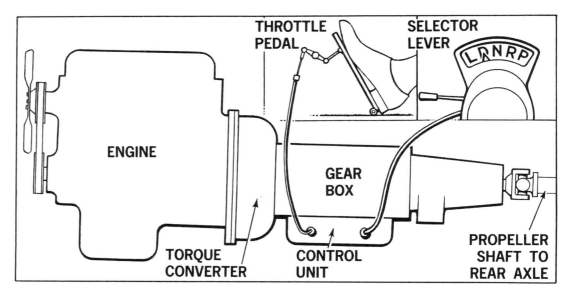

The inside story of the car with no clutch

by GORDON WILKINS

Production

They are still too expensive in relation to our car prices and living standards. They usually mean a slight increase in fuel consumption which doesn't matter in the United States where petrol costs a few pence per gallon but is serious for us when tax raises it to nearly 7s. per gallon. Finally, people fear that automatic transmissions will be difficult and expensive to repair. (In fact they usually last longer than a normal clutch and gearbox.)

I'm sure that price is the main snag. DAF have no difficulty in selling all their cars with automatic transmission. Their simple lightweight belt drive allows them to sell at prices fully competitive against conventional cars, but when British Leyland offer one of the world's finest automatic transmissions, the four-speed AP at £90 extra on a Mini, only three buyers in every 100 order it. It's a vicious circle because more orders would mean bigger production which would mean lower prices, which would mean more orders.

The DAF Variomatic drive is by far the simplest and cheapest. The rear wheels are driven by two cogged belts riding on pulleys which are formed from a pair of cones. The cones approach each other or move further apart under the action of centrifugal weights and pistons connected to the manifold, so the pulley diameter varies and so does the gear ratio.

There are no steps or jerks because the drive is varying continuously all the time. It's used not only on small cars but on mopeds, snow scooters, light military vehicles and machine tools.

Most other automatic transmissions use a fluid drive of some sort. The simplest kind is the fluid coupling. It's like an orange cut in two, with the fruit removed so that only the segments remain and it is immersed in oil. One half is connected to the engine and one to the car wheels.

As the oil circulates from one to the other it makes a smooth automatic clutch. This was used with a self-change gearbox on pre-war Daimlers and other cars. With a planetary automatic gearbox, it figures on the Mercedes automatic transmission. It also figured on the original Hydra-Matic transmission used by General Motors and by Rolls Royce up to last year.

Next step forward is to put a third element consisting of a ring of blades in between the two halves of the orange. This acts on the oil like the fulcrum of a lever and enables the fluid coupling to increase the torque. This is a torque converter and it gives an automatic change of gear ratio varying smoothly up to the point where the slip between the two halves ceases. It then functions as an ordinary clutch and you are in top gear.

Action

Unfortunately the range of ratios is not wide enough to cover all conditions from climbing a steep hill with a full load to driving flat-out on the level with a light load, so there has to be a gearbox as well.

This is usually a set of two or three planetary gears (a sun wheel surrounded by planet wheels inside a ring gear) which can be brought into action by band brakes or clutches to help the torque converter and it is the engagement of these planetary gears that causes the slight jerks that are usually felt when the driver kicks down the accelerator for extra acceleration or hill climbing.

With the complicated brain box needed to tell the transmission when to change gear, the whole thing is difficult and costly to make. After serious teething troubles, British Leyland had to do as the Americans do and build a special air conditioned factory to keep the dust out of the oilways in the control system of the AP automatic.

To cut the cost and complication, a half-way system is now catching on. You use a torque converter with a normal gearbox and an automatic clutch which disconnects the drive for gear changing by means of an electric contact built into the knob of the gear lever. Thanks to the torque converter there is much less need for gear changing and when a change has to be made you simply push the lever from one position to the next. There is no clutch pedal to worry about. This system is used on a wide variety of cars from high performance machines like the Porsches and the NSU RO 80 to the humble VW.

Narrow

But what about the five speed gearbox? This has long been a normal fitting on fast cars built for keen drivers like Aston Martins, Alfa Romeos, Ferraris, Porsches and the sports Fiats but it is now coming within reach of the ordinary driver on the Austin Maxi.

The more gear ratios you have the more you can get out of your engine. The extreme example is the 125 c.c. racing motor cycles where astronomical revs extract a fantastic amount of power from egg-cup sized cylinders but it only comes in over a very narrow range of revs, so they use transmissions with twelve speeds or more and the driver is incessantly changing gear to keep the little engine screaming 'on the cam'.

Nothing as extreme as that would do for an ordinary road car but revs are rising—6,000 rpm. is commonplace and there are small car engines running up to over 8,000 rpm. The driver who uses the revs gets through the traffic faster.

The spread of motorways also encourages the use of more ratios because you need a high cruising gear to give the engine an easy time when cruising fast even if it means changing down for acceleration and hill climbing. This is the main reason behind the five speed gearbox on the Maxi. Four speeds for normal driving and fifth to provide relaxed motorway cruising. It pays dividends in quieter running, reduced wear and in fuel economy.

Bursting at the seams, we had to move into something bigger

by CHARLES GOVEY

PICKING a car to suit one person is tricky enough: picking a car to suit all the family is ten times worse.

First there's the wife to consider—and the colour of the car isn't the only thing she's interested in if she's a driver herself. There are also three children over five who all have firm ideas about the car *they* want.

Then there are aged parents to take on trips, weekend visitors with *their* children, neighbours' children to be ferried to school under a complicated rota system. Just a bit much for the ordinary family saloon.

But it wasn't just weight of numbers that drove us into the big car category. Comfort was another factor. My wife has a theory that while most cars are fun for the drivers, few are much fun for passengers after about 20 miles.

Cars with hard suspension, cars that accelerate fiercely, cars with little engines buzzing away under your feet . . . all are non-fun for passengers in her book. And since she is always the passenger on family trips, her views have to be considered.

So a nice, big, comfortable, non-buzzing car it had to be. But which one? For months we let our minds wander over most of the possibilities, checking on likely second-hand prices and maintenance costs.

But after all this careful planning, the car we finally chose was a wild bit of impulse-buying. Suddenly we spotted a white Zephyr Mark IV estate gleaming on the forecourt of, of all places, a Volkswagen garage.

For some reason this was one we hadn't considered—perhaps because there are so few about. I certainly hadn't seen one on the second-hand market before.

Just two years old, 32,000 on the clock, and the asking price was £875—little more than half the cost when new. Without demur, they lopped £25 off the price and agreed to take an old Prefect in part exchange.

After a short test drive we were hooked. Hardly was my signature dry on the order form when my wife rushed into the office: "Don't sign, don't sign! My feet won't reach the pedals."

It took just a moment to locate not only the lever which eases the front bench forward but another one to adjust the angle of the steering wheel. Even the salesman didn't know about that.

We got an awful lot of car for our money. Two huge sofas instead of seats, that great loading compartment at the back, and a lot of little extra comforts you don't get on smaller cars—including a handsome push-button radio that alone seemed worth more than the old banger we'd traded in.

Of course there were some teething troubles. The next day I was back at the garage with a loose window-winder in my hand. "Anybody would think I was buying a brand new car," I said rather tartly to the mechanic.

Maybe it is a buyer's market at the moment. Maybe this was just an extraordinarily nice garage. But they cheerfully fixed everything we found to complain about—from a worn gear-lever pin and a faulty windscreen wiper motor to the two tatty rear tyres.

We've had the car a couple of months now and believe we know the best and the worst. It certainly answers everything we asked for in the way of space and comfort. The family even survived a long holiday haul to North Wales without a trace of travel sickness—a miracle for us.

You can't of course turn on a sixpence or park in a Mini-space. But once you get used to the width and that enormous bonnet stretching in front of you, it's amazing what you can do.

The car handles easily in town traffic and on the motorway settles down to a sedate 70 with very little effort and absolutely no noise.

You would never call it a nippy car and it's a dead loss for budding world champions who like to chicane their way through slower moving traffic. But with half a dozen people on board, maybe that's no bad thing.

No doubt the bigger V6 engine would give the extra woomph you sometimes feel you need. But then second-hand buyers can't always be choosers. And against that you have to weigh up the much more reasonable running costs. Insurance is little more than for the average family saloon, and fuel consumption is averaging out around 22 to the gallon—with a tune-up I'm even hoping for a little more.

I suppose you never quite fall as madly in love with a big car the way you do with a daintier model. It's rather like falling for a big girl. Her attractions are obvious enough—maybe too obvious. But once you've been cosseted by her ample charms, it spoils you for anything else.

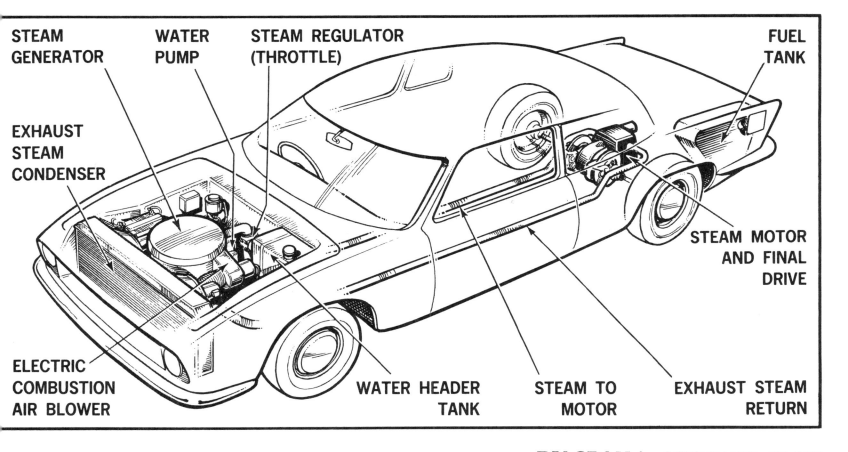

STEAM GENERATOR WATER PUMP STEAM REGULATOR (THROTTLE) FUEL TANK

EXHAUST STEAM CONDENSER

STEAM MOTOR AND FINAL DRIVE

ELECTRIC COMBUSTION AIR BLOWER

WATER HEADER TANK STEAM TO MOTOR EXHAUST STEAM RETURN

DIAGRAM by LEONARD CLOW

STEAM – the old power in new clothes

by DAVID BENSON

S A SMALL boy my favourite pastime was finding a steam powered road-roller ironing out the asphalt on new roads. These giant machines with their huge flywheels and incredible front wheels were a source of infinite fascination. I used to have terrible nightmares in which I was rolled flat underneath one of these slow puffing juggernauts.

Steam power was the first form of locomotion where the vehicle was independent of an outside influence and is therefore basic to every form of modern propulsion. Steam power freed man from the horse.

Now, the top automobile engineers in the world are reconsidering the future of the internal combustion engine and are prepared to take a whole new approach on propulsion units for the future.

Air pollution caused by diesel and petrol engines has become such a problem with the vast increases in traffic in recent years that some way must be found to reduce this serious hazard to city life. And although it is possible to minimise exhaust pollution on present day motor cars it is also highly expensive. Steam provides the ideal answer.

Sealed

According to Donald Healey, Britain's most successful sports car designer, the reason for the new turn to steam is that it "reduces waste by products to an absolute minimum, because it can maintain a fixed fuel air ratio at all times". So carbon pollution is reduced to a minimal level.

It is perhaps ironic that in an era when man is capable of landing on the moon the steam car is the project for the future.

The first recorded auto-mobile (self propelled vehicle) was a two-foot wooden platform with four wooden wheels. On board was a sealed kettle type arrangement with a coal fire underneath. It fed steam through a narrow spout

directly onto a miniaturised water wheel connected to the front wheels of the craft. It achieved a speed of two and a half miles per hour and was built by Ferdinand Verbiest, a Belgian priest, in 1668.

The most famous steam car was the classic Stanley Steamer, one of which still runs each year in the London to Brighton Veteran rally.

Development of the steam engine, has always been hampered by the necessity to use flame and easy burning fuels like coal and

coke. In addition, the heat exchangers (either radiators or steam coils) have had to be massive to propel effectively a reasonable size vehicle.

But in recent years the development of the "flash" boiler system has meant that the potential steam designer can use crude oil as a basic fuel and get full steam pressure in a matter of seconds. So far, four major motor engineering companies have been working on this type of engine.

The giant General Motors Corporation in America—the largest car maker in the world—has built two experimental cars, the SE-101 and SE-124. As yet, neither car is ready for production but as feasibility studies they could be converted into production models in less than 12 months.

From Britain, Healey has already produced a prototype engine, boiler and drive unit and placed it in a go-kart in which he has been trundling around his Devon estate.

Racing

Dr. Trevor Lamb of ICI is prepared to back further research into the all-essential heat exchangers for steam engines and has offered Healey the help of his company.

Back in America, Andy Granatelli who controls the STP oil additive company with long association with the Indianapolis 500 mile race is experimenting with a steam powered racing car for next year's event. And the Lear Motor Corporation—backed by the multi-millionaire industrialist William Lear—has already built a steam powered racing car which made its debut at the New York motor show earlier this year.

So the steam car that really began life 300 years ago looks like creeping back into the space age.

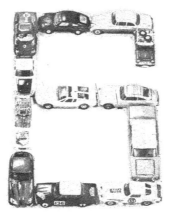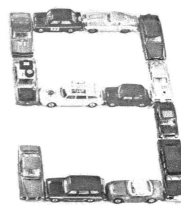

1969

YOUR A to Z GUIDE

A.C. 428

7-LITRE Ford-engined luxury speed model with many detail advances; safety facia with recessed instruments and new gear lever to US requirements, door warning lights, revised cooling system, better fresh air ventilation, redesigned seats. Rubber bushes replace rose joints in rear suspension pivots. Frua styled the coupé and convertible bodies. Electric window controls, twin-circuit servo brakes, limited-slip differential are standard.

CLOSE-UP
Eight-cyl.; o.h.v.; 104.9 × 101.1 mm.; 6,989 c.c.; 345 b.h.p. gross; 10.5 to 1 comp; Ford 4-choke carb.; 4-speed, 6.68, 4.86, 3.72, 2.88 to 1; cen. lvr. Ford auto. opt.; susp. f. and r. ind. coil; 2-door; 2-seat; disc servo brks.; max. 145 m.p.h.; cruise, 115; m.p.g. 13-18; whl. base 8ft.; track f. 4ft. 7in., r. 4ft. 8in.; lgth. 14ft. 6in.; width 5ft. 7in.; ht. 4ft. 3in.; g.c. 7in.; turng. cir. 35ft.; kerb wt. 29 cwt.; tank 15 gals.; 12-volt.

£4,775 + £1,461 p.t. = £6,236

ALFA ROMEO GIULIA 1300GT

ALFA loaf is better than no bread, so if you can't quite afford the 1750 Spider Veloce, this gives you the racy Pininfarina line at about £450 less. With two twin-choke Webers the smooth twin-cam engine is eager for action and a five-speed gearbox helps you make the most of it. Anti-roll bars front and rear ensure road holding in the Alfa tradition.

CLOSE-UP
Four-cyl.; o.h.c.; 74 × 75 mm.; 1,290 c.c.; 92 b.h.p.; 9 to 1 comp;. 2 Weber 2-choke carbs.; 5-speed 15.03, 9.05, 6.17, 4.55, 3.91 to 1; cen. lvr.; susp. f. ind. coil, r. coil; 2-door; 2-seat; disc servo brks.; max. 107 m.p.h.; cruise 95; m.p.g. 24-27; whl. base, 7ft. 4½in. track f. 4ft. 3½in., r. 4ft. 2in.; lgth. 13ft. 11½in.; width 5ft 4½in.; ht. 4ft. 2¾in.; g.c. 5½in., turng. cir. 34ft.; kerb wt 19¾ cwt.; tank 10½ gals.; 12-volt.

£1,340 + £409 p.t. = £1,749

ALFA ROMEO 1750 GT VELOCE

STATE run industry sometimes produce more than memos, red tape and excuses; for example this top model in the Alfa range. But it has a private enterprise body by Bertone (the state shapes were terrible). Though rear suspension is not independent, steering and handling set a high standard and there are disc brakes all round. Cylinder head and block are in light alloy with removable cylinder liners.

CLOSE-UP
Four-cyl.; o.h.c.; 80 × 88.5 mm.; 1,779 c.c.; 122 b.h.p.; 9.5 to 1 comp.; 2 twin-choke Weber carbs.; 5-speed, 13.56, 8.17, 5.54, 4.10, 3.24 to 1; cen. lvr.; susp. f. ind. coil, r. coil; 2-door; 2/4-seat; disc servo brks.; max. 118 m.p.h.; cruise 105; m.p.g. 20-26; whl. base 7ft. 8½in.; track f. 4ft. 4in., r. 4ft. 2in.; lgth. 13ft. 4⅞in.; width 5ft. 2½in.; ht. 4ft. 3¾in.; g.c. 6in.; turng. cir. 39ft.; kerb wt. 21 cwt.; tank 10 gals.; 12-volt.

£1,762 + £538 p.t. = £2,300

Abbreviations—g.c.—ground clearance; susp.—suspension; f.—front; r.—rear; comp.—compression; s.v.—side-valves; o.h.v.—overhead valves; o.h.c.—overhead camshaft; hyd.—hydraulic

AMERICAN MOTORS HORNET

HOT on the trail of Ford's Maverick comes the Hornet, the second of the new sub-compacts with which the Americans hope to stem the rising flood of imported cars, but like the Maverick it could not be more conventional, with its in line water cooled engine, coil spring front suspension and rigid rear axle on half-elliptic springs. At least the buyer gets a big choice of engines, three sixes and a V8.

CLOSE-UP

Six-cyl.; o.h.v.; 78.1×76.2 mm.; 3,262 c.c.; 128 b.h.p. gross; 8.5 to 1 comp.; Carter carb.; 3-speed, axle ratio 3.08 to 1; col. lvr. auto. opt.; susp., f. ind. coil, r. half elliptic; 2/4-door; 5-seat; drum brks.; max. 90 m.p.h.; cruise 80; m.p.g. 20-23; whl. base 9ft.; track f. 4ft. 9½in., r. 4ft. 9in.; lgth. 14ft. 11½in.; width 5ft. 11½in.; ht. 4ft. 4¾in.; g.c. 5½in.; turng. cir. 36ft. 3in.; kerb wt. 24½ cwt.; tank 14 gals.; 12-volt.

ASTON MARTIN DB6 MK II

ALIMENTARY, my dear Watson. A computer decides the duration of the squirt as six injectors punch fuel into inlet ports to give the same power as the Weber-carburetter Vantage engine, with greater flexibility and 20 per cent lower fuel consumption. 0-100 mph in 15 sec. they say, but power figures are now secret. Wider rims with low-profile tyres, flared wings and more enveloping seats are other features.

CLOSE-UP

Six-cyl.; o.h.c.; 96×92 mm.; 3,995 c.c.; b.h.p. not revealed; 8.9 to 1 comp.; 3 SU carbs. or Brico injection; 5-speed, 10.29, 6.64, 4.64, 3.77, 3.14 to 1; cen. lvr. BW auto. opt.; susp. f. ind. coil, r. coil; 2-door; 4-seat; disc servo brks.; max. 150 m.p.h.; cruise, 130; m.p.g. 12-15; whl. base 8ft. 5½in.; track f. 4ft. 6in.; r. 4ft. 5½in.; lgth. 15ft. 2in.; width 5ft. 6in.; ht. 4ft. 5½in.; g.c. 5in.; turng. cir. 34ft.; kerb wt. 29 cwt.; tank 19 gals.; 12-volt.

£3,700 + £1,133 p.t. = £4,833

ASTON MARTIN DBS V8

MAGNIFICENT new light alloy V8 engine with fuel injection and four overhead camshafts puts the DBS among world performance leaders. Crisp style is now enhanced by light alloy wheels. Lavish equipment includes power steering, collapsible column, halogen headlamps, electric window lifts, heated rear window, passenger foot rest, safety lamps in door edges, tinted glass, adjustable dampers.

CLOSE-UP

Eight-cyl.; o.h.c.; 100×85 mm.; 5,340 c.c.; b.h.p. not revealed; 9 to 1 comp.; Bosch injection; 5-speed, 10.27, 6.35, 4.32, 3.54, 2.99 to 1; cen lvr.; susp., f. ind. coil, r. de Dion coil; 2-door; 4-seat; disc servo brks.; max. 170 m.p.h.; cruise 140; m.p.g. 12-16; whl. base 8ft. 6⅞in.; track f. and r. 4ft. 11in.; lgth. 15ft. 0½in.; width 6ft.; ht. 4ft. 4½in.; g.c. 5½in.; turng. cir. 38ft.; kerb wt. 34 cwt.; tank 21 gals.; 12-volt.

£5,281 + £1,616 p.t. = £6,897

AUSTIN 3-LITRE

TAKE the body space of the 1800, add a long tail with bigger luggage boot and a long nose with six-cylinder engine driving the rear wheels and you have Austin's recipe for 3-litre luxury. Steering and brakes are power assisted, automatic transmission is optional and the Hydrolastic suspension has a levelling device to keep height constant regardless of load.

CLOSE-UP

Six-cyl.; o.h.v.; 83.3×88.9 mm.; 2,912 c.c. 123 b.h.p. 9 to 1 comp.; 2 SU carbs.; 4-speed, 13.43, 8.48, 5.49 to 1; cen. lvr., L de N overdrive or BW auto. opt.; susp. f. and r. ind. rubber-hyd., hyd. levelling; 4-door; 5/6-seat; servo brks., disc front; max. 104 m.p.h. cruise 85; m.p.g. 18-22; whl. base 9ft. 7½in.; track f. 4ft. ½in., r. 4ft. 8in.; lgth. 15ft. 5¾in.; width 5ft. 6¾in.; ht. 4ft. 8¾in.; g.c. 6½in.; turng. cir. 40ft.; kerb wt. 25 cwt.; tank 15½ gals.; 12-volt.

£1,152 + £455 p.t. = £1,507

Abbreviations—g.c.—ground clearance; susp.—suspension; f.—front; r.—rear; comp.—compression; s.v.—side-valves; o.h.v.—overhead valves; o.h.c.—overhead camshaft; hyd.—hydraulic.

209

AUSTIN MAXI

FIVE times five. Five seats, five doors, five-bearing engine, five speed gearbox and five wheels, the fifth neatly stowed under the rear floor. Britain's first saloon with station wagon versatility. It has fold-away rear seats, lift-up rear door and plus points like servo brakes, radial-ply tyres, reclining front seats. Transverse engine of course, and front-wheel-drive.

CLOSE-UP

Four-cyl.; o.h.c.; 76.2×81.28 mm.; 1,485 c.c.; 74 b.h.p.; 9 to 1 comp.; SU carb.; 5-speed, 13.4, 8.4, 5.75, 4.2, 3.3 to 1; cen. lvr.; susp. f. and r. ind. rubber-hyd.; 5-seat; disc/drum servo brks.; max 92 m.p.h.; cruise 85, m.p.g. 26-30; whl. base 8ft. 8in.; track f. 4ft. 5¾in.; r. 4ft. 5½in.; lgth. 13ft. 2½in.; width 5ft. 4in.; ht. 4ft. 7in.; g.c. 5½in.; turng. cir. 30ft. 6in.; kerb wt. 19½ cwt.; tank 10 gals.; 12-volt.

£748 + £231 p.t. = £979

AUSTIN 1300 GT

AUSTIN with Action. Inspired by the two-door Austin America, one of the top ten imports into the USA, the four-door 1300 GT has similar exterior and high-style interior, but gets extra performance from a twin-carburetter engine. Road holding is up-graded to match with lowered Hydrolastic suspension, a rear anti-roll bar and stronger auxiliary rear springs. Roof is vinyl-covered.

CLOSE-UP

Four-cyl.; o.h.v.; 70.6×81.3 mm.; 1,275 c.c.; 70 b.h.p.; 8.8 to 1 comp.; 2 SU carbs.; 4-speed, 12.89, 8.09, 5.23, 3.65 to 1; cen. lvr.; susp. f. and r. ind. rubber-hyd.; 4-door; 4/5-seat; disc/drum brks.; max 95 m.p.h.; cruise 85; m.p.g. 28-33; whl. base 7ft. 9½in.; track f. 4ft. 3½in., r. 4ft. 2⅞in.; lgth. 12ft. 2¾in.; width 5ft. 0⅜in.; ht. 4ft. 5in.; g.c. 5⅛in.; turng. cir. 34ft. 9in.; kerb wt. 16¾ cwt.; tank 8 gals.; 12-volt.

£695 + £214 p.t. = £909

AUSTIN HEALEY SPRITE MK. IV

LAST of the leprechauns. Riley's Elf has got the chop but you can still meet Sprites and Midgets in the woodland glades. New grille, divided rear bumper, modern silver-spoke wheels and a cute new cockpit add interest to this long established small sports car, marketed under Austin Healey and MG names. Reclining seats, a hotter heater, winding windows and a snug convertible top cosset the customers.

CLOSE-UP

Four-cyl.; o.h.v.; 70.6×81.3 mm.; 1,275 c.c.; 64 b.h.p.; 8.8 to 1 comp.; 2 SU carbs.; 4-speed, 13.5, 8.09, 5.73, 4.22 to 1; cen. lvr.; susp. f. ind. coil, r. half-elliptic; 2-door; 2-seat; hyd. brks., disc front; max 95 m.p.h.; cruise 80; m.p.g. 30-34; whl. base 6ft. 8in.; track f. 3ft. 10⅛in., r. 3ft. 8¾in.; lgth. 11ft. 5¼in.; width 4ft. 7in.; ht. 4ft. 0⅜in.; g.c. 5⅛in.; turng. cir. 32ft.; kerb wt. 14 cwt.; tank 6 gals.; 12-volt.

£577 + £179 p.t. = £756

AUDI 100 LS

CUCKOO in the Nest. Built by VW's Auto Union subsidiary, the 100 LS outsells VW's own 411 and has been an instant success in Britain. Longer, lower, wider than the Super 90, with more legroom and bigger boot, it scores on fuel economy and top gear acceleration besides ride and road holding. The canted Heron-head engine drives the front wheels via an all-synchro gearbox.

CLOSE-UP

Four-cyl.; o.h.v.; 81.5×84.4 mm.; 1,760 c.c.; 100 b.h.p.; 10.2 to 1 comp.; Solex twin-choke carb.; 4-speed, 13.19, 7.54, 5.28, 3.76 to 1; cen. lvr.; susp. f. ind. coil, r. tors. bar; 4-door; 5-seat; servo brks. disc front; max. 101 m.p.h.; cruise 90; m.p.g. 23-26; whl. base 8ft. 9½in.; track f. 4ft. 7½in., r. 4ft. 8¼in.; lgth. 15ft. 2½in.; width 5ft. 8¾in.; ht. 4ft. 8¼in.; g.c. 6¼in.; turng. cir. 32ft. 6in.; kerb wt. 20½ cwt.; tank 12¾ gals.; 12-volt.

£1,128 + £347 p.t. = £1,475

Abbreviations—g.c.—ground clearance; susp.—suspension; f.—front; r.—rear; comp.—compression; s.v.—side-valves; o.h.v.—overhead valves; o.h.c.—overhead camshaft; hyd.—hydrau

BENTLEY T TYPE

JUBILEE celebrations this year have reminded us of Bentley's glorious past but the Le Mans-winning days are over. Today's Bentley buyer demands more than an open body and a thunderous engine so the T-type provides silent 100 m.p.h. cruising, smooth new torque converter transmission, triple-circuit brakes, electric windows, electric adjustment of seat height, slope and reach, and self levelling all-independent suspension.

CLOSE-UP

Eight-cyl.; o.h.v.; 104.1×91.4 mm.; 6,230 c.c.; b.h.p. not revealed; 9 to 1 comp.; 2 SU carbs.; 3-speed auto., 7.64, 4.56, 3.08 to 1; col. lvr.; susp. f. and r. ind. coil, hyd. levelling; 2 or 4-door; 5-seat; disc. hyd. servo brks.; max. 120 m.p.h.; cruise 100; m.p.g. 13-16; whl. base 9ft. 11½in.; track f. and r. 4ft. 9½in.; lgth. 16ft. 11½in.; width 5ft. 11in.; ht. 4ft. 11½in.; g.c. 7in.; turng. cir. 38ft.; kerb wt. 41½ cwt.; tank 24 gals.; 12-volt.

£6,045+£1,849 p.t. = £7,894

BMW 1600

BMW's brilliant progress gained new impetus from this fast, compact four-seater with their sturdy overhead cam engine, which is now the cheapest model in the range. Strut type front suspension and trailing wishbones at rear give terrific road grip and cornering power. Then to gild the lily they stretched the engine to two litres to make the 2002 one of the world's fastest cars through traffic.

CLOSE-UP

Four-cyl.; o.h.c.; 84×71 mm.; 1,573 c.c.; 85 b.h.p.; 8.6 to 1 comp.; Solex carb.; 4-speed, 16.7, 8.95, 5.85, 4.37 to 1; cen. lvr.; susp. f. and r. ind. coil; 2-door; 4-seat; disc/drum brks, servo. opt.; max. 98 m.p.h.; cruise, 85; m.p.g. 24-27; whl. base 8ft. 2½in.; track f. and r. 4ft. 4in.; lgth. 14ft. 1½in.; width 5ft. 4in.; ht. 4ft. 7½in.; g.c. 6½in.; turng. cir. 31ft. 6in.; kerb wt. 19 cwt.; tank 10 gals.; 12-volt.

£1,070+£329 p.t. = £1,399

BMW 2500/2800

THE new big BMWs made an instant hit with their excellent engines and high performance, fine ride and stable road holding. The luxurious interiors feature colourful velour upholstery with adjustable headrests and a very modern, legible instrument panel. Power steering and automatic transmission are among the options. Illuminated switches show coloured reminder lights for hazard warning flasher, heated rear window, fog lamps. 2800 has self-levelling rear suspension.

CLOSE-UP

Six-cyl.; o.h.c.; 71.6×86 mm.; 2,494 c.c.; 150 b.h.p. or 80×86 mm., 2,788 c.c.; 170 b.h.p. 9 to 1 comp.; 4-speed, 14.01, 7.57, 5.0, 3.64 to 1; cen. lvr.; susp. f. and r. ind. coil; 4-door; 5-seat; disc servo brks.; max. 118/124 m.p.h.; cruise 100-105; m.p.g. 22-26; whl. base 8ft. 10in.; track f. 4ft. 8½in.; r. 4ft. 9⅝in.; lgth 15ft. 5in.; width 5ft. 8½in.; ht. 4ft. 9in.; g.c. 5⅜in.; turng. cir. 31ft. 6in.; kerb wt. 25½-26¼ cwt.; tank 16½ gals.; 12-volt.

BOND EQUIPE 2-LITRE GT

AMALGAMATION of Bond and Reliant unites enormous know-how in the production of good looking, well finished glass fibre bodies. This convertible on the latest Vitesse 6 chassis has the new rear suspension which transformed the road holding and the latest more powerful engine. You can push the hood down without leaving the driving seat. Leg room for rear passengers is limited making this virtually a 2+2 but the luggage boot is large.

CLOSE-UP

Six-cyl.; o.h.v.; 74.7×76 mm.; 1,998 c.c.; 104 b.h.p.; 9.25 to 1 comp.; 2 Stromberg carbs; 4-speed, 10.31, 6.92, 4.86, 3.89 to 1; cen. lvr., L de N overdrive opt.; susp. f. ind. coil, r. ind. transv. leaf; 2-door; 2/4-seat; hyd. brks., disc front; max. 105 m.p.h.; cruise 90; m.p.g. 26-28; whl. base 7ft. 7½in; track f. 4ft. 1in., r. 4ft.; lgth. 13ft. 10in.; width 5ft. 1½in.; ht. 4ft. 4½in.; g.c. 6½in.; turng. cir. 25ft.; kerb wt. 18½ cwt.; tank 9 gals.; 12-volt.

£998+£307 p.t. = £1,305

BRISTOL 411

VASTLY improved, the Bristol earns its new model number with bigger engine, revised styling, improved power steering, limited-slip differential. Chrysler supply engine and transmission which give 0-100 m.p.h. in about 1 sec. Safety features include steel chassis, collapsible column, two separate braking systems, through-flow ventilation. Improvements and extra tax add about £1,000 to the price but you can have any colour you like.

CLOSE-UP
Eight-cyl.; o.h.v.; 107.9×85.7 mm.; 6,277 c.c.; 335 b.h.p. gross; 10 to 1 comp.; Carter 4-choke carb.; 3 speed auto., 7.52, 4.45, 3.07 to 1; cen. lvr; susp., f. ind. coil, r. torsion bar; 2-door; 4-seat; disc servo brks.; max. 138 m.p.h.; cruise, 110; m.p.g. 14-16; whl. base, 9ft. 6in.; track f. 4ft. 6in.; r. 4ft. 7in.; lgth 16ft. 1in.; width 5ft. 8in.; ht. 4ft. 9½in.; g.c. 5in.; turng. cir., 39ft. 6in.; kerb wt. 33¼ cwt.; tank 18 gals.; 12-volt.

£5,358 + £1,639 p.t. = £6,997

BUICK RIVIERA

BUICK'S luxury sporting coupé has longer bonnet, new grille and bumpers, covered rear wheels, wide rear window for 1970 and a new bigger engine of 7,475 c.c. is available to order. A "time modulated chock control" weakens off after 6-12 sec. to avoid needless air pollution. Wide-based tyres have glass reinforcement. Electric locks secure doors and boot lid.

CLOSE-UP
Eight-cyl.; o.h.v.; 106×99 mm.; 7,457 c.c.; 370 b.h.p. gross; 10.25 to 1 comp.; Rochester 4-choke carb.; 3-speed auto, 8.48, 5.06, 3.42 to 1; col. lvr.; susp. f. ind. coil, r. coil; 2-door; 6-seat; drum servo brks., disc front opt.; max. 125 m.p.h.; cruise 100; m.p.g. 12-16; wh. base. 9ft. 11in.; track f. 5ft. 3½in., r. 5ft. 3in.; lgth. 17ft. 11¼in.; width 6ft. 7¾in.; ht. 4ft. 5½in.; g.c. 5in.; turng. cir. 44ft. 4in.; kerb wt. 38¾cwt.; tank 17½gals; 12-volt.

£3,882 + £1,188 p.t. = £5,070

BUICK GS 455

NOT one of the big Buicks, it's only 16ft. 8¾in. long but it has a useful little engine of 7½ litre delivering 350 horsepower. If that proves inadequate a power pack is available with dual exhaust and special camshaft. Optional items include a steering wheel on which you can sound the horn by squeezing the rim and a collapsible space saving spare tyre which can be inflated from a compressed air bottle.

CLOSE-UP
Eight-cyl.; o.h.v.; 109.5×99 mm.; 7,457 c.c.; 350 b.h.p. gross; 10 to 1 comp.; Rochester 4-choke carb.; 3-speed Turbo-Hydramatic auto. 9.69, 5.78, 3.91 to 1; col. lvr; susp. f. ind. coil, r. coil; 2-door; 4-seat; disc/drum servo brks.; max. 118 m.p.h.; cruise 95; m.p.g. 12-16; wh. base 9ft. 4in.; track f. 4ft. 11½in., r. 4ft. 11in.; lgth. 16ft. 8¾in.; width 6ft. 3½in.; ht. 4ft. 5½in.; g.c. 5½in.; turng. cir. 39ft. 10in.; kerb wt. 33½ cwt.; tank 16¾ gals. 12-volt.

CADILLAC ELDORADO

THE world's biggest production engine, a V8 of 8,165 c.c. giving 400 horsepower, at least on the test bed, is Cadillac's boast for 1970. With it comes a new, stronger rear axle. New signal seeking radio locks on to stereo, AM or FM stations. There are many mechanical improvements and 21 colours, plus 167 internal trim combinations in cloth, vinyl and leather to choose from.

CLOSE-UP
Eight-cyl.; o.h.v.; 8,165 c.c.; 400 b.h.p. gross; 10.5 to 1 comp.; Rochester 4-choke carb.; 3-speed auto., 7.61, 4.54, 3.07 to 1; col. lvr.; susp. f. ind. torsion bar, r. half-elliptic; 2-door; 4-seat; disc/drum servo brks.; max. 120 m.p.h.; cruise 100; m.p.g. 12-16; whl. base 10ft.; track f. 5ft. 3½in., r. 5ft. 3in.; lgth. 18ft. 5in.; width 6ft. 8in.; ht. 4ft. 5¾in.; g.c. 5½in.; turng. cir. 41ft. 3in.; kerb wt. 49 cwt.; tank 21¾ gals.; 12-volt.

£4,860 + £1,487 p.t. = £6,347

Abbreviations—g.c.—ground clearance; susp.—suspension; f.—front; r.—rear; comp.—compression; s.v.—side-valves; o.h.v.—overhead valves; o.h.c.—overhead camshaft; hyd.—hydraulic

CHEVROLET CAPRICE

RE-STYLED for 1970, this big Chevrolet has a wider track and glass-reinforced tyres. Colours and trim are new too. Optional equipment includes electrically operated door locks and boot lid, automatic safety latches on seat backs and stereo tape system. The radio aerial is built into the windscreen. Choice of coupé or saloon bodies and V8 engines from 5.7 to 7.4 litres.

CLOSE-UP
Eight-cyl.; o.h.v.; 107.9×101.6 mm.; 7,440 c.c.; 345 b.h.p. gross; 10.25 to 1 comp.; Rochester 4-choke carb.; 3-speed Turbo-Hydramatic auto., 8.01, 5.23, 3.31 to 1; col. lvr.; susp. f. ind. coil, r. coil; 4-door; 5-seat; disc/drum servo brks.; max. 120 m.p.h.; cruise 100; m.p.g. 12-14; whl. base 9ft. 11in.; track. f. and r. 5ft. 2½in.; lgth. 17ft. 11¾in.; width 6ft. 7¾in.; ht. 4ft. 6½in.; g.c. 5¼in.; turng. cir. 43ft. 6in.; kerb wt. 35⅝ cwt.; tank 19½ gals.; 12-volt.

CHEVROLET MONTE CARLO

DON'T blame Princess Grace. This new prestige model seems to have more Milwaukee than Monaco in it, but it was conceived by the shrewd Chevrolet team, who sell over two million cars a year—far more than the whole British motor industry combined. Choice of four V8 engines from 5.7 to 7.4 litres; disc front brakes and glass fibre tyres. Transmission-controlled ignition is a new feature.

CLOSE-UP
Eight-cyl.; o.h.v.; 101.6×89.4 mm.; 5,737 c.c.; 300 b.h.p. gross; 10.2 to 1 comp.; Rochester 4-choke carb.; 3-speed, Turbo-Hydramatic auto., 8.01, 5.23, 3.31 to 1; col. lvr.; susp. f. ind. coil, r. coil; 2-door; 5-seat; disc/drum servo brks.; max. 115 m.p.h.; cruise 95; m.p.g. 14-18; whl. base 9ft. 8in.; track f. and r. 4ft. 11in.; lgth. 17ft. 1¾in.; width 6ft. 3⅝in.; ht. 4ft. 4⅞in.; g.c. 5½in.; turng. cir. 44ft. 6in.; kerb wt. 21¾ cwt.; tank 16¾ gals.; 12-volt.

CHRYSLER 300

ONE of 15 Chrysler models for 1970. It has a wider rear track for increased stability, rubber insulators for front frame and rear axle to cut road noise and vibration and a rubber coupling in the steering column. Headlamps are concealed and there are new full width tail lamps for 1970. A warning buzzer chides drivers who leave the car with the ignition key in the lock.

CLOSE-UP
Eight cyl.; o.h.v.; 109.7×95.2 mm.; 7,206 c.c.; 350 b.h.p. gross; 10 to 1 comp.; Holley 4-choke carb.; 3-speed, Torque-flite auto. 6.76, 4.0, 2.76 to 1; col. lvr.; susp. f. ind. torsion bar, r. half-elliptic; 2-door; 5-seat; disc/drum servo brks.; max. 120 m.p.h.; cruise 95; m.p.g. 12-15; whl. base 10ft. 3½in.; track f. 5ft. 2½in., r. 5ft. 2in.; lgth. 18ft. 8in.; width 6ft. 7½in.; ht. 4ft. 7in.; g.c. 8in.; turng. cir. 47ft.; kerb wt. 38¾ cwt.; tank 19 gals.; 12-volt.

CITROEN AMI-8

NEW to the UK, this Citroen family model was recently restyled to look less like one of Emmett's drawings, but it's still unique. It retains the basic simplicity of the 2CV; flat-twin air-cooled engine, front-wheel-drive, suspension by leading and trailing arms interconnected by coil springs with cast iron inertia dampers, which gives a gently undulating ride. Disc front brakes are new; an automatic clutch is optional.

CLOSE-UP
Two-cyl.; air-cooled; o.h.v.; 74×70 mm.; 602 c.c.; 32 b.h.p.; 9 to 1 comp.; Solex twin-choke carb.; 4-speed, 21.71, 11.12, 7.44, 5.49 to 1; facia lvr.; susp. f. and r. ind. coil; 4-door; 4-seat; drum brks.; max. 75 m.p.h.; cruise 65; m.p.g. 38-40; whl. base 7ft. 10½in.; track f. 4ft. 1½in., r. 4ft.; lgth. 12ft. 11in.; width 5ft.; ht. 4ft. 10¼in.; g.c. 6in.; turng. cir. 37ft.; kerb wt. 14¼ cwt.; 5½ gals.; 12-volt.

£495+£154 p.t. = £649

Abbreviations—g.c.—ground clearance; susp.—suspension; f.—front; r.—rear; comp.—compression; s.v.—side-valves; o.h.v.—overhead valves; o.h.c.—overhead camshaft; hyd.—hydraulic.

CITROEN DS 21 PALLAS

THE most luxurious car in the Citroen range this year has a further improvement to its seats. A new patterned jersey material has been designed for the centre panels of the seat and squab which provides more comfort and support. It is a sophisticated car up to the highest continental standards and now Citroen's electronic fuel injection system is offered as a factory option.

CLOSE-UP
Four-cyl.; o.h.v.; 90×85.5 mm.; 2,175 c.c.; 128 b.h.p.; 8.75 to 1 comp.; Electronic injection; 4-speed, 14.22, 8.48, 5.55, 3.71 to 1; dash lvr.; susp. f. and r. ind. hyd.-pneu.; 4-door; 5/6-seat; hyd. disc/drum servo brks.; max. 112 m.p.h.; cruise 95; m.p.g. 23-28; whl. base 10ft. 3in.; track f. 4ft. 11in., r. 4ft. 3½in.; lgth. 15ft. 10in.; width 5ft. 10½in.; ht. 4ft. 9⅜in.; g.c. 5¾in.; turng. cir. 36ft.; kerb wt. 25½ cwt; tank 14 gals.; 12-volt.

£1,624 + £498 p.t. + £2,122

DAF 33

FROM the land of the bulb fields and windmills comes a car that has no equivalent anywhere else—the latest version of Daf's pioneer baby with flat twin air cooled engine and the simple silent stepless automatic transmission by rubber belts. The engine is designed for flat out motorway cruising. The interior is well finished (safety locks on tip up front seats) and the boot holds a lot of luggage.

CLOSE-UP
Two-cyl.; o.h.v. air cooled; 85.5×65 mm.; 746 c.c.; 28 b.h.p.; 7.5 to 1 comp.; Solex carb.; auto. belt drive 16.4 to 3.9 to 1; cen. lvr.; susp. f. ind. trans. leaf, r. ind. coil; 2-door; 4-seat; drum brks.; max. 65 m.p.h.; cruise 65; m.p.g. 38-48; whl. base 6ft. 8½in.; track f. and r. 3ft. 10½in.; lgth. 11ft. 10½in.; width 4ft. 9in.; ht. 4ft. 6½in.; g.c. 6⅜in.; turng. cir. 33ft.; kerb wt. 13¼ cwt; tank 7 gals.; 6-volt.

£467 + £145 p.t. = £612

DAF 55 COUPE

NO extra charge for automatic transmission there isn't any other kind. Daf's famous belt drive uses pulleys which expand or contract according to speed and throttle opening. It also acts like a limited slip differential to give maximum grip on ice and snow. Renault built the 1100 engine and Michelotti styled the saloon and coupé bodies. The spare wheel over the engine leaves the boot free to carry maximum luggage.

CLOSE-UP
Four-cyl.; o.h.v.; 70×72 mm.; 1,108 c.c.; 45 b.h.p.; 8.5 to 1 comp.; Solex carb.; variable-ratio belt auto. 14.87 to 3.73 to 1; cen. lvr.; susp. f. ind. transv. leaf, r. ind. coil; 2-door; 2/4-seat; drum/disc brks.; max. 85 m.p.h.; cruise 87; m.p.g. 27-33; whl. base 7ft. 4½in.; track f. 4ft. 2½in., r. 4ft. 1½in.; lgth. 12ft. 8¾in.; width 5ft. 0⅝in.; ht. 4ft. 3½in.; g.c. 6½in.; turng. cir. 31ft.; kerb wt. 15½ cwt.; tank 8⅜ gals.; 12-volt.

£732 + £226 p.t. = £958

DATSUN 1800

NEW to Britain, this Japanese four door, five seater saloon resembles the 1600 in general style but has more developed safety features, crushable front end, safety steering and redesigned interior. The four cylinder in line engine has a chain driven overhead camshaft. Gears can be three on the column, four on the floor or BW automatic. Suspension is independent all round with coil struts at front, semi trailing arms and coils at the rear.

CLOSE-UP
Four-cyl.; o.h.c.; 85×80 mm.; 1,815 c.c.; 103 b.h.p. gross; 8.3 to 1 comp.; Hitachi twin-choke carb.; 4-speed, 12.51, 7.44, 4.84, 3.7 to 1; cen. lvr.; susp. f. and r. ind. coil; 4-door; 5-seat; disc/drum brks.; max. 100 m.p.h.; cruise 90; m.p.g. 25-28; whl. base 8ft. 7½in.; track f. 4ft. 3¾in., r. 4ft. 3½in.; lgth. 14ft. 0½in.; width 5ft. 3½in.; ht. 4ft. 7in.; g.c. 7¼in.; turng. cir. 35ft.; kerb wt. 19½ cwt.; tank 11 gals.; 12-volt.

Abbreviations—g.c.—ground clearance; susp.—suspension; f.—front; r.—rear; comp.—compression; s.v.—side-valves; o.h.v.—overhead valves; o.h.c.—overhead camshaft; hyd.—hydraul

DAIMLER SOVEREIGN

LUXURY and compactness symbolises the new Daimler Sovereign, a 4/5 seater of high performance. Its 6-cylinder twin overhead camshaft engine is offered in two capacities—2.8 litre and 4.2 litre—with a choice of manual transmission with overdrive or fully automatic. Its anti-dive geometry for the front suspension is quite a thing. It is a promising newcomer by Daimler out of Jaguar.

CLOSE-UP
Six-cyl.; o.h.c.; 83 × 86 mm.; 2,792 c.c.; 180 b.h.p. gross; 9 to 1 comp.; or 92.7 × 106 mm.; 4,235 c.c.; 245 b.h.p.; 8 to 1 comp.; two SU carbs.; 4-speed and overdrive, 13.22, 8.67, 6.33, 4.55 to 1 or 10.53, 6.75, 4.49, 3.54 to 1; cen. lvr.; susp. f. and r. ind. coil; 4-door; 4-seat; disc servo brks.; max. 115-120 m.p.h.; cruise 100; m.p.g. 14-19; whl. base 9ft. 0⅞in.; track f. 4ft. 10in., r. 4ft. 10¼in.; lgth. 15ft. 9⅝in.; width 5ft. 9¾in.; ht. 4ft. 4⅞in.; g.c. 6in.; turng. cir. 36ft.; kerb wt. 31¼ cwt.; tank 23 gals.; 12-volt.

DAIMLER LIMOUSINE

IT costs nearly £5,000 but it's cheap at the price. Where else can you get such regal splendour, performance, comfort and road-holding for the money? Jaguar's all independent suspension and twin cam engine ensure the 110 m.p.h. performance and imperturbable riding qualities. The veteran craftsmen of Vanden Plas make the body and trim the opulent interior. Electric windows and division glass optional.

CLOSE-UP
Six-cyl.; o.h.c.; 92 × 106 mm.; 4,235 c.c.; 245 b.h.p. gross; 8 to 1 comp.; 2 SU carbs.; 3-speed BW auto, 8.5, 5.1, 3.4 to 1; col. lvr.; susp. f. and r. ind. coil; 4-door; 7-seat; disc servo brks.; max. 110 m.p.h.; cruise 95; m.p.g. 12-16; whl. base 11ft. 9in.; track f. and r. 4ft. 10in.; lgth. 18ft. 10in.; width 6ft. 7in.; ht. 5ft. 3¾in.; g.c. 7in.; turng. cir. 46ft.; kerb wt. 42¾ cwt.; tank 12 gals.; 12-volt.

£3,732 + £1,142 p.t. = £4,874

DODGE CHALLENGER

DODGE'S Challenger, smallest in the new range, could be a giant-killer. Nine models including hardtops and convertibles. Bucket seats have inbuilt headrests and a six-way adjuster is optional. Air pilots will feel at home with the roof light console which flashes warnings for "low fuel" "door ajar" or "Seat belts not fastened". 1970 engines are coloured according to capacity; blue, yellow, or orange for the hot one.

CLOSE-UP
Eight-cyl.; o.h.v.; 99.3 × 84.07 mm.; 5,210 c.c.; 230 b.h.p. gross; 9.2 to 1 comp.; Carter carb.; 3-speed Torqueflite auto, 8.88, 5.17, 2.94 to 1; cen. lvr.; susp. f. ind. torsion bar, r. half-elliptic; 2-door; 4/5-seat; disc/drum servo brks.; max. 120 m.p.h.; cruise 100; m.p.g. 14-18; whl. base 9ft. 4in.; track f. 4ft. 11½in., r. 4ft. 10¾in.; lgth. 15ft. 11¼in.; width 6ft. 4¼in.; ht. 4ft. 3½in.; g.c. 5in.; turng. cir. 39ft.; kerb wt. 29 cwt.; tank 19 gals.; 12-volt.

FERRARI DINO

THE mid-engine formula is catching on fast, for modern sports cars. It gives tremendous roadholding but its a stylist's nightmare and no one has yet evolved a body to equal Pininfarina's design for the Dino which has a V6 4 o.h.c. engine mounted transversely ahead of the rear wheels. The engine has light alloy block, wet liners, transistor ignition and the gearbox has five speeds.

CLOSE-UP
Six-cyl.; o.h.c.; 86 × 57 mm.; 1,987 c.c.; 180 b.h.p.; 9 to 1 comp.; 3 Weber 2-choke carbs.; 5-speed, 15.1, 8.86, 6.46, 5.10, 3.86 to 1; cen. lvr.; susp. f. and r. ind. coil; 2-door; 2-seat; disc servo brks.; max. 145 m.p.h.; cruise 120; m.p.g. 18-21; whl. base 7ft. 5¾in.; track f. 4ft. 7⅞in., r. 4ft. 7⅞in.; lgth. 13ft. 9¾in.; width 5ft. 5¾in.; ht. 3ft. 7¾.; g.c. 4¼in.; turng. cir. 43ft.; kerb wt. 18 cwt.; tank 13½ gals.; 12-volt.

£4,780 + £1,463 p.t. = £6,243

Abbreviations—g.c.—ground clearance; susp.—suspension; f.—front; r.—rear; comp.—compression; s.v.—side-valves; o.h.v.—overhead valves; o.h.c.—overhead camshaft; hyd.—hydraulic.

FERRARI 365 GTB/4

FERRARI is as natural for fast cars as Ferragamo for shoes or Fontana for clothes among Italy's jet set. Previous Ferrari coupes have V12 engines with one overhead camshaft to each bank; this one has two each side plus oil radiator, six carburetters, rear mounted gearbox and limited slip differential. Pininfarina designed the advanced two seater coupe with four faired in headlamps; Scaglietti builds it.

CLOSE-UP
Twelve-cyl.; o.h.c.; 81×71 mm.; 4,390 c.c.; 345 b.h.p.; 9.3 to 1 comp.; six Weber twin-choke carbs; 5-speed 10.13, 6.96, 5.21, 4.12, 2.34 to 1; cen. lvr.; susp. f. and r. ind. coil; 2-door; 2-seat; disc servo brks.; max. 175 m.p.h.; cruise 150; m.p.g. 12-14; whl. base 7ft. 10½in.; track f. 4ft. 7in.; r. 4ft. 7¾in.; lgth. 14ft. 6in.; width 5ft. 7in.; ht. 4ft.; g.c. 5½in.; turng. cir. 29ft. 10in.; kerb wt. 24 cwt.; tank 20 gals.; 12-volt.

£6,700+£2,050 p.t. = £8,750

FIAT 500L

L is for Luxury on Fiat's shrimp-sized town and shopping car. Standard features are sun roof, reclining seats, fitted carpets, oddments tray between front seats and radial ply tyres. Distinguishing marks; big curved overriders on plated bumpers, front and rear. Twin-cylinder air-cooled engine with a tiny thirst mounted at the rear. The 500 has passed the million mark and is still going strong.

CLOSE-UP
Two-cyl.; o.h.v.; air cooled; 67.4×70 mm.; 499 c.c.; 18 b.h.p.; 7.1 to 1 comp.; Weber carb.; 4-speed, 18.9, 10.6, 6.6, 4.4 to 1; cen. lvr.; susp. f. ind. transv. leaf, r. ind. coil; 2/door; 2/4-seat; drum brks.; max. 62 m.p.h.; cruise 55; m.p.g. 47-52; whl. base 6ft. 0½in.; track f. 3ft. 8in., r. 3ft. 8½in.; lgth. 9ft. 9in.; width 4ft. 4in.; ht. 4ft. 4in.; g.c. 5in.; turng. cir. 28ft. 3in.; kerb wt. 9⅞ cwt.; tank 4½ gals.; 12-volt.

£393+£122 p.t. = £515

FIAT 124S

A bigger engine raises power from 60 to 70 b.h.p. and torque is up for swifter acceleration on this super version of Fiat's popular family car. Bigger clutch, higher gearing, servo brakes, new quieter rear suspension with no torque tube are features. Door handles are recessed. Reversing lamp is provided. 124S has four headlamps. An intermittent wiper switch deals with drizzle and mud spray from lorries.

CLOSE-UP
Four-cyl.; o.h.v.; 80×71.5 mm.; 1,438 c.c.; 70 b.h.p.; 9 to 1 comp.; Weber twin-choke carb.; 4-speed 15.54, 8.89, 5.78, 4.1 to 1.; cen. lvr.; susp. f. ind. coil; r. coil; 4-door; 4-seat; disc brks.; max 93 m.p.h.; cruise 80; m.p.g. 27-32; whl. base 7ft. 11½in.; track f. 4ft. 4¼in.; r. 4ft. 3⅛ in.; lgth. 13ft. 3½in.; width 5ft. 3½in.; ht. 4ft. 7¼in.; g.c. 4¾in.; turng. cir. 35ft.; kerb wt. 18¼ cwt.; tank 8½ gals.; 12-volt.

£740+£228 p.t. = £968

FIAT 128

FROM Fiat's new factory at Rivalta emerges the new 128. Their first big scale venture with transverse engine and front drive, it follows successful experience with the Autobianchi Primula. Replacing the 1100, it conveys four in comfort with smooth, free-revving over-square engine, good ride, light steering. Ingenious rear suspension with transverse leaf spring leaves maximum free space in the luggage boot. The clever transmission uses the minimum number of gears.

CLOSE-UP
Four-cyl.; o.h.c.; 80×55.5 mm.; 1,116 c.c.; 55 b.h.p.; 8.8 to 1 comp.; Weber carb.; 4-speed, 14.6, 9.1, 5.9, 4.2 to 1; cen. lvr.; susp. f. ind. coil, r. ind. transv. leaf; 2/4 door; 4-seat; hyd. brks.; disc front; max. 90 m.p.h.; cruise 80; m.p.g. 33-36; whl. base 8ft. 0⅜in.; track f. 4ft. 3½in., r. 4ft. 3⅜in.; lgth. 12ft. 8in.; width 5ft. 2½in.; ht. 4ft. 5in.; g.c. 4¾in.; turng. cir. 34ft.; kerb wt. 15½ cwt.; tank 8¼ gals.; 12-volt.

Abbreviations—g.c.—ground clearance; susp.—suspension; f.—front; r.—rear; comp.—compression; s.v.—side-valves; o.h.v.—overhead valves; o.h.c.—overhead camshaft; hyd.—hydraulic.

FIAT 130

WITH a large part of the European popular car market safely in the bag, Fiat now bid boldly for a slice of the luxury car business with this beautifully finished discreetly styled five-seater of highly original design. The V6 engine has two overhead camshafts belt driven, automatic transmission or five-speed. Strut type suspension all round gives excellent ride and roadholding.

CLOSE-UP
Six-cyl.; o.h.c.; 96 × 66 mm.; 2,866 c.c.; 140 b.h.p.; 8.3 to 1 comp.; Weber twin-choke carb.; 5-speed, 14.47, 7.76, 5.18, 3.73, 3.24 to 1; cen. lvr., BW auto opt.; susp. f. ind. torsion bar, r. ind. coil; 4-door; 5-seat; disc servo brks.; max. 112 m.p.h.; cruise 100; m.p.g. 18-22; whl. base 8ft. 11in.; track f. 4ft. 9in., r. 4ft. 9½in.; lgth. 15ft. 7in.; width 5ft. 11in.; ht. 4ft. 8⅝in.; g.c. 6¾in.; turng. cir. 35ft. 8in.; kerb wt. 28½ cwt.; tank 17½ gals.; 12-volt.

FORD CAPRI 3-LITRE

THE biggest engine yet offered in the Capri. The Dagenham V6 of 3-litres delivers the same power as the 2.3 litre V6 in the German version. As usual the basic car forms the starting point; you choose your specification from three packs of goodies including items like reclining seats, separate rear seats, dual horns, wide rim wheels, steering wheel lock, extra interior light and extra exterior bright metal.

CLOSE-UP
Six-cyl.; o.h.v.; 93.66 × 72.41 mm.; 2,994 c.c.; 128 b.h.p.; 8.9 to 1 comp.; twin-choke Weber carb.; 4-speed, 10.18, 7.12, 4.54, 3.22 to 1; cen. lvr.; susp. f. ind. coil, r. half-elliptic; 2-door; 4-seat; disc/drum brks.; max. 115 m.p.h.; cruise 100; m.p.g. 20-23; whl. base 9ft. 4¾in.; track f. 4ft. 5in., r. 4ft. 4in.; lgth. 13ft. 11⅛in.; width 5ft. 4⅝in.; ht. 4ft. 2⅜in.; g.c. 4½in.; turng. cir. 32ft.; kerb wt. 21¼ cwt.; tank 13½ gals.; 12-volt.

FORD ESCORT 1100/1300

THE extra doors don't mar the clean line of Ford's fast selling family model but they should open new doors for it in export markets. Total sales are already around 340,000 and it is one of the most popular Fords ever built in Britain. Rear doors have child proof locks and push buttons lock all doors from inside. Escorts have now scored a score of International race and rally victories.

CLOSE-UP
Four-cyl.; o.h.v.; 81 × 53.3 mm.; 1,098 c.c.; 49 b.h.p., or 81 × 63 mm.; 1,298 c.c.; 58 b.h.p.; 9 to 1 comp.; Ford carb.; 4-speed, 15.08, 9.01, 5.88, 4.125 to 1; cen. lvr.; susp. f. ind. coil, r. half elliptic; 2 or 4-door; 4-seat; brks. disc front and servo opt.; max. 79/83 m.p.h.; cruise, 72-78; m.p.g. 30-34; whl. base, 7ft. 10½in.; track f. 4ft. 0½in., r. 4ft. 1¾in.; lgth. 13ft. 4in.; width 5ft. 1¾in.; ht. 4ft. 7in.; g.c. 6½in.; turng. cir. 30ft.; kerb wt. 15¼ cwt.; tank 9 gals.; 12-volt.

1100 from £512 + £160 p.t. = £672
1300 from £592 + £181 p.t. = £773

FORD CORSAIR 2000 E

FORD'S bargain priced entry in the 2000 c.c. executive category has the vinyl covered top and matt black interior which are today's conventional symbols of prestige and luxury. The V4 pushrod engine is rough but rugged. Good points are the brakes, the all-synchromesh gearbox with remote control and the vast luggage boot. Extractor ventilation keeps driver and passengers alert and untired on long trips.

CLOSE-UP
Four-cyl.; o.h.v.; 93.7 × 72.4 mm.; 1,996 c.c., 97 b.h.p.; 8.9 to 1 comp.; Weber carb.; 4-speed, 11.25, 7.59, 5.28, 3.77 to 1; cen. lvr.; susp. f. ind. coil, r. half-elliptic; 4-door; 5-seat; disc/drum servo brks.; max. 96 m.p.h.; cruise 85; m.p.g. 21-25; whl. base 8ft. 5in.; track f. 4ft. 2½in., r. 4ft. 1½in.; lgth. 14ft. 8½in.; width 5ft. 3½in.; ht. 4ft. 9in.; g.c. 6in.; turng. cir. 36ft. 6in.; kerb wt. 20¼ cwt.; tank 10 gals.; 12-volt.

£868 + £265 p.t. = £1,133

FORD CORTINA SUPER

THIS is the luxury version of the highly successful and well-proven Cortina range. It comes with either two or four doors and has a host of choices. For instance the Cortina Super can be fitted with an automatic transmission or a 4-speed gear box; either floor or column gear change; and there is a choice of bench or individual front seats. All this with the power of a 1600 c.c. crossflow engine.

CLOSE-UP
Four-cyl.; o.h.v.; 81×78 mm.; 1,599 c.c.; 71 b.h.p.; 9 to 1 comp.; Ford carb.; 4-speed, 13.82, 9.34, 5.50, 3.9 to 1; cen. lvr. BW auto. opt.; susp. f. ind. coil, r. half-elliptic; 2 4-door; 4/5-seat; disc/drum brks.; max. 87 m.p.h.; cruise 78; m.p.g. 27-30; whl. base 8ft. 2in.; track f. 4ft. 5½in., r. 4ft. 3in.; lgth. 14ft.; width 5ft. 5in.; ht. 4ft. 7¾in.; g.c. 6½in.; turng. cir. 30ft.; kerb wt. 17½ cwt.; tank 10 gals.; 12-volt.

From **£670 + £205** p.t. = **£875**

FORD ZEPHYR

NOT exactly Ford's best seller, but a familiar model that has had a lot of development over the years and gets a new series of improvements for 1970. Choice of V4 or V6 engines. There are fade resistant disc brakes on all four wheels. The spare wheel is up front with the engine to leave the boot entirely free for luggage. Automatic transmission is among the options.

CLOSE-UP
Four-cyl.; o.h.v.; 93.7×72.4 mm.; 1,996 c.c.; 88 b.h.p.; 8.9 to 1 comp. (Six-cyl.; 93.7×60.3 mm.; 2,495 c.c.; 112 b.h.p.; 9 to 1 comp.); Zenith carb.; 4-speed, 16.3, 8.7, 5.6, 3.7 to 1 (Six, 12.3, 8.6, 5.5, 3.9 to 1); col. lvr.; susp. f. and r. ind. coil; 4-door; 5/6-seat; disc servo brks.; max. 88/96 m.p.h.; cruise 78/85; m.p.g. 18/26; whl. base 9ft. 7in.; track f. 4ft. 9in., r. 4ft. 10in.; lgth. 15ft. 5in.; width, 5ft. 11½in.; ht. 4ft. 10½in.; g.c. 6in.; turng. cir. 35ft.; kerb wt. 24¼/25¾ cwt.; tank 15 gals.; 12-volt.

Four: **£747 + £228** p.t. = **£975**
Six: **£807 + £247** p.t. = **£1,054**

FORD 20M

SOMETHING from Cologne that you can't get from Dagenham; a good looking big coupe with a sporting air. This one has a 2.3 litre V8 engine with four speed box. The brakes have dual circuits with discs in front and the well planned equipment includes automatic choke, reversing lamps, alternator, electric clock, sealed cooling system with two year anti-freeze, steering column lock, four-jet screen washer and reclining seats.

CLOSE-UP
Six-cyl.; o.h.v..; 84×60 mm.; 1,998 c.c.; 90 b.h.p.; 8 to 1 comp.; Solex carb.; 4-speed, 12.6, 7.3, 5.8, 3.7 to 1; cen. lvr.; susp. f. ind. coil, r. half-elliptic; 2-door; 4-seat; disc/drum servo. brks.; max. 97 m.p.h.; cruise 85; m.p.g. 24-28; whl. base 8ft. 10½in.; track f. 4ft. 8½in., r. 4ft. 7½in.; lgth. 15ft. 6in.; width 5ft. 9in.; ht. 4ft. 10¾in.; g.c. 6⅛in.; turng. cir. 35ft. 6in.; kerb wt. 22 cwt.; tank 10 gals.; 12-volt.

£1,235 + £379 p.t. = **£1,614**

FORD MUSTANG MACH I

FORD'S best selling sporting car replies to the growing competition with new front and rear styling, on seven different models with a choice of nine engines; two sixes and seven V8s, driving through a choice of three transmissions, three-speed manual, four-speed manual or automatic. New features include oval steering wheel, high-backed seats, glass reinforced tyres, tamper proof odometer to defeat shady used car dealers.

CLOSE-UP
Eight-cyl.; o.h.v.; 105×101 mm.; 7,015 c.c.; 330 b.h.p. gross; 10 to 1 comp.; Autolite 4-choke carb.; 4-speed, 8.1, 5.9, 4.5, 3.5 to 1; cen. lvr. Ford auto. opt.; susp. f. ind. coil, r. half-elliptic; 2-door; 2/4 seat; disc/drum servo brks.; max.135 m.p.h.; cruise 110; m.p.g. 15-20; whl. base 9ft.; track f. and r. 4ft. 10½in.; lgth. 15ft. 7½in.; width 5ft. 11½in.; ht. 4ft. 3½in.; g.c. 7in.; turng. cir. 37ft. 6in.; kerb wt. 25½ cwt.; tank 13½ gals.; 12-volt.

Abbreviations—g.c.—ground clearance; susp.—suspension; f.—front; r.—rear; comp.—compression; s.v.—side-valves; o.h.v.—overhead valves; o.h.c.—overhead camshaft; hyd.—hydraulic.

FORD MAVERICK

WITH imports taking 12 per cent of the American market, the Maverick is the first of a new generation of home-built "compacts" to stem the tide. Design is strictly conventional with in-line six-cylinder engine at front driving a rear axle on half-elliptic springs. Engines can be 2.8 or 3.4 litres; transmission three-speed manual, three-speed semi-automatic or fully automatic.

CLOSE-UP

Six-cyl.; o.h.v.; 93.4×79.5 mm.; 3,380 c.c.; 120 b.h.p. gross; 8.7 to 1 comp.; Ford carb.; 3-speed, 10.5, 5.72, 3.08 to 1; col. lvr. auto-opt.; susp. f. ind. coil, r. half-elliptic; 2-door; 4-seat; drum brks.; max. 90 m.p.h.; cruise 80; m.p.g. 21-23; whl. base 8ft. 7in.; track f. and r. 4ft. 7½in.; lgth. 14ft. 11⅛in.; width 5ft. 10⅝in.; ht. 4ft. 4¼in.; g.c. 5½in.; turng. cir. 36ft. 4in.; kerb wt. 22½ cwt.; tank 12¾ gals.; 12-volt.

GILBERN INVADER

INVADER ousts Genie from the production line of the only Welsh car maker. The glass fibre body has recessed door handles, new lamp styling, revised wheel arches. Springs are softer; front suspension has twin wishbones instead of single upper arm. A Panhard rod now locates the rear axle and brakes are servo assisted. They say the Ford V6 engine rushes it up to 100 mph in 25 seconds.

CLOSE-UP

Six-cyl.; o.h.v.; 93.7×72.4 mm.; 2,994 c.c.; 141 b.h.p.; 8.9 to 1 comp.; Weber twin-choke carb.; 4-speed, 10.55, 7.38, 4.71, 3.34 to 1; cen. lvr. L de N overdrive or BW auto opt.; susp. f. ind. coil, r. coil; 2-door; 4-seat; servo brks., disc front; max. 125 m.p.h.; cruise 110; m.p.g. 18-23; whl. base 7ft. 8¾in.; track f. 4ft. 6in., r. 4ft. 6½in.; lgth. 13ft. 3in.; width 5ft. 5in.; ht. 4ft. 4in.; g.c. 6in.; turng. cir. 31ft.; kerb wt. 19¾ cwt.; tank 14 gals.; 12-volt.

£1,840+£562 p.t. = £2,402

GINETTA G15

THERE'S a waiting list as this small Essex outfit builds up production of its unusual sports coupé with twin-carb. Hillman Imp engine at the rear. Current output is about 100 a year. Body is glass fibre on a tubular steel chassis with wishbones and coil springs at front, trailing arms and coils at rear. Front brakes are discs. A new feature is an optional sun roof.

CLOSE-UP

Four-cyl.; o.h.c.; 68×60 mm.; 875 c.c.; 51 b.h.p.; 10.1 to 1 comp.; 2 Stromberg carbs.; 4-speed, 16.6, 8.9, 5.7, 4.14 to 1; cen. lvr.; susp. f. and r. ind. coil; 2-door; 2-seat; disc/drum brks.; max. 98 m.p.h.; cruise 85; m.p.g. 32-35; whl. base 6ft. 10in.; track f. 4ft. 1in., r. 4ft. 0¾in.; lgth. 12ft. 0¼in.; width 4ft. 9in.; ht. 3ft. 8½in.; g.c. 6in.; turng. cir. 33ft.; kerb wt. 9½ cwt.; tank 7 gals.; 12-volt.

£799+£244 p.t. = £1,043

HILLMAN GT

LONDON to Sydney may not be your normal beat, but some of the rugged power of the Marathon winner is yours in this fast family saloon. Wide-rim wheels, racing stripes and high-backed seats with neck rests hint at the performance delivered by the 94 bhp twin-carburetter engine. Padded steering wheel covered in leather cloth and binnacle-mounted tachometer aid the performance image.

CLOSE-UP

Four-cyl.; o.h.v.; 81.5×82.5 mm.; 1,725 c.c.; 94 b.h.p.; 9.2 to 1 comp.; Two Zenith carbs.; 4-speed, 12.41, 7.92, 5.15, 3.7 to 1; cen. lvr.; susp. f. ind. coil, r. half-elliptic; 4-door; 4/5-seat; disc/drum brks.; max. 100 m.p.h.; cruise 90; m.p.g. 25-30; whl. base 8ft. 2½in.; track f. and r. 4ft. 4½in.; lgth. 14ft.; width 5ft. 3½in.; ht. 4ft. 8in.; g.c. 6¾in.; turng. cir. 34ft.; kerb wt. 18⅞ cwt.; tank 10 gals.; 12-volt.

£735+£227 p.t. = £962

Abbreviations—g.c.—ground clearance; susp.—suspension; f.—front; r.—rear; comp.—compression; s.v.—side-valves; o.h.v.—overhead valves; o.h.c.—overhead camshaft; hyd.—hydraulic.

HILLMAN IMP

BLOCK Buster. Priced to beat the sales blockage created by high taxes and credit curbs, the latest Imp retains the essential advantages of the eager smooth-revving light alloy engine with overhead camshaft, the all-round independent suspension and the load-carrying convenience of the lift-up rear window and fold-down rear seat. Speeds up to 80 mph are possible and fuel consumption up to 45 mpg.

CLOSE-UP

Four-cyl.; o.h.c.; 68×60 mm.; 875 c.c.; 39 b.h.p.; 10 to 1 comp.; Solex carb.; 4-speed, 16.59, 8.91, 5.70, 4.14 to 1; cen. lvr.; susp. f. and r. ind. coil; 2-door; 4-seat; drum brks.; max. 80 m.p.h.; cruise 75; m.p.g. 40; whl. base 6ft. 10in.; track f. 4ft. 2⅜in., r. 4ft.; lgth. 11ft. 7in.; width 5ft. 0¼in.; ht. 4ft. 6in.; g.c. 5½in.; turng. cir. 30ft. 6in.; kerb wt. 14⅛ cwt.; tank 6 gals.; 12-volt.

£435+£135 p.t. = £570

HILLMAN MINX

LOWEST priced model in a range of Hillman, Singer, Humber and Sunbeam cars that has transformed the Rootes image. Lighter, livelier and right up to date in style, the Minx now has disc front brakes. The engine is 1496 c.c. with manual gearbox; 1725 with automatic transmission. The Minx de luxe has a centre console and fitted carpets. A station wagon is available too.

CLOSE-UP

Four-cyl.; o.h.v.; 81.5×71.6 mm.; 1,496 c.c.; 60 b.h.p; 8.4 to 1 comp.; Zenith Stromberg carb.; 4-speed, 13.04. 8.32, 5.41, 3.89 to 1; cen. lvr.; susp. f. ind. coil, r. half-elliptic; 4-door; 4/5 seat; disc/drum brks.; max. 80 m.p.h.; cruise 70; m.p.g. 30-34; whl. base 8ft. 2½in.; track f. and r. 4ft. 4in.; lgth. 14ft.; width 5ft. 3½in.; ht. 4ft. 8in.; g.c. 6¾in.; turng. cir. 33ft. 6in.; kerb wt. 18¼ cwt.; tank 10 gals.; 12-volt.

£625+£193 p.t. = £818

HONDA 1300

HONDA uses his motor cycle experience in car design with a revolutionary overhead cam air-cooled engine mounted transversely, and driving the front wheels. Front suspension uses coil spring struts and the rear borrows an idea from Ford light trucks with long crossover swing axles on half-elliptic springs. The claimed performance should put it at the top of its class and they say the engine is quiet for an air-cooled unit.

CLOSE-UP

Four-cyl.; o.h.c. air-cooled; 74×75.5 mm.; 1,298 c.c.; 9 to 1 comp.; Keihin carb.; 4-speed, 12.81, 7.63, 5.38, 4.08 to 1; cen. lvr.; susp. f. ind. coil, r. ind. half-elliptic; 4-door; 4-seat; disc brks.; max. 108 m.p.h.; cruise 90; whl. base 7ft. 4½in.; track f. 3ft. 11⅞in., r. 4ft. 0⅜in.; lgth. 12ft. 7½in.; width 4ft. 9in.; ht. 4ft. 5in.; g.c. 5½in.; turng. cir. 31ft. 6in.; kerb wt. 15½ cwt.; tank 9 gals.; 12-volt.

HUMBER SCEPTRE

LAST survivor of a long line of Humbers, the Sceptre offers compact luxury at a keen price. Four headlamps, special wheel discs, vinyl roof covering are matched inside by wood veneer facia, adjustable steering column, reclining seats. Standard transmission is four speed synchromesh with overdrive on third and top; automatic transmission is optional. Rear window is electrically heated.

CLOSE-UP

Four-cyl.; o.h.v.; 81.5×82.5 mm.; 1,725 c.c.; 88 b.h.p.; 9.2 to 1 comp.; 2 Stromberg carbs.; 4-speed, 13.04, 8.32, 5.41, 3.89 to 1; L de N overdrive; cen. lvr.; susp. f. ind. coil, r. half-elliptic; 4-door; 4-seat; servo brks., disc/drum; max. 97 m.p.h.; cruise 80; m.p.g. 25-30; whl. base 8ft. 2½in.; track f. and r. 4ft. 4in.; lgth. 14ft. 1½in.; width 5ft. 4in.; ht. 4ft. 8in.; g.c. 6¾in.; turng. cir. 33ft. 6in.; kerb wt. 19½ cwt.; tank 10 gals.; 12-volt.

£925+£284 p.t. = £1,209

ISO RIVOLTA FIDIA 350

USING the Chevrolet Corvette engine and gearbox in an Italian built platform chassis, the late Signor Rivolta built up a reputation for very fast, comfortable roadworthy GT cars. Bodywork of the first cars was by Bertone but Ghia builds this new four-door model capable of accelerating in a sustained rush from a standstill to over 140 m.p.h. Among the equipment are electrically operated windows and safety lamps in the door edges.

CLOSE-UP

Eight-cyl.; o.h.v.; 101.6×82.5 mm.; 5,359 c.c.; 350 b.h.p. gross; 10.25 to 1 comp.; Holley 4-choke carb.; 5-speed, 9.04, 5.82, 4.07, 3.31, 2.74 to 1; cen. lvr.; susp. f. ind. coil, r. de Dion coil; 4-door; 4-seat; disc servo brks.; max. 142 m.p.h.; cruise 115; m.p.g. 11-14; whl. base 9ft. 4½in.; track f. and r. 4ft. 7½in.; lgth. 16ft. 3⅝in.; width 5ft. 10½in.; ht. 4ft. 4in.; g.c. 4¾in.; turng. cir. 44ft.; kerb wt. 32¼ cwt.; tank 23 gals.; 12-volt.

JAGUAR 420G

THIS is one of the largest cars available in Europe and is the top-of-the-range Jaguar model in terms of size, cost and prestige. It has plentiful accommodation for five or even six adults and a truly cavernous luggage boot. All this is propelled by a 4.2 litre, twin overhead camshaft, three carburetter engine. It has manual transmission—with or without overdrive or fully automatic. Electric lift windows and air conditioning are optional.

CLOSE-UP

Six-cyl.; o.h.c.; 92×106 mm.; 4,235 c.c.; 255 b.h.p. gross; 8 to 1 comp.; 3 SU carbs.; 4-speed, 10.76, 6.98, 4.7, 3.54 to 1; cen. lvr.; susp. f and r. ind. coil; 4-door; 4/5-seat; disc servo brks.; max. 122 m.p.h.; cruise 105; m.p.g. 15-18; whl. base 10ft.; track f. and r. 4ft. 10in.; lgth. 16ft. 10in.; width 6ft. 4in.; ht. 4ft. 6½in.; g.c. 6½in.; turng. cir., 37ft. 3in.; kerb wt. 35½ cwt.; tank 20 gals.; 12-volt. **£2,044 + £627 p.t. = £2,671**

JAGUAR XJ6

DEMAND exceeds supply and people have been paying over the odds on the home market reckoning that the Jaguar is still unbeatable value at a premium price. Low centre of gravity, race-proved independent suspension, wide-radial tyres give exemplary road grip and cornering power. 2.8 or 4.2-litre engine.

CLOSE-UP

Six-cyl.; o.h.c. 83×86 mm.; 2,792 c.c.; 180 b.h.p. gross; 9 to 1 comp.; 2 SU carbs.; 4-speed, 12.5, 8.14, 5.93, 4.27 to 1; or 92.7×106 mm.; 4,235 c.c.; 245 b.h.p. gross; 9 to 1 comp.; 4-speed, 10.38, 6.74, 4.92, 3.54 to 1; cen. lvr. L de N overdrive or BW auto. opt.; susp. f. and r. ind. coil; 4-door; 4-seat; disc servo brks.; max. 115-120 m.p.h.; cruise 100; m.p.g. 15-19; whl. base 9ft. 0¾in.; track f. 4ft. 10in., r. 4ft. 10½in.; lgth. 15ft. 9⅝in.; width 5ft. 9¾in.; ht 4ft. 4⅞in.; g.c. 6in.; turng. cir. 36ft.; kerb wt. 31¼/32½ cwt.; tank 23 gals.; 12-volt.

2.8 Litre £1,530 + £470 p.t. = £2,000
4.2 Litre £1,894 + £581 p.t. = £2,475

JAGUAR E TYPE 2+2

THE legendary fast coupé at an unbeatable price. Maximum speed may be a bit down since they took the fairings off the headlamps, but 135 m.p.h. is enough for most people and even with optional automatic transmission it will do 0-100 m.p.h. in about 19 seconds. Luxurious comfort for two adults plus one more or two children at the rear and a good deal of luggage, which is easy to load through the lift-up rear window.

CLOSE-UP

Six-cyl.; o.h.c.; 92.1×106 mm.; 4,235 c.c.; 265 b.h.p. gross; 9 to 1 comp.; 3 SU carbs.; 4-speed, 8.23, 5.34, 3.90, 3.07 to 1; cen. lvr., auto. opt.; susp. f. torsion bar, r. ind. coil; 2-door; 2/4-seat; disc servo brks.; max. 135 m.p.h.; cruise 115; m.p.g. 18-20; whl. base 8ft. 9in.; track f. and r. 4ft. 2in.; lgth. 15ft. 4½in.; width 5ft. 5½in.; ht. 4ft. 2in.; g.c. 5½in.; turng. cir. 41ft.; kerb wt. 26½ cwt.; tank 18 gals.; 12-volt.

£2,022 + £620 p.t. = £2,642

JENSEN FF II

FERGUSON Formula four-wheel-drive and Dunlop Maxaret non-skid braking give this Jensen unmatched safety, whether accelerating fast to 100 or over, or stopping suddenly on slippery surfaces. New for 1970; restyled interior, reclining seats with detachable headrests, collapsible steering column, larger fuel tank, improved front suspension. Four-speaker radio, electric windows, hazard warning flasher, first aid kit are included.

CLOSE-UP
Eight-cyl.; o.h.v.; 108×86 mm.; 6,276 c.c.; 330 b.h.p. gross; 10 to 1 comp.; Carter 4-choke carb.; 3-speed auto., 7.05, 4.16, 2.88 to 1; col. lvr.; susp. f. ind. coil, r. half-elliptic; 2-door; 4-seat; disc servo brks. with Maxaret; max. 130 m.p.h.; cruise 110; m.p.g. 12-15; whl. base 9ft. 1in.; track f. and r. 4ft. 8¼in.; lgth. 15ft. 11in.; width 5ft. 9in.; ht. 4ft. 5in.; g.c. 5in.; turng. cir. 39ft.; kerb wt. 34 cwt.; tank 20 gals.; 12-volt.
£5,900 + £1,805 p.t. = £7,705

JENSEN INTERCEPTOR II

SLIGHT styling changes now make it easier to tell rear-drive Interceptor from all-wheel-drive FF. Interceptor offers swift, silent travel in the grand manner. Standard comforts are electrically controlled windows, radio aerial, filler flap. Also included are clock, reversing lights, fire extinguisher, headrests, steering column lock, low profile radial tyres and razor socket.

CLOSE-UP
Eight-cyl.; o.h.v.; 108×86 mm.; 6,276 c.c.; 330 b.h.p. gross; 10 to 1 comp.; Carter 4-choke carb.; 3-speed auto., 7.05, 4.16, 2.88 to 1; col. lvr.; susp. f. ind. coil, r. half-elliptic; 2-door; 4-seat; disc servo brks.; max. 132 m.p.h.; cruise 110; m.p.g. 15-18; whl. base 8ft. 9in.; track f. 4ft. 7⅞in., r. 4ft. 8⅝in.; lgth. 15ft. 8in.; width 5ft. 9in.; ht. 4ft. 5in.; g.c. 5½in.; turng. cir. 38ft.; kerb wt. 31¼ cwt.; tank 20 gals.; 12-volt.
£4,470 + £1,368 p.t. = £5,838

LAMBORGHINI ISLERO

THE fame of Lamborghini's beautifully built twelve cylinder speed models was such that Britons made the pilgrimage to the factory to buy left hand drive models long before he had an agent here. Now the Islero with the low built coupé body of deceptively simple line by Marrazzi comes with right hand drive. Chassis is square section tube, suspension is by wishbones and coil springs all round.

CLOSE-UP
Twelve-cyl.; o.h.c.; 82×62 mm.; 3,929 c.c.; 335 b.h.p.; 9.8 to 1 comp.; 6 Weber twin-choke carbs.; 5-speed, 10.31, 8.81, 4.99, 4.09, 3.31 to 1; cen. lvr; susp. f. and r. ind. coil; 2-door; 2/4-seat; disc servo brks.; max.165 m.p.h.; cruise 140; m.p.g. 12-15; whl. base 8ft. 4¼in.; track f. and r. 4ft. 6¼in.; lgth. 14ft. 10in.; width 5ft. 8in.; ht. 4ft. 2in.; g.c. 5in.; turng. cir. 37ft. 9in.; kerb wt. 25 cwt.; tank 23 gals.; 12-volt.
£6,120 + £1,830 p.t. + £7,950

LAMBORGHINI ESPADA

A sure-fire traffic stopper, the Espada has no chassis, but a unit structure built by Bertone with seats for four and luggage space behind. To keep the dramatic lines at the right angle regardless of load variations, it has self levelling suspension and air conditioning is an optional extra. The light alloy V12 engine has four overhead camshafts and six twin choke carburetters.

CLOSE-UP
Twelve-cyl.; o.h.c.; 82×62 mm.; 3,929 c.c.; 320 b.h.p.; 9.5 to 1 comp.; six Weber twin-choke carbs.; 5-speed, 10.31, 7.07, 4.99, 4.09, 3.31 to 1; cen. lvr.; susp. f. and r. ind. coil; 2-door; 4-seat; disc servo brks.; max. 155 m.p.h.; cruise 135; m.p.g. 14-16; whl. base 8ft. 8¼in.; track f. and r. 4ft. 10½in.; lgth. 15ft. 6in.; width 6ft. 0in.; ht. 3ft. 11in.; g.c. 4½in.; turng. cir. 37ft. 9in.; kerb wt. 33¾ cwt.; tank 21 gals.; 12-volt.
£7,900 + £2,395 p.t. = £10,295

LANCIA FULVIA RALLYE

QUICK off the mark, light and nimble, the Fulvia coupé shows quality in every detail. Power comes from an overhead-cam V4 driving the front wheels. Doors, bonnet and boot lid are light alloy to save weight. The works team is now making a hit in international rallies. The Fulvia saloon has been given a longer wheelbase, more rear seat room and bigger boot.

CLOSE-UP
Four-cyl.; o.h.c.; 77×70 mm.; 1,298 c.c.; 87 b.h.p.; 9 to 1 comp.; 2 Solex 2-choke carbs.; 4-speed, 13.65, 8.06, 5.25, 3.7 to 1; cen. lvr.; susp. f. ind. transv. leaf, r. half-elliptic; 2-door; 2/4 seat; disc brks.; max 104 m.p.h.; cruise 95; m.p.g. 29-33; whl. base 7ft. 8in.; track f. 4ft. 3¼in.; r. 4ft. 2⅜in.; lgth. 13ft. 0½in.; width 5ft. 1½in.; ht. 4ft. 3½in.; g.c. 5in.; turng. cir. 34ft.; kerb wt. 18 cwt.; tank 8½ gals.; 12-volt.

£1,299 + £399 p.t. = £1,698

LANCIA FLAVIA 2000 COUPE

HIGH class, high speed carriage with graceful new body by Pininfarina giving 2+2 accommodation and good luggage space. Powered by new 2-litre flat-four light alloy engine. Full width grille carries four quartz iodine headlights. Disc brakes on Lancia Duplex servo assisted system with independent circuits front and rear. Headroom is good and padded headlining ensures silence at 100 m.p.h.

CLOSE-UP
Four-cyl.; o.h.v.; 89×80 mm.; 1,991 c.c.; 130 b.h.p. gross; 9 to 1 comp.; Solex twin-choke carb.; 4-speed, 11.7, 6.8, 4.8, 3.54 to 1; cen. lvr.; susp. f. ind. transv. leaf, r. half-elliptic; 2-door; 4-seat; disc servo brks.; max. 112 m.p.h.; cruise 100; m.p.g. 24-27; whl. base 8ft. 1⅛in.; track f. 4ft. 4in., r. 4ft. 2⅜in.; lgth. 14ft. 10¾in.; width 5ft. 3¼in.; ht. 4ft. 4⅜in.; g.c. 5¼in.; turng. cir. 36ft.; kerb wt. 23¼ cwt.; tank 12 gals.; 12-volt.

£2,225 + £682 p.t. = £2,907

LINCOLN CONTINENTAL MK III

THIS 2-door coupé is one of the top prestige cars from Ford of America. Its equipment is lavish with aids like power-assisted disc brakes at front, power-assisted steering and simple-as-pie automatic transmission. Believe it or not this svelte model comes in more than a score of colours and with a wide choice of leathers and woodwork inside.

CLOSE-UP
Eight-cyl.; o.h.v.; 110.7×97.7 mm.; 7,544 c.c.; 365 b.h.p. gross; 10.5 to 1 comp.; Autolite 4-choke carb.; 3-speed Turbo Drive auto, 6.89, 4.09, 2.8 to 1; col. lvr.; susp. f. ind. coil, r. coil; 2-door; 4-seat; disc/drum servo brks.; max. 120 m.p.h.; cruise 90; m.p.g. 10-15; whl. base 9ft. 9¼in.; track f. and r. 5ft. 2in.; lgth. 18ft.; width 6ft. 7⅜in.; ht. 4ft. 6in.; g.c. 5½in.; turng. cir. 42ft.; kerb wt. 42½ cwt.; tank 19 gals.; 12-volt.

LOTUS ELAN S.4

WIND-CHEATING lines and G-cheating cornering power reflect the Lotus racing background. Steel backbone chassis with front-mounted Lotus-Ford engine and all-independent suspension; glass fibre body with electric windows. Headlamps pop up fast enough for daytime flashing. Elan comes as coupé or convertible; Elan+2 has longer wheelbase, occasional seats in the rear, and is available with coupé body only.

CLOSE-UP
Four-cyl.; o.h.c.; 83×73 mm.; 1,558 c.c.; 105 b.h.p.; 9.5 to 1 comp.; 2 Weber 2 choke carbs.; 4-speed, 11.2, 7.58, 5.28, 3.77 to 1; cen. lvr.; susp. f. and r. ind. coil; 2-door; 2-seat; disc brks.; max. 115 m.p.h.; cruise 100; m.p.g. 23-26; whl. base 7ft.; track f. 3ft. 11in., r. 4ft. 1in.; lgth. 12ft. 1¼in.; width 4ft. 8in.; ht. 3ft. 10in.; g.c. 6in.; turng. cir. 31ft.; kerb wt. 13½ cwt.; tank 10 gals.; 12-volts.

£1,486 + £456 p.t. = £1,942

Abbreviations—g.c.—ground clearance; susp.—suspension; f.—front; r.—rear; comp.—compression; s.v.—side-valves; o.h.v.—overhead valves; o.h.c.—overhead camshaft; hyd.—hydraulic.

LOTUS EUROPA S2

BRITONS Last. This mid-engined light-weight, shipped to thirty-five countries to boost the export drive is at last available to British buyers. Engine and transmission from the Renault 16 with bigger valves, special camshaft, higher compression and different carburetter to produce 82 bhp at 6,000 rpm. Streamlined glass fibre body on a steel backbone chassis. Electric windows standard, servo brakes optional.

CLOSE-UP

Four-cyl.; o.h.v.; 76×81 mm.; 1,470 c.c.; 82 b.h.p. 10.25 to 1 comp.; Solex twin-choke carb.; 4-speed 12.85, 8.01, 5.27, 3.67 to 1; cen. lvr.; susp. f. and r. ind coil; 2-door; 2-seat; disc/drum brks.; max. 115 m.p.h. cruise 100; m.p.g. 30-35; whl. base 7ft. 7in.; track f. 4ft 5in.; r. 4ft. 5¼in.; lgth. 13ft. 1½in.; width 5ft. 4½in.; ht 3ft. 7in.; g.c. 6½in.; turng. cir. 40ft.; kerb wt. 12½ cwt. tank 7 gals.; 12-volt.

£1,275 + £392 p.t. = £1,667

MARCOS 3-LITRE

OUT of the wood. Moving from their riverside mill at Bradford on Avon to a fine new factory, Marcos shed the plywood chassis that has been their unique feature since the beginning and adopt a new one in steel tubes. The engines are Ford. The 3-litre V6 is the performance leader, but the Show brings a new 2-litre V4 to replace the 1600.

CLOSE-UP

Six-cyl.; o.h.v.; 93.7×72.4 mm.; 2,994 c.c.; 144 b.h.p. gross; 8.9 to 1 comp.; Weber twin-choke carb.; 4-speed, 11.91, 8.33, 5.31, 3.77 to 1, L de N overdrive; cen. lvr.; susp. f. ind. coil, r. coil; 2-door; 2-seat; disc/drum servo brks.; max. 130 m.p.h.; cruise, 110; m.p.g. 20-25; whl. base 7ft. 5in.; track f. 4ft. 2½in., r. 4ft. 4in.; lgth. 13ft. 4½in.; width 5ft. 3¾in.; ht. 3ft. 9½in.; g.c. 5in.; turng. cir. 28ft.; kerb wt. 16½ cwt.; tank 10 gals.; 12-volt.

£1,790 + £560 p.t. = £2,350

MAZDA 1500

SPORTY saloon with a quality air, styled in Italy by Bertone, built in Japan for world markets. Simple suspension with coil springs in front, half elliptic at rear, gives quite good ride and roadholding. Like so many Japanese engines this one is extremely flexible, with terrific low speed slogging power in top gear. It uses a compound twin choke carburetter on which only one choke operates for low speed running.

CLOSE-UP

Four-cyl.; o.h.c.; 78×78 mm.; 1,490 c.c.; 77 b.h.p. gross; 8.2 to 1 comp.; Nikki carb.; 4-speed, 15.3, 9.0 5.9, 4.1 to 1; col. lvr. BW. auto. opt.; susp. f. ind. coil r. half-elliptic; 4-door; 4/5-seat; disc/drum brks.; max 92 m.p.h.; cruise 80; m.p.g. 27-33; whl. base 8ft. 2⅜in. track f. 4ft. 4⅜in., r. 4ft. 4in.; lgth. 14ft. 4in.; width 5ft. 4½in.; ht. 4ft. 7½in.; g.c. 7in.; turng. cir. 29ft.; kerb wt. 20½ cwt.; tank 11 gals.; 12-volt.

MASERATI GHIBLI

BREATHTAKING elegance of line marks out the Ghibli coupé body styled by Giugiaro and built by Ghia on the same tubular chassis that is used for Vignale's four seater Mexico coupé. The Ghibli is also available as convertible. The engine is a light alloy V8 with four overhead camshafts chain driven. The disc brakes have twin circuits and twin servos.

CLOSE-UP

Eight-cyl.; o.h.c.; 94×85 mm.; 4,719 c.c.; 290 b.h.p.; 8.5 to 1 comp.; 4 twin-choke Weber carbs.; 5-speed, 9.83, 6.36, 4.34, 3.31, 2.98 to 1; cen. lvr.; susp. f. ind. coil, r. half-elliptic; 2-door; 2-seat; disc servo brks.; max. 174 m.p.h.; cruise 150; m.p.g. 13-15; whl. base 8ft. 4½in.; track f. 4ft. 8⅝in., r. 4ft. 7⅞in.; lgth. 15ft. 0¾in.; width 5ft. 10⅞in.; ht. 3ft. 9⅜in.; g.c. 5⅛in.; turng. cir. 36ft.; kerb wt. 28 cwt.; tank 22 gals.; 12-volt.

£7,795 + £2,384 p.t. = £10,179

MASERATI V8 QUATTROPORTE

UNLIKE the coupé Maseratis, the big luxurious four door saloon has a unit structure with separate front sub frame carrying the light alloy V8 engine. Frua does the bodywork and there is a choice of 4.2 or 4.7 litre engines with five-speed ZF gearbox and limited slip differential for those who like to stir their own or Borg Warner automatic for those who prefer to sit and steer.

CLOSE-UP

Eight-cyl.; o.h.v.; 94×85 mm.; 4,719 c.c.; 300 b.h.p. gross; 8.5 to 1 comp.; 4 Weber twin-choke carbs.; 5-speed, 9.66, 6.22, 4.35, 3.54, 3.0 to 1; cen. lvr.; BW auto. opt.; susp. f. ind. coil, r. half-elliptic; 4-door; 5-seat; disc servo brks.; max. 148 m.p.h.; cruise 110; m.p.g. 15-18; whl. base 9ft. 0¼in.; track f. 4ft. 6¾in., r. 4ft. 7½in.; lgth. 16ft. 4in.; width 5ft. 8in.; ht. 4ft. 5in.; g.c. 7in.; turng. cir. 36ft.; kerb wt. 33½ cwt.; tank 18 gals.; 12-volt.

£6,454+£1,974 p.t.=£8,428

MERCEDES BENZ 220

THE Mercedes star shines brightly on the "New Generation" cars. 220 is the four-cylinder model, quiet, comfortable and impeccably finished, with fine road holding from the new trailing arm rear suspension. The brakes can be used hard thanks to inbuilt anti-dive characteristics. For those who prefer six cylinders there are several saloons and the sporty new 250 coupe, with carburetter or injection engines.

CLOSE-UP

Four-cyl.; o.h.c.; 87×92.4 mm.; 2,197 c.c.; 105 b.h.p.; 9 to 1 comp.; Stromberg carb.; 4-speed, 15.91, 9.38, 5.75, 4.08 to 1; cen. lvr., MB auto. opt.; susp f. and r. ind. coil; 4-door; 4/5-seat; disc servo brks.; max. 104 m.p.h.; cruise 95; m.p.g. 18-22; whl. base 9ft. 0¼in.; track f. 4ft. 8¾in., r. 4ft. 8⅝in.; lgth. 15ft. 4½in.; width 5ft. 9⅝in.; ht. 4ft. 8⅝in.; g.c. 6¾in.; turng. cir. 32ft.; kerb wt. 25¼ cwt.; tank 14¼ gals.; 12-volt.

£1,867+£572 p.t.=£2,439

MERCEDES-BENZ C111

MILLIONAIRES need not apply; it's to be seen but not sold. With this sensational two-seater coupe powered by a three-rotor Wankel engine just ahead of the rear axle, Mercedes Benz continue development of a design that points the way to the future. Chassis like a Grand Prix car, five-speed gearbox, gas-filled shock absorbers—and glass fibre body with built-in roll bar feature on the experimental series.

CLOSE-UP

Three-rotor Wankel; 1,800 c.c.; 280 b.h.p.; Bosch fuel injection; 5-speed, final drive 3.77 to 1; cen. lvr.; susp. f. and r. ind. coil; 2-door; 2-seat; disc servo brks.; max. 162 m.p.h.; cruise 140; whl. base 8ft. 7⅛in.; track f. 4ft. 6⅜in., r. 4ft. 6in.; lgth. 13ft. 10½in.; width 5ft. 10⅞in.; ht. 3ft. 8¼in.; kerb wt. 21¾ cwt.; tank 26¼ gals.; 12-volt.

MERCEDES BENZ 300 SEL 3.5

LATEST development in the immense Mercedes Benz range is the light alloy 3.5-litre V8 engine which goes in the 300 SEL saloon, and in the 280 SE coupe and convertible which now have a lower bonnet and grille line because the V8 is lower than the ohc six. Electronic fuel injection and transistorised ignition mark the engine as an ultra modern unit. Photo shows 280 SE convertible.

CLOSE-UP

Eight-cyl.; o.h.c.; 92×65.8 mm.; 3,499 c.c.; 200 b.h.p. 9.5 to 1 comp.; Bosch injection; 4-speed, 14.94, 8.23, 5.17, 3.69 to 1; col. or cen. lvr., MB auto opt.; susp. f. and r. ind. coil, pneu. opt.; 4-door; 5-seat; disc servo brks.; max. 125 m.p.h.; cruise 110; m.p.g. 16-22; whl. base 9ft. 4¼in.; track f. 4ft. 10⅜in., r. 4ft. 10½in.; lgth. 16ft. 4⅞in.; width 5ft. 11¼in.; ht. 4ft. 7½in.; g.c. 6¼in.; turng. cir. 38ft. 6in.; kerb wt. 32¾ cwt.; tank 18 gals.; 12-volt.

Abbreviations—g.c.—ground clearance; susp.—suspension; f.—front; r.—rear; comp.—compression; s.v.—side-valves; o.h.v.—overhead valves; o.h.c.—overhead camshaft; hyd.—hydraulic.

MINI 1275 GT

MINI with muscle. Push-in-the-back to gear acceleration comes from the single carburetter 1,275 c.c. engine behind the new extended front. Close-ratio all-synchro gearbox pushes performance near to the level of the Mini Cooper (which continues with the previous body style). The plated wheels with wide rims are new, so are winding windows, interior styling and better seats (reclining backrests optional).

CLOSE-UP
Four-cyl., o.h.v.; 70.64×81.33 mm.; 1,275 c.c.; 5 b.h.p.; 8.8. to 1 comp.; S.U. carb.; 4-speed, 11.0, 6.6., 4.67, 3.44 to 1; cen. lvr., AP auto opt.; susp. f. and r. ind. rubber-hydraulic; 2-door; 4-seat; disc/drum servo brks.; max. 90 m.p.h.; cruise 80; m.p.g. 28-3 whl. base 6ft. 8in.; track f. 3ft. 11½in.; lgth. 10ft 5½in.; width 4ft. 7½in.; ht. 4ft. 5in.; g.c. 6in.; turng. cir 28ft. 6in.; kerb wt. 13 cwt.; tank 5½ gals.; 12-volt.

£637 + £197 p.t. = £834

MINI CLUBMAN

BREAKING the family ties, the Mini stands on its own at last; not Austin or Morris, just Mini. Bold new front, five inches longer, improves engine access. Doors are wider for easy entry, hinges are concealed. Windows wind up, seats are comfortable at last, the facia is new and there's face-level fresh air for driver and front passenger. Electrics have negative earth.

CLOSE-UP
Four-cyl.; o.h.v. 64.6×76.2 mm.; 998 c.c.; 38 b.h.p.; 8.3 to 1 comp.; SU carb.; 4-speed, 12.49, 7.46, 4.85, 3.44 to 1; cen. lvr., auto. opt.; susp, f. and r. ind. rubber-hyd.; 2-door; 4-seat; drum brks.; max 78 m.p.h.; cruise 70; m.p.g. 32-40; whl. base 6ft. 8in.; track f. 3ft. 11¾in., r. 3ft. 9⅞in.; lgth. 10ft. 5in.; width 4ft. 7½in.; ht. 4ft. 4in.; g.c. 6⅛in.; turng. cir. 28ft. 6in.; kerb wt. 12¼ cwt.; tank 5⅞ gals.; 12-volt.

£550 + £170 p.t. = £720

MONTEVERDI 400 SS

PETER Monteverdi, Swiss newcomer to the London show began building racing cars then turned to road cars with simple but striking objectives; the speed of a Grand Prix car, easy driving for women, safe braking and easy service. He builds his own chassis with engines and transmissions from Chrysler and bodies from Frua or Fissore. Safety steering column and other features are designed to meet American Regulations.

CLOSE-UP
Eight-cyl.; o.h.v.; 109.7×95.25 mm.; 7,206 c.c.; 39 b.h.p. gross; 10 to 1 comp.; two 4-choke Carter carbs 4-speed, 8.63, 5.47, 4.6, 2.88 to 1; cen. lvr., auto opt susp. f. ind. coil, r. de Dion coil; 2-door; 2/4-seat; servo brks.; max. 168 m.p.h.; cruise 145; m.p.g. 12-16 whl. base 8ft. 2⅜in.; track f. 4ft. 9½in., r. 4ft. 7⅞in lgth. 14ft. 11½in.; width 5ft. 10½in.; ht. 4ft. 0½in g.c. 5½in.; turng. cir. 39ft.; kerb wt. 31 cwt.; tank 2 gals.; 12-volt.

MG 1300

AFTER starting life with a single carburetter, then a low power twin-carb. unit, this two-door saloon with the sporty appearance at last has an engine worthy of the badge on the grille. It produces 70 b.h.p. to give quick acceleration and a maximum speed in the high nineties. Higher compression, bigger ports, new exhaust system, different carburetters explain the extra power. It's economical on fuel too.

CLOSE-UP
Four-cyl.; o.h.v.; 70.6×81.3 mm.; 1,275 c.c.; 70 b.h.p.; 9 to 1 comp.; 2 SU carbs.; 4-speed, 12.81, 8.08, 5.20, 3.64 to 1; cen. lvr.; susp. f. and r. ind. rubber-hyd.; 2-door; 4-seat; disc/drum brks.; max. 96 m.p.h.; cruise 83; m.p.g. 30-34; whl. base 7ft. 9½in.; track f. 4ft. 3⅛in., r. 4ft. 2⅞in.; lgth. 12ft. 2¾in.; width 5ft. 0⅞in.; ht. 4ft. 5in.; g.c. 6in.; turng. cir. 34ft. 9in.; kerb wt. 16¾ cwt.; tank 8 gals.; 12-volt.

Abbreviations—g.c.—ground clearance; susp.—suspension; f.—front; r.—rear; comp.—compression; s.v.—side-valves; o.h.v.—overhead valves; o.h.c.—overhead camshaft; hyd.—hydrauli

MG MGB

NO longer just for the helmet and goggles crowd, today's MGB comes as cosy convertible with optional moulded hard top, or as 2+2 GT coupe. New grille and bumpers, silver-spoke wheels, a more luxurious interior with new instrument panel and more comfortable seats are among the quality touches. Headrests are optional and the GT can have an electrically heated rear window.

CLOSE-UP
Four-cyl.; o.h.v.; 80.2×89 mm.; 1,798 c.c.; 95 b.h.p.; 8.9 to 1 comp.; two SU carbs.; 4-speed, 14.21, 8.66, 5.37, 3.91 to 1; cen. lvr.; susp. f. ind. coil, r. half-elliptic; 2-door; 2-seat; disc/drum brks.; max. 108 m.p.h.; cruise 85; m.p.g. 25-28; whl. base 7ft. 7in.; track f. 4ft. 1in., r. 4ft. 1¼in.; lgth. 12ft. 9¼in.; width 5ft.; ht. 4ft. 1¼in.; g.c. 5in.; turng. cir. 32ft.; kerb wt. 18⅛ cwt.; tank 12 gals.; 12-volt.

MORGAN PLUS 8

MORGAN first built three wheelers and the Plus 8 savours of Vintage motoring but in more comfort. Rover V8 engine rockets it from 0-100 in 19 seconds. Ride still pretty rugged. Concessions to comfort loving customers include heater, simple hood and detachable side screens. Luggage space behind the rear seats takes more than a towel and a toothbrush but don't try a cabin trunk.

CLOSE-UP
Eight-cyl.; o.h.v.; 89×71 mm.; 3,530 c.c.; 168 b.h.p.; 10.5 to 1 comp.; 2 S.U. carbs.; 4-speed, 10.48, 6.16, 4.25, 3.53 to 1; cen. lvr.; susp. f. ind. coil, r. half-elliptic; 2-door; 2-seat; disc/drum servo brks.; max. 124 m.p.h.; cruise 105; m.p.g. 20-23; whl. base 8ft. 2¼in.; track f. 4ft. 11½in., r. 4ft. 2⅜in.; lgth. 12ft. 9in.; width 4ft. 9¾in.; ht. 4ft. 1in.; g.c. 6in.; turng. cir. 38ft.; kerb wt. 17¼ cwt.; tank 13½ gals.; 12-volt.
£1,155+£352 p.t. = £1,507

MORGAN PLUS 4 2-SEATER

WITH the disappearance of Triumph's four cylinder engine, Morgan concentrate on the Ford Cortina GT for their lower priced cars and the Four/Four is available for road use with single carburetter and 70 b.h.p. or in competition form with twin choke carburetter and 90 b.h.p. It has the classic Morgan sliding pillar front suspension and front brakes are discs.

CLOSE-UP
Four-cyl.; o.h.v.; 81×78 mm.; 1,599 c.c.; 70 b.h.p.; 9 to 1 comp.; Zenith carb.; 4-speed, 12.2, 8.3, 5.7, 4.1 to 1; cen. lvr.; susp. f. ind. coil, r. half-elliptic; 2-door; 2-seat; disc/drum brks.; max. 94 m.p.h.; cruise 85; m.p.g. 25-28; whl. base 8ft.; track f. 3ft. 11in., r. 4ft. 1in.; lgth. 12ft.; width 4ft. 8in.; ht. 4ft. 4in.; g.c. 6½in.; turng. cir. 33ft. 9in.; kerb wt. 13 cwt.; tank 8½ gals.; 12-volt.
£755+£233 p.t. = £988

MORRIS MINOR 1000

THIS is the ever-green model of the entire British Leyland range. The original Issigonis design has been little changed in more than 10 years but despite its age the public still want it in many body styles that include two-door saloon, 4-door saloon and a spacious station wagon. The car is still very functional by modern standards.

CLOSE-UP
Four-cyl.; o.h.v.; 64.6×83.7 mm.; 1,098 c.c.; 48 b.h.p.; 8.5 to 1 comp.; SU carb.; 4-speed, 15.27, 9.16, 5.96, 4.22 to 1; cen. lvr.; susp. f. ind. torsion bar, r. half-elliptic; 2/4-door; 4-seat; drum brks.; max. 78 m.p.h.; cruise 68; m.p.g. 28-34; whl. base 7ft. 2in.; track f. 4ft. 2½ in., r. 4ft. 2½in.; lgth. 12ft. 4in.; width 5ft. 1in.; ht. 5ft.; g.c. 6¾in.; turng. cir. 33ft.; kerb wt. 15½ cwt.; tank 6½ gals.; 12-volt.
£500+£155 p.t. = £655

Abbreviations—g.c.—ground clearance; susp.—suspension; f.—front; r.—rear; comp.—compression; s.v.—side-valves; o.h.v.—overhead valves; o.h.c.—overhead camshaft; hyd.—hydraulic.

MORRIS 1800 MK II S

GAS flowed head, higher compression, twin SUs, free-flow exhaust produce an extra 10 horsepower enabling the 1800 to live up to the image created by its excellent performance in the London-Sydney Marathon. It does almost 100 m.p.h. but on 100 octane fuel. Modified front suspension permits quicker steering, power steering optional. Better seats and unbeatable interior space.

CLOSE-UP
Four-cyl.; o.h.v.; 80.26 × 88.9 mm.; 1,798 c.c.; 97 b.h.p.; 9.5 to 1 comp.; 2 SU carbs.; 4-speed, 12.77, 7.98, 5.37, 3.88 to 1; cen. lvr.; susp. f. and r. ind. rubber hydraulic; 4-door; 5-seat; disc/drum servo brks.; max. 100 m.p.h.; cruise 88; m.p.g. 22-24; whl. base 8ft. 10in.; track f. 4ft. 8in., r. 4ft. 7½in.; lgth. 13ft. 10¾in.; width 5ft. 7in.; ht. 4ft. 8in.; g.c. 6½in.; turng. cir. 37ft.; kerb wt. 23¼ cwt.; tank 10½ gals.; 12-volt.
£845 + £260 p.t. = £1,105

MOSKVICH

RUGGEDLY built to stand the hammering it takes on Russia's rotten roads, the Moskvich is heavy but practical. A full tool kit and inspection lamp are included because D.I.Y. is the only kind of service it's likely to get on its home ground and there are a lot of points to grease. Reclining seats, heater, radio, coat hooks are standard equipment. Brakes are self adjusting.

CLOSE-UP
Four-cyl.; o.h.c.; 82 × 70 mm.; 1,479 c.c.; 80 b.h.p. gross; 8.8 to 1 comp.; K-59 carb.; 4-speed, 16.1, 10.2, 6.1, 4.2 to 1; col. lvr.; susp. f. ind. coil, r. half-elliptic; 4-door; 4/5-seat; hyd. brks.; max. 87 m.p.h.; cruise 75; m.p.g. 28-32; whl. base 7ft. 10½in.; track f. 4ft. 0¾in., r. 4ft. 0½in.; lgth. 13ft. 5½in.; width 5ft. 1½in.; ht. 4ft. 10½in.; g.c. 7in.; turng. cir. 35ft.; kerb wt. 18½ cwt.; tank 10 gals.; 12-volt.
£508 + £171 p.t. = £679

NSU 1000 C

EAST-WEST engine, but it's at the south end driving the rear wheels. It has an overhead camshaft and it's air cooled. It makes this roomy four seater saloon one of the fastest things in its class and the all independent suspension gives road holding to match. If you think that rear engined cars don't carry much luggage, take a peep into the big bin under the front bonnet.

CLOSE-UP
Four-cyl.; o.h.c.; 69 × 67 mm.; 996 c.c.; 40 b.h.p.; 7.5 to 1 comp.; Solex carb.; 4-speed, 16.5, 9.1, 5.8, 4.2 to 1; cen. lvr.; susp. f. and r. ind. coil; 2-door; 4-seat; drum brks.; max. 80 m.p.h.; cruise 70; m.p.g. 33-38; whl. base 7ft. 4½in.; track f. and r. 4ft. 1½in.; lgth. 12ft. 5in.; width 4ft. 10½in.; ht. 4ft. 5½in.; g.c. 7in.; turng. cir. 29ft.; kerb wt. 12¾ cwt.; tank 8 gals.; 6-volt.
£530 + £164 p.t. = £694

NSU Ro 80

FABULOUS ride and cornering, superb finish and equipment, an individual shape that turns out to be efficiently streamlined, a nice semi-automatic transmission with torque converter and three speeds (just push the lever to shift); with so many star points you almost forget it is also unique in Europe with its tiny twin rotor Wankel engine, which revs fast with little fuss or noise.

CLOSE-UP
Twin-rotor Wankel; 995 c.c.; 115 b.h.p.; 9 to 1 comp.; 2 Solex carbs.; 3-speed, semi-auto., 9.98, 5.87, 3.83 to 1; cen. lvr.; susp. f. and r. ind. coil; 4-door; 5-seat; disc servo brks.; max. 112 m.p.h.; cruise 100; m.p.g. 18-23; whl. base 9ft. 4¾in.; track f. 4ft. 10½in., r. 4ft. 8½in.; lgth. 15ft. 8in.; width 5ft. 9¼in.; ht. 4ft. 7½in.; g.c. 6½in.; turng. cir. 38ft. 9in.; kerb wt. 24¾ cwt.; tank 18 gals.; 12-volt.
£1,745 + £536 p.t. = £2,281

OLDSMOBILE TORONADO

EXPOSED instead of concealed headlamps, sleeker bumpers, identify the 1970 Toronado and interior trim is more tasteful. A new door lock option automatically unlocks the tilting front backrest when a door is opened. Power locks let the driver lock both doors and boot lid electrically. The big V8 engine features new bearing design and rotating valve lifters for still longer life.

CLOSE-UP

Eight-cyl.; o.h.v.; 105 × 108 mm.; 7,457 c.c.; 375 b.h.p. gross; 10.25 to 1 comp.; Rochester 4-choke carb.; 3-speed Hydra-Matic, 7.64, 4.56, 3.08 to 1; col. lvr.; susp. f. ind. torsion bar, r. half-elliptic; 2-door; 4-seat; disc/drum servo brks.; max. 130 m.p.h.; cruise 100; m.p.g. 10-15; whl. base 9ft. 11in.; track f. 5ft. 3½in., r. 5ft. 3in.; lgth. 17ft. 11in.; width 6ft. 6¾in.; ht. 4ft. 4¾in.; g.c. 5in.; turng. cir. 42ft. 9in.; kerb wt. 40½ cwt.; tank 20 gals.; 12-volt.

£3,882 + £1,188 p.t. = £5,070

OLDSMOBILE HOLIDAY 4-4-2

REAL bonnet scoops gulp real air to fill the cylinders of a V8 engine stretched from 6½ to 7½ litres. New choke mechanism for faster warm-up, new bearing design and valve rotators should make engines still more durable. Transmission is Turbo-Hydra-matic with torque converter. Options include a single switch that locks doors electrically. When a door is opened, tilting seat backs are unlocked.

CLOSE-UP

Eight-cyl.; o.h.v.; 104.7 × 107.9 mm.; 7,457 c.c.; 365 b.h.p. gross; 10.5 to 1 comp.; Rochester 4-choke carb.; 3-speed Turbo Hydra matic auto., 7.61, 4.54, 3.07 to 1; col. lvr.; susp. f. ind. coil, r. coil; 2-door; 5-seat; disc/drum servo brks.; max. 120 m.p.h.; cruise 95; m.p.g. 12-15; whl. base 9ft. 4in.; track f. and r. 4ft. 11in.; lgth. 15ft. 11½ ins.; width 6ft. 4½in.; ht. 4ft. 4¾in.; g.c. 5½in.; turng. cir. 40ft.; kerb wt. 34 cwt.; tank 16¾ gals.; 12-volt.

OPEL KADETT

GENERAL Motors, Germany, offers a choice of nine basic Kadett models; two notch-back saloons, two fastback saloons, a two-door coupe, a high performance Rallye coupe and two estate cars. Equipment includes energy absorbing steering column, steering wheel lock, clock, lights for boot, bonnet, glove box, reversing lamps, two-speed wipers, child-proof safety locks and safety mirror with breakaway bracket.

CLOSE-UP

Four-cyl.; o.h.v.; 75 × 61 mm.; 1,078 c.c.; 45 b.h.p.; 7.8 to 1 comp.; Solex carb.; 4-speed, 15.07, 8.59, 5.16, 3.89 to 1; cen. lvr.; susp. f. ind. transv. leaf, r. coil; 2/4-door; 4-seat; drum brks.; max 76 m.p.h.; cruise 70; m.p.g. 29-35; whl. base 7ft. 11½in.; track f. 4ft. 1½in., r. 4ft. 2½in.; lgth. 13ft. 8½in.; width 5ft. 2in.; ht. 4ft. 7½in.; g.c. 5¾in.; turng. cir. 30ft. 9in.; kerb wt. 15¼ cwt.; tank 8¾ gals.; 12-volt.

£614 + £188 p.t. = £802

OPEL COMMODORE

A big, impressive coupe from General Motors, Germany, with side windows and quarter lights that wind down, leaving the whole side open for summer days. Saloons are also made, with two or four doors and the GS is a sports version with 130 b.h.p. engine that does about 115 m.p.h. The latest GM automatic transmission, made in Strasbourg, is an optional extra.

CLOSE-UP

Six-cyl.; o.h.v.; 87 × 69.8 mm.; 2,490 c.c.; 129 b.h.p.; 9.5 to 1 comp.; Solex carb.; 4-speed, 12.21, 7.69, 4.88, 3.56 to 1; cen. lvr.; susp. f. ind. coil, r. coil; 2-door; 4/5-seat; disc/drum servo brks.; max. 105 m.p.h.; cruise 85; m.p.g. 20-22; whl. base 8ft. 9in.; track f. and r. 4ft. 7½in.; lgth. 15ft.; width 5ft. 9in.; ht. 4ft. 3½in.; g.c. 7in.; turng. cir. 33ft.; kerb wt. 22¾ cwt.; tank 14½ gals.; 12-volt.

Abbreviations—g.c.—ground clearance; susp.—suspension; f.—front; r.—rear; comp.—compression; s.v.—side-valves; o.h.v.—overhead valves; o.h.c.—overhead camshaft; hyd.—hydraulic.

229

PEUGEOT 204

AN early recruit to the transverse engine and front-wheel-drive formula, the Peugeot does it in style with overhead camshafts, light alloy block, wet cylinder liners and five main bearings. Gears are in the sump as in Issigonis designs. The engine is smooth revving and economical. Coil strut front suspension and trailing arms at rear. Still newer is 304 with 1,288 c.c. engine and front like the 504.

CLOSE-UP

Four-cyl.; o.h.c.; 75×64 mm.; 1,130 c.c.; 53 b.h.p.; 8.8 to 1 comp.; Solex carb.; 4-speed, 15.15, 9.25, 6.06, 4.23 to 1; col. lvr.; susp. f. and r. ind. coil; 4-door; 4-seat; disc/drum brks.; max. 86 m.p.h.; cruise 78; m.p.g. 27-30; whl. base 8ft. 6in.; track f. 4ft. 4in., r. 4ft. 1½in.; lgth. 13ft.; width 5ft. 1½in.; ht. 4ft. 7in.; g.c. 5½in.; turng. cir. 31ft. 2in.; kerb wt. 16¾ cwt.; tank 9¼ gals.; 12-volt.

£812 + £250 p.t. = £1,062

PEUGEOT 504

A CHARMER from Paris, though opinions are divided about the styling. It's solid and well finished, capable of high cruising speeds and fade-free braking. The engine comes with single carburetter at 75 b.h.p. or with Kugelfischer injection giving 90 b.h.p. Front seats have built-in head rests. Rubber inserts reduce scars on bumpers. Sunshine roof is optional. Instruments include voltmeter and a transistor clock.

CLOSE-UP

Four-cyl.; o.h.v.; 84×81 mm.; 1,796 c.c.; 90 b.h.p.; 8.3 to 1 comp.; Kugelfischer injection; 4-speed, 13.83, 8.18, 5.32, 3.78 to 1; cen. lvr.; susp. f. and r. ind. coil; 4-door; 5-seat; disc servo brks.; max. 106 m.p.h.; cruise 90; m.p.g. 25; whl. base 8ft. 11⅞in.; track f. 4ft. 7¾in., r. 4ft. 5⅜in.; lgth. 14ft. 8⅝in.; width 5ft. 6½in.; ht. 4ft. 9½in.; g.c. 6¼in.; turng. cir. 35ft.; kerb wt. 23½ cwt.; tank 12¼ gals.; 12-volt.

£1,282 + £394 p.t. = £1,676

PLYMOUTH SPORT FURY

THE high performance version of the Chrysler Group's mass market popular model features concealed headlamps, a vinyl rub strip on the body side, premium tail lamps and premium door trim with puff padding highlights, if you know what that means. There are 18 exterior colours and six colour options for the vinyl roof in tortoise, alligator or boar grains. To dazzle the opposition you can have new "strobe" stripes in three colours of reflective tape.

CLOSE-UP

Eight-cyl.; o.h.v.; 109.7×95.25 mm.; 7,210 c.c.; 350 b.h.p. gross; 10 to 1 comp.; Carter 4-choke carb.; 4-speed, 8.77, 6.39, 4.60, 3.31 to 1; cen. lvr.; susp. f. ind. torsion bar, r. half-elliptic; 2 or 4-door; 5-seat; disc/drum brks.; max. 118 m.p.h.; cruise 95; m.p.g. 13-18; whl. base 10ft.; track f. 5ft. 2¼in., r. 5ft. 2in.; lgth. 17ft. 11¼in.; width 6ft. 7⅝in.; ht. 4ft. 7¼in.; g.c. 5½in.; turng. cir. 42ft. 9in.; kerb wt. 29¾ cwt.; tank 19 gals.; 12-volt.

PONTIAC GRAND PRIX

SAID to have the longest bonnet in the business, and you can have a new 7-litre engine underneath if a mere 6.5 litres isn't enough. Three speeds are standard. Optional are Turbo-Hydra-Matic or four speed manual box with floor lever. A new headlamp delay system lets driver see by the headlights for 60 seconds after turning off the light switch to reach front door or garage.

CLOSE-UP

Eight-cyl.; o.h.v.; 104.7×95.2 mm.; 6,556 c.c.; 348 b.h.p. gross; 10.5 to 1 comp.; Rochester 4-choke carb.; 4-speed, 8.94, 6.67, 5.18, 3.55 to 1; cen. lvr., auto. opt.; susp. f. ind. coil, r. half-elliptic; 2-door; 5/6-seat; disc/drum brks., servo opt.; max. 120 m.p.h.; cruise 100; m.p.g. 13-17; whl. base 9ft. 10in.; track f. 5ft. 2in., r. 5ft. 6½in.; lgth. 17ft. 6½in.; width 6ft. 1in.; ht. 4ft. 4½in.; g.c. 5½in.; turng. cir. 38ft. 6in.; kerb wt. 28 cwt.; tank 15½ gals.; 12-volt.

PORSCHE 911S

THIS famous sports coupé with the air-cooled six-cylinder rear engine comes in three versions; T, E, S, with engines increased from 1,971 to 2,195 c.c. to give gross powers of 142, 175 or 200 b.h.p. and better torque for still easier overtaking. E and S have Bosch injection. There is a de luxe E and lightweight competition S. Photo shows Targa version with removeable coupé top.

CLOSE-UP

Six-cyl.; o.h.c.; air-cooled; 84×66 mm.; 2,195 c.c.; 200 b.p.h. gross; 9.9 to 1 comp.; Bosch injection; 5-speed, 13.68, 8.37, 5.85, 4.61, 3.28 to 1; cen. lvr.; susp. f. and r. ind. torsion bar; 2-door; 2/4-seat; disc brks.; max. 143 m.p.h.; cruise 120; m.p.g. 23-26; whl. base 7ft. 5¼in.; track f. 4ft. 6in.; r. 4ft. 5½in.; lgth. 13ft. 9in.; width 5ft. 3⅜in.; ht. 4ft. 4in.; g.c. 6½in.; turng. cir. 31ft.; kerb wt. 21½ cwt.; tank 13½ gals.; 12-volt.

RELIANT REBEL

"THEY don't make them like that any more" . . . But Reliant does; sturdy steel chassis, front engine, rear drive, all in simple design that is easy to maintain. The glass fibre body won't rust and is easy to mend after slight shunts. There are big doors and a good rear seat and you cover up to 50 miles per gallon, but there's no synchromesh on first gear.

CLOSE-UP

Four-cyl.; o.h.v.; 60×61 mm.; 701 c.c.; 31 b.h.p.; 8.4 to 1 comp.; Zenith carb.; 4-speed, 18.7, 10.7, 6.4, 4.4 to 1; cen. lvr.; susp. f. ind. coil, r. half elliptic; 2-door; 4-seat; drum brks.; max. 70 m.p.h.; cruise 60; m.p.g. 40-50; whl. base 7ft. 5in.; track f. 4ft., r. 3ft. 10½in.; lgth. 11ft. 6in.; width 4ft. 10in.; ht. 4ft. 3¾in.; g.c. 4in.; turng. cir. 27ft.; kerb wt. 10¾ cwt.; tank 6 gals.; 12-volt.

£495+£153 p.t. = £648

RELIANT SCIMITAR

FROM making modest three wheelers and light vans, Reliant now a member of the Hodge Group has built up a widespread reputation for well built high performance GT coupés with glass fibre bodies styled by Ogle. The Scimitar uses the V6 Zephyr or Zodiac engines in 2.5 or 3 litres sizes with three carburetters, and on Continental motorways it will cruise happily at over 100 m.p.h. in overdrive.

CLOSE-UP

Six-cyl.; o.h.v.; 94×60 mm.; 2,495 c.c.; 112 b.h.p.; 9 to 1 comp.; Zenith carb.; 4-speed, 11.3, 7.9, 5.1, 3.6 to 1; cen. lvr.; susp. f. ind. coil, r. coil; 2-door; 2/4-seat; disc/drum brks.; max. 113 m.p.h.; cruise 98; m.p.g. 22-27; whl. base 7ft. 8½in.; track f. 4ft. 3½in., r. 4ft. 2½in.; lgth. 13ft. 11in.; width 5ft. 4in.; ht. 4ft. 3½in.; g.c. 6in.; turng. cir. 35ft.; kerb wt. 20½ cwt.; tank 21 gals.; 12-volt.

£1,133+£349 p.t. = £1,482

RENAULT 10

THIS distinguished Frenchman has a new 52 b.h.p., 1,289 c.c. engine with a 5-bearing crankshaft, sealed cooling system and disc brakes all round. An outstanding feature of the Renault 10 is the luxury of the seating and the standard appointments including adjustable fresh air vents, and a heater/demister with booster fan. The model also has anti-theft locks, windscreen washer and—unusual for these days—a starting handle.

CLOSE-UP

Four-cyl.; o.h.v.; 73×77 mm.; 1,289 c.c.; 52 b.h.p.; 8 to 1 comp.; Solex carb.; 4-speed, 14.93, 9.28, 6.11, 4.25 to 1; cen. lvr.; susp. f. ind., r. ind.; 4-door; 4-seat; disc brks. all round; max. 86 m.p.h.; cruise 70; m.p.g. 32-40; whl. base 7ft. 5½in.; track f. 4ft. 1½in., r. 4ft. 0in.; lgth. 13ft. 9½in.; width 5ft. 0in.; ht. 4ft. 6in.; g.c. 6in.; turng. cir. 30ft. 6in.; kerb wt. 1,742 lb.; tank 8½ gals.; 12-volt.

£592 10+£183 6 8 p.t. = £775 16 8

Abbreviations—g.c.—ground clearance; susp.—suspension; f.—front; r.—rear; comp.—compression; s.v.—side-valves; o.h.v.—overhead valves; o.h.c.—overhead camshaft; hyd.—hydraulic.

RENAULT 6

CLEAN cut design combines something of the R 16 style with R4 compactness and economy. Based on R4 chassis, it has the same size engine but Gordini mods increase the power. Lift-up rear door reveals almost station wagon capacity. A load sensitive valve prevents rear brakes locking. Powerful heater and good ventilation are plus points. After a successful first year on the Continent, it makes its London debut at this year's show.

CLOSE-UP
Four-cyl.; o.h.v.; 58×80 mm.; 845 c.c.; 34 b.h.p.; 8 to 1 comp.; Solex carb.; 4-speed, 14.87, 9.27, 5.99, 4.25 to 1; facia lvr.; susp. f. and r. ind. torsion bar; 5-door; 4/5-seat; drum brks.; max 73 m.p.h.; cruise 65; m.p.g. 34-37; whl. base 7ft. 10½in.; track. f 4ft. 2¼in., r. 4ft. 1in.; lgth. 12ft. 7⅝in.; width 5ft. 0½in.; ht. 4ft. 11in.; g.c. 6in.; turng. cir. 32ft.; kerb wt. 14¾ cwt.; tank 7 gals.; 12-volt.

RENAULT 12

JUST when everyone is climbing on Renault's five door utility band wagon, they get off themselves and produce a saloon of strictly conventional shape with four doors and a big boot. But the mechanical side is full of interest, with coil spring struts above the top wishbones in front and an axle on trailing arms and coil spring struts at the rear. Reclining seats, and Renault's usual comprehensive heater ventilation system with extractor grilles.

CLOSE-UP
Four-cyl.; o.h.v.; 73×77 mm.; 1,289 c.c.; 60 b.h.p.; 8.5 to 1 comp.; Solex carb.; 4-speed, 13.68, 8.43, 5.25, 3.89 to 1; cen. lvr.; susp. f. and r. ind. coil; 4-door; 5-seat; disc/drum brks.; max. 90 m.p.h.; cruise 80; m.p.g. 35; whl. base 8ft.; track f. and r. 4ft. 3¾in.; lgth. 14ft. 3in.; width 5ft. 4½in.; ht. 4ft. 8½in.; g.c. 6in.; turng. cir. 32ft. 9in.; kerb wt. 16¼ cwt.; tank 11 gals.; 12-volt.

ROLLS-ROYCE SILVER SHADOW L.W.B.

SHADOWS lengthen. Best selling Rolls-Royce now available with longer body and electric drop division for those who can afford a chauffeur's wages *and* SET. Twin air conditioners permit different climates front and rear. Chauffeurless paupers can have it divisionless to enjoy the four inches extra rear legroom and wider rear doors. The American-inspired safety-cushioned interior with recessed controls is now supplied to all markets.

CLOSE-UP
Eight-cyl.; o.h.v.; 104.1×91.4 mm.; 6,230 c.c.; b.h.p. not revealed; 9 to 1 comp.; 2 S.U. carbs.; 4-speed auto., 11.75, 8.1, 4.46, 3.08 to 1; col. lvr.; susp. f. and r. ind. coil, hyd. levelling; 2/4-door; 5-seat; disc servo brks.; max. 116 m.p.h.; cruise 100; m.p.g. 11-14; whl. base 13ft. 11½in.; track f. and r. 4ft. 9½in.; lgth. 17ft. 3¾in.; width 6ft.; ht. 4ft. 8¾in.; g.c. 6½in.; turng. cir. 38ft.; kerb wt. 41½ cwt.; tank 24 gals; 12-volt.
£6,095+£1,865 p.t. = £7,960

ROLLS-ROYCE PHANTOM VI

GOOD enough for a queen, this is the choice of the British Royal Family, seen on State occasions in many different parts of the world. Two separate air conditioning systems now permit different climates in front and rear compartments. The engine gains extra power from the new cylinder heads developed for the Silver Shadow. Rear compartment is upholstered in West of England Cloth, the front in top grade English hide.

CLOSE-UP
Eight-cyl.; o.h.v.; 104.14×91.44 mm.; 6,230 c.c.; b.h.p. not revealed; 9 to 1 comp.; 2 SU carbs.; 3-speed auto., 9.65, 5.76, 3.89 to 1; col. lvr.; susp. f. ind. coil, r. half-elliptic; 4-door; 7-seat; drum servo brks.; max. 100 m.p.h.; cruise 85; m.p.g. 12; whl. base 12ft. 1in.; track f. 5ft. 0¾in., r. 5ft. 4in.; lgth. 19ft. 10in.; width 6ft. 7in.; ht. 5ft. 9in.; g.c. 6½in.; turng. cir. 48ft. 9in.; kerb wt. 50½ cwt.; tank 23 gals.; 12-volt.
£10,050+£3,073 p.t. = £13,123

Abbreviations—g.c.—ground clearance; susp.—suspension; f.—front; r.—rear; comp.—compression; s.v.—side-valves; o.h.v.—overhead valves; o.h.c.—overhead camshaft; hyd.—hydraulic.

ROVER 2000 TC

BRITAIN'S pioneer Securicar with world famous safety features in structure and interior design gains the extra urge from twin carburetters to keep up with the competition but it needs 100 octane fuel. Unique front suspension with horizontal coil springs and De Dion rear axle, combine to give superb ride and remarkable roadholding. Heating and ventilation are among the best available.

CLOSE-UP

Four-cyl.; o.h.c.; 85.7 × 85.7 mm.; 1,978 c.c.; 108 b.h.p.; 10 to 1 comp.; coil ign.; 2 SU carbs.; 4-speed, 12.83, 7.55, 4.92, 3.54 to 1; cen. lvr.; susp f. ind. coil, r. de Dion coil; 4-door; 4-seat; disc servo brks.; max 110 m.p.h.; cruise 98; m.p.g. 23-27; whl. base 8ft. $7\frac{1}{2}$in.; track f. 4ft. $5\frac{1}{2}$in., r. 4ft. $4\frac{1}{2}$in.; lgth. 14ft. $10\frac{1}{2}$in.; width 5ft. $6\frac{1}{4}$in.; ht. 4ft. $7\frac{3}{4}$in.; g.c. $6\frac{1}{2}$in.; turng. cir. 31ft. 6in.; kerb wt. $24\frac{3}{4}$ cwt.; tank 12 gals.; 12-volt.

£1,200 + £369 p.t. = £1,569

ROVER 3500

A light alloy V8 engine fitting snugly where the four in line resided brings an impressive increase in performance without impairing good balance and safe roadholding. Smooth and quiet as no four can ever be it swishes along without effort but not everyone likes the automatic transmission with rather low shift points and no manual box is available. Usual excellent Rover finish and safety minded interior.

CLOSE-UP

Eight-cyl.; o.h.v.; 88.9 × 71 mm.; 3,532 c.c.; 160 b.h.p.; 10.5 to 1 comp.; 2 SU carbs.; 3-speed BW auto, 7.36, 4.47, 3.08 to 1; cen. lvr.; susp. f. ind. coil, r. de Dion coil; 4-door; 4-seat; disc servo brks.; max. 117 m.p.h.; cruise 98; m.p.g. 18-20; whl. base 8ft. $7\frac{1}{2}$in.; track f. 4ft. $5\frac{1}{2}$in., r. 4ft. $3\frac{3}{4}$in.; lgth. 14ft. $11\frac{3}{4}$in.; width 5ft. 6in.; ht. 4ft. 8in.; g.c. $7\frac{1}{2}$in.; turng. cir. 32ft. 6in.; kerb wt. $26\frac{1}{4}$ cwt.; tank 15 gals.; 12-volt.

£1,400 + £430 p.t. = £1,830

SAAB 99

LONG awaited right hand drive models of Saab's new car with the Triumph-built engine are now arriving. Builders of famous supersonic fighters, Saab's put the same effort into quality control on this subsonic family model. Reclining seats with adjustable headrests. Heated rear window, hazard warning flasher, illuminated ignition switch and safety lock on the gear lever are interesting features.

CLOSE-UP

Four-cyl.; o.h.c.; 83.5 × 78 mm.; 1,709 c.c.; 80 b.h.p.; 8.8 to 1 comp.; Zenith carb.; 4-speed, 14.3, 9.07, 5.8, 4.22 to 1; cen. lvr. BW auto. opt.; susp. f. ind. coil, r. coil; 2-door; 4/5-seat; disc servo brks.; max. 96 m.p.h.; cruise 85; m.p.g. 28-32; whl. base 8ft. $1\frac{1}{4}$in.; track f. 4ft. $6\frac{3}{4}$in., r. 4ft. $7\frac{1}{8}$in.; lgth. 14ft. $3\frac{1}{4}$in.; width 5ft. $4\frac{3}{4}$in.; ht. 4ft. $8\frac{5}{8}$in.; g.c. $6\frac{5}{8}$in.; turng. cir. 33ft. 6in.; kerb wt. $21\frac{1}{4}$ cwt.; tank $10\frac{1}{2}$ gals.; 12-volt.

SIMCA 1100

FRONT-DRIVE from Rootes! Simca's British sales network is now run by Rootes and some of their dealers will handle this transverse-engined front-drive model. Outstanding handling and safety have permitted a boost of 4 b.h.p. in engine output. New facia has space for tachometer or clock. Steering is improved to eliminate vibration. The top model has more luxurious seats; servo brakes are optional.

CLOSE-UP

Four-cyl.; o.h.v.; 74 × 65 mm.; 1,118 c.c.; 60 b.h.p.; 9.6 to 1 comp.; Solex carb.; 4-speed, 15.19, 9.15, 6.02, 4.26 to 1; cen. lvr., semi-auto opt.; susp. f. and r. ind. torsion bar; 3/5 door; 4-seat; disc/drum brks.; max. 88 m.p.h.; cruise 78; m.p.g. 30-34; whl. base 8ft. $3\frac{1}{8}$in.; track f. 4ft. $5\frac{3}{4}$in., r. 4ft. $3\frac{5}{8}$in.; lgth. 12ft. $11\frac{1}{4}$in.; width 5ft. $2\frac{1}{2}$in.; ht. 4ft. $9\frac{3}{8}$in., g.c. $5\frac{1}{2}$in.; turng. cir. 36ft.; kerb wt. $17\frac{1}{4}$ cwt.; tank $9\frac{1}{4}$ gals.; 12-volt.

£624 + £194 p.t. = £818

Abbreviations—g.c.—ground clearance; susp.—suspension; f.—front; r.—rear; comp.—compression; s.v.—side-valves; o.h.v.—overhead valves; o.h.c.—overhead camshaft; hyd.—hydraulic.

SIMCA 1501S

YANKS in Paree collaborate in running Chrysler's French factory which offers this up-graded 1501 for 1970. New grille with rectangular long-range lamps. Sports steering wheel, imitation wood facia with circular dials, pedal-operated wiper-washer are features. All 1501 models now get Special's 80 b.h.p. engine. An electrically heated rear window is optional.

CLOSE-UP

Four-cyl.; o.h.v.; 75.2×83 mm.; 1,475 c.c.; 80 b.h.p.; 9.3 to 1 comp.; Solex or Weber carb.; 4-speed, 13.93, 8.17, 5.28, 3.38; cen. lvr.; susp. f. ind. coil, r. coil; 4-door; 4-seat; disc/drum brks.; max. 92 m.p.h.; cruise 80; m.p.g. 25-28; whl. base 8ft. 3½in.; track f. 4in., r. 4ft. 3in.; lgth. 14ft. 7½in.; width 5ft. 2in.; ht. 4ft. 6in.; g.c. 5½in.; turng. cir. 32ft. 3in.; kerb wt. 20 cwt.; tank 12 gals.; 12-volt.

£882+£273 p.t. = £1,155

SINGER CHAMOIS Mk II

THE Impish Chamois is available in two forms; saloon with handy lift-up rear window for shopping expeditions, sports with sloping coupe tail. The coloured side mouldings are white for saloon, red for sports. There are four headlamps and the dummy grille incorporates the lock for the front boot. The well finished interior includes a full width facia with a good range of instruments including voltmeter and oil pressure gauge.

CLOSE-UP

Four-cyl.; o.h.c.; 68×60.4 mm.; 875 c.c.; 39 b.h.p.; 10 to 1 comp;. Solex carb.; 4-speed, 16.59, 8.90, 5.70, 4.13 to 1; cen. lvr.; susp. f. and r. ind. coil; 2-door; 4-seat; drum brks.; max. 77 m.p.h.; cruise 68; m.p.g. 40; whl. base 6ft. 10in.; track f. 4ft. 2½in., r. 4ft. 0½in.; lgth. 11ft. 7in.; width 5ft. 0¼in.; ht. 4ft. 6½in.; g.c. 6¼in.; turng. cir. 30ft. 6in.; kerb wt. 14½ cwt.; tank 10 gals.; 12-volt.

£535+£166 p.t. = £701

SINGER VOGUE

THIS is a car in a bracket which appeals to motorists with sporting interests. It is a 5-seater with reclining front seats and the usual luxury interior with a lot of wood that distinguishes most Rootes models. Power-assisted brakes control the Vogue's snappy 1,725 c.c. engine and there is an option for fully automatic transmission or an overdrive. A worthy and trusty example of the best Rootes engineering.

CLOSE-UP

Four-cyl.; o.h.v.; 81.5×82.5 mm.; 1,725 c.c.; 74 b.h.p.; 9.2 to 1 comp.; Stromberg carb.; 4-speed, 12.41, 7.92, 5.15, 3.7 to 1; cen. lvr., L de N overdrive or BW. auto. opt.; susp. f. ind. coil, r. half-elliptic; 4-door; 4/5-seat; disc/drum brks.; max. 87 m.p.h.; cruise 75; m.p.g. 27-30; whl. base 8ft. 2½in.; track f. and r. 4ft. 4in.; lgth. 14ft. 1½in.; width 5ft. 3½in.; ht. 4ft. 8in.; g.c. 6¾in.; turng. cir. 34ft.; kerb wt. 18½ cwt.; tank 10 gals.; 12-volt.

£818+£252 p.t. = £1,070

SKODA 110L

AMID the miseries of military occupation, the Czechs and Slovaks have managed to produce a restyled Skoda with longer front, new rear end, more powerful engine. All Skodas have remarkably full equipment for their modest price, including lockable fuel filler and engine compartment, reclining front seats and fold away rear seats for extra luggage space, radiator blind and powerful heater.

CLOSE-UP

Four-cyl.; o.h.v.; 72×68 mm.; 1,107 c.c.; 49 b.h.p.; 8.8 to 1 comp.; Jikov carb.; 4-speed, 16.87, 9.41, 6.26, 4.26 to 1; cen. lvr.; susp. f. and r. ind. coil; 4-door; 4-seat; disc/drum brks.; max. 84 m.p.h.; cruise 75; m.p.g. 30-33; whl. base 7ft. 10½in.; track f. 4ft. 2½in., r. 4ft. 1½in.; lgth. 13ft. 8in.; width 5ft. 4in.; ht. 4ft. 7in.; g.c. 7in.; turng. cir. 35ft. 4in.; kerb wt. 16¼ cwt.; tank 7 gals.; 12-volt.

SUNBEAM ALPINE

FAMILY Fastback. Bearing the name previously carried by the Rootes sports two-seaters, the new Alpine is a full four-seater coupe with roomy luggage boot. The Rapier body shell brings the free sideways vision of pillarless styling and the 80 bhp engine gives lively performance with tolerable running costs. Teak veneer facia, centre console and high-backed safety seats highlight the interior.

CLOSE-UP
Four-cyl.; o.h.v.; 81.5 × 82.55 mm.; 1,725 c.c.; 88 b.h.p.; 9.2 to 1 comp.; Zenith Stromberg carb.; 4-speed, 13.04, 8.32, 5.41, 3.89 to 1; cen. lvr.; susp. f. ind. coil, r. half-elliptic; 2-door; 4-seat; disc/drum servo brks.; max. 90 m.p.h.; cruise 80; m.p.g. 27-30; whl. base 8ft. 2½in.; track f. and r. 4ft. 4in.; lgth. 14ft. 6in.; width 5ft. 4¾in.; ht. 4ft. 7in.; g.c. 5in.; turng. cir. 34ft.; kerb wt. 19¾ cwt.; tank 15 gals.; 12-volt.

£830 + £256 p.t. = £1,086

SUNBEAM RAPIER H 120

WITH lightning thrust, the Rapier now takes on all comers in the 100 m.p.h. cruising class. Fastback lines and pillarless sides give good vision and the lighted boot is cavernous. Front seats are adjustable for rake and reach, and upholstery is in breathing Ambla. Tuning by Holbay raises engine output from 88 to 105 b.h.p. Four speeds plus Laycock de Normanville overdrive make the most of it.

CLOSE-UP
Four-cyl.; o.h.v.; 81.5 × 82.5 mm.; 1,725 c.c.; 105 b.h.p.; 9.6 to 1 comp.; 2 Weber twin-choke carbs.; 4-speed and L de N overdrive, 12.14, 7.75, 5.04, 3.89 to 1; cen. lvr., auto. opt.; susp. f. ind. coil, r. half-elliptic; 2-door; 4-seat; disc/drum servo brks.; max. 112 m.p.h.; cruise 95; m.p.g. 24-28; whl. base 8ft. 2½in.; track f. and r. 4ft. 4in.; lgth. 14ft. 6½in.; width 5ft. 4¾in.; ht. 4ft. 7in.; g.c. 5in.; turng. cir. 34ft.; kerb wt. 20¾ cwt.; tank 16 gals.; 12-volt.

£1,150 + £353 p.t. = £1,503

SUNBEAM STILETTO

STYLISH little sports coupe with more to it than meets the eye. Agile and economical it can carry four adults or two with plenty of luggage in the front locker and on the fold down rear seats. The opulent interior features fine reclining seats and comprehensive instruments. The roof is vinyl covered. Probably no rear engine car has better road holding or better gear shift.

CLOSE-UP
Four-cyl.; o.h.c.; 68 × 60.4 mm.; 875 c.c.; 51 b.h.p.; 10 to 1 comp.; 2 Zenith-Stromberg carbs.; 4-speed, 16.59, 8.91, 5.70, 4.14 to 1; cen. lvr.; susp., f. and r., ind. coil; 2-door; 4-seat; drum servo brks.; max. 88 m.p.h.; cruise 80; m.p.g. 35-42; whl. base 6ft. 10in.; track f. 4ft. 2⅝in., r. 4ft.; lgth. 11ft. 7in.; width 5ft. 0½in.; ht. 4ft. 4½in.; g.c. 5⅓in.; turng. cir. 30ft. 6in.; kerb wt. 14⅜ cwt.; tank 6 gals.; 12-volt.

£620 + £192 p.t. = £812

TOYOTA COROLLA 1100

OUTWARDLY conventional, the little Corolla has a willing smooth running engine and can be ordered with a low cost automatic transmission consisting of torque converter and two-speed planetary gearbox. Coming soon is the Spinter, a striking sports coupé with a specially tuned engine, but it may not arrive in time for the show.

CLOSE-UP
Four-cyl.; o.h.v.; 75 × 61 mm.; 1,077 c.c.; 73 b.h.p. gross; 10 to 1 comp.; Aisan twin-choke carb.; 4-speed, 15.53, 8.65, 5.84, 4.22 to 1; cen. lvr.; susp. f. ind. coil and transv. leaf, r. half-elliptic; 2-door; 4-seat; disc/drum brks.; max. 95 m.p.h.; cruise 85; m.p.g. 30; whl. base 7ft. 6in.; track f. 4ft. 0⅜in.; r. 4ft.; lgth. 12ft. 3in.; width 4ft. 10½in.; ht. 4ft. 6⅜in.; g.c. 6½in.; turng. cir. 30ft.; kerb wt. 14¾ cwt.; tank 8 gals.; 12-volt.

£611 + £178 p.t. = £789

Abbreviations—g.c.—ground clearance; susp.—suspension; f.—front; r.—rear; comp.—compression; s.v.—side-valves; o.h.v.—overhead valves; o.h.c.—overhead camshaft; hyd.—hydraulic.

TOYOTA CORONA

BESIDE the latest version of the Corona, with its 82 hp engine, Toyota are introducing the new 1900 with overhead camshaft engine which looks like being one of the hottest things in its class. With an oversquare engine delivering 105 b.h.p. gross it will accelerate from 0-50 m.p.h. in under 8 seconds and comes complete with station seeking radio, reclining seats, steering lock and low profile tyres.

CLOSE-UP

Four-cyl.; o.h.v.; 78×78 mm.; 1,490 c.c.; 82 b.h.p. gross; 8.3 to 1 comp.; Aisan 2-choke carb.; 4-speed 13.59, 7.81, 5.18, 3.7 to 1; cen. lvr.; susp. f. ind. coil, r. half- elliptic; 4-door; 4/5 seat; disc/drum brks.; max. 90 m.p.h.; cruise 80; m.p.g. 28-33; whl. base 7ft. 11½in. track f. and r. 4ft. 2in.; lgth. 13ft. 5¾in.; width 5ft. 1in. ht. 4ft. 8in.; g.c. 6¾in.; turng. cir. 32ft. 6in.; kerb wt 18¾ cwt.; tank 9⅞ gals.; 12-volt.

£685 + £225 p.t. = £910

TOYOTA CROWN DE LUXE

HALF a world away from the Land of the Rising Sun, with all the transport costs that this implies, the big Toyota still provides luxury and lavish equipment at a startlingly low price. Modern overhead camshaft six cylinder engine with manual or automatic transmission, a station seeking radio with electrically operated aerial, reading lamps for rear passengers, reclining front seats, tinted glass, tool kit, reversing lamps, courtesy lamps in rear doors.

CLOSE-UP

Six-cyl.; o.h.c.; 75×85 mm.; 2,253 c.c.; 115 b.h.p. gross; 8.8 to 1 comp.; Aisan 2-choke carb.; 3-speed, 13.37, 7.17, 4.37 to 1; cen. lvr. 4-speed or Toyoglide auto. opt.; susp., f. ind. coil, r. coil; 4-door; 5/6-seat; disc/drum servo brks.; max. 95 m.p.h.; cruise 85; m.p.g. 19-21; whl. base 8ft. 10½in.; track f. 4ft. 6in., r. 4ft. 6¼in.; lgth. 15ft. 3⅜in.; width 5ft. 7in.; ht. 4ft. 8⅞in.; g.c. 6¾in.; turng. cir. 34ft.; kerb wt. 25¼ cwt.; tank 14⅞ gals.; 12-volt.

£1,145 + £352 p.t. = £1,497

TRIUMPH HERALD 13/60

STEADY mechanical development and concentration on improving quality have kept the Herald selling well against more recent competitors. A neater facia with recessed switches and a new front with Vitesse style wings kept it up to date but it still retains the swing axle rear suspension instead of the more costly type on the Vitesse. Swing up bonnet and wings for free access to engine, steering, brakes, suspension.

CLOSE-UP

Four-cyl.; o.h.v.; 73.7×76 mm.; 1,296 c.c.; 61 b.h.p. 8.5 to 1 comp.; Solex carb.; 4-speed, 15.4, 8.9, 5.7, 4.1 to 1; cen. lvr.; susp. f. ind. coil, r. ind. transv. leaf; 2-door 4-seat; disc/drum brks.; max. 85 m.p.h.; cruise 80 m.p.g. 32-36; whl. base 7ft. 7½in.; track f. 4ft. 1in. r. 4ft.; lgth. 12ft. 9in.; width 5ft.; ht. 4ft. 4in.; g.c. 6¾in.; turng. cir. 25ft.; kerb wt. 17 cwt.; tank 6 gals.; 12-volt.

£583 + £180 p.t. = £763

TRIUMPH 2500 PI

AFTER a year with the 2½ litre injection engine in the old 2000 body, Triumph introduce a Michelotti face-lift for both models; longer front, bigger boot, plus wider rear track and wider rims for still more tenacious roadholding. New facia, adjustable-rake steering column. Steering lock for 1970. Brushed nylon seats and Swedish style single-action seat belts are among the optional equipment.

CLOSE-UP

Six-cyl.; o.h.v.; 74.7×95 mm.; 2,498 c.c.; 132 b.h.p.; 9.5 to 1 comp.; Lucas injection; 4-speed, 11.31, 7.24, 4.78, 3.45 to 1; cen. lvr.; L de N overdrive or BW auto. opt.; susp. f. and r. ind. coil; 4-door; 5-seat; disc/drum servo brks.; max. 106 m.p.h.; cruise 95; m.p.g. 23-27; whl. base 8ft. 10in.; track f. 4ft. 4½in., r. 4ft. 4⅞in.; lgth. 15ft. 4¼in.; width 5ft. 5in.; ht. 4ft. 8in.; g.c. 6in.; turng. cir. 33ft.; kerb wt. 26 cwt.; tank 14 gals.; 12-volt.

Abbreviations—g.c.—ground clearance; susp.—suspension; f.—front; r.—rear; comp.—compression; s.v.—side-valves; o.h.v.—overhead valves; o.h.c.—overhead camshaft; hyd.—hydraulic

TRIUMPH GT 6

FAST, neat two seater coupé with big luggage platform, reached through lift-up rear window. Mark II engine with extra power still gives good economy for the performance; latest rear suspension gives real road grip with no vices. New features are adjustable-slope seats, more padding, stronger structure, black surround to windscreen.

CLOSE-UP

Six-cyl.; o.h.v.; 74.7×76 mm.; 1,998 c.c.; 104 b.h.p.; 9.25 to 1 comp.; 2 Stromberg carbs.; 4-speed, 8.66, 5.82, 4.11, 3.27 to 1; cen. lvr. L de N overdrive opt.; susp. f. ind. coil, r. ind. transv. leaf; 2-door; 2-seat; disc/drum brks.; max. 110 m.p.h.; cruise 90; m.p.g. 26; whl. base 6ft. 11in.; track f. and r 4ft. 1in.; lgth. 12ft. 3in.; width 4ft. 9in.; ht. 3ft. 11in.; g.c. 4in.; turng. cir. 25ft. 3in.; kerb wt. 17¼ cwt.; tank 9¾ gals.; 12-volt.
£902 + £278 p.t. = £1,180

TRIUMPH TR6 PI

HERE is a worthy and exciting replacement of last year's model. Its petrol injection engine is even further hotted up to give swift getaway and smooth top-speed motoring. The new model will be especially popular in the United States where fans are always keen to own British sports cars. Independent rear suspension gives a glide-ride. Re-styling was by Karmann.

CLOSE-UP

Six-cyl.; o.h.v.; 74.7×95 mm.; 2,498 c.c.; 150 b.h.p.; 9.5 to 1 comp.; Lucas injection; 4-speed, 10.83, 6.93, 4.58, 3.45 to 1; cen. lvr.; susp. f. and r. ind. coil; 2-door; 2/3-seat; disc/drum servo brks.; max. 120 m.p.h.; cruise 100; m.p.g. 20-24; whl. base 7ft. 4in.; track f. 4ft. 2½in., r. 4ft. 1¾in.; lgth. 12ft. 11in.; width 4ft. 9½in.; ht. 4ft. 2in.; g.c. 5in.; turng. cir. 33ft.; tank 11¼ gals.; 12-volt.
£1,046 + £321 p.t. = £1,367

TRIUMPH VITESSE MK II

SPEEDY soft top. Lovers of al fresco motoring owe a debt to Triumph who keep on making convertibles in a variety of styles and powers. Specially good value is the Vitesse, a 100 m.p.h. four-seater at a very modest price. Improved rear suspension introduced a year ago avoids sudden changes of wheel camber; gives much better road holding and skid resistance. Like the Herald from which it was developed, it has unbeatable ease of access to the engine.

CLOSE-UP

Six-cyl.; o.h.v.; 74.7×76 mm.; 1,998 c.c.; 104 b.h.p.; 9.25 to 1 comp.; 2 Stromberg carbs.; 4-speed, 10.31, 6.92, 4.86, 3.89 to 1; cen. lvr., L de N overdrive opt.; susp. f. ind. coil, r. ind. transv. leaf; 2-door; 4-seat; disc-drum brks.; max. 105 m.p.h.; cruise 90; m.p.g. 25-28; whl. base, 7ft. 7½in.; track f. 4ft. 1in., r. 4ft. 1⅛in.; lgth. 12ft. 9in.; width 5ft.; ht. 4ft. 5in.; g.c. 5½in.; turng. cir. 25ft.; kerb wt. 18½ cwt.; tank 8¾ gals.; 12-volt.
£780 + £241 p.t. = £1,021

TVR TUSCAN

FLYER from the fish and chip circuit. The Blackpool-built Tuscan has a Ford V6 engine in a light tubular chassis with all-independent coil spring suspension and impact-resistant glass fibre body with built-in roll bar. Alloy wheels carry radial ply tyres; brakes are servo assisted with discs in front. Similar-looking Vixen S2 has Speedwell-tuned 100 b.h.p. Cortina engine.

CLOSE-UP

Six-cyl.; o.h.v.; 93.7×72.4 mm.; 2,994 c.c.; 136 b.h.p.; 8.9 to 1 comp.; Weber carb.; 4-speed, 10.47, 7.33, 4.67, 3.31 to 1; cen. lvr. L de N overdrive opt.; susp. f. and r. ind. coil; 2-door; 2-seat; disc/drum brks.; max. 124 m.p.h.; cruise 110; m.p.g. 23-26; whl. base 7ft. 6in.; track f. 4ft. 5in.; r. 4ft. 6in.; lgth. 12ft. 1in.; width 5ft. 4in.; ht. 4ft.; g.c. 5in.; turng. cir. 27ft.; kerb wt. 18 cwt.; tank 15 gals.; 12-volt.
£1,930 + £434 p.t. = £2,364

Abbreviations—g.c.—ground clearance; susp.—suspension; f.—front; r.—rear; comp.—compression; s.v.—side-valves; o.h.v.—overhead valves; o.h.c.—overhead camshaft; hyd.—hydraulic.

237

VAUXHALL VIVA DE LUXE

HANDSOME is as handsome does and the Viva's clean cut good looks are matched by quiet running and good handling. It is now available in nearly 30 models, two door, four door and station wagon with engines from a pushrod 1100 to an overhead cam 2-litre. There are Brabham specials for the sportsman and automatic transmissions for those who don't want to be bothered.

CLOSE-UP
Four-cyl.; o.h.v.; 77.8×61 mm.; 1,159 c.c.; 47 b.h.p. 8.5 to I comp.; Solex carb.; 4-speed, 14.64, 8.61, 5.46, 3.9 to I; cen. lvr. BW. auto opt.; susp. f. ind. coil, r. coil; 2/4-door; 4-seat; drum brks. disc front opt.; max. 78 m.p.h.; cruise 70; m.p.g. 29-34; whl. base 7ft. 11¾in.; track f. and r. 4ft. 3in.; lgth. 13ft. 5in.; width 5ft. 3in.; ht. 4ft. 5in.; g.c. 5in.; turng. cir. 31ft. 9in.; kerb wt. 15¼ cwt.; tank 8 gals.; 12-volt.

£580+£180 p.t. = £760

VAUXHALL VICTOR 2000

HIGH cornering power, good ride and well arranged controls encourage full use of the extra performance that comes from the 2-litre engine replacing the normal Victor's 1600. A small turning circle makes parking easy and the steering is collapsible. The overhead camshaft engine gives relaxed cruising at 85 and it will touch 100 in the right conditions. Low profile tyres, disc front brakes, alternator. VX 4/90 is the new hot one.

CLOSE-UP
Four-cyl.; o.h.c.; 95.25×69.24 mm.; 1,975 c.c.; 88 b.h.p.; 8.5 to I comp.; Zenith carb.; 3-speed, 11.18, 6.38, 3.9 to I; col. lvr. 4-speed or BW auto opt.; susp. f. ind. coil, r. coil; 4-door; 5-seat; disc/drum brks.; max. 95 m.p.h.; cruise 95; m.p.g. 23-26; whl. base 8ft. 6in.; track f. and r. 4ft. 6½in.; lgth. 14ft. 8½in.; width 5ft. 7in.; ht. 4ft. 4¾in.; g.c. 5¼in.; turng. cir. 33ft. 4in.; kerb wt. 21 cwt.; tank 12 gals.; 12-volt.

£760+£235 p.t. = £995

VAUXHALL VENTORA II

VAUXHALL'S Ventora ventures into the luxury class and emerges victorious. Cresta engine in Victor body makes it fast car for the money with swift and effortless hill climbing. 0-100 m.p.h. in 38 seconds isn't bad. Comfortable conveyance for four, vast luggage space. Good heater-ventilation system. Automatic choke for simple starting. Steering wheel is padded and collapsible. Service required only every 6,000 miles.

CLOSE-UP
Six.-cyl.; o.h.v.; 92×82.6 mm.; 3,294 c.c.; 124 b.h.p. 8.5 to I comp.; Zenith carb.; 4-speed, 8.69, 6.17, 4.66, 3.45 to I; cen. lvr. L de N overdrive or Powerglide auto opt.; susp. f. ind. coil, r. coil; 4-door; 5-seat; disc/drum servo brks.; max. 103 m.p.h.; cruise 88; m.p.g. 20-23; whl. base 8ft. 6in.; track f. 4ft. 6¾in., r. 4ft. 6½in.; lgth. 14ft. 8½in.; width 5ft. 7in.; ht. 4ft. 4in.; g.c. 6¼in.; turng. cir. 34ft.; kerb wt. 24¼ cwt.; tank 1 gals.; 12-volt.

£970+£299 p.t. = £1,269

VAUXHALL CRESTA

AMERICAN style and space with no dollar premium to pay. Luton-built with lots of space for 5 people and an enormous boot, this is budget priced 100 m.p.h. travel for large families. Reclining front seats have thick rolls on top to protect rear passengers, and detail equipment covers most motoring needs. A long established model, it is further improved for 1970. The engine is a powerful in-line six and a smooth automatic transmission is optional.

CLOSE-UP
Six-cyl.; o.h.v.; 92×82 mm.; 3,294 c.c.; 123 b.h.p.; 8.5 to I comp.; Zenith carb.; 3-speed, 9.0, 5.13, 3.45 to I; col. lvr. 4-speed or L de N overdrive opt.; susp. f. ind. coil, r. half-elliptic; 4-door; 5-seat; brks.; max. 100 m.p.h.; cruise 87; m.p.g. 16-19; whl. base 8ft. 11½in.; track f. 4ft. 7¼in.; r. 4ft. 8½in.; lgth. 15ft. 5in.; width 5ft. 10in.; ht. 4ft. 8in.; g.c. 5¼in.; turng. cir. 36ft. 6in.; kerb wt. 24⅞ cwt.; tank 15 gals.; 12-volt.

£876+£270 p.t. = £1,146

Abbreviations—g.c.—ground clearance; susp.—suspension; f.—front; r.—rear; comp.—compression; s.v.—side-valves; o.h.v.—overhead valves; o.h.c.—overhead camshaft; hyd.—hydraulic

VW 1600 TL

THE Schnozzle Durante style of the 411 extends to the middle-range 1600 models with a 4½-inch nose-lengthening operation that adds 1½ cubic feet to the luggage space. Though overshadowed by the Beetle's success, sales have passed 1¾ million. Slight improvements to the engine, new bumpers, new rear lamps are 1970 changes. The 1600 TL fast-back coupe also has a modified tail.

CLOSE-UP

Four-cyl.; o.h.v.; 85.5×69 mm.; 1,584 c.c.; 54 b.h.p.; 7.7 to 1 comp.; two Solex carbs.; 4-speed, 15.68, 8.49, 5.2, 3.67 to 1; cen. lvr.; susp. f. and r. ind. torsion bar; 2-door; 4-seat; disc/drum brks.; max. 84 m.p.h.; cruise 84; m.p.g. 27-32; whl. base 7ft. 10½in.; track f. 4ft. 3⅝in.; r. 4ft. 5in.; lgth 13ft. 10¼in.; width 5ft. 4⅝in.; ht. 4ft. 9⅞in.; g.c. 5⅞in.; turng. cir. 36ft. 5in.; kerb wt. 18¾ cwt.; tank 8¾ gals.; 12-volt.

VW 1500

THIS is the standard and orthodox version of the latest Beetle. Its claim, with an air-cooled rear engine, that "air cannot freeze and air cannot boil" still holds good after more than 20 years of the popular Volkswagen model. Every year a few more additions keep the car up-to-date. It is cheap to run and cheap to maintain and you will see these cars all over the world.

CLOSE-UP

Four-cyl.; o.h.v.; air cooled; 83×69 mm.; 1,493 c.c.; 44 b.h.p.; 7.5 to 1 comp.; Solex carb.; 4-speed, 15.68, 8.49, 5.20, 3.67 to 1; cen. lvr.; susp. f. and r. ind. torsion bar; 2-door; 4-seat; disc/drum brks.; max. 80 m.p.h.; cruise 75; m.p.g. 30-34; whl. base 7ft. 10½in.; track f. 4ft. 3½in., r. 4ft. 5½in.; lgth. 13ft. 3 in.; width 4ft. 11in.; ht. 4ft. 11in.; g.c. 6in.; turng. cir. 36ft.; kerb wt. 17 cwt.; tank 8¾ gals.; 12-volt.

VW—PORSCHE

END to Middle. First move away from VW's exclusively rear-engine formula comes with this mid-engined sports two-seater available with the four-cylinder 411 injection engine or (at much higher price) the six-cylinder Porsche. Headlamps retract electrically. The glass fibre top is detachable, leaving roll-over bar in position. There are good-sized luggage lockers front and rear.

CLOSE-UP

Four-cyl. air-cooled; o.h.v.; 90×66 mm.; 1,679 c.c.; 80 b.h.p.; 8.2 to 1 comp.; Bosch injection; or six-cyl.; o.h.c.; 80×66 mm.; 1,991 c.c.; 110 b.h.p.; 8.6 to 1 comp.; two 3-choke Weber carbs.; 5-speed, 13.69, 8.37, 5.85, 4.61, 3.49 to 1; cen. lvr.; 4-speed Porsche semi-auto. opt.; susp. f. ind. tors. bar, r. ind. coil; 2-door; 2-seat; disc brks.; max. 110/125 m.p.h.; cruise 100/115; m.p.g. 23-29; whl. base 8ft. 0⅛in.; track f. 4ft. 4¼in., r. 4ft. 6¼in.; lgth. 13ft. 1in.; width 5ft. 5in.; ht. 4ft.; g.c. 4¾in.; turng. cir. 36ft.; kerb wt. 18 cwt.; tank 13 gals.; 12-volt.

VOLVO 144S

STURDY Swedish four cylinder saloon, built to last with lots of rear leg room and an enormous luggage boot. Remarkable front seats with reclining backrests and a gadget which changes the shape to fit your back. As EFTA members, Volvo use many British parts but had second thoughts when strikes stopped supplies. Not very light to drive, but loyal owners keep coming back for more.

CLOSE-UP

Four-cyl.; o.h.v.; 88.9×80 mm.; 1,985 c.c.; 100 b.h.p.; 8.5 to 1 comp.; 2 SU carbs.; 4-speed, 12.83, 8.16, 5.57, 4.10 to 1; cen. lvr. L de N overdrive opt.; susp. f. ind. coil, r. coil; 4-door; 5-seat; disc servo brks.; max. 100 m.p.h.; cruise 90; m.p.g. 23-26; whl. base 8ft. 6½in.; track f. and r. 4ft. 5in.; lgth. 15ft. 3in.; width 5ft. 8in.; ht. 4ft. 8½in.; g.c. 7in.; turng. cir. 31ft.; kerb wt. 22¾ cwt.; tank 12¾ gals.; 12-volt.

£1,200 + £368 p.t. = £1,568

Abbreviations—g.c.—ground clearance; susp.—suspension; f.—front; r.—rear; comp.—compression; s.v.—side-valves; o.h.v.—overhead valves; o.h.c.—overhead camshaft; hyd.—hydraulic.

VOLVO 164

ALL the Volvo virtues, a strong, comfortable reliable car with a quiet, smooth, six-cylinder engine which allows loyal Volvo owners to move up from four cylinders without leaving the family. Upholstery is leather; front seats are fully reclining. The engine has seven bearings for smoothness and a heated manifold for slow running to keep the exhaust free of unburned hydrocarbons. Sun roof and auto transmission optional.

CLOSE-UP

Six-cyl.; o.h.v.; 88.9×80 mm.; 2,979 c.c.; 130 b.h.p. 9.2 to I comp.; 2 Zenith-Stromberg carbs.; 4-speed and L de N overdrive, 11.67, 7.42, 5.07, 3.73 to I; cen. lvr. BW auto opt.; susp. f. ind. coil, r. coil; 4-door; 5-seat; disc servo brks.; max. 110 m.p.h.; cruise 98; m.p.g. 19-23; whl. base 8ft. 10½in.; track f. and r. 4ft. 5in.; lgth. 15ft. 6in.; width 5ft. 8½in.; ht. 4ft. 9in.; g.c. 6½in.; turng. cir. 28ft. 9in.; kerb wt. 25½ cwt.; tank 12¾ gals.; 12-volt.

£1,400+£430 p.t. = £1,830

WARTBURG KNIGHT

THE Communist Party line remains unchanged but the grille is now matt black and there is a new facia with circular instruments. On this East-German state-built family saloon modifications to the three-cylinder two-stroke engine produce an extra 5 b.h.p. and more torque. The axle ratio is altered to match, giving quieter cruising.

CLOSE-UP

Three-cyl.; two-stroke; 73.5×78 mm.; 991 c.c.; 50 b.h.p.; 7.5 to I comp.; BVF carb.; 4-speed, 14.14, 9.45, 6.06, 4.24 to I; cen. lvr.; susp., f. and r. ind. coil; 4-door; 4/5-seat; drum brks.; max. 75 m.p.h.; cruise 65; m.p.g. 26-30; whl. base 8ft. 0½in.; track f. 4ft. 1½in., r. 4ft. 1¾in.; lgth. 13ft. 10in.; width 5ft. 5in.; ht. 4ft. 9¾in.; g.c. 5¾in.; turng. cir. 29ft.; kerb wt. 17¾ cwt.; tank 9½ gals.; 12-volt.

£532+£165 p.t. = £697

WOLSELEY 18/85 MK II

INNER space is complemented by greater comfort. Reclining front seats with individual arm rests, deeper rear seat with folding armrest. New door trim, deeper pile carpet, safety rocker switches, better-placed fresh air vents, gayer colours, help explain the £83 rise in pre tax price. There's also an extra-power S version. Servo brakes and power steering are standard. Heated rear window and automatic transmission optional.

CLOSE-UP

Four-cyl.; o.h.v.; 80.26×88.9 mm.; 1,798 c.c.; 85 b.h.p. gross; 9 to I comp.; S.U. carb.; 4-speed, 12.7, 7.98, 5.37, 3.88 to I; cen. lvr., BW auto opt.; susp. f. and r. ind. rubber hydraulic; 4-door; 5-seat; servo brks., disc front; max. 90 m.p.h.; cruise 80; m.p.g. 22-27; whl. base 8ft. 10in.; track f. 4ft. 8in., r. 4ft. 7½in.; lgth. 14ft. 2½in.; width 5ft. 7in.; ht. 4ft. 8¼in.; g.c. 6¼in.; turng. cir. 37ft.; kerb wt. 23¼ cwt.; tank 10½ gals.; 12-volt.

£928+£286 p.t. = £1,214

WOLSELEY HORNET

THE Hornet is basically a Mini with winding windows and a big boot that adds ten inches to the length, and a Wolseley radiator grille, but of course the radiator is inside the front wings, the engine is mounted crosswise and it drives the front wheels. With a single carburettor and 998 c.c., pulling power is a strong point and Hydrolastic suspension soaks up the bumps in a satisfactory way. Its companion the Riley Elf has now gone the way of all Rileys.

CLOSE-UP

Four-cyl.; o.h.v.; 64.6×76.2 mm.; 998 c.c.; 38 b.h.p.; 8.3 to I comp.; SU carb.; 4-speed, 13.6, 8.2, 5.3, 3.8 to I; cen. lvr. AP auto. opt.; susp. f. and r. ind. rubber-hyd.; 2-door; 4-seat; disc/drum brks.; max. 77 m.p.h.; cruise 70; m.p.g. 38-41; whl. base 6ft. 8in.; track f. 3ft. 11⅛in., r. 3ft. 9⅞in.; lgth. 10ft. 10in.; width 4ft. 7⅜in.; ht. 4ft. 5in.; g.c. 6in.; turng. cir. 28ft. 6in.; kerb wt. 12⅞ cwt.; tank 5½ gals.; 12-volt.

£535+£166 p.t. = £701

Abbreviations—g.c.—ground clearance; susp.—suspension; f.—front; r.—rear; comp.—compression; s.v.—side-valves; o.h.v.—overhead valves; o.h.c.—overhead camshaft; hyd.—hydraulic

CAR ESTATE REVIEW

AUSTIN 1300 COUNTRYMAN

WITH no rear overhang the load platform is shorter than some, but wheels at the corners plus Hydrolastic all-independent suspension make this a family freighter with outstanding ride and road holding. Transverse engine of course, and front-wheel-drive with many detail improvements to give quieter running and longer mechanical life. Leg room for front and rear passengers is outstanding.

CLOSE-UP

Four-cyl.; o.h.v.; 70.6 × 81.3 mm.; 1,275 c.c.; 60 b.h.p.; 8 to 1 comp.; SU carb.; 4-speed, 12.85, 8.09, 5.23, 3.65 to 1; cen. lvr.; susp. f. and r. ind. rubber-hyd.; 4-door; 4-seat; disc/drum brks.; max. 88 m.p.h.; cruise 78; m.p.g. 31-34; whl. base 7ft. 9½in.; track f. 4ft. 3½in., r. 4ft. 2¾in.; lgth. 12ft. 2¾in.; width 5ft. 0½in.; ht. 4ft. 5in.; g.c. 6in.; turng. cir. 34ft. 9in.; kerb wt. 15½ cwt.; tank 8 gals.; 12-volt.

£645 + £199 p.t. = £844

CITROEN SAFARI

HERE is a station wagon that appeals to the sophisticated owner of a twin-purpose car. Over the years it has been a world favourite thanks to many in-built assets. These include Citroen's hydraulic-pneumatic suspension that irons out the pot-holes and bumps and its self-levelling device that keeps the headlamp beam true and level despite the load.

CLOSE-UP

Four-cyl.; o.h.v.; 90 × 85.5 mm.; 2,175 c.c.; 104 b.h.p.; 8.75 to 1 comp.; Weber twin-choke carb.; 4-speed, 14.21, 8.49, 5.58, 3.73 to 1; col. lvr.; susp. f. and r. ind. hyd.-pneu.; 5-door; 7-seat; disc/drum servo brks.; max. 109 m.p.h.; cruise 90; m.p.g. 21-23; whl. base 10ft. 3in.; track f. 4ft. 11in., r. 4ft. 3in.; lgth. 16ft. 6in.; width 5ft. 10½in.; ht. 5ft. 0½in.; g.c. 5¾in.; turng. cir. 36ft.; kerb wt. 27 cwt.; tank 14 gals.; 12-volt.

£1,624 + £498 p.t. = £2,122

DAF 55 ESTATE

DAFS come with three kinds of engine; two air cooled flat twins and the water cooled four cylinder Renault used in this practical small station wagon. All have the same automatic transmission using reinforced rubber belts which adjusts itself continuously to provide the best ratio for all conditions. Swing axle rear suspension limits cornering speeds but gives quite a good ride.

CLOSE-UP

Four-cyl.; o.h.v.; 70 × 72 mm.; 1,108 c.c.; 45 b.h.p.; 8.5 to 1 comp.; Solex carb.; variable-ratio belt auto., 3.87 to 3.73 to 1; cen. lvr.; susp. f. ind. transv. leaf, r. ind. coil; 3-door; 4-seat; disc/drum brks.; max. m.p.h.; cruise 84; m.p.g. 30-36; whl. base 7ft. 4½in.; track f. 4ft. 2½in., r. 4ft. 1½in.; lgth. 12ft. 8¾in.; width 5ft. 0⅛in.; ht. 4ft. 6⅜in.; g.c. 6¾in.; turng. cir. 31ft.; kerb wt. 15¾ cwt.; tank 8⅜ gals.; 12-volt.

£702 + £217 p.t. = £919

Abbreviations—g.c.—ground clearance; susp.—suspension; f.—front; r.—rear; comp.—compression; s.v.—side-valves; o.h.v.—overhead valves; o.h.c.—overhead camshaft; hyd.—hydraulic.

241

DATSUN 1000

EASY to park, easy to load and easy to run with its economical 1000 c.c. engine, the Datsun is a well finished little three door wagon with a lot of load capacity. Plated bars prevent bulky loads damaging rear quarter windows. Front seats have reclining backrests. Mechanical design is utterly orthodox but quite practical. Standard equipment on de luxe wagons includes overriders, dual horns, two-speed wipers, fuel filler lock.

CLOSE-UP
Four-cyl.; o.h.v.; 73×59 mm.; 988 c.c.; 62 b.h.p. gross; 8.5 to 1 comp.; Hitachi carb.; 3-speed, 13.89, 7.11, 4.11 to 1; col. lvr., 4-speed opt.; susp. f. ind transv. leaf, r. half-elliptic; 3-door; 4-seat; drum brks.; max 84 m.p.h.; cruise 74; m.p.g. 33-35; whl. base 7ft. 5⅜in.; track f. 3ft. 10⅞in., r. 3ft. 10⅝in.; lgth 12ft. 6⅜in.; width 4ft. 8⅜in.; ht. 4ft. 3in.; g.c. 6¼in.; turng. cir. 27ft.; kerb wt. 13½ cwt.; tank 7½ gals.; 12-volt. **£597+£184 p.t. = £781**

FORD CORTINA 1600 ESTATE

PROPELLED by Ford's powerful five bearing engine, this good looking station wagon offers a six foot flat floor with the rear seat folded and reasonably adequate rear passenger space with it up. A practical moulded rubber carpet covers the rear floor. Through flow ventilation keeps occupants fit and alert. Good brakes and a powerful handbrake give safety margins for heavy loads.

CLOSE-UP
Four-cyl.; o.h.v.; 81×78 mm.; 1,599 c.c.; 71 b.h.p.; 9 to 1 comp.; Ford carb.; 4-speed, 13.82, 9.34, 5.50, 3.9 to 1; cen. lvr. BW auto. opt.; susp. f. ind. coil, r. half-elliptic; 5-door; 4/5-seat; disc/drum brks.; max. 86 m.p.h.; cruise 75; m.p.g. 23-26; whl. base 8ft. 2in.; track f. 4ft. 5½in.; r. 4ft. 3in.; lgth. 14ft. 2in.; width 5ft. 5in.; ht. 4ft. 9in.; g.c. 6½in.; turng. cir. 30ft. 3in.; kerb wt. 19¼ cwt.; tank 8 gals.; 12-volt. **£765+£234 p.t. = £999**

FORD ESCORT ESTATE

AN Escort can be anything from a low priced family car with big space and a small thirst to a broad shouldered racing champion with twin cam engine and tyres like a Grand Prix car. You can spend hundreds or thousands on it. But for all round utility and value for money it's hard to beat the Estate car which has one of the roomiest bodies in its class.

CLOSE-UP
Four-cyl.; o.h.v.; 80.9×63 mm.; 1,298 c.c.; 54 b.h.p.; 9 to 1 comp.; Ford carb.; 4-speed, 13.76, 8.23, 5.85, 4.13 to 1; cen. lvr.; susp. f. ind. coil, r. half-elliptic; 3-door; 4-seat; drum brks.; max. 85 m.p.h.; cruise 75; m.p.g. 26-30; whl. base 7ft. 10in.; track f. 4ft. 1in., r. 4ft. 2in.; lgth. 13ft. 5in.; width 5ft. 1⅜in.; ht. 4ft. 7in.; g.c. 6¼in.; turng. cir. 29ft.; kerb wt. 16¼ cwt.; tank 9 gals.; 12-volt. **£642+£196 p.t. = £838**

FIAT 124 ESTATE

FIVE door station wagon version of one of Europe's most successful family cars. Practical, no-gimmick design with an eager 1.2 litre push rod engine that has a small thirst, for its performance. Latest rear suspension with four radius arms and Panhard rod improves road holding, reduces noise. Disc brakes all round have pressure limiting valves to prevent rear wheels locking. Front wings carry repeater indicators for safety in traffic.

CLOSE-UP
Four-cyl.; o.h.v.; 73×71.5 mm.; 1,197 c.c.; 60 b.h.p.; 8.8 to 1 comp.; Solex 2-choke carb.; 4-speed, 16.1, 9.9, 6.4, 4.3 to 1; cen. lvr.; susp. f. ind. coil, r. coil; 5-door; 4/5-seat; disc brks.; max. 86 m.p.h.; cruise 78; m.p.g. 32; whl. base 7ft. 11½in.; track f. 4ft. 4in., r. 4ft. 3½in.; lgth. 13ft. 2½in.; width 5ft. 4in.; ht. 4ft. 7½in.; g.c. 4½in.; turng. cir. 35ft.; kerb wt. 17 cwt.; tank 8½ gals.; 12-volt. **£750+£231 p.t. = £981**

Abbreviations—g.c.—ground clearance; susp.—suspension; f.—front; r.—rear; comp.—compression; s.v.—side-valves; o.h.v.—overhead valves; o.h.c.—overhead camshaft; hyd.—hydraulic.

HILLMAN HUSKY

WITH useful carrying space extending right from front to rear bumper, the Husky is a small car with big carrying capacity; 3¾ cu.ft. in front and up to 50 in the rear with the back seat folded away. The willing Imp o.h.c. engine is canted over under the rear floor. The single lift-up tailgate makes loading easy. The engine has a sealed cooling system and oil level can be checked without moving the luggage.

CLOSE-UP
Four-cyl.; o.h.c.; 68 × 60.4 mm.; 875 c.c.; 39 b.h.p.; 10 to 1 comp.; Solex carb.; 4-speed, 16.59, 8.91, 5.70, 4.14 to 1; cen. lvr.; susp. f. and r. ind. coil; 3-door; 4-seat; drum brks.; max. 78 m.p.h.; cruise 70; m.p.g. 33-36; whl. base 6ft. 10in.; track f. 4ft. 1½in., r. 4ft.; lgth. 11ft. 9in.; width 5ft. 0¼in.; ht. 4ft. 10in.; g.c. 6⅛in.; turng. cir. 31ft.; kerb wt. 14¾ cwt.; tank 6 gals.; 12-volt.

£545 + £169 p.t. = £714

MINI CLUBMAN ESTATE

THIS is British Leyland's estate version of the new Mini Clubman which comes with many modern additions. It is the ideal model for the wife who wants a compact little car for town work but also needs its greater carrying capacity for taking the children to school. It has a bold new front, ease-of-entry doors and a brand new dashboard and face-level fresh air for the car's occupants.

CLOSE-UP
Four-cyl.; o.h.v.; 64.6 × 76.2 mm.; 998 c.c.; 38 b.h.p.; 8.3 to 1 comp.; SU carb.; 4-speed, 12.49, 7.46, 4.85, 3.44 to 1; cen. lvr., auto. opt.; susp. f. and r. ind. rubber-hyd.; 4-door; 4-seat; drum brks.; max 78 m.p.h.; cruise 70; m.p.g. 32-40; whl. base 6ft. 8in.; track f. 3ft. 11⅜in., r. 3ft. 9⅞in.; lgth. 11ft. 1in.; width 4ft. 7½in.; ht. 4ft. 5in.; g.c. 6⅛in.; turng. cir. 29ft.; kerb wt. 12¼ cwt.; tank 5½ gals.; 12-volt.

£583 + £180 p.t. = £763

PEUGEOT 204 ESTATE

PEUGEOT gives the family man a Break (French for Station Wagon). With transverse light alloy overhead cam engine and front wheel drive, road holding is good and safe in the wet though it rolls on corners. Floors have durable rubber mats. The load platform is low and the roof has inbuilt mounting points for a roof rack. Compact, but roomier than it looks.

CLOSE-UP
Four-cyl.; o.h.c.; 75 × 64 mm.; 1,130 c.c.; 53 b.h.p.; 8.8 to 1 comp.; Solex carb.; 4-speed, 15.6, 9.25, 6.06, 4.23 to 1; col. lvr.; susp. f. and r. ind. coil; 5-door; 4-seat; disc/drum servo brks.; max. 86 m.p.h.; cruise 77; m.p.g. 29-34; whl. base 8ft. 6in.; track f. 4ft. 4in., r. 4ft. 1½in.; lgth. 13ft.; width 5ft. 1½in.; ht. 4ft. 7in.; g.c. 5½in.; turng. cir. 31ft.; kerb wt. 17¾ cwt.; tank 9¼ gals.; 12-volt.

£864 + £266 p.t. = £1,130

RELIANT SCIMITAR GT/E

EXPEDITIOUS executive estate with longer, wider chassis than the coupé, more interior space and a softer ride. Rear axle is well located by radius arms with coil spring struts; a limited slip differential is optional. Lift up the rear window to load. Weight is low and performance high, thanks to the glass fibre body. Engines and gearboxes by Ford guarantee easy servicing.

CLOSE-UP
Six-cyl.; o.h.v.; 93.7 × 72.4 mm.; 2,994 c.c.; 128 b.h.p.; 9 to 1 comp.; Weber carb.; 4-speed, 11.31, 7.92, 5.05, 3.58 to 1; cen. lvr., L de N overdrive opt.; susp. f. ind. coil, r. coil; 3-door; 2/4-seat; disc/drum brks.; max. 120 m.p.h.; cruise 100; m.p.g. 21-24; whl. base 8ft. 4in.; track f. 4ft. 7¼in., r. 4ft. 5in.; lgth. 14ft. 2½in.; width 5ft. 5in.; ht. 4ft. 4½in.; g.c. 5in.; turng. cir. 35ft.; kerb wt. 22¾ cwt.; tank 17 gals.; 12-volt.

£1,375 + £422 p.t. = £1,797

RENAULT 4

RIDE tall in Renault's low priced but room＜
utility wagon that combines big car space wit＜
baby car price and running costs. Long suppl＜
torsion bars float it over the worst bumps, bu＜
it rolls on corners and heavy loads tilt the nos＜
so levers are provided to reset the headlam＜
beam quickly when the load is changed. ＜
steering column lock is standard. Gear chang＜
is a push-pull affair on the instrument panel.

CLOSE-UP
Four-cyl.; o.h.v.; 58×80 mm.; 845 c.c.; 27 b.h.p＜
8.1 to 1 comp.; Solex carb.; 4-speed, 15.68, 8.50, 5.6＜
4.28 to 1; facia lvr.; susp. f. and r. ind. torsion ba＜
5-door; 4/5 seat; drum brks.; max. 68 m.p.h.; crui＜
60; m.p.g. 37-45; whl. base 8ft. 0½in.; track f. 4f＜
1¼in., r. 4ft. 0¾in.; lgth. 12ft.; width 4ft. 10¼in.; ht. 5ft＜
g.c. 7¾in.; turng. cir. 30ft.; kerb wt. 12⅝ cwt.; tan＜
5¾ gals.; 6-volt.

£467+£145 p.t. = £612

ROVER 2000 ESTATE

HANDSOME estate car by Crayford the
conversion specialists, retains its Rover character while adding a little extra something of
their own design. Retained are Rover rear
wings but roof is new. Rear door is in aluminium, hinged at the top. A bench rear seat takes
the place of shaped rear seats. Extras include
Webasto roof, dog grille, electric window lifts,
tinted glass.

CLOSE-UP
Four-cyl.; o.h.c.; 85.7×85.7 mm.; 1,978 c.c.; 90 b.h.p.;
9 to 1 comp.; SU carb.; 4-speed, 12.83, 7.55, 4.92,
3.54 to 1; cen. lvr.; susp. f. ind. coil, r. de Dion coil;
5-door; 4/5-seat; disc/servo brks.; max. 100 m.p.h.;
cruise 85; m.p.g. 23-26; whl. base, 8ft. 7½in.; track f.
4ft. 5⅜in., r. 4ft. 4½in.; lgth. 14ft. 10½in.; width 5ft.
6¼in.; ht. 4ft. 6¾in.; g.c. 7¼in.; turng. cir. 32ft.; kerb
wt. 25¼ cwt.; tank 15 gals.; 12-volt.

£1,830+£557 p.t. = £2,387

SIMCA 1100 ESTATE

THESE individualistic cars from Simca＜
Chrysler-controlled French factory are no＜
handled in Britain by Rootes. With transvers＜
engine and front drive, they resemble no Roote＜
product and the styling is not everyone's idea＜
but they have fine roadholding, good ride an＜
high performance for engine size with a modes＜
thirst for fuel. Two door and four door saloon＜
and station wagons with various trim an＜
equipment options.

CLOSE-UP
Four-cyl.; o.h.v.; 74 × 65 mm.; 1,118 c.c.; 56 b.h.p＜
8.2 to 1 comp.; Solex carb.; 4-speed, 15.39, 9.15, 6.0＜
4.26 to 1; cen. lvr.; susp. f. and r. ind. torsion ba＜
3 or 5-door; 4-seat; disc/drum brks.; max. 80 m.p.h＜
cruise 75; m.p.g. 31-35; whl. base 8ft. 3¼in.; trac＜
f. 4ft. 5¼in., r. 4ft. 3½in.; lgth 12ft. 11¼in.; widt＜
5ft. 2in.; ht. 4ft. 10in.; g.c. 5½in.; turng. cir. 36ft＜
kerb wt.17¾ cwt.; tank 9¼ gals.; 12-volt.

£671+£208 p.t. = £879

SINGER VOGUE ESTATE

HERE is an ideal car in a medium sized range
for the busy family man who also wants to
carry around loads for business purposes. The
car's long, crisp lines make it a good looker. It
has a 1,725 c.c. engine that can more than cope
with five people and a lot of luggage. Brakes
are servo assisted; there is a choice of three
transmissions.

CLOSE-UP
Four-cyl.; o.h.v.; 81.5×82.5 mm.; 1,725 c.c.; 74 b.h.p.;
9.2 to 1 comp.; Stromberg carb.; 4-speed, 12.41,
7.92, 5.15, 3.7 to 1; cen. lvr.; L de N overdrive or BW
auto opt.; susp. f. ind. coil, r. half-elliptic; 5-door;
4/5-seat; disc/drum servo brks.; max. 88 m.p.h.; cruise
78; m.p.g. 27-30; whl. base 8ft. 2½in.; track f. and r.
4ft. 4in.; lgth. 14ft. 4½in.; width 5ft. 3½in.; ht. 4ft. 8in.;
g.c. 6¾in.; turng. cir. 33ft. 6in.; kerb wt. 19¾ cwt.;
tank 10 gals.; 12-volt.

£919+£283 p.t. = £1,202

Abbreviations—g.c.—ground clearance; susp.—suspension; f.—front; r.—rear; comp.—compression; s.v.—side-valves; o.h.v.—overhead valves; o.h.c.—overhead camshaft; hyd.—hydrauli＜

TRIUMPH 2000 ESTATE

LONG nose, wide head are not usually the key to social success, but on Triumph's 1970 station wagon they mean improved appearance and extra engine power. The re-styled front is matched by a new interior while the GT6 cylinder head, with bigger ports raises maximum speed of the saioon to a genuine 100 mph and probably not much less for the station wagon.

Six-cyl.; o.h.v.; 74.7×76 mm.; 1,998 c.c.; 90 b.h.p.; 9.5 to 1 comp.; 2 Stromberg carbs.; 4-speed, 13.45, 8.61, 5.68, 4.1 to 1; cen. lvr. BW auto. opt.; susp. f. and r. ind. coil; 5-door; 5/6-seat; disc/drum servo brks.; max. 95 m.p.h.; cruise 80; m.p.g. 22-25; whl. base 8ft. 10½in.; track f. 4ft. 4¼in.; r. 4ft. 2in.; lgth. 14ft. 6½in.; width 5ft. 5in.; ht. 4ft. 8in.; g.c. 6½in.; turng. cir. 29ft. 6in.; kerb wt. 24 cwt.; tank 11½ gals.; 12-volt.

VAUXHALL VIVA 1600 ESTATE

SMOOTH flowing lines provide a lot of space within a stylish exterior. There's a vast range of trim and equipment options. Rear seat folds away to create a five-foot load platform. Not the biggest load carrier nor the most economical but it's fast. Same capacity and lower fuel bills are still available with the 1100 engine at much lower price.

CLOSE-UP

Four-cyl.; o.h.c.; 85.7×69.2 mm.; 1,599 c.c.; 83 b.h.p. gross; 8.5 to 1 comp.; Zenith carb.; 4-speed, 11.49, 8.17, 5.82, 4.12 to 1; cen. lvr. BW auto. opt.; susp. f. ind. coil, r. coil; 3-door; 4-seat; disc/drum brks.; max. 88 m.p.h.; cruise 78; m.p.g. 20-24; whl. base 7ft. 11¾in.; track f. and r. 4ft. 3in.; lgth. 13ft. 5in.; width 5ft. 3in.; ht. 4ft. 5¼in.; g.c. 4¾in.; turng. cir. 31ft. 9in.; kerb wt. 18⅜ cwt.; tank 12 gals.; 12-volt.

£705 + £218 p.t. = £923

VW 411E VARIANT

FOUR-EYED Four-Eleven. Revised frontal styling with four halogen headlamps identifies the latest edition of the big VW and a new three-door station wagon is added to the range. Electronic fuel injection with new pistons and heads gives the flat four air-cooled engine an extra five horsepower. First VW with coil spring suspension, the 411 also has a powerful petrol-burning heater.

CLOSE-UP

Four-cyl.; o.h.v.; 90×66 mm.; 1,679 c.c.; 80 b.h.p.; 8.2 to 1 comp.; Bosch injection; 4-speed, 14.91, 10.36, 6.22, 3.91 to 1; cen. lvr.; susp. f. and r. ind. coil; 3-door; 5-seat; disc/drum brks.; max. 90 m.p.h.; cruise 90; m.p.g. 25; whl. base 8ft. 2½in.; track f. 4ft. 6¾in., r. 4ft. 2¾in.; lgth. 14ft. 11¼in.; width 5ft. 5in.; ht. 4ft. 10⅝in.; g.c. 5¼in.; turng. cir. 37ft. 5in.; kerb wt. 23 cwt.; tank 11 gals.; 12-volt.

VOLVO 145S ESTATE

145 has single-carb. 75 b.h.p. engine; 145S has twin-carb. 100 b.h.p. unit. Both use the same strong, spacious body, well-built and comfortable. 145S has sporty performance and good roadholding. There's a special under floor compartment for valuables, the brakes have twin circuits to guarantee both front and one rear working in the event of pipe failure or leak.

CLOSE-UP

Four-cyl.; o.h.v.; 88.9×80 mm.; 1,986 c.c.; 100 b.h.p.; 8.7 to 1 comp.; 2 SU carbs.; 4-speed, 13.46, 8.56, 5.85, 4.3 to 1; cen. lvr. L de N overdrive opt.; susp. f. ind. coil, r. coil; 5-door; 5-seat; disc servo brks.; max. 105 m.p.h.; cruise 88; m.p.g. 20-23; whl. base 8ft. 6½in.; track f. and r. 4ft. 5¼in.; lgth. 15ft. 3in.; width 5ft. 8in.; ht. 4ft. 9in.; g.c. 7in.; turng. cir. 30ft. 10in.; kerb wt. 22¼ cwt.; tank 13½ gals.; 12-volt.

£1,300 + £399 p.t. = £1,699

IT USED to be "P.B.I." for the long-suffering infantryman. Nowadays it could just as well be "P.B.M." for the long-suffering motorist. So far as the law is concerned, there is no section of the community more sat upon, more beset by the authorities, more likely to end up in court than drivers.

Lord Goddard, when Lord Chief Justice, once calculated that there were more than 1,000 offences a motorist could commit. Today there are many more. As A.A. Director-General A. C. Durie has said: "The imposition almost weekly of new motoring regulations imposes an impossible burden on the undermanned police and makes a mockery of justice."

The wonder is that, despite everything, most car owners still find pleasure in driving. According to an A.A. survey nine out of ten motorists still enjoy being at the wheel.

Yet official figures show that well over a million drivers are convicted of motoring offences every year. More than 60% of all people convicted in our courts are drivers! We are the biggest single group of "criminals" in the country.

Driving can still be a pleasure—despite the rules

by FENTON BRESLER

And when you look at motoring law, it's no wonder. It is a maze of regulations, sections and sub-sections of Acts and a whole forest of reported cases. From the moment you climb into the driving seat of a car, it is almost impossible not to become a potential law-breaker.

It's not simply the expected offences that cause the trouble. Most sensible motorists would expect there to be laws against drunken driving, dangerous driving, careless driving, driving while uninsured and driving without a licence.

And you cannot reasonably complain about the prudent enforcement of "no waiting" and parking restrictions designed to keep our largely inadequate roads as uncongested as possible. But if a policeman wants to get you for some pettifogging technical offence, it is all too easy. Just look at some of these recent prosecutions and see if you think they really were justified:

● A COLLEGE lecturer, with a 41-years' clean driving record, was stuck at lights jammed at red. Slowly he moved across. A policeman spotted him—and he was successfully prosecuted for "failing to conform to traffic lights."

● A HOUSEWIFE parked her car in a municipal car park in a small Buckinghamshire town. She put her money in a meter that should have produced a ticket. But it was out of order. Result: she was summonsed—and convicted—of "failing to affix a machine-issued car park ticket in a prominent and conspicuous place on and facing to the front of her vehicle," contrary to a local order made under the 1960 Road Traffic and Road Improvement Act. Although nobody denied she had paid and it quite clearly was not her fault she didn't have a ticket!

● A SURREY learner-driver housewife and her instructor were convicted of giving other motorists too large a warning of her novice status. By exhibiting an "L" plate three times the size specified by the regulations.

● A 25-YEAR-OLD Suffolk carpenter did not send his licence to court when writing to plead guilty to a speeding charge. He was arrested at work, handcuffed and put in the cells overnight.

● A DORSET businessman unloaded goods outside a customer's premises, then drove round the corner, parked his car—and returned to complete the unloading. In both streets you could only park for loading and unloading. He was summonsed for parking in the side street. The local magistrates threw out the case—but the police appealed. Result: the High Court directed the magistrates to convict. If the car had remained in the same street throughout the whole process of unloading and carrying the goods onto the premises, the driver would probably have been all right. But by moving the empty vehicle round the corner—to clear the main road!—he had ended "the unloading," and earned himself a conviction.

Under present-day ideas, even sensible laws —such as those penalising dangerous or careless driving—are turned on their head. And made to impose what many consider an unduly heavy burden on motorists.

It is the law of England, and has been such since two fairly recent Criminal Appeal Court decisions, that you can drive dangerously carefully! It may sound Irish, but that is English law.

As Mr. Justice Veale has said, it is no longer a defence to say that you were "a most incompetent person doing his best" or "even a good driver doing his best in very difficult circumstances."

Objectively speaking, if you are guilty of a dangerous or careless piece of driving, that's it! You are liable to be convicted. Even though it may have been due to a momentary error of judgment or you were quite truthfully doing your best.

Some years ago, Mr. Frank Milton, the present Chief Metropolitan Magistrate, said, when sitting at the North London Magistrates' Court: "Is it necessary, every time there is a bump, for everybody to come rushing along here?

"There is no need to bring every careless motorist to a magistrates' court. Many cases could be dealt with in a civil court. Our courts are highly suitable for dealing with people who are reckless or thoroughly incompetent. But many motorists make mistakes which only amount to small acts of carelessness."

I wish more policemen heeded these words. Almost any piece of momentary carelessness on the roads could—as the law now stands—be blown up to form the basis of a successful prosecution. And all too often this happens.

What makes this prosecution mania of the late sixties so serious for motorists is the "totting up" procedure. Three endorsements—and you are in grave danger of losing your licence. Although your offences may, in themselves, be comparatively minor.

Most motorists would probably agree with Mr. Ronald Horsman, president of the Justices Clerks Society, when he called in June for a revision of the system. The law was far too inflexible, he said.

But I'm afraid there is not much hope of any change in the law that might *favour* the motorist. He is the fall-guy of successive governments and of successive Ministers of Transport. In official circles, it is never our inadequate and antiquated roads that are to blame for our undoubted traffic problems. It is always the "P.B.M."— the motorist.

With all these gadgets, why bother about the car!

by DENNIS MAY

FOR the legions of owner-customisers, buying a new car is just a beginning. At once the accessory and engine conversion purveyors—represented in strength at Earls Court—start baiting their tender traps.

By the time he runs short on wolf-repellent, the poorer by anything from a few pounds to £1,000 but happy, he'll be going faster, and/or accelerating quicker, and/or using less petrol, and/or sitting prettier, and/or buffering himself and his family against motoring hazards, and/or seeing more clearly by night and in fog, and/or enjoying higher-fi broadcast noises.

Devices that genuinely pay dividends—more mpg or more speed and acceleration, or with luck a little of both—are everybody's sweetheart.

Examples: the Cheetah fuel economiser and three rival makes of low-power-loss cooling fan—Kenlowe, Aerofan and Wood-Jeffreys' Auto Electric.

Suitable for any car so long as it isn't fuel-injected, and bolted between the carburetter and inlet manifold flanges, the Cheetah cheats the petrol-thirst bogy by putting calculated kinks in the entering mixture's path, thereby improving atomisation.

It costs only 70s., and can be fitted in half an hour or less. On a Mini, it gave a *Motor* tester gains of over 2 mph and nearly 3½ mpg. (**Cheetah Conversions, 28, White Hart Lane, N22.**)

Perhaps the best known of the three fans mentioned is the Kenlowe (I had an E-type Jaguar with one myself and formed a high opinion of it). Electrically driven and thermostatically controlled, it cuts in at 87 deg. C. and out again at 84 deg., obviously absorbing no engine power.

Prices start at £13 14s. 6d. and there's an unconditional 12-months guarantee. (**Kenlowe Accessories, Burchetts Green, Maidenhead, Berks.**)

Similar in principle is the slightly more expensive **Auto Electric,** of which **Wood-Jeffreys** say 'the motor is good for two million miles—the first service is then due'.

The Aerofan (**Aerofan Ltd., Broadway, Worcs.**) is different again and, at 79s. 6d., much cheaper. Drive is mechanical, by a normal belt, but the four spring-loaded blades fine-off as engine speed rises, pitch-up as it drops. A 9 per cent reduction in power absorption, plus lengthened belt life, plus much abated noise, are bonuses claimed.

Special road wheels and trims, some of them just easy on the eye, others benefiting road holding by cutting unsprung weight, or stability by virtue of extra rim width, are a current rage, lending sports and GT cars that in-at-elbow, up-at-heel look. Prices vary enormously, depending on whether you're shopping for smartness alone or smartness plus practical effect.

High in this second category come the expensive Minilite eight-spoke magnesium wheels, made in separate types for rallycross, rally or circuit racing service but with no bar against buyers who just want the glory without the risk. (**Tech Del, 32 Telford Way, W3.**)

A mite less pricy but also strong on lightness, strength and looks are the rival Dunlop and Revolution products (former marketed by **GT Wheels and Accessories, Eaton Bray, Dunstable, Beds.,** latter by **Revolution Wheels, Cranbourne Close, Horley, Surrey).**

Then of course there are many designs of wheel trim that achieve 'mag' appearance without punishing the purse unduly, typified by the Alexander Super-Mag embellisher (**Alexander Engineering, Haddenham, Aylesbury, Bucks.).**

Sports type steering wheels, either visibly wood rimmed or leather gaitered and with their triple light-alloy spokes tastefully pierced, are doing booming business.

Watch out at the Show—at the factors' stands where the makers themselves aren't exhibiting—

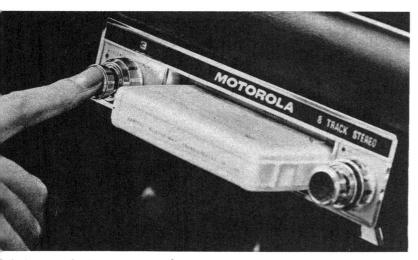

Eight-track stereo tape player

Instrument panel: oil check and seat belt indicator

for the wares of such specialists as **Les Leston, Karobes, Super Accessories, Alexander Engineering, Simon Green, Intertech, Formula and Astrali.** Les Leston (Claremont Rd., Cricklewood, NW2) charges £8 10s. 0d. for flat wheels of this type, £8 17s. 0d. for dished ones, which is about average.

What's new or recent in the safety harness line? The Britax Automatic belt, for one. Fundamental to automatics is the self-locking characteristic . . . when all's well you have full freedom of movement, at the moment of impact or high-force inertia it restrains you automatically.

Another Britax speciality—why don't more parents use it?—is the Star Rider child's safety seat, complete with midriff and shoulder straps (**Britax Ltd., Proctor Works, Byfleet, Surrey**).

A quick release push-button is built into the buckle of their latest belts by **Kangol Ltd. of Carlisle,** and is also featured by Romac in the Superdrive range of belts, the plastic buckles of which, incidentally, don't merely meet but actually exceed BS strength standards (**Holt Products Ltd., 12 Sydenham Rd., Croydon, Surrey**).

Facia instruments making their Earls Court debut will include stylish examples of Italian and British gauges from Veglia Borletti and Alexander Engineering respectively.

The former, imported by **Harry Moss (London) Ltd. (424 Kingston Rd., SW20)** have standard-diameter dials, are calibrated in metric or Imperial units to choice, measure rpm, speed, time, oil pressure, oil and water temperature, amps and battery condition; clear white numerals jump out of the black faces at you.

The Alexander series, launched last month with an impulse tachometer (other new instruments are in the Alexander Engineering pipeline) have the same easy-to-read quality. Tacho price £12 19s. 6d.

'Do not trust to deceitful lamplight', Ov⟨ ⟩ warned, but *he* lived two thousand years t⟨ ⟩ early to experience Britain's first tungsten hal⟨ ⟩ gen double-dipping headlamp system: the ou⟨ ⟩ come of collaboration between Philips Electrica⟨ ⟩ who supply the twin-filament Duplo PH4 bul⟨ ⟩ and Joseph Lucas.

Elements in the asymmetrical beam cast are ⟨ ⟩ long-range spear of light scanning the left-han⟨ ⟩ side of the road and a cleanly cut-off spread ⟨ ⟩ the right.

Wipac's new auxiliary lamps for the Fo⟨ ⟩ Capri, with rectangular stainless steel bowls, a⟨ ⟩ mated spot and fog lights, priced at £5 10s. 0⟨ ⟩ with quartz halogen bulbs, £4 with norm⟨ ⟩ bulbs. They are FoMoCo part-numbered item⟨ ⟩ and thus obtainable from all Ford dealers.

Also new: distinctively styled Monza a⟨ ⟩ Monte Carlo driving and fog lamps from **Hel⟨ ⟩ Automobile Equipment, Hanworth Lan⟨ ⟩ Chertsey, Surrey.**

Monza is round, Monte Carlo square, bo⟨ ⟩ have quartz halogen bulbs, 6 and 12 volt system⟨ ⟩ catered for. Prices from £6 9s. 0d. to £6 19s. 6⟨ ⟩

please turn to page ⟨ ⟩

Slim line tachometer   **Water temperature gauge, battery condition indicator and oil pressure gauge**

It's the little things that brighten your travel!

continued from page 63

...lus 17s. for the necessary relay and mounting brackets together.

Another goody in the same class is Miller's Type 35/36 spot and fog lamp sets, designed to harmonise with current grille shapes. The 36 one, with bowls that would be rectangular if their ends weren't rounded, have quartz iodine bulbs and cost £4 complete with switches and cables (**H. Miller and Co. Ltd., Aston Brook St., Birmingham 10**).

Now let's reflect awhile on mirrors, like for example Wingards's Silverline, S-Type and Multi-Angle models, the last named in a recently launched Mk II version. All three are attractively shaped, give a wide range of hindsight vision (**Wingard Ltd., Kingsham Rd., Chichester, Sussex**).

The **Magnatex Flo-Line** wing mirror, using spring-back mounting is sold in flat and convex forms, and meets European and U.S. safety standards. Prices £1 13s. 0d. flat, £1 15s. 6d. convex.

Low back-pressure silencers, some with dual tail pipes which look impressive as well as ungagging the spent gases, are popular with sporting drivers, and many are to be seen around Earls Court.

Peco are forefronters in this field, with a name for euphoniously gruff exhaust notes; their twin-outlet Big Bore silencers, tailored to a wide range of volume-produced cars of the get-up-and-go *genre*, start at £3 6s. 6d. (**Peco Silencers Ltd., Birkenhead, Lancs.**).

Rather similar in looks but different in having straight-through acoustic chambers, are Taurus silencers, also in single and dual tail pipe types (**Taurus Performance Tuning Ltd., Handforth, Wilmslow, Ches.**).

But if you measure merit by spout multiplication, one of the Cooper sports silencers, with *three* flues, has to be reckoned with. This, in common with all Cooper mufflers is guaranteed to conform to the current anti-noise regulations. (**Desmond Cooper and Co. (Motor Components) Ltd., Solihull, Warks.**)

New radios include an attractive two-role model from Hitachi of Japan, the KM-1100T, which can be slotted into a facia aperture and powered off the car battery or alternatively used as a portable using its own built-in batteries. KM-1100T (imported by **Lee Products (Great Britain) Ltd., 10 Clifton St., EC2**), has long, medium and FM wave bands, measures 4×3×8in. as fitted to a car, is for 6 or 12 volt electrical systems.

Alike in its double role, car-cum-walkabout, is the RAD-15 (**Fidelity Radio Ltd., Olaf St., W11**) with push-button selection for long, medium and FM wavebands, speaker grilles on both sides of the cabinet, sockets provided for

tape recording and earphones, price £22 1s. 0d.

Stereo tape players for car installation took a welcome step down the price ladder with the recent launch of an eight-track model by **Motorola Automotive Products Ltd.** at £39 18s. 6d.

This includes two 5¼in. matching speakers for sub-facia and rear parcel-shelf mounting, gives a maximum of forty minutes' playing on four programmes.

For back-seat passengers who, even en route, can't tear themselves away from the television (but strictly not for drivers), **Crown Radio Ltd., 137 Goswell Rd., EC1,** import from Japan the Crown 7TV-105 car television, reasonably priced at £73 15s. 0d.

This has a 10in. screen, operates on 625 lines (BBC-2), voltages are 240 a.c. or 12 volts. Surprisingly light and compact, the Crown weighs 6½lbs., measures only 9¼×8¼×7½in. The bill includes a daylight viewing screen and a pair of earphones.

S.C. Johnson and Son Ltd. (Johnson's Wax) has introduced Liquid Rally, a long-life paintwork beautifier that removes dirt without disturbing wax film, if any. A 10oz. tin costs 7s. 6d.

Hozelock Ltd., Haddenham, Aylesbury, Bucks., has a new hose nozzle with a particularly wide range of fine/coarse adjustability, gunning water in a Scotch mist type spray or stair-rod jet.

Then for an engine you could eat your breakfast off, **Porzelack Ltd., Townsend Lane, Liverpool 13,** have a line of heat-resistant paints—10s. 6d. for a 5oz. aerosol. Choice of colours: bronze, aluminium, green, red, black.

Finally there are the almost infinitely various tuning kits and treatments that together make a sub-industry.

Leaders include **Downton Engineering,** specialising in cars built on British Leyland's Longbridge/Abingdon axis; **Jack Brabham Conversions Ltd.** for Vauxhall Vivas; **V. W. Derrington Ltd.**—more steam for most British makes, **Weber Carb. Agency/Allard Motor Co. Ltd.,** stacked high with supercharging know-how; **Super-Sport of Acton, London,** for Cortina GT crossflow engines—aggressive cams, h.c. pistons, special inlet manifolds to take a second Weber, cylinder heads with reworked fireplaces; **Broadspeed Engineering,** with tuning forks at the disposal of go-faster BMC and Ford owners; and many, many others, spread nationwide.

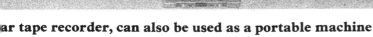

Car tape recorder, can also be used as a portable machine

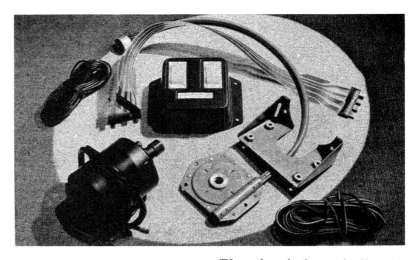

Electric window winding kit

Learning to drive? Then leave your corsets at home!

by
KATHARINE HADLEY

KATHARINE HADLEY: PICTURE BY RONALD DUMONT

EVERYBODY has seen the lady learner doing her comedy act, bouncing and jerking right at traffic lights. Yet curiously, if a man does it, nobody laughs.

Far worse is the male driver who has 'female driver neurosis'.

Men who belong to the fast car variety, conquering every women driver with a compulsive dangerous overtake put the accident rate up. So do those who yell or violently whistle at the girl behind the wheel and so distract her attention.

That a female driver syndrome still exists in 1969 is depressing especially as the breathalyser, cheaper insurance for women, and the suburban spread—where shopping facilities are often a car journey away—are sending more and more women to the driving school.

Steady

The British School of Motoring, with its 160 branches and 1,500 staff, reports that while overall learning is going down a little, the number of women learners is going up.

If you want to learn, go to a registered driving school rather than let Uncle Fred teach you—because he'll pass on all his bad driving habits.

Tony Camp, 64, and 33 years an instructor, told me: "Bad habits are worse losing than getting. Nasty things like lax deportment at the wheel. I've just been teaching a sheik who had an awful slouch. I kept telling him, but he went on slouching. Well in the end I said: 'If you don't do what you're told, you won't pass'. I mean, nobody's going to pass you with bad deportment, even if you are a prince".

Qualified instructors know what to look for. Their nerves are steady, they use dual control cars, and aren't anti-female drivers. They take the view that women are neither better nor worse than men—simply as good.

My own instructor, 28-year-old Eddy Simmonds, said: "Women drivers have less accidents than men but that's because they normally cover fewer miles. Women are less aggressive on the roads but men counter this advantage because they have mechanical know-how."

Control

One tip for women: "Drive bare-foot—it makes for greater control of the car; whatever you do don't drive in high heels."

Eddy also advises against: tight corsets and boned long-line bras that hamper breathing and rapid movement; and skimpy skirts and loose bra straps that you will be continually adjusting.

When you pass your test—experts say the average number of hours pre-test is around 18—ask your instructor to advise on a suitable ca

Mr. Camp said: "For at least the first tw years after passing the test the best car for woman, who often has children, is the ordina family car."

So keep the flashy car dreams on ice, don ruin your relationship with Fred, uncle or no who is always secretly terrified you are going wrap his smashing motor round a keep-left sig

Sensible

When the 'L' plates are off and you have yo sensible car keep watching the road. Don relax so much that you treat your car as drawing room on wheels, like the lady who sa at green lights so engrossed in chat with he friend that she didn't notice the line of ca behind.

Finally an infuriated gentleman got out an said "Madam, exactly which shade of green ar you waiting for?"

It gets us a bad name.

EFFORTLESS

...the luxury of automatic motoring at no extra cost – with DAF

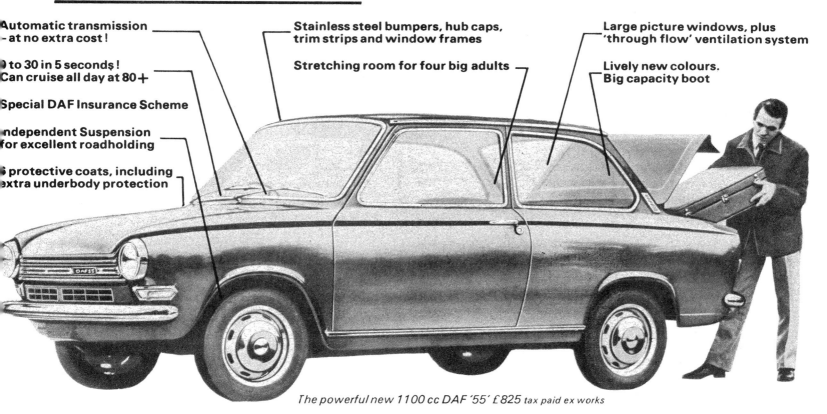

Automatic transmission – at no extra cost!

Stainless steel bumpers, hub caps, trim strips and window frames

Large picture windows, plus 'through flow' ventilation system

0 to 30 in 5 seconds! Can cruise all day at 80+

Stretching room for four big adults

Lively new colours. Big capacity boot

Special DAF Insurance Scheme

Independent Suspension for excellent roadholding

6 protective coats, including extra underbody protection

The powerful new 1100 cc DAF '55' £825 tax paid ex works

DAF makes automatic motoring possible for your next car. Carefree, effortless, *fully automatic* motoring, free from constantly changing gears up and down, down and up! With DAF there are just *two* pedals. One to go. One to stop. This feature is not an expensive extra as it is on other cars, *but is included at no extra cost!*

And they're tough, this 1970 range of DAF cars, station wagons, sports coupe. Rally proved (DAF was first 1100 cc car in the London to Sydney Marathon) and backed by an *outstandingly comprehensive guarantee*, including unlimited mileage for one year. These new DAF cars embody all the experience of one of Europe's largest manufacturers of all-automatic cars.

Look closer and you'll discover a mass of other worthwhile 'extras' – again at no extra cost. Like a heater, de-misters, screen washer, safety locks, radial tyres. Incidentally DAF's automatic drive ensures that you always get 'drive' even in snow and slush . . . and you can expect over 30,000 miles from these tyres with normal driving. With petrol, too, DAF cars make every gallon go a phenomenally long way. Some do over 40 to the gallon on cheapest petrol. Above all, these are *sensible* cars . . . .

Which is probably why you'd like to know more. So simply fill in the coupon. It's the first step towards stepping into a DAF – *and enjoying your first AUTOMATIC Test Drive!* It's all completely free and puts you under no obligation.

For 1970, DAF offers you a choice of 8 new models, all fully automatic, from as little as £639 *tax paid ex works*

The versatile, spacious DAF '44' Estate £874 tax paid ex works

Sleek, fast, luxurious, the DAF '55' Sports Coupe £958 tax paid ex works

automatic

van Doorne's Automobiel Fabrieken of Holland

OVER 1000 STRONG DEALER NETWORK THROUGHOUT THE U.K. AND EUROPE

These Automatic **DAF** Cars sound just what I'm looking for!
Please send me your free colour brochure of the new DAF '33', '44', and '55' ranges of cars and name of my nearest DAF Dealer.

NAME .... (I am over 17)

ADDRESS ....

....

My usual shopping town is .... My phone no. ....
To Dept. MSR , DAF Motors (G.B.) Ltd.,
Hanworth Park, Uxbridge Road, Feltham, Middx.   (01-890 0161/6)

251

Announcing the new Sunbeam Alpine.
A pretty, expensive car that only costs £1,085.*

Pretty it is, expensive it isn't.

When you pay £1,085* for a car you expect a certain amount.

With the Alpine you get more.

A line and finish that looks more like £2,000.

Creature comforts that include high-back front seats, and through-flow ventilation and heating.

A 1725 c.c. engine that takes you to 50 mph in around 11 secs., up to 90 mph, and up to 34 mpg.

And servo-assisted brakes with front discs.

Then to add to the expensive look there are things like a veneered facia. Centre console. All of this makes you feel good.

We could tell you a whole lot more about the new Alpine.

But we'd like you to see for yourself. Compare it with other cars at the price.

We believe that if you see it you'll believe.

The new fastback Sunbeam Alpine. Only £1,085* (automatic or overdrive extra)—just one of the remarkable Rapier family. See also the Sunbeam Rapier £1,242* and the Sunbeam Rapier H.120 £1,503*.

*ex-works price inc. p.t. (seat belts, over-riders and wing mirrors extra)

SUNBEAM

SUNBEAM ROOTES

The new Hillman GT. 100 mph. £961*

All spark plugs are the same

"You must be joking."

If all spark plugs were the same, why would Graham Hill have insisted on Autolite?

He knew that the 1968 World Championships couldn't be won with just any spark plugs.

He knew that only Autolite could deliver the performance and total reliability he needed to win the biggest prize in motor racing.

And now, Jackie Stewart, the runaway leader in this year's World Championship, is also using Autolite.

If you take your motoring seriously enough to compare one spark plug against another, you'll insist on Autolite, too.

They cost around 6/- each.

You'll probably see other plugs offered at lower prices.

But you won't see Graham Hill or Jackie Stewart buying them.

AUTOLITE MOTOR PRODUCTS LTD., ENFIELD, MIDDX.

Compare! After the great insurance revolution Alpha is <u>still</u> the only motor policy to offer all this!

Premiums related to just one factor— YOUR AGE!

Comprehensive insurance tailored for the average private car owner

Cover for passenger liability For all drivers with no exclusions

£50 cover for your personal effects

Easy Monthly Payments

FREE GREEN CARD

Over 31's pay only 25/- monthly

Policy written in plain English

Personal injury claims and many others free from excess

Caravan towing and most rallies covered

Freedom to drive other cars

Freedom to let others drive your car

Up to age 31 your premium reduces £3 every year

Claims offices for every area

Class 1 business use allowed

WINDSCREEN COVER

Easiest-ever application —just fill in his form and post it today!

Freedom from the dilemma of no-claim bonuses — Alpha premiums are net!

One scale of premiums for all cars — and that includes sports cars!

You are fully protected right from the start. No messing about with cover notes!

No variations, no endorsements Alpha terms are standard for everyone!

Continuous protection Alpha takes care of renewal for you — automatically

Legal costs up to £1000 — even for the 17-year old driver!

Proposal Form

Issued BY MIDLAND NORTHERN & SCOTTISH INSURANCE COMPANY LIMITED
Alpha House, 120 Kings Road, Reading, RG1 3BU

PROPOSAL FORM The date you enter here must allow time for postal delays

| COMMENCEMENT OF INSURANCE | | |
| DAY | MONTH | YEAR |

PROPOSER'S SURNAME

FORENAMES

FULL ADDRESS

BLOCK CAPITALS PLEASE

PROPOSER'S AGE (years)

DATE OF BIRTH — DAY MONTH YEAR

PROPOSER'S OCCUPATION

DECLARATION

I hereby declare that:

To the best of my knowledge and belief I do not suffer from any physical defect.

I have not been convicted of any of the following offences:
a) Driving without due care and attention (within the last three years)
b) Reckless or dangerous driving (within the last five years)
c) Causing death by reckless or dangerous driving (within the last ten years)
d) Driving under the influence of drink or drugs (within the last ten years)

I have not been involved in more than two accidents or losses in the previous three years in connection with any motor vehicle owned or used by myself.

The above items (1 to 3) apply to anyone who to my knowledge will drive the motor car insured under the policy.

The car to be insured is my property or is being purchased by me under a purchase agreement and is registered in my name.

I have not withheld any information likely to affect acceptance of this proposal, that the information given herein is true and correct.

I agree that if this proposal in any particular is filled in by any other person such person shall be deemed to be my agent and not the agent of the Company and this proposal and declaration shall be the basis of the contract between me and MIDLAND NORTHERN & SCOTTISH INSURANCE COMPANY LIMITED

I agree that this is a legally binding proposal for twelve months insurance at a premium determined by the Company.

PROPOSER'S SIGNATURE   DATE

PROPOSER'S NATIONALITY

PROPOSER'S COUNTRY OF ORIGIN

CAR REGISTRATION No.

MANUFACTURER

MODEL

TYPE OF BODY

CUBIC CAPACITY

SEATING CAPACITY

YEAR OF MANUFACTURE

DATE OF PURCHASE (approx.) MONTH YEAR

A1/8 **462**

This form to be used when insuring the motor car specified above or any subsequent replacement. Business use is extended to the Policyholder in person, but excludes commercial travelling. The Company reserves the right to decline any proposal. The policy is issued for 12 months.

BANKER'S ORDER

This Banker's Order or a National Giro standing order (form available on request) must be completed before the proposal will receive consideration. We regret we cannot accept any form of cash payment.

Please pay to the MIDLAND NORTHERN & SCOTTISH INSURANCE COMPANY LIMITED at Barclays Bank Limited, Head office collection account—sorting code No. **27-00-84**

the sum of £ __ (See column 1 of premiums table) on the __ 19 __ and then £ __ (See column 2 of premiums table) Enter date insurance is to commence

each month following until further notice, quoting policy number

THE MANAGER

| FOR OFFICE USE ONLY | |

BANK CODE At top right-hand corner of most cheques

NAME

ACCOUNT No. (if any)

DATE __ 19

SIGNATURE

AFFIX 2d STAMP HERE

Post to Midland Northern & Scottish Insurance Co. Ltd.
Head Office: Alpha House, 120 Kings Road, Reading, RG1 3BU
Northern Ireland post to: Alpha House, 3 Rosemary St, Belfast BT1 1QP

Here's why, every month, thousands come over to Alpha!

Monthly payments. Just fill in the form —we and your bank do the rest! Because your initial payment is equal to three months' instalments, your first year's policy is paid in full by the ninth month. If your payments continue after that we automatically renew your policy—and we reduce your premium if you are under 31.

Your age	Column 1 Initial payment	Column 2 Monthly payments	Col.3 total annual premium
31 & over	£3.15. 0	£1. 5. 0	£15. 0. 0
30	£4.10. 0	£1.10. 0	£18. 0. 0
29	£5. 5. 0	£1.15. 0	£21. 0. 0
28	£6. 0. 0	£2. 0. 0	£24. 0. 0
27	£6.15. 0	£2. 5. 0	£27. 0. 0
26	£7.10. 0	£2.10. 0	£30. 0. 0
25	£8. 5. 0	£2.15. 0	£33. 0. 0
24	£9. 0. 0	£3. 0. 0	£36. 0. 0
23	£9.15. 0	£3. 5. 0	£39. 0. 0
22	£10.10. 0	£3.10. 0	£42. 0. 0
21	£11. 5. 0	£3.15. 0	£45. 0. 0
17 to 20	£12. 0. 0	£4. 0. 0	£48. 0. 0

For Northern Ireland add 15/- to the initial payment and 5/- to the monthly instalment

Driving other cars. When you borrow a friend's car Alpha covers you for claims made upon you by the owner if you are to blame—something which no other insurance company will do, as far as we know.

Others driving your car. The tables below show your maximum liability for collision damage whoever the driver may be. Claims arising from any cause other than collision are free from all excess.

Table A The limit of your liability	Driver's age at time of collision				
	17-20	21-23	24-27	28-30	31 & over
Policyholder, wife (or husband) of policyholder driving.	£35	£30	£25	£20	£10
Son or daughter driving.	£50	£40	£30	£20	£10
Other drivers.	£150	£75	£50	£30	£10

Table B Liability for sports or modified cars.	Driver's age at time of collision			
	17-23	24-27	28-30	31 & over
Policyholder, wife (or husband) or son or daughter of policyholder driving.	£200	£150	£100	£10
Other drivers.	£300	£200	£100	£10

For collisions on Continent £10 is added to these figures.

Passenger liability and legal costs. The full range of cover, including legal costs up to £1,000 and unlimited passenger liability, is extended to the very young, the elderly, the inexperienced driver, and even the learner. There are no special loadings, exclusions or endorsements.

Only your age counts. The premium and excess tables A and B apply without alteration wherever you live in England, Scotland or Wales, and to private cars of all makes and sizes up to six-seaters.

Claims free from excess. Loss of personal effects, windscreen damage, fire and theft arising from any cause other than collision are completely free from excess. So are personal injury claims even if they result from a collision.

Rallies and towing. You are covered for local rallies which are purely tests of navigational skill, treasure hunts or similar events—but not racing, pace-making or similar trials. You are covered also for liability to third parties when towing a caravan or trailer.

Free Green Card. You pay no extra premium when you take your car on a Continental holiday. The Green Card is issued for up to three months.

Sports cars. The same premium as any other car. There has to be a higher rate of excess for younger drivers, but for 31's the maximum liability remains at £10.

Business use. Alpha is a class 1 comprehensive policy and therefore allows limited business use. It does not allow others to drive your car on business, neither does it cover hiring, commercial travelling, or any purpose connected with the motor trade.

PLEASE NOTE...
The Road Vehicles (Registration and Licensing) Regulations 1964 require that whoever is registered as the owner shall be the person by whom the vehicle is kept and used. We cannot, therefore, issue a valid policy in the name of a parent if the principal user of the car is in fact the son, for instance.

As it is illegal for any insurance company to back-date cover, the date of commencement you give on the proposal form must allow reasonable time for postal delays.

The Alpha policy is limited to vehicles registered in the private car category. It is not valid for those in the motor-cycle or goods carrying categories. Owners of three-wheelers and vans are advised to check their registration details.

We regret we cannot issue the Alpha policy to service personnel on duty abroad or to people living outside the U.K.

Our acceptance of higher powered cars has to be kept in proportion, so if you own such a car we may not be able to offer you an Alpha policy for the time being.

Midland Northern & Scottish Insurance Company Limited, Alpha House, 120 Kings Road, Reading RG1 3BU

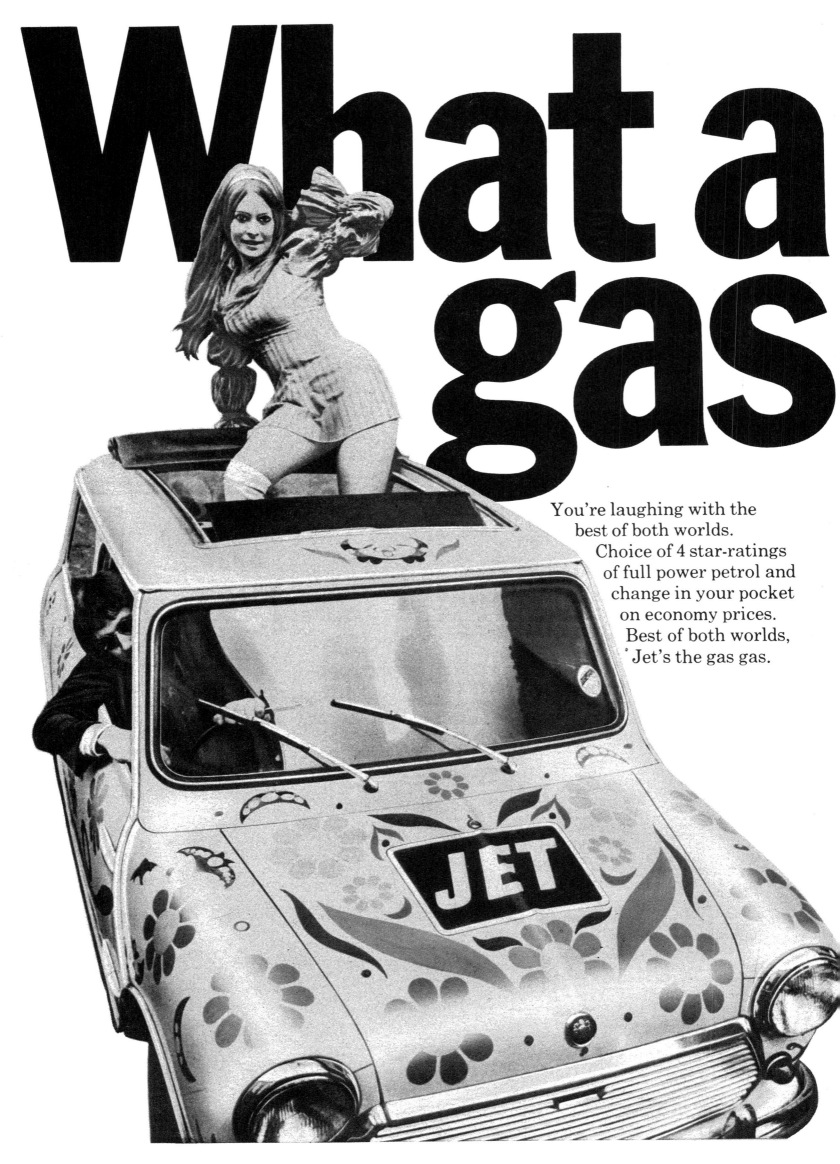

What a gas

You're laughing with the best of both worlds. Choice of 4 star-ratings of full power petrol and change in your pocket on economy prices. Best of both worlds, Jet's the gas gas.

JET